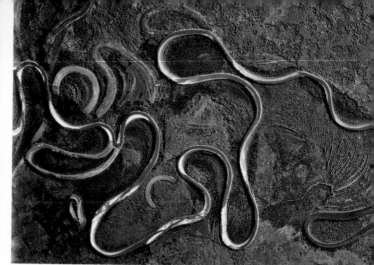

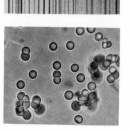

THE PHYSICAL SCIENCES  AN INTRODUCTION

Stephen S. Winter *PROFESSOR, STATE UNIVERSITY of NEW YORK at BUFFALO*

Harper & Row, Publishers *NEW YORK, EVANSTON, AND LONDON*

Library of Congress Catalog Card Number: 67–10813

To my parents

Max and Anna Winter

Contents

Preface

This book grew out of a physical science survey course that I taught at the University of Minnesota several years ago. Most of the students were freshmen from the College of Science, Literature, and Arts, although there were also upperclassmen and a sizable contingent from Elementary Education. All had at least two characteristics in common: they coupled a strong interest in other fields with a less pronounced interest and meager backgrounds in science and mathematics, and they used the course as a means of satisfying the university's laboratory science requirement. In the first two quarters, we dealt with topics from astronomy, physics, and chemistry; the third quarter, on geology, was optional and was taught by a member of the geology department.

It is very difficult to decide how to do justice to "science" in a course of this nature. The intent is clearly to make the student "scientifically literate," a charming phrase whose truth is self-evident and whose meaning is undefined. The selection of content does not, by itself, determine the value of the course. All physical science is appropriate content, and with so few weeks available for instruction, topics have to be chosen and treated with the greatest selectivity. Indeed, each year I varied the subject matter slightly in an attempt to find the sequence that seemed most appropriate to my aims. But while the content differed, the treatment did not, and the course attained

its identity from the manner in which the topics were developed.

This book is based on the same principles as the course. Its first aim is to teach science, not to teach about science. It tries to provide the student with an orientation toward his physical surroundings. Sufficient description is given throughout so that he knows the referents of the vocabulary of science: knows the difference between a planet, a star, a gaseous nebulosity, and a galaxy, for instance, or the behavior of solids, liquids, and gases under changing conditions of pressure and temperature. This orientation extends to the conceptual as well as the observational components of science, and an attempt is made to stress the contribution that both components make to the description and understanding of nature—which is what science is. The interplay of the conceptual framework with observational data is one theme that runs through the book.

Observational data and invented concepts in science can be seen to interact in a small number of empirical and conceptual processes, and illustration of these processes was the second criterion for the development of the content of this book. The logic of science is taught mostly by implication during the development of the various topics; it is discussed directly only on occasion, in order to make explicitly clear what might, without such discussion, remain implicit and hidden. The topic kinetic theory, for instance, provides an excellent vehicle to demonstrate the use of derivation, deduction, prediction, and empirical verification. Hence it is developed in such a way that the scientific procedures employed will be clear to the student, although these procedures are commented upon only occasionally. Other topics are developed in such a manner as to illustrate different characteristics of the growth of scientific knowledge: atomic structure, for instance, is taken up as an example of experiment and model building; the explanations of periodicity and bonding are seen as an example of the merging of diverse strands of theory and experimentation. As far as possible, each chapter shows the advances of concepts and experiments that have created the scientific knowledge of today.

Considerable attention is given to the acts of human creativity that are required in the inductive steps of the scientific methods and that underlie all great experiments. As far as possible, science is shown as a human activity—a creation of the human brain that matches what is found in nature. Scientific explanations are not, of course, infallible, and in some chapters enough history is given to demonstrate the painfully slow refinement of our understanding. While the stress is definitely on the human inventions in science, history in itself is not an important part of this book. Where historical treatment might cause trouble by requiring the learning and unlearning of complex and outdated conceptions, history is avoided.

There is more material in the book than can be taught in one semester or two quarters because I have included all topics that seemed relevant. The user must choose those topics that are suited to the course he is teaching. I have tried to write the book so that there are many ways of abbreviating it without loss of continuity. The chapters on astronomy can be dropped as a block, as can the chapters on geology; several of the chapters on physics and chemistry can be omitted. Such omissions would not destroy the basic aims of the book since each of the various methods of science appears in several chapters. While selection would necessarily reduce the description of what scientists have learned about the universe, the procedures by which the knowledge has been won would still be well illustrated.

The book has benefited from the advice of a number of colleagues. Professors Otto H. Johnson, Maurice M. Kreevoy, and Rufus W. Lumry looked at my early drafts and helped me with the planning. Professor Charles V. Clemency did a critical review of the chapters on geology and made many important suggestions for revision and clarification. Professor Robert C. Kochersberger read a number of chapters and helped to assess their clarity. Professor Marion A. Panzarella also discussed a part of the book with me. My sincere thanks to them for sharing their ideas and giving me their judgment. Clearly they are not responsible for shortcomings of this book.

My sincere thanks also to Arthur J. Hannah and Arthur I. Rothman, who helped me with several of the illustrations.

The typing of the manuscript was expertly done by Mrs. Sandra Yarnes and Mrs. Gail Hoffman, with the help of my wife, Bettina, who in addition aided me in the many tasks required for the completion of this book. My indebtedness to them can be appreciated only by another first author.

STEPHEN S. WINTER

Chapter 1

Astronomy

Most of us hold strange notions about the earth. We "know" that the earth moves though certainly it seems still enough. We "know" that the sun stands still though we can see it rise, move across the sky, and set. We know this because it is what we have been taught. The greatest of the Greek philosophers, Aristotle (384–322 B.C.), did not know what we know. He would not have disagreed with us on what we see. He observed as we do that the sun rises and sets. He felt the stillness of the earth as we feel it. But he believed what he saw and felt, and since he was not taught as we are, his "knowledge" was the very opposite of ours.

In science as in all affairs, knowledge comes from two sources: observation and interpretation. We glance about and then form ideas about what we have ob-

1

FIG. 1-1

Reproduction of a plate from Astronomique Discourse, *1557, by Jacques Bassantin.* (Harvard College Library)

served. The observations are usually direct and straightforward; the ideas often complex and ingenious. The observations relate to what we see "out there"; the ideas are formed in our minds, within us. The observations are largely noncontroversial; the ideas are changeable, at times controversial. Indeed, some scientific ideas have been accepted just because they were liked, and others rejected because disliked.

Obviously our disagreement with Aristotle is not about observations. It is about his and our interpretation of these observations. What we "know" (what we have been taught) represents one set of ideas. We like and accept them for good reasons. He accepted another set of ideas which he, too, liked for what seemed good reasons to him.

The development of ideas about the universe illustrates very clearly how ideas and observations go hand in hand in the development of knowledge. We begin this book by describing the observations and ideas that evolved into the presently accepted theory of the solar system.

2

North

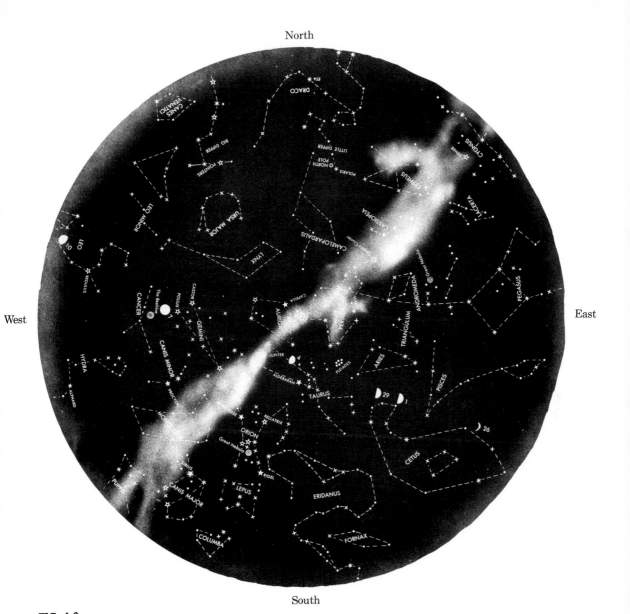

West

East

South

FIG. 1-2

The night sky in the United States in January. If the map is held overhead, it reproduces the pattern of the stars seen about 10:30 P.M. local standard time on January 1, 9:30 P.M. on January 15, and 8:30 P.M. on January 31. The locations of the moon and Jupiter are given for January, 1964. Note that they are very near each other in the sky. (American Museum of Natural History, New York)

THE CELESTIAL SPHERE

To orient ourselves among the heavenly bodies, we consider the sky a huge sphere on which the stars are placed. This is the *celestial sphere*. We map certain portions of that sphere by the star patterns that ap-

pear in them, the *constellations*. The constellations have names like Taurus, the bull, Pisces, the fish, and Cygnus, the swan, though only someone with very great imagination can see the outlines of these animals in the star patterns. Yet, as Fig. 1–1 shows, the connections were once considered quite real. Today such attempts to relate the

3

star patterns to the outlines of animals or other figures are no longer common; however, the ancient names are still used to designate various regions of the celestial sphere as we use the names of states or countries on a map. On the star map (Fig. 1–2) which represents the sky for January, 1964, for instance, the moon is shown moving from near Pisces through Taurus, Gemini, Cancer to Leo. Jupiter is in Pisces.

The celestial sphere makes a daily rotation about the earth, the *diurnal motion.* Its results are shown in Fig. 1–3. The stars rise in the east, move across the sky, and set in the west. So does the sun. To relate the sky we see to a star map, two definitions are helpful. Both are determined by *our* position on earth. The *zenith* is the point in the sky vertically overhead. (Ze-

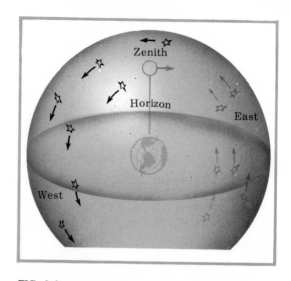

FIG. 1-4

Because the celestial sphere moves toward the west during the night, the zenith moves eastward and the stars that are visible also change. Constellations disappear beneath the horizon in the west and new ones appear in the east.

FIG. 1-3

Tracks of stars with a time exposure of about 7 hours' duration and the camera pointing north. The short bright arc is the North Star, Polaris, which is a short distance from the celestial north pole. The arcs result from the rotation of the celestial sphere, the diurnal motion. (Lick Observatory Photograph)

nith was between Auriga and Perseus at the times shown in Fig. 1–2.) As the celestial sphere rotates to the west, the zenith moves eastward among the constellations (Fig. 1–4). New stars continuously appear at zenith. The *horizon* is the great circle on the celestial sphere that divides the visible hemisphere from the invisible one. It is as far as we can see the stars. (The star map, Fig. 1–2, ends on the horizon at the times shown on the map.) The horizon, too, moves on the celestial sphere. A star that appears on the eastern horizon at sundown rotates to near zenith at midnight and sets on the western horizon about sunrise. Zenith and horizon depend on the observer's position on earth. There are also definitions that focus on the celestial sphere itself.

The diurnal motion of the celestial sphere occurs about two points, the north *celestial pole* located near the North Star, Polaris, and its southern counterpart. The great circle halfway between them is the *celestial equator.* In this respect celestial geography resembles terrestrial geography. The celestial poles and the celestial equator are simply the extensions of our poles and our equator on the celestial sphere.

ANNUAL CHANGES

The appearance of the night sky changes in the course of a year. From night to night, the stars slip somewhat farther to the west; new constellations appear in the east while others move toward the sun and become lost in its much brighter light. The constellation Orion with its bright stars Rigel and Betelgeuse, for instance, appears most brilliantly in the winter. From November to January it is directly overhead in the evening sky. However, it moves westward toward the sun, and by late spring it is no longer visible at night. It remains in the daytime portion of the sky until late summer. Then it reappears in the eastern sky as an early-morning constellation and gradually moves back westward into the evening sky.

The changes in the stellar landscape from night to night are the result of the sun's motion along the celestial sphere (Fig. 1–5). As the sun changes position among the

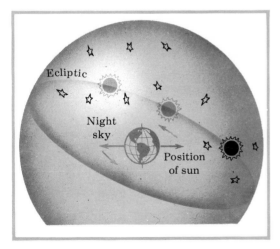

FIG. 1-5

As the sun moves along the ecliptic, the stars of the celestial sphere which are in the opposite direction—in the night sky—change. In the course of 1 year all constellations become visible at night from some part of the earth.

stars, it obscures different constellations by its bright light. At the same time the stars which are away from the sun—in the night sky—also change. This means that only in the course of a year do all the stars of the celestial sphere become visible.

The sun sweeps the entire celestial sphere each year. The twelve constellations through which it moves are called the constellations of the *zodiac*, famous because of their importance in astrology. The path of the sun is called the *ecliptic*. The ecliptic is a circle inclined 23.5° to the celestial equator. (Of course, the sun cannot be seen against the constellations of the zodiac because its brightness obscures them. But one can note the stars that appear just after the sun sets or just before the sun rises and thus locate the ecliptic.)

The sun is on the ecliptic to the north of the celestial equator during our summertime and to the south during our winter. For people living in the southern hemisphere of the earth, however, the seasons are reversed because summer and winter are determined by whether the sun is in the same or in the opposite direction of the celestial equator. The times of the year when the sun on its path along the ecliptic crosses the celestial equator are the *vernal* and *autumnal equinoxes,* which mark the beginning of spring and of fall, respectively.

MOON AND PLANETS

All heavenly bodies are carried along the celestial sphere in its diurnal motion. But like the sun, the moon and planets also move among the constellations. The moon's motion is by far the most rapid. From one night to the next, it advances about 15° and, indeed, one can easily spot its motion among the stars in a few hours. If one night the moon is near zenith at midnight (full moon), 7 days later it has already moved near the eastern midnight horizon (quarter moon). It makes a full transit of the celestial sphere in about 29 days in a west-to-east direction. The 29-day cycle of the moon is, of course, the origin of our months.

It is not difficult to distinguish the sun and moon from the stars because of their size and their brilliance. The planets, on the other hand, appear as points of light like the stars. They are recognized chiefly by their motion. (The word planet derives from a Greek word meaning wanderer.) Planets' motions are slow, much slower than that of the moon. While they are also generally in the direction west-to-east, their motions are not as regular as that of the moon. Planets were already known in some detail to the astronomers of ancient Greece and Babylon. Their apparently irregular progress among the stars caused great concern and was basic to the development of various theories of the universe.

One final aspect of the motion of the moon and the planets is of interest. All of them always appear in the sky among the constellations of the zodiac. They move only through a band of the celestial sphere about 10° to the north and south of the ecliptic.

FROM ARISTOTLE TO PTOLEMY

All the observations we have described so far can be made with the naked eye. They were known to the ancient astronomers and formed the observational part of ancient knowledge. To those observations the Greek philosophers added two fundamental ideas to make the universe comprehensible.

The first idea was of heavenly perfection. It probably arose from the observed contrast between things terrestrial and things celestial, though undoubtedly a religious element was present. On earth irregularity, change, and decay are the mark of all things. Earthly objects, whether animate or inanimate, take on all kinds of shape or form; they crumble and decay; they are born, live, and die. In contrast, the heavens seem regular and permanent. Diurnal mo-

tion occurs day after day without change, and so do the transits of the moon and the sun. Moreover, the orbits seem to describe circles, the most regular and perfect of the closed curves. This evidence of the perfection of the heavens strongly impressed the Greek philosophers. When they attempted to make sense of their astronomical observations, the perfect curve, a circle, and the perfect solid, a sphere, were foremost in their thinking.

The stillness of the earth, which was the second fundamental idea added to the observations, probably arose directly from sense impressions. It seems like the obvious conclusion to anyone who has not been taught as we have. Yet the idea of a stationary earth, too, was mixed with theological overtones, especially after the rise of Christianity. (The religious notion later proved much harder to displace.) The theological argument ran something like this. Is not man unique in creation? Then surely his abode, the earth, is unique too, motionless and at the center of the moving heavenly bodies. It could not be simply one of the wandering planets.

The system of the universe shown in Fig. 1–6 arose from these two ideas and the basic observations: (1) the diurnal motion of the entire celestial sphere; (2) the yearly motion of the sun among the stars in addition to its daily motion with them; (3) the monthly motion of the moon among the stars in addition to its daily motion with them; (4) the somewhat more complex motions of the planets among the stars. The earth resides motionless at the center. Around it are the heavenly bodies, each planet on a separate sphere, and the stars all together. The spheres are coupled so that all can make the daily rotation— diurnal motion—together, but loose enough so that each planet can make its own motions as well. Next to the earth is the sphere of the moon. It makes a separate rotation every month. Then comes the sphere of Mercury and then that of Venus, each with its appropriate motion. The

FIG. 1-6

The simple geocentric universe from a text by Gassendi published in 1658. (Yerkes Observatory Photograph)

sphere of the sun comes next with separate rotation every year. The spheres of Mars, Jupiter, and Saturn follow. Finally comes the starry sphere, which rotates daily and carries all other spheres with it.

Eight spheres apparently did not seem "right." The number 8 never had much mystical significance and must have seemed unlike the kind of number the Creator would have chosen to form the perfect pattern of the universe. Hence the ancient cosmologists added more spheres, invisible but necessary to round out heavenly perfection. Gassendi had two crystalline heavens; other authors had only one. Their function is not entirely clear. Beyond was the primum mobile, a sort of motor which set all other spheres in motion.

Unfortunately this simple system adhered to the two ideas behind its construction more perfectly than to the observed motions of the planets. Two groups of observations in particular could not easily be made to fit the scheme. Mercury and Venus are never seen very far from the sun. For instance, if on a few successive nights Venus progressively appears higher in the

sky at sunset and therefore sets somewhat later in the evening, soon she reverses her course and moves closer to the sun again until she fades into the sunset. Her next appearance, then, is in the morning. She appears just before sunup, moves farther from the sun, and then returns toward the sun. The same is true of Mercury. Both seem to wobble in the sky from before to behind the sun.

Motion such as this is almost impossible to construct into the set of spheres of Aristotle. To obtain it, the spheres of Mercury and of Venus would have to oscillate back and forth rather than follow the steady, "perfect" motion of a circular orbit. Clearly something was wrong with the construction.

The second group of observations that disturbed the Aristotelian system is known as *retrograde motion*. While planets generally move from west to east among the stars, at times they reverse themselves and for a short period move in the opposite direction before resuming their general eastward paths. Their orbits describe short loops among the stars (Fig. 1–7), the retrograde motion.

Retrograde motion, too, clashes with the perfection of the circular orbits. Some rather arbitrary timing device would have to be incorporated into the primum mobile in order to produce the retrograde motions of the planets at the observed intervals. To state the problem in a nutshell: The Aristotelian system was fully in accord with the preconceived ideas of heavenly perfection. It predicted *approximately* what was observed. But when some of the finer details, such as the behavior of Mercury and Venus or retrograde motion, were introduced, the simple rotation of concentric spheres could not describe what was observed.

Fortunately for Greek thought, a rather simple way out of the dilemma was found which did not require the overthrow of the basic preconceived ideas. Neither the perfection of circular motion nor the stillness of the earth had to be abandoned in the

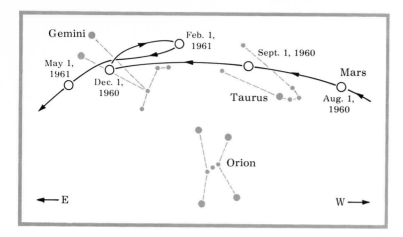

The positions of Mars on the celestial sphere between August, 1960, and May, 1961. From December 1, 1960, to February 1, 1961, Mars appeared to be moving in a westerly direction, the retrograde motion.

FIG. 1-7

more sophisticated Ptolemaic system, named after the author of the book *Almagest* (Ptolemy, ca. 90–168), in which the system was preserved for the Middle Ages.

The sun and moon behaved perfectly in the Aristotelian system and were left to revolve along their spheres in the Ptolemaic system. But each of the planets was displaced from its sphere to a little circle which had its center on that sphere. The combinations of circles—the large ones, called *deferents,* sweeping around the earth and the small ones, called *epicycles,* rotating around a point on the deferent—together described very well what was ac-

tually observed. The deferent of Mercury and Venus moved together with the deferent of the sun. Thus their motion from before to behind the sun resulted from the rotation of the epicycle which sometimes pushed the planet ahead of the sun and sometimes pushed it behind the sun (Fig. 1–9). And while the deferents of the other planets were not connected to that of the sun, the epicyclic motion of Mars, Jupiter, and Saturn also caused their retrograde motion. Thus by the addition of epicycles to the Aristotelian spheres, the idea of circular motion (on at least two circles per planet) was preserved and the observed motion of

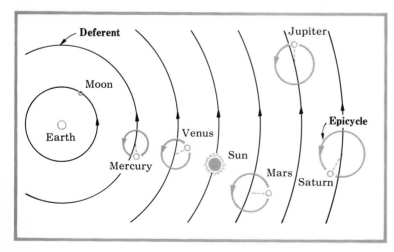

One of the simpler diagrams of the universe using the Ptolemaic theory of epicycles. In the most complex constructions, as many as 88 separate circles were needed to produce agreement between construction and observation.

FIG. 1-8

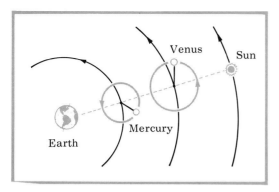

FIG. 1-9

Because the motion of the deferents of Mercury and Venus was tied to the motion of the sun, these two planets never moved far from it. The motion of their epicycles sometimes moved them a little ahead of the sun—into the predawn sky—or a little behind the sun—into the early evening sky.

the planets was described with much greater accuracy.

In this form the earliest ideas about the structure of the universe were transmitted to the Middle Ages. If observation had not improved in that period, or if men had been content to place their faith entirely in the perfection of the ideas rather than the accuracy of their observations, it might be our system still. Except for minor deviations, this construction predicted the motion of the moon (the months), of the sun (the seasons), of the planets, and of the stars. But minor deviations were noted and astronomers set out to improve the construction.

COPERNICUS

One of the problems of the Ptolemaic system was that it predicted retrograde motion only approximately. When the planet on the epicycle and the deferent both rotate in the same sense, the system predicts more rapid progress for a planet than is actually observed in the sky. Half a cycle later, when the planet on the epicycle and the deferent rotate in opposite senses, predicted progress is less than observed progress.

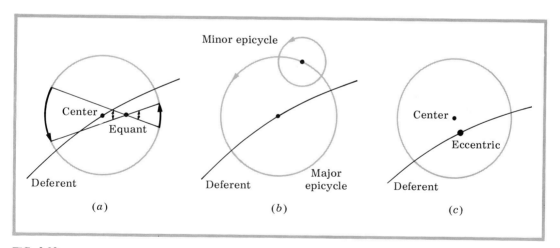

FIG. 1-10

(a) *Equant. The planet moves along a circular orbit through equal angles with respect to a point off the center of the circle in equal time periods. Thus, when the planet is near the equant on its orbit, it moves more slowly; when far away from the equant, more rapidly.* (b) *Major and minor epicycles. Additional epicycles were used to obtain more complex motion. The planet moves along an epicycle which revolves around a point on another epicycle which itself revolves around a deferent.* (c) *Eccentric. The planet moves along a circular orbit, but the center is not on the deferent. Thus the planet moves closer to and farther away from the deferent, and its apparent motion in the sky also changes.*

Again rather arbitrary timing was required in the Ptolemaic system to speed up and slow down motion as needed. But such arbitrariness was contrary to the basic philosophical idea of heavenly perfection upon which the system was founded. Hence other means had to be found to make the motion uniform again. Different astronomers used different devices for that purpose.

One construction chosen to preserve motion which was uniform in some respect and yet produced changing speeds was the *equant* (Fig. 1–10*a*). The equant is a point off the center of the circle around which motion is uniform. Thus the planet moves more slowly on the portion of the circle near the equant and more rapidly away from it—giving the needed changing speed —but its angular change with respect to the equant remains uniform. A second construction to achieve the same purpose was the introduction of minor epicycles to rotate around major epicycles (Fig. 1–10*b*). A third construction used by some astronomers was the *eccentric* (Fig. 1–10*c*), a circle like the epicycle whose center, however, was a point off the deferent. All these additional constructions rather cluttered up the basic Ptolemaic universe and, worse still, left medieval scholars in somewhat of a dilemma. Surely in His wisdom, the Creator would not have made such confusing systems, but if He did, just which one did He create?

Since the two basic ideas of the Ptolemaic system—circular orbits and a stationary earth—led to horribly complex constructions with 80 or more equants, epicycles, or eccentrics, one of the ideas had to be given up to simplify the system. This was done by Copernicus (1473–1543), a Polish cleric and astronomer, who felt that above all the perfection of circular orbits had to be maintained. Hence, he moved the center of the universe to the sun and introduced a moving earth. The basis of his thought is best given in his own language, taken from his book *De Revolutionibus Orbium Coelestium:*

In the first place we must observe that the Universe is spherical. This is either because that figure is the most perfect, as not being articulated but whole and complete in itself; or because it is the most capacious and therefore best suited for that which is to contain and preserve all things; or again because all the perfect parts of it, namely, Sun, Moon, and Stars are so formed; or because all things tend to assume this shape, as is seen in the case of drops of water and liquid bodies in general if freely formed. No one doubts that such a shape has been assigned to the heavenly bodies.

Copernicus's basic argument, of course, went right back to ancient Greece, where similar ideas produced the first systems. Indeed, he was particularly concerned that uniform circular motion had been debased when devices like eccentrics and equants with their off-center points were introduced:

Nevertheless, despite these irregularities, we must conclude that the motions of these bodies are ever circular or compounded of circles. For the irregularities themselves are subject to a definite law and recur at stated times, and this could not happen if the motions were not circular, for a circle alone can thus restore the place of a body as it was. So with the Sun which, by compounding of circular motions, brings ever again the changing days and nights and the four seasons of the year. Now therein it must be that divers motions are conjoined, since the simple celestial body cannot move irregularly in a single circle. For such irregularity must come of unevenness either in the moving force (whether inherent or acquired) or in the form of the revolving body. Both these alike the mind abhors regarding the most perfectly disposed bodies.

Since geocentric orbits could not describe the actual motions of the planets without devices that "the mind abhors," Copernicus abandoned that system. He displaced it with one compounded of 34 deferents and epicycles around a stationary sun. To bolster the scientific justification for the change he introduced and to get men to believe in his system, he added a philosophic rationale as well: "In the middle of all sits the Sun enthroned. In this most beautiful temple could we place this luminary in any better position from which he can illuminate the whole at once? . . . So sits the Sun as upon a royal throne ruling his children the planets which circle round him." Thus Copernicus argued for a heliocentric system in which the sun is surrounded by the planets moving in circular orbits (Fig. 1–11).

After he had finished these arguments, however, Copernicus seems to have been

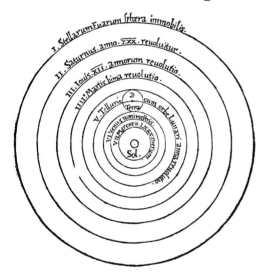

FIG. 1-11

Copernicus's universe. The sun is stationary at the center and an immobile sphere of fixed stars encloses the moving planets. This simple system gives only the basic heliocentric structure of Copernicus. To obtain agreement with observed motions, he also had to use epicycles. From De Revolutionibus Orbium Coelestium, *1566. (Yerkes Observatory Photograph)*

struck by the enormous implications of the change he introduced. Did the construction really represent the situation of sun, moon, and planets, was it a model of the universe, or was it merely a geometrical construction that helped astronomers with their work but left the earth "really" at the center of the universe, unique in creation? To remove man to an insignificant planet far from the sun ran counter to dogma and was, therefore, heretical. While the last quotation leaves little doubt about Copernicus's beliefs, in the remainder of *De Revolutionibus* he confined himself to the geometry and left the fundamental question alone. Yet we, who have accepted the heliocentric universe not only as a pretty and simple construction but as "reality," cannot avoid that question. Why do we believe in this system which we could regard simply as a diagram, helpful but not necessarily "real"?

One aspect of the Copernican construction rests on purely scientific arguments. Some of the observed behavior of planets requires that they revolve about the sun, not the earth. But that some planets revolve around the sun does not in turn require that the earth revolve around the sun. All observed behavior could still be fitted into an earth-centered system although it would be far more complex than the sun-centered one. The heliocentric system too rests on belief, not on evidence alone.

We have discussed the basic beliefs on which the earlier systems were built. What are our basic beliefs, those which are fundamental to the heliocentric system? One is a belief in simplicity. It is as if modern man had substituted simplicity for circularity as the criterion of divine perfection. We generally accept those ideas which strike us as simple. A second basis for our belief is the elegance or "prettiness" of the heliocentric construction. It joins all observations in one grand, though simple, scheme. This too encourages belief in the idea behind it. Finally, we base our belief in the heliocentric system on a faith in regularity. The earth is a nonluminous body like the planets; it shines by reflecting sunlight. Therefore it is much more plausible to let the earth circle the sun like Mercury, Venus, Mars, Jupiter, and Saturn than to reserve for it a unique place in the universe. Our faith in regularity thus reinforces the other bases for our belief in a revolving earth and a motionless sun. From these beliefs, which contrast with the basic beliefs held by Aristotle, comes our knowledge of a moving earth. That knowledge, of course, also contrasts with Aristotle's "knowledge."

THE COPERNICAN SYSTEM

The Copernican system has the sun motionless at the center of the solar system, the stars motionless at its extremes, and the planets—including the earth—revolving around the sun. Only the moon retains its orbit around the earth and is carried along with the earth. The earth makes a complete revolution around the sun in 1 year; Mercury and Venus in periods shorter than a year; and Mars, Jupiter, and Saturn in periods longer than 1 year.

This construction explains why the sun appears against different constellations at different times during the year and also the different stellar landscapes as the seasons pass along. The straight line earth-sun-stars sweeps a circle on the celestial sphere every year (Fig. 1–12). Therefore the sun moves among the stars from day to day and the opposite side of the earth, the night side, faces different constellations. The Copernican system also shows the cause of the phases of the moon. As the moon revolves around the earth every month, the portion that is illuminated by the sun and also visible on earth depends upon the relative positions of sun, earth, and moon (Fig. 1–13). With the moon "behind" the earth, its entire illuminated face is visible (full moon); when it is "in

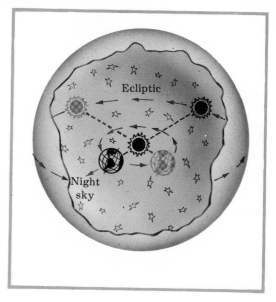

FIG. 1-12

As the earth revolves around the sun, the star background against which the sun appears changes. Also, the stars away from the sun and in the night sky change. In the course of a year the sun makes a complete sweep of the celestial sphere along the ecliptic and all stars become visible from some part of the earth. (Compare this construction with the geocentric construction of Fig. 1–5.)

front" of the earth, the visible surface is entirely dark (new moon); in positions between these extremes, a part of the illuminated face is visible. The Copernican construction explains *eclipses of the moon*, times when the moon falls in the shadow of the earth and is therefore unilluminated though at full-moon position (Fig. 1–14), and *eclipses of the sun*, times when the moon passes directly between the earth and the sun and therefore hides the sun in broad daylight.

Retrograde motion, too, is explained by the Copernican system (Fig. 1–15). We see planets against the stars, which are very far away compared to the distance to the planets. From night to night, both the planet and the earth progress along their orbits. A planet that one night is at A' appears among the stars at A'' when viewed from the earth at A. Several nights later

FIG. 1-13

Phases of the moon. As the moon revolves around the earth, different parts are illuminated by the sun and are also visible from earth. This gives rise to the phases of the moon. (Lick Observatory Photographs)

Eclipses of the sun and of the moon. An eclipse of the moon occurs when the moon passes into the shadow of the earth and becomes partly or totally dark. An eclipse of the sun occurs when the moon passes directly between the sun and the earth and blocks part of the sun's disk.

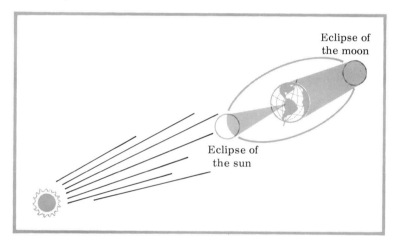

FIG. 1-14

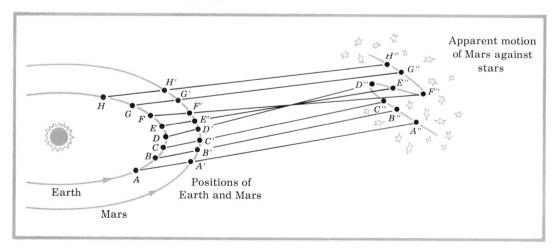

FIG. 1-15

Retrograde motion. Because the earth and Mars move at different speeds along orbits of different sizes, Mars seems to be moving backward among the stars whenever the two planets happen to be near each other in their revolutions around the sun. The same phenomenon occurs with the other planets.

13

the planet is at B', the earth at B, and the planet appears against the stars at B''. Progress along its orbit then places the planet at C', D', E', etc., while at the same time the earth moves to C, D, E, etc., and the position of the planet among the stars appears at C'', D'', E'', etc. But because the planet and the earth move at different speeds, the positions A'', B'', C'', D'', . . . of the planet among the stars appear to make the looping, retrograde motion.

Finally, the Copernican system explains why neither Mercury nor Venus is ever seen in the sky far from the sun. The orbits of Mercury and Venus are smaller than the earth's orbit. Thus (Fig. 1–16) as seen from the earth these two planets can only appear a few degrees to the east or the west of the sun. They are never near the midnight zenith, where the planets with orbits larger than the earth's can appear.

To explain the diurnal motion, Copernicus had to introduce a daily rotation of the earth around its axis. This rotation, from west to east, makes all heavenly bodies rise daily in the east and set in the west.

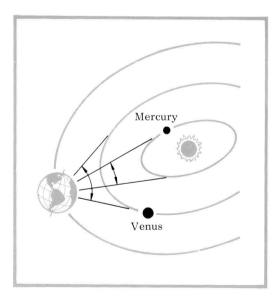

FIG. 1-16

Because the orbits of Mercury and Venus are smaller than that of the earth, they always appear a small angular distance away from the sun.

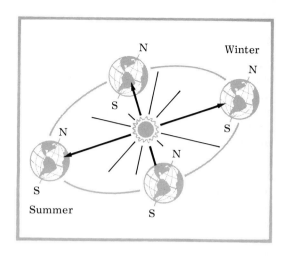

FIG. 1-17

Because the earth's axis is inclined, during part of the earth's revolution around the sun its rays reach the northern hemisphere most directly—our summer—and during other parts of the revolution they reach the southern hemisphere most directly—our winter. At intermediate times the rays strike most directly near the equator—fall and spring.

In the Copernican system the celestial sphere does not rotate daily and sweep all heavenly bodies along with it; it is at rest and appears to move only because the earth rotates.

The axis of the earth's rotation is inclined by 23.5° to the plane of its yearly revolution. This is the cause of the angle between the celestial equator and the ecliptic. When the earth's axis is tipped toward the sun (Fig. 1–17), the sun is above the celestial equator and it is summertime. When the axis, 6 months later, is tipped away from the sun, the sun appears to the south of the celestial equator and it is winter in the northern hemisphere. The fact that the planets are always seen in the constellations of the zodiac means that they revolve in about the same plane as the earth.

But the system was not without flaws, and objections were quickly raised. One question asked was: Why doesn't the earth fly apart from its rapid rotation, as a stone flies off when twirled on a string? The answer given to this question was another question: Why doesn't the celestial sphere fly apart in the Ptolemaic system since, being so much larger, it has to rotate even faster? But then it was asked: Why don't we notice strong winds as the earth rotates under the air? The answer was because the air sticks to the earth and is carried around with it. These objections were easily met. Far more difficult was the question: Why don't the stars move when viewed from one end of the earth's orbit and then, 6 months later, from the other (Fig. 1–18)? This phenomenon, known as *stellar parallax,* was a more crucial test, for it is inherent in the Copernican system although it had never been observed.

Parallax results when an object is viewed from different positions. For instance, if you raise your finger in front of you and then view it alternately with the left and right eyes, the finger seems to move back and forth. The cause is the slight separation between the eyes which, as a matter of fact, helps us gauge distances. But if you view a line at the far end of the classroom, some 20 or more feet away, first with the left and then with the right eye, the line doesn't wiggle back and forth. Parallax is appreciable only if the distance between the

two viewing positions (the eyes are about 2 in. apart) is large compared to the distance to the object seen. If the distance is small (2 in. compared to 20 ft), then parallax is not noticed.

The explanation given for the absence of observed stellar parallax was the one described in the last paragraph. It was asserted that the stars are too far away. But since it was known that the distance from one point on the earth's orbit to its opposite point is many millions of miles, the answer was hard to believe. It required that the stars be billions of miles away. Today we know that this is the correct answer. We know that the nearest star is about 25 million million miles away because its parallax and those of several thousand stars have been measured. Parallaxes usually are expressed by means of the angle made by the two lines of sight. The largest of them, that of the nearest star, is only 1.5 seconds of arc. The displacement of that star when viewed at 6-month intervals is about the same as the displacement of a line 4 miles away when seen first with the left and then with the right eye.

These were the major objections to the Copernican system, all of which could be answered although not all answers were

Stellar parallax. When seen from different parts of the earth's orbit, a nearby star should appear to move against the background of more distant stars.

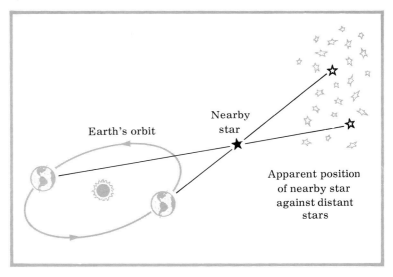

Earth's orbit

Nearby star

Apparent position of nearby star against distant stars

FIG. 1-18

FIG. 1-19

The phases of Venus. When only part of Venus's illuminated disk is visible from the earth, Venus must be near and her apparent size is large. When the entire illuminated disk is also visible from earth, she must be at the opposite side of the sun, far away, and her apparent size is much smaller. (Lowell Observatory Photograph)

when more fully illuminated. The predictions of the Copernican system are easily confirmed by observation (Fig. 1–19); they were first noted by Galileo.

Galileo, moreover, made another discovery with his telescope that tended to establish the Copernican system more firmly. He found that Jupiter is surrounded by four moons which circle the planet as our moon circles our earth. This was direct evidence that there are at least some heavenly bodies that do not circle the earth. It helped to displace the earth from the center of the universe. This discovery, particularly, made the Copernican system more than a mere geometrical construction and helped to confirm its "reality."

KEPLER

In spite of its successes, the Copernican system did not accomplish all its author had hoped it would. Regular motion along heliocentric circular orbits did not improve the description of the motion of the planets among the stars in keeping with the improvement in observational techniques. While calculations with his system were simpler, they were still not perfectly accurate. It remained for an astronomer and mathematician, Johannes Kepler (1571–1630), to perfect the system to the state in which we know it today.

Like Copernicus, Kepler tried to devise a simple system from which one could calculate the location of the planets among the stars. Kepler, however, had two advantages over Copernicus. First, he was trained as a mathematician with a greater command over various aspects of that discipline. Second, he had available the extremely accurate observations of his employer, Tycho Brahe (1546–1601), a Danish astronomer who had spent his life in the study of the stars and who had invented several instruments for making celestial observations more accurate.

One change that Kepler introduced was

believed. But the Copernican system had advantages that could not be matched by the Ptolemaic, though these were not confirmed until some years later when an Italian scientist, Galileo Galilei (1564–1642), constructed the first telescope and used it to observe the heavens.

Both the Copernican and the Ptolemaic systems predict that we should observe phases of the planet Venus just as we observe phases of the moon, although these cannot be observed without a telescope because Venus is too small an object in the sky. With a telescope the phases are easily seen and provide a test of the two systems. Whereas the Ptolemaic system predicts that the size of Venus should be about the same whether partially or more fully illuminated, the Copernican system predicts that she should appear larger when part of her surface is dimmed and smaller

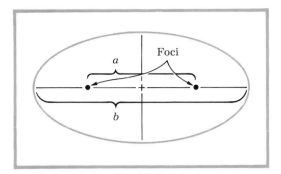

FIG. 1-20

Ellipse. An ellipse is a slightly squashed circle. It has two foci placed symmetrically with respect to its center, which help define the shape of the ellipse. The extent to which an ellipse differs from a circle is given by its eccentricity, a number obtained by dividing the distance between the foci by the distance along the major axis (a/b in the diagram). When the foci are near each other, the eccentricity is small and the ellipse approaches a circle in appearance.

in the shape of the planetary orbits. Instead of using circular orbits, he used elliptical orbits to account for the observation that planets are not always equidistant from the sun. An ellipse can be thought of as a squashed circle. Whereas the circle has one center, which is equidistant from all points on the circle, the ellipse has two *foci* which have a similar function with regard to the points on the ellipse.[1] The extent to which an ellipse differs from circularity is expressed by a number called the *eccentricity* of the ellipse. Most planetary orbits have small eccentricities; this means that they are nearly circular. Kepler expressed his findings in a statement now known as Kepler's *first law*: *The planets revolve around the sun in elliptical orbits with the sun at one of the foci of the ellipse.* This law made plain how the planets could at certain times move farther away from the sun than at others, something that circular orbits alone could not achieve.

In his *second law* Kepler accounted for the observed change in the velocity of mo-

[1]The precise definition of an ellipse is the locus of all points the sum of whose distance from two fixed points, the foci, is constant.

tion of the planets: *Planets sweep out equal areas with respect to the sun in equal times.* This law relates to the triangle made by the sun and the planet on two different days (Fig. 1–21). The areas of these triangles remain constant. If the planet is very far from the sun on its elliptical path, the altitude of the triangle is large. Its base must, therefore, be small, meaning that the planet travels slowly. When the planet is near the sun, on the other hand, the altitude is small, the base large, and the planet moves a larger distance along the orbit. Thus the changing speed of the planets follows a more sophisticated, yet regular, pattern.

Finally, in Kepler's *third law* there is a description of the relationship between the period of revolution of a planet (the time for a complete orbit) and its distance from the sun. For all planets *the square of the period of revolution is proportional to the distance to the sun, cubed.* In algebraic form, $T^2 = kR^3$; T equals the period of revolution and R the mean distance to the sun. The third law gives another regularity of the motion of planets. The speed with which they move is related to their distance from the sun. Kepler seems to have considered his third law his greatest achieve-

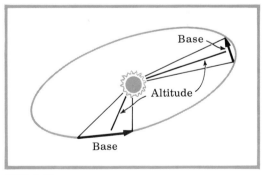

FIG. 1-21

The law of equal areas. When a planet is near the sun in its orbit, the altitude of the triangle is small and the planet must move a larger distance in a day to sweep out the same area than when it is far away from the sun and the altitude of the triangle is large. (The area of a triangle is ½ × base × altitude.)

ment. He was very much given to numerology and sought some mystical numerical relationships among the planets. After many futile attempts, he found such a relationship in the third law.

With these three laws, Kepler described the solar system essentially as we know it today. New planets—whose motions obey Kepler's three laws—have been discovered with the aid of telescopes. The position of planets is now known more accurately, and a number of other features of the solar system have been observed. All the new discoveries fit Kepler's scheme. The short but turbulent period from Copernicus to Kepler changed the ideas about the universe from those which were Aristotle's "knowledge" to those which constitute our "knowledge."

Questions and Problems

1. Make a diagram showing the relative positions of earth, moon, and sun at new moon; quarter moon; full moon.

2. During which hours of the day is the moon visible from a point on earth at new moon? quarter moon? full moon?

3. The moon revolves around the earth in a west-to-east direction. With the aid of a diagram determine in which direction the moon appears to move against the stars.

4. The earth revolves around the sun in a west-to-east direction. With the aid of a diagram determine in which direction the stars appear to move from day to day.

5. Indianapolis, Ind., and Denver, Colo., are both 39°45′N. Denver is about 30° farther west. How many hours apart are they with reference to the celestial sphere? Do both have the same zenith? at the same instant? on the same day?

6. Pittsburgh, Pa., and Miami, Fla., are exactly north-south of one another. Pittsburgh is 15° north of Miami. How many hours apart are they with reference to the celestial sphere? Do both have the same zenith? at the same instant? on the same day?

7. Does the zenith move eastward at the North Pole? at the equator? Can any planet ever be seen at zenith in Miami (25°N)? New Orleans, La. (30°N)? Memphis, Tenn. (35°N)? Philadelphia, Pa. (40°N)? Minneapolis, Minn. (45°N)?

8. If there are intelligent beings on Mars, do they ever see Venus at their midnight? Do they see the earth at midnight? Jupiter? Explain.

9. Construct a diagram for the solar system in which the earth remains motionless, the sun revolves around the earth, and the other planets revolve around the sun. (HINT: Think of the motions of the earth and the moon.)

10. Draw a diagram to show how the Copernican system predicts the phases of Venus; how the Ptolemaic system predicts the phases of Venus. Any difference? How does the size difference arise?

11. Does Venus ever present a phase which compares with the phase of the new moon? Does Mercury? Mars? Jupiter? Explain.

12. Is the time interval between the times when the sun is directly overhead on successive days the same throughout the year? Explain.

13. What geometric figure is the ellipse with maximum eccentricity? minimum eccentricity?

14. Which two apparently irregular aspects of planetary motion were shown to follow regular laws if elliptical orbits are assumed?

15. What role did each of the following play in the change from the Ptolemaic to the Copernican system? (a) epicycles, (b) retrograde motion, (c) stellar parrallax, (d) Jupiter's moons, (e) Venus's phases, (f) Venus's size.

16. Cite one bit of evidence which definitely demonstrates that (a) the moon is not a planet revolving around the sun; (b) Mars has an orbit larger than the earth's; (c) Venus has an orbit smaller than the earth's.

17. Draw an ellipse by putting two pins in a piece of cardboard. Loop a piece of string firmly around the pins. Then run a pencil point inside the string (Fig. 1–22) all around the two pins, pushing the pencil outward so that the string bulges. The result is an ellipse for which the two pins are the foci. Suppose your ellipse is a planetary orbit and your string is exactly three times as long as the distance

between the pins; compare the planet's orbital speed when it cuts the line which passes through the foci near the sun and away from the sun. At what point does the planet travel $1\frac{1}{2}$ times as fast as at the far point?

18. Use the data in Table 2—1 to confirm Kepler's third law for Venus, Jupiter, and Pluto. (HINT: Establish the value of k by means of the earth's orbit, $T = 1$ year and $R = 1$ AU.)

19. Define and explain the cause of retrograde motion of the planets, eclipses of the moon and of the sun, stellar parallax.

20. The earth rotates from west to east. How does that explain that the sun, moon, and stars seem to rise in the east and set in the west?

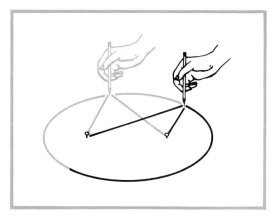

FIG. 1-22 *How to draw an ellipse.*

Suggestions for Further Reading

Texts on astronomy that give more information on all aspects of astronomy include:

Abell, George: *Exploration of the Universe*, Holt, Rinehart, and Winston, Inc., New York, 1964.

Baker, Robert H.: *Astronomy*, 8th ed., D. Van Nostrand Company, Inc., Princeton, N.J., 1964.

Hoyle, Fred: *Astronomy*, Doubleday & Company, Inc., Garden City, New York, 1962. Also treats historical developments.

Krogdahl, W. S.: *The Astronomical Universe*, 2d ed., The Macmillan Company, New York, 1962.

Wyatt, Stanley P.: *Principles of Astronomy*, Allyn and Bacon, Inc., Boston, 1964.

Books that treat the historical development of theories of the solar system are:

Armitage, Angus: *The World of Copernicus*, Mentor Books, New York, 1947 (paperback). A biography of Copernicus, with a discussion of the ideas that preceded him and the consequences of his work.

Koestler, Arthur: *The Sleepwalkers*, The Macmillan Company, New York, 1959. A very readable account of the lives of Copernicus, Kepler, and Galileo, and their contributions to astronomy.

Kuhn, Thomas: *The Copernican Revolution*, Vintage Books, Random House, New York, 1959 (paperback). A discussion of the sequence of ideas that preceded and followed Copernicus, with a thorough evaluation of his contribution.

Munitz, Milton K.: *Theories of the Universe*, The Free Press, Glencoe, Ill., 1957. Contains excerpts from the writings of early astronomers as well as interpretive statements by later authors.

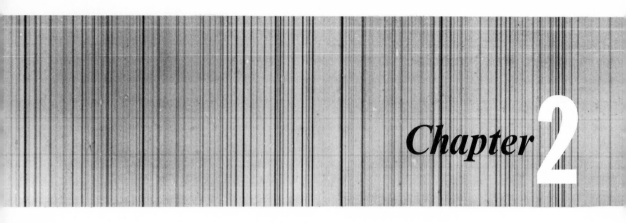

Chapter 2

The Constituents of the Solar System

The telescope, invented by Galileo, made possible the thorough study of the heavenly bodies, a study that has continued ever since and has added major new discoveries almost yearly. The telescope is a device for gathering and focusing the dim light of faint stars, thus bringing out details that are hidden to observation with the naked eye. How it functions is briefly discussed in Chap. 15. But the telescope was only the first of a series of improvements in the observational techniques of astronomy. Separation of starlight into its component colors gives information on the temperatures, composition, and velocity of motion of the stars and has led to theories concerning stellar evolution. Photographic techniques have extended the power of telescopes, since photographic plates can be exposed for a long time and thus gather light too faint to be observed visually. Finally, and most recently, the radio telescope, which detects radio signals emitted by celestial bodies, has added still another technique for finding out what is happening in the universe.

Chapters 2 and 3 describe some of the major characteristics of our solar system and of the stars beyond. The last chapter of this book describes galaxies of stars and some speculations concerning the past and future of the universe.

THE PLANETS

The major inhabitants of the solar system are the planets. While there are only six (including the earth) visible to the naked eye, three others have been discovered with the aid of telescopes, the last as recently as 1930. The planets can be divided into two groups, the inner or terrestrial planets—Mercury, Venus, Earth, and Mars—which are relatively small and of fairly high density, and the outer planets—Jupiter, Saturn, Uranus, Neptune, and Pluto—which are, with the exception of Pluto, much larger and much less dense. All planets revolve about the sun in elliptical orbits. Except for Pluto's orbit, which is inclined 17° from the plane of the earth's orbit, planetary orbits lie in nearly the same plane (Fig. 2–1). This explains why the planets are always

seen in the region of the zodiac. With the exception of the orbits of Mercury and Pluto, planetary orbits are very nearly circular. The distance from the earth to the sun, for instance, varies only from 91.4 million miles in our winter to 94.4 million miles in our summer. All planets revolve around the sun in the same west-to-east direction with speeds that vary according to Kepler's third law.

Table 2–1 gives the vital statistics of the planets. The mean distances from the sun are given in terms of the *astronomical unit*, AU, the mean distance between the earth and the sun (92.9 million miles). The table shows the basis for the distinctions between the inner and the outer planets. Mercury, Venus, Earth, and Mars are small and dense. Four of the outer planets, in contrast, are huge. The smallest of these, Uranus, has a diameter about four times as great, and a mass about fourteen times as great, as those of the earth, which is the largest of the inner planets. But the density of the outer planets is much smaller, showing that they must be differently constituted. The rotation of the outer planets is also much greater than that of the inner planets, especially when one considers their far greater size. Of the outer planets only Pluto is an enigma. The best estimates of its size, mass, and period of rotation make it more like the inner planets though it is, of course, the outermost of

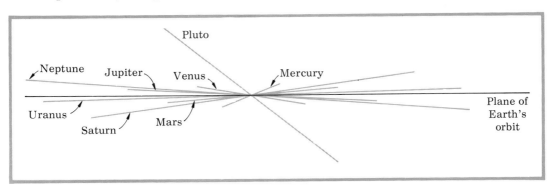

FIG. 2-1

Except for the orbit of Pluto, which is inclined 17° from the plane of the earth's orbit, planetary orbits lie very nearly in the same plane. (Orbit sizes are not to scale.)

TABLE 2-1

Some characteristics of the planets

Planet	Distance from sun (AU)	Period of revolution	Inclination of orbit	Eccentricity of orbit	Period of rotation
Mercury	0.39	88 days	7.0°	0.206	88 days
Venus	0.72	225 days	3.4°	0.007	30 days(?)
Earth	1.000	365 days	···	0.017	24 hr
Mars	1.52	687 days	1.9°	0.093	24.6 hr
Jupiter	5.20	11.9 years	1.3°	0.048	9.9 hr
Saturn	9.54	29.5 years	2.5°	0.056	10.2 hr
Uranus	19.19	84 years	0.8°	0.047	10.7 hr
Neptune	30.07	165 years	1.8°	0.009	15.8 hr
Pluto	39.52	248 years	17.1°	0.249	?
Sun	···	···	···	···	25–35 days
Moon	···	27.3 days	5.1°	0.055	27.3 days

all. It is also interesting to note that Jupiter, the largest of the planets, contains more mass than all the other bodies in the solar system added together except the sun. All that, however, constitutes only about 0.1 percent of the matter in the solar system. The rest is in the sun.

EARTH

Of all the planets, the earth is obviously the most interesting to man. The earth revolves in an orbit of mean distance 92.9 million miles from the sun in the period of 365.256 days. The slight excess over 365 days requires that every fourth year, a leap year, has 366 days, though in each century this adds 1 day too many; therefore the century years, except for those divisible by 400, are not leap years. Before the present calendar was adopted, with leap years to consume the approximately ¼ day by which the period of revolution differs from 365, considerable confusion existed in dates. Indeed, because of the calendar difficulties, Easter had slipped back into late winter. A calendar reform instituted by Pope Gregory XIII in 1582 had to wipe out 10 days before

establishing our present Gregorian calendar, which has served well since.

In addition to its revolution about the sun, the earth rotates daily about an axis that is inclined 23.5° toward the plane of its orbit. The inclination of the earth's

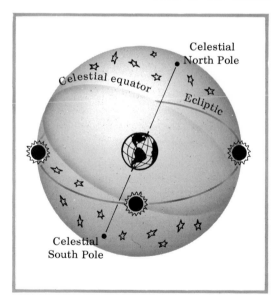

FIG. 2-2

The relative position of the celestial equator, which is determined by the earth's axis of rotation, and the ecliptic, which is determined by the position of the sun among the stars, produces the seasons.

Diameter (miles)	Density (grams/cm^3)	Number of satellites
3,000	4.1	
7,700	4.9	
7,900	5.52	1
4,200	3.85	2
86,600	1.33	12
71,000	0.71	9
32,000	1.26	5
28,000	1.61	2
3,600(?)	3.3(?)	?
864,000	1.41	
2,100	3.34	

axis is responsible for the rise of the ecliptic above and below the celestial equator, and also for the seasons (Fig. 2–2). In the northern hemisphere the earth's axis is inclined toward the sun in the summer. Consequently the sun appears above the equator. In the winter the axis is inclined away from the sun and the sun appears below the equator. This inclination is responsible for the summer and winter temperatures. When the sun is high above the equator in the summer, its rays are concentrated over a smaller area of the earth's surface than when the sun is below the equator and its rays strike at an angle (Fig. 2–3). Moreover, they have a shorter path through the atmosphere and less of their energy is dissipated. These factors

lead to the higher summer temperatures. They are more important than the distance to the sun in determining the temperatures, since the earth is about 3 million miles closer to the sun in the northern winter than in the northern summer.

The rapid rotation of the earth, which carries the equator around at a rate of about 1,000 mph, causes a slight bulge in that region with a corresponding flattening at the poles. The polar diameter of the earth is about 7,900 miles; its equatorial diameter is about 27 miles greater. This flattening of the earth at the poles is, of course, evidence for its rotation and confirmation of Copernicus's theory. However, records sent back by artificial satellites since 1957 have cast some doubt on the exact shape of the earth. It seems that the southern hemisphere is somewhat more pointed than the northern hemisphere, giving the earth a pear-shaped appearance. How to interpret that shape is not certain.

Contrary to the implications of statements such as "to the ends of the earth" which have reached us from antiquity, the ancient Greeks knew quite well that the earth was spherical. They knew it from observations of how ships appear on the horizon, mast first, then deck, then the entire ship (Fig. 2–4). They had also observed the circular shadow of the earth on the moon during lunar eclipses. Indeed, they knew not only the shape of the earth; they knew its diameter as well.

The first determination of the earth's diameter is due to Eratosthenes, an Alex-

When the sun's rays strike the earth more directly, more energy is received per unit area. This produces the higher summer temperatures. In the wintertime, the energy falls on a much larger area because of the oblique angle of contact. Winter temperatures are consequently lower.

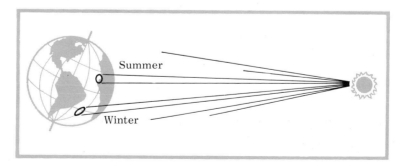

FIG. 2-3

The fact that ships seem to rise as they approach port is an indication of the spherical shape of the earth.

FIG. 2-4

andrian astronomer, who made the calculation in 235 B.C. Eratosthenes noted that at Syene (near the site of the present Aswan Dam in southern Egypt) a stick placed vertically into the ground casts no shadow at noon of the longest day of the year. At Alexandria, 488 miles to the north, at the same time a stick casts a shadow. He measured the lengths of the stick and its shadow; from these measurements he determined the diameter of the earth by the method of similar triangles (Fig. 2–5). The height of the stick and the length of the shadow told him the magnitude of the angle O. Since the line *OP* to the center of the earth, *P*, intersects the two parallel sun rays *MO* and *NP*, $\angle P = \angle O$. The angle *P* is to 488 miles as 360° is to the circumference of the earth, and the circumference of a circle is πd, in which *d* is the diameter. The value obtained by Eratosthenes, translated into miles, was 7,820 miles, not quite 100 miles less than the value accepted today.

THE MOON

The earth's nearest neighbor in the universe is the moon, which travels around the earth in an elliptical orbit with a mean distance of about 240,000 miles. Bodies like the moon which revolve around planets are known as *satellites*. Among the satellites, the moon is a very big one. Its diameter, 2,160 miles, is about one-fourth as great as

the earth's and only one-third smaller than that of the planet Mercury. Among satellites, it is exceeded in size by only four of the nearly thirty known satellites of the big, outer planets. In contrast, the two satellites of Mars, a planet of about the earth's size, are only about 10 miles in diameter.

Because the moon rotates in the same period as it revolves around the earth, al-

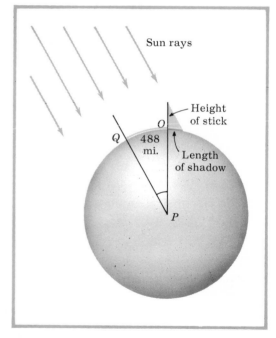

FIG. 2-5

From the shadow cast by a stick at O, Eratosthenes computed the angle at O and at P. Knowing the angle P and the distance between O and Q, he could compute the circumference of the earth.

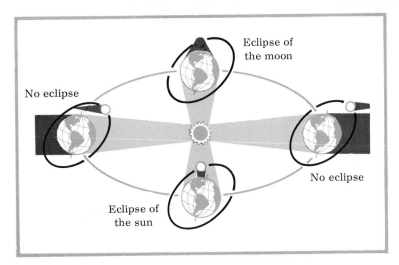

Eclipses occur whenever earth, moon, and sun are in a straight line. Since the moon's orbit is inclined to the orbit of the earth, when the moon passes between earth and sun or behind the earth, it may be above or below the line of sight and an eclipse need not occur.

FIG. 2-6

most half of its surface is forever hidden from our direct view. One of the results of programs to explore outer space, however, has been pictures of the back side of the moon. In 1960 Russia sent the first rocket to circle the moon, and the pictures transmitted back show that the surface features of its hidden portions are like those visible from the earth.

Eclipses of the sun occur when the moon passes directly between the earth and the sun, and lunar eclipses when it passes through the earth's shadow. At first thought, one might expect an eclipse of each kind every month, a solar eclipse at new moon and a lunar eclipse at full moon. The orbit

of the moon, however, is inclined at an angle of about 5° to the plane of the earth's orbit (Fig. 2–6). This means that most times at full or new moon, the moon is above or below the plane of the earth's orbit and does not pass through the line of sight. As a result, there are only between four and seven eclipses annually, at least two and no more than five of each kind. The eclipses may be total—complete blocking of the light—or partial. The character of an eclipse depends on whether the moon is directly in the line of sight or slightly above or below it. Even when the moon is directly in the line of sight, the eclipse may be total or annular (Fig. 2–7), de-

FIG. 2-7

Annular eclipse of sun, observed in Australia on April 8, 1959. (Photo by Ronald W. Boggis, Perth, Australia)

pending on whether the moon is near or far from the earth in its elliptical orbit. Actual seeing of an eclipse is further limited to certain regions of the earth, since it must be night at the place of observation for a lunar eclipse and daytime for a solar eclipse. The moon remains in the eclipsing position for a few hours at most.

The moon revolves about the earth in the period of 27.32 days if measured against the stars, the *sidereal* month, or just over 29.5 days if measured against the sun, the *synodic* month (Fig. 2–8). The difference arises from the fact that the earth, too, is revolving, and that in the course of a month, it is about 30° farther in its orbit around the sun. The earth's orientation with respect to the stars has therefore changed while the moon completes its sidereal orbit. The moon must catch up to the earth in the period between full moon and full moon; this takes about 2 days.

The moon's density is similar to that of the inner planets, and its composition is probably like that of the earth. The most striking difference is the complete absence of an atmosphere on the moon, making it possible to study its surface features in great detail with telescopes. These studies have recently been complemented by close-up pictures, sent by television, from rockets that circled the moon, and by the crash-landing and then, in 1966, the "soft"-landing of television cameras. Further explorations, including manned landing, are actively pursued as this book goes to press.

Some of the details of the moon's surface are noticeable even with the naked eye. Its darker and brighter areas turn out, on observation with the telescope, to be flat plains and rugged mountain areas (Fig. 2–9). From the shadows cast by the mountain ranges, it is possible to estimate the height to which they rise above the plains (Fig. 2–10). The highest visible lunar mountain is about 26,000 ft high, just a bit shorter than Mount Everest. However, the most notable features of the moon are its craters. Some 30,000 craters are distinguishable from earth, and the pictures transmitted back by moon probes show tens of thousands more. They range in size from great walled plains, 150 miles in diameter, to craters a few feet across and barely visible in the televised pictures (Fig. 2–11). From a number of craters *rays* emanate,

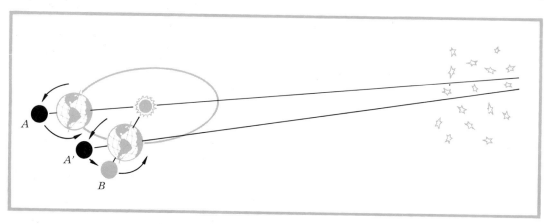

FIG. 2-8

The difference between the sidereal month and the synodic month arises from the fact that when the moon has completed one orbit with respect to the stars (A—A'), it is not back to the full-moon position. About two additional days are needed before it reaches the full-moon position again (B) directly in line with earth and sun. Hence the time for a synodic (solar) month is about 2 days longer than the time for a sidereal month, the time for a complete orbit.

FIG. 2-9

Telescopic view of the moon. Note the flat, dark areas called maria, *the craters, and the white streaks or rays emanating from the large craters.* (Lick Observatory Photograph)

light-colored streaks 5 to 10 miles wide, which pass over mountains and plains for distances of up to 1,500 miles.

The origin of the moon's craters is in some doubt. One suggestion is that they are the result of volcanic activity as we find it on earth. The other suggestion, which seems somewhat more plausible, is that the craters are the result of collisions with meteors (see below). The tremendous force of impact of the meteor compresses and melts

the moon's surface. This leads to an explosion, the result of which is the crater. The debris from the biggest explosions could be distributed in the form of the rays. The plausibility of this theory is supported by several similar craters on earth formed from explosions of meteors. The absence of an atmosphere on the moon explains why there are so many craters there and so few on earth. Smaller meteors, big enough, however, to cause craters of con-

A mountain range on the moon. From the length of the shadows it is possible to compute the height of the mountains. (Lick Observatory Photograph)

siderable size, are "burned out" in the earth's atmosphere and never reach the ground. Also, our atmosphere causes "weathering" of surface features, with rapid (astronomically speaking) changes. The moon lacks the protection of an atmosphere and, having no weather, maintains craters for much longer times.

The absence of a lunar atmosphere makes the moon an ideal spot for astronomical observations, and it is quite likely that an observatory will be established there soon after man arrives. (Currently the arrival is planned for about 1970). Many of the undesirable effects of the earth's atmosphere are absent there. On the other hand, a lunar astronomer would certainly need protection from the impact of tiny meteors which, though much smaller than bullets, would strike him with much higher velocities.

MERCURY

Mercury is a planet only a little larger than the moon; it is very near the sun. Its mean distance is only 36 million miles and its period of revolution 88 days. We have already mentioned that because of its small orbit, it is never seen far from the sun in the sky. Also, as a result of its position inferior to the earth, it shows phases. Like the moon, Mercury has its period of rotation equal to its period of revolution and always shows the same face to the sun. This face reaches a temperature of about 410°C whereas the reverse face seems to be near absolute zero, −273°C. These temperature conditions almost certainly preclude the existence of anything that we might call life on Mercury.

The orbit of Mercury has a relatively large eccentricity, 0.2. In contrast to the orbits of other planets, which are fixed against the celestial sphere, that of Mercury rotates slowly. This phenomenon, called *precession*, was partly unexplained until this century. Its explanation became one of the major triumphs of Einstein's theory of relativity.

Mercury, the smallest planet in the solar system, has no satellite.

VENUS

The planet Venus is very much of an enigma. Because of a dense atmosphere, consisting mostly of carbon dioxide and water vapor or ice crystals, it is impossible to see its surface. Hence very little is known about surface conditions. It has not been possible to establish exactly the period of rotation of Venus. Even the status of the atmosphere is in dispute, with some interpretations of the data indicating a high temperature and others a low one. If Venus's atmosphere is hot, it is unlikely that life could exist there in spite of the presence of water, which is now considered the most essential ingredient of any lifelike form, even bacteria. If Venus's atmosphere is cold, like ours, life would be quite possible because in size and other characteristics Venus resembles the earth.

FIG. 2-11

Left: *Part of the last picture televised by the F-a camera of Ranger VII, taken from 3.7 miles above the moon's surface, on July 31, 1964. The insets are pictures of small parts of the same area transmitted by the partial-scan cameras from distances down to 1,000 ft. They show craters that are as small as 3 ft in diameter.* (NASA/Jet Propulsion Laboratory Photo) Right: *One of the early pictures televised by Surveyor I, which landed softly on the moon on June 1, 1966. The moon's surface is rock strewn and several small craters appear at the left.*(NASA/Jet Propulsion Laboratory Photo)

Venus is the planet that comes nearest to the earth, being only about 25 million miles away under rare, favorable approaches of the two planets. In size it is also most nearly like the earth. Venus, like Mercury, has no satellite.

MARS

After Venus, the nearest planet to the earth is Mars, which comes within 35 million miles of the earth. In many respects Mars too resembles the earth quite closely: it has a thin atmosphere; it probably has weather; it has seasons during which a polar cap forms and disappears while a greenish belt grows from the equator outward and recedes again (Fig. 2–12); its day is about 24 hrs long; and its temperature changes from about 10°C to about −70°C, not unlike the variations in our arctic regions. But Mars's surface is as crater-filled as the moon's, and its atmosphere apparently has neither oxygen nor water vapor. Despite the growing green belt which strongly suggests some sort of vegetation, it is very doubtful that such a highly developed form of life exists there if, indeed, any form of life exists there at all.

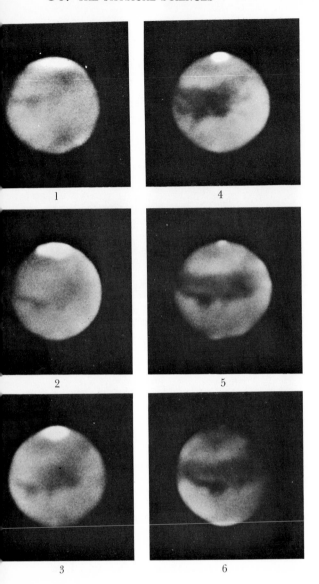

1

4

2

5

3

6

FIG. 2-12

Seasonal changes on Mars. The size of the white polar cap decreases with the onset of the Martian summer while the size of the dark area seems to grow from the equator upward. The dark area may indicate the presence of something "alive" on Mars although the pictures sent back by Mariner IV (Fig. 24-3) make a nonliving explanation much more likely. (Lowell Observatory Photographs)

Another aspect of Mars at one time figured strongly in the suggestion of life on Mars. The Italian astronomer Schiaparelli (1835–1910) in 1877 observed something

resembling "the finest thread of spider's web drawn across the disk." These fine lines he called canals. It was an unfortunate name, because some people with great imagination quickly transformed the observed network of lines into a system of irrigation canals, dug by intelligent beings, the Martians. Although other observers have noted surface features resembling fine lines, there is considerable uncertainty whether they run together into the spider's web pattern seen by Schiaparelli or whether they are simply some random aspects of surface detail.

Mars is known as the red planet. Its surface is distinctly reddish when viewed with the telescope, and even with the naked eye a reddish tint can be observed. It has two small satellites which revolve about the planet very rapidly, the larger one making three revolutions daily. In 1954 another mysterious feature of Mars was noticed—a big W, 1,000 miles in length. At first it was thought the W merely represented a strange cloud formation, but the same form reappeared in 1956 and 1958. There is no explanation for this appearance or for the canals if they do, indeed, exist.

THE LARGE OUTER PLANETS

Beyond Mars there is a gap in the solar system occupied by the asteroids, which we shall discuss later. Then comes the biggest of the outer planets, Jupiter.

The outer planets differ considerably in all respects from the inner planets. In addition to their size, their rapid rotation, their many satellites, and their much lower temperatures—ranging from about −130°C on Jupiter to about −200°C on Neptune—the structure of these planets is completely unlike that of the inner planets. The inner planets, except for Mercury, have a surface surrounded by an atmosphere. The outer planets probably have a very thin atmosphere that gets denser and denser as one approaches their centers, becoming much more compressed than matter on earth but without a distinct surface (Fig. 2–13). The compressed atmosphere may end at a small, rocky core. The atmosphere and compressed portions of the outer planets must contain much hydrogen, the lightest element, since their average densities are so very low.

Jupiter is by far the largest of the outer planets, and because of its great mass it seems to have influenced the orbits of a number of heavenly bodies. Its surface shows considerable marking, bright and dark bands and spots appearing and disappearing from time to time. One, the great red spot, which at times has covered an elliptical area 30,000 miles long, has persisted for nearly 100 years. The exact cause of these markings is not known. They have helped, however, to determine the period of rotation of the planet, which is about 10 hrs. The equator of Jupiter whips around at the rate of over 25,000 mph. With the invention of radio astronomy, bursts of intense radio signals have been detected from

FIG. 2-14

Jupiter, with the great red spot on the upper hemisphere. By noting its rate of motion, the period of rotation of the planet can be obtained. The photograph also shows one of Jupiter's satellites, in the upper right, and the satellite's shadow just above the great red spot. (Photograph from the Mount Wilson and Palomar Observatories)

Jupiter. What causes them is also unknown, though they may come from the Jovian equivalent of thunderstorms. Jupiter has the prodigious number of 12 satellites.

Probably the prettiest of all planets is Saturn (Fig. 2–15), with its rings that are clearly visible with even a low-power telescope. Saturn is the last of the planets visible with the naked eye. While the planet itself has a diameter of only 71,000 miles, its rings extend 100,000 miles farther, being about 171,000 miles in diameter. The rings are only about 10 miles thick.

The rings of Saturn consist of small ice and rock particles that revolve around the planet, the faster the closer to the planet's surface. Indeed, the inner edge of the rings moves more rapidly than the planet itself. Saturn has nine satellites in addition to the rings.

The next planet, Uranus, was discovered in 1781 by the English astronomer, Sir William Herschel (1738–1822), more or less by accident. After that discovery a search

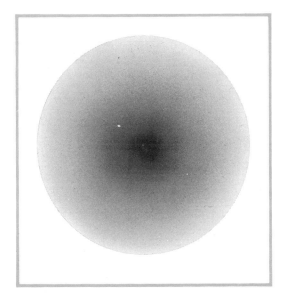

FIG. 2-13

The probable structure of the outer planets. A thin gaseous atmosphere becomes denser and denser toward the center and perhaps ends at the surface of a rocky core.

FIG. 2-15

Saturn and its rings. Under higher-power magnification, another break in the rings becomes visible, dividing the brighter, inner ring into two. (Photograph from the Mount Wilson and Palomar Observatories)

of records of the past 100 years showed that Uranus had been seen about 20 times before, but had always been set down as a star. Because of Uranus's 84-year period of revolution, the existing records were inadequate to calculate its orbit when it was discovered, and it took 40 more years of observation before enough data had been gathered. Then it became apparent that Uranus did not follow the calculated path, but was disturbed by still another heavenly body, correctly assumed to be an undiscovered planet.

The most notable feature of Uranus is the direction of its axis of rotation. The axis lies nearly in the plane of its orbit so that the planet rotates at approximately a right angle to the direction of its revolution about the sun.

The disturbance of Uranus's orbit led to calculations of the location of the other planet which would cause the observed deviations. Two young mathematicians, Urbain Leverrier (1811–1877) in France and John Couch Adams (1819–1892) in England, independently carried out this work and both predicted the identical position for the undiscovered planet in 1846. Leverrier was fortunate, however, in persuading the German astronomer Johann Galle

(1812–1910) to look for it. Galle found the planet Neptune after only a half hour's search within 1° of the place assigned it by Leverrier. Though Adams had finished his calculations a few weeks earlier than Leverrier, he had no luck in persuading British astronomers to look for Neptune. Until his unsuccessful attempt to direct a search for it came to light, Adams was thus deprived of his rightful claim to share the credit for the discovery. Today both men are generally listed as codiscoverers.

This little anecdote probably illustrates two things in the progress of science. First, that often, when the circumstances are ripe for a discovery, many workers independently make the same discovery. Second, as in all enterprises, luck plays a part in success. Galle's willingness to observe the right region of the sky coupled with the British astronomers' refusal gave Leverrier rather than Adams first claim to the discovery of Neptune.

The last planet to be discovered is Pluto, which is peculiar in several ways. First is the large eccentricity of its orbit, which brings it closer to the sun than Neptune at its *perihelion* (nearest the sun) position, though its mean distance is nearly 10 AU greater than Neptune's. Also, Pluto's orbit is inclined at a greater angle, 17°, than that of any other planet so that it dips in and out of the zodiac. Finally, unlike the outer planets, Pluto is a small planet with a diameter smaller than that of the earth. Its great distance and small size, which make it very dim in the sky, have left some doubts about its characteristics.

THE ASTEROIDS

The space between Mars and Jupiter is occupied by the *asteroids*, a large number of chunks of matter, irregular in shape and in their orbits. It is estimated that there are at least 30,000 asteroids, about 2,000 of which have already been observed long enough and often enough to calculate their orbits. Most of the asteroids are small, between 1 and 50 miles in diameter, and their masses all together add up to no more than perhaps 5 percent of the mass of the moon. The largest asteroid observed has a diameter of only about 500 miles. Their irregular shapes suggest that they may be fragments of a larger body or larger bodies.

In addition to questions of their origin, the asteroids are of great interest because some of them come extremely close to the earth. Several have passed within 1 to 3 million miles from the earth. While most asteroids have roughly circular orbits lying between the orbits of Mars and Jupiter, there are others with highly eccentric and often highly inclined orbits for which their huge neighbor, Jupiter, seems to be partly responsible (Fig. 2–16). The orbit of the asteroid Icarus, for instance, reaches inside the orbit of Mercury, and that of the asteroid Hidalgo as far out as the orbit of Saturn. Some of these highly eccentric orbits cut across the earth's orbit and suggest that an encounter with an asteroid is

not entirely out of the question. Fortunately most of the asteroids are so small that an encounter would not have catastrophic consequences unless the point of contact happened to be a populated area.

METEORS AND COMETS

While an encounter with an asteroid is unlikely, the earth daily collides with millions of *meteors*, much smaller particles from outer space, most of which are no larger than a pinhead. It has been estimated that the earth picks up more than 10 tons daily in meteor dust.

Meteors are too small to be seen until they enter the earth's atmosphere. Then, in collision with the atmospheric gases, they heat to incandescence and become visible as "shooting stars" in the sky. Occasionally a very large and very bright one, a "fireball," is seen.

Meteors enter the earth's atmosphere at all times of day and night, but there are

Orbits of asteroids. Most asteroids occupy the space between the orbits of Mars and Jupiter; Hidalgo, however, reaches as far as Saturn. While Adonis and Apollo intersect the earth's orbit, their orbits are inclined and an encounter with them will not occur.

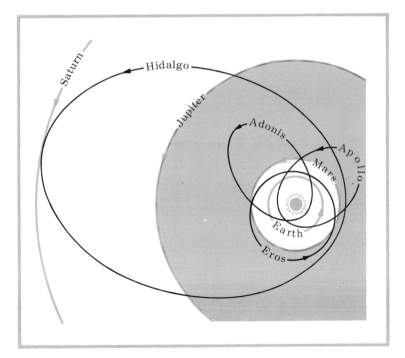

FIG. 2-16

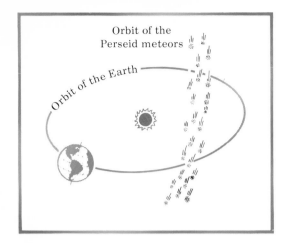

FIG. 2-17

The Perseid meteor shower occurs every year when the earth's orbit intersects a region of debris which comes from the direction of the constellation Perseus and which probably is cometary material. (After "Astronomy" by Robert H. Baker, Van Nostrand, Princeton, N.J., 1964)

FIG. 2-18

At least seven bright Leonid meteors and twice that many faint ones were photographed in a 2-min exposure on November 17, 1966, by Dave McLean. The Leonid meteor shower, which originates from the direction of the constellation Leo (not shown in the photograph), intersects the earth's orbit every 33 years. It usually provides a spectacular show, with 1,000 or more meteors visible per minute in the early morning. (Wide World Photos)

times of the year when the earth seems to be cutting across belts of debris which give rise to meteor showers. One shower, the Perseids, comes from the direction of the constellation Perseus and hits the earth with regularity and brilliance in the 2 or 3 weeks around August 11. A number of other meteor showers have been identified and return at more or less regular intervals (Fig. 2–18). Meteors are best seen in the

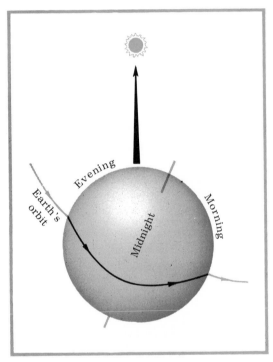

FIG. 2-19

In the morning hours, the earth faces toward the direction of revolution and the incidence of visible meteors is much greater. (After "Astronomy" by Robert H. Baker, Van Nostrand, Princeton, N.J. 1964)

early morning hours, when the direction of rotation of the earth is opposed to the direction of entry of meteors, increasing the number that become visible (Fig. 2–19). There is strong evidence to suggest that meteor showers are produced by remnants of material ejected from a comet or remaining when a comet has disappeared.

Comets are the true wanderers in the solar system. Nearly all have orbits that take them from far beyond Pluto to about the earth's orbit or even nearer the sun. Many are known to have closed elliptical orbits and to return at long intervals. Probably the most famous of these is Halley's comet, which has been recorded since 240 B.C. and returns every 76 years.

A period of 76 years is short for a comet, and it is not certain whether comets that have been observed only once return after perhaps hundreds of years or whether their orbits never close, making them visitors from beyond the solar system. The best guess at the moment is that they never entirely escape from the sun but have orbits of very great length and eccentricity.

Comets consist of a *nucleus*, a loose structure of ices with metallic and rock particles embedded in them, only about 1 mile in diameter. Surrounding the nucleus is the *coma*, some 10,000 to a million miles in diameter. The structure of the coma is so loose that the density of comets is probably no more than half an ounce per cubic mile. As a comet approaches the sun, its coma grows in diameter, and when the comet reaches a distance of between 2 and 3 AU from the sun, it grows a spectacular tail (Figs. 2–20 and 2–21). The tail results from the vaporizing of the ices in the nucleus and their expulsion due to the pressure of the sun's radiation. Consequently comet's tails always point away from the sun, trailing the comet as it approaches,

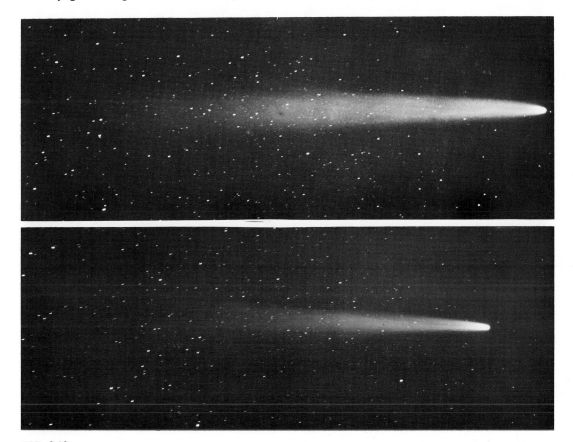

FIG. 2-20

Two pictures of Halley's comet taken 3 days apart. Note the growth of the tail and the coma. Also note that stars are clearly visible through the tail, indicating its slight density. (Photographs from the Mount Wilson and Palomar Observatories)

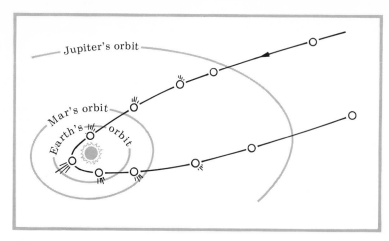

Diagram of the orbit of a comet. The comet consists of a small coma only on most of its orbit, which may extend far beyond the orbit of Pluto. When the comet comes as close as the orbit of Jupiter, the coma grows. Still closer, the comet grows a tail which always points away from the sun. The orbits of comets probably close into ellipses of great eccentricity.

FIG. 2-21

and preceding it as it recedes from the sun.

The expulsion of material from the nucleus ultimately leads to a comet's demise. The disappearance of at least one comet has been recorded. Biela's comet had been tracked for five returns at about 6-year intervals before it seemed to divide in 1846. In 1852 it reappeared as two comets which have not been seen since. But in 1872, 1885, and 1898, when the earth intersected the orbit of Biela's comet, pronounced meteor showers were observed; these, however, have since disappeared too.

make up about 95 percent of the material that enters the earth's atmosphere. The largest known stony meteorite, weighing somewhat more than a ton, fell in Furnas County, Nebraska, on February 18, 1948. Another, about one-third as large, fell at Paragould, Arkansas, in 1930. Large stones probably are less common than large irons because the iron meteorites offer greater resistance to fracture in their path through the atmosphere and on impact.

Two explosive impacts of meteorites have been recorded, both in Siberia. Both have

METEORITES

Occasionally a chunk of matter encountered by the earth is large enough to penetrate the atmosphere and land on the earth's surface. It is then called a *meteorite* and is one source of extraterrestrial material available for study. The other source is dust collected by manned and unmanned spacecraft.

Most of the meteorites are quite small, though some 35 meteorites weighing more than a ton have been discovered. The large meteorites are almost all "*irons*," consisting of nickel-iron alloys. Large "*stones*," consisting of iron-magnesium silicates are quite rare. On the other hand, stony meteorites

FIG. 2-22

The Ahnighito meteorite, a 34½-ton "iron." (American Museum of Natural History, New York)

FIG. 2-23

The largest stony meteorite found. It weighs over 1 ton and was part of a large fall of meteorites in Norton County, Kan., and Furnas County, Nebr., on February 18, 1948. (Reproduced by permission from "Catalog of the Collections of the Institute of Meteoritics, University of New Mexico," by Lincoln LaPaz, University of New Mexico Press, Albuquerque, N. Mex., 1965; photo by Meleski)

produced moonlike craters. The first, in 1911, devastated an area 20 to 30 miles in radius and created a number of craters more than 100 ft in diameter. The second, on February 12, 1947, behaved similarly. There is one large meteorite crater in the United States, the Barringer meteorite crater in Arizona, dating from before Columbus's time. The Barringer is nearly a mile in diameter, 570 ft deep, and rimmed by walls that rise 135 ft above the surrounding plain. Until the recent suggestion that some lakes may be water-filled meteorite craters, the Barringer crater was thought to be the largest impact crater on earth.

The only other notable inhabitant of the solar system is the sun itself. Since it is also the nearest and therefore most familiar of the stars, we shall discuss it in the next chapter in conjunction with the other stars.

FIG. 2-24

The Barringer meteor crater near Winslow, Ariz. Despite several attempts to find the meteorite which might have produced this large crater, it has not been found. (Photo by Dorsey Hager)

Questions and Problems

1. From the data given, complete Eratosthenes' computation of the diameter of the earth.

2. Suppose the sun was only three times as far as the moon; approximately what portion of the moon would be illuminated at quarter moon?

3. Is there a "sidereal" day? a "synodic" day? Explain.

4. Jupiter completes an orbit in about 12 years. What angular distance does it move in 4 hrs? Can this be easily noticed without a telescope? (Assume that a moon diameter, about ½°, can easily be determined. Ignore earth motion.)

5. Repeat the computation of Question 4 for the moon.

6. How long is the day on Mercury? Mars? Saturn? How long is the year on these planets?

7. Why does the surface temperature decrease on the planets, the further they are from the sun?

8. Use the data of Kepler's third law computed in Question 18 of Chap. 1 to determine the mean distance of an asteroid which has a period of 6 years.

9. What are the maximum and minimum distances between Earth and Venus? Earth and Mars?

10. It is possible though not likely for one planet to block another planet from our view. Which planets can Mars block? Venus?

11. Use a road map and the scale of 1 in. = 1 AU to draw planetary orbits to scale. Locate the sun at your hometown. Do all orbits fit on the map? If not, change the scale.

12. Compute the mass of Jupiter; of Saturn. Compare them with the mass of the earth.

13. Describe meteors, meteorites, asteroids, comets.

Suggestions for Further Reading

Texts on astronomy that contain more extensive discussions of the constituents of the solar system are listed at the end of Chap. 1.

Recent astronomical discoveries are in the magazine *Sky and Telescope*, Sky Publishing Company, Cambridge, Mass.

Books that describe the constituents of the solar system are:

Watson, Fletcher G.: *Between the Planets*, Anchor Books, Doubleday & Company, Inc., Garden City, N.Y., 1962 (paperback). Asteroids, comets, meteors, and meteorites.

Whipple, Fred L.: *Earth, Moon, and Planets*, Harvard University Press, Cambridge, Mass., 1963.

Chapter 3

Stars and Galaxies

With the exception of the sun, the stars are so far away that even in the most powerful telescopes they appear merely as dots of light. Yet modern techniques of observation coupled with the theories of astrophysics have permitted astronomers to build a picture of the universe which is surprisingly detailed. Foremost in this work is the analysis of the spectra of stars, the components of the light which they emit. From spectrum analysis one can obtain the temperature, composition, and motion of the stars. This in turn leads to inferences concerning their sizes and ages. Information about the age of stars leads to suggestions of a pattern of growth and decline of stars so that we have today some indication of their life cycles. Yet, most of the inferences drawn depend upon our knowledge of the details of the one star that is near us, the sun. In studying the heavens, the astronomer is like the pilot who has never landed in some foreign country but has flown over it often at high altitude. By noting carefully and repeatedly what he sees there, though at great height, and assuming that what he sees is similar to what he knows at home, he can piece together a fairly good account of life in the country he has never visited. Home, in astronomy, is the sun. Its study is therefore one of the most important fields of astronomy.

THE SUN

The sun is by far the dominant object in the solar system. It is at the focus of the elliptical orbits of all planets, asteroids, comets, and meteors—all the solar-system bodies except the satellites. Through its mass the sun maintains them in their paths. Its mass is more than 300,000 times as great as that of the earth; more than 1,000 times as large as that of the largest planet, Jupiter. Its diameter is 864,000 miles: if the earth were at the sun's center, the moon's orbit would be a little more than halfway to the sun's surface. The sun's density is low, 1.41, like that of the outer planets, indicating that it is composed mostly of hydrogen. It rotates in a period

of about 25 days near the solar equator and about 35 days near the solar poles. This means, of course, that its structure cannot be as rigid as that of the earth and that considerable shearing action occurs in the sun. Other evidences of turbulence in the sun's structure confirm its nonrigidity.

The interior of the sun is known only from theoretical researches. Near the center the temperature is about 20 million °C, and the density is at least five times as great as the greatest density known on the surface of the earth. Progressively outward from the center, both the temperature and the density decrease gradually until at the visible surface the temperature is only 4500°C and the density perhaps one-thousandth of the density of our atmosphere.

One might ask how we can tell about conditions in the interior of the sun when we have no direct methods for observation. What kind of theory can describe that which cannot be seen? Actually the problem is fairly easy to formulate in principle, though solutions are by no means easily obtained.

A simplified formulation considers energy pressure and gravitational pressure. As we mentioned in connection with comets' tails, radiant energy generates a pressure on matter. The energy produced at the center of the sun presses on the layer around it; the energy produced in that layer presses on

The total amount of energy emitted by the sun equals the amount received by a square inch on the earth's surface multiplied by the number of square inches of area on the sphere whose diameter is 1 AU.

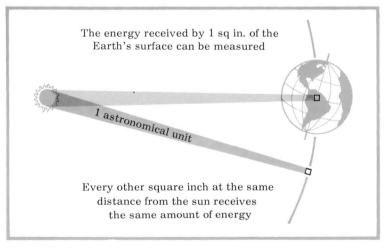

The energy received by 1 sq in. of the Earth's surface can be measured

1 astronomical unit

Every other square inch at the same distance from the sun receives the same amount of energy

FIG. 3-1

the next layer out; and so on. If we consider the sun as a series of layers, then each layer presses against the next one out. The tendency to expand because of this pressure is balanced by the gravitational attraction between the particles in each of the layers. And since the sun is and has been a stable star for millions of years, the outward radiation pressure and the inward pull of gravity must exactly balance one another. Then, from the known mass of the sun (which gives the total attraction) and the energy that pours forth from its surface, it is possible to calculate the conditions that must exist in its interior to maintain the balance. These conditions depend on the density and temperature at the center.

The calculation requires a knowledge of the amount of energy that is emitted by the sun's surface. To obtain it, we first measure the amount of solar energy received by the earth's surface (corrected for atmospheric absorption). Then we consider the following (Fig. 3–1). If the sun radiates equally in all directions, every square inch of a giant sphere constructed around the sun at the distance of the earth will receive the same amount of energy as a square inch on the earth's surface. The total amount of energy generated by the sun is the measured amount of energy received by 1 sq in. multiplied by the number of square inches on that sphere. That number, as we know from geometry, is $4\pi r^2$. The amount of solar radiation turns out to be prodigious. Each square yard of the sun's surface pours out 70,000 horsepower each second.

The visible surface of the sun, called the *photosphere*, is a layer about 250 miles thick. Through it pours all the energy emitted by the sun. Seen through the telescope, the photosphere has a mottled appearance which can be resolved into bright *granules* surrounded by narrow darker spaces (Fig. 3–2). The granules are from 150 to 900 miles in diameter but last only a few minutes. They consist of hot gases

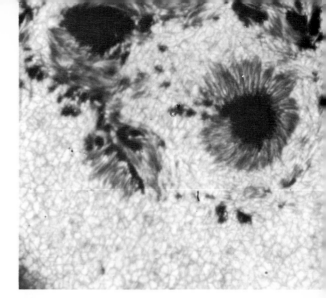

FIG. 3-2

Granules around a sunspot group, taken from a stratospheric balloon. The lighter "fluffy" regions are the granules consisting of hot gases. The dark areas are the much larger and cooler sunspots. (Project Stratoscope of Princeton University, sponsored by NSF, ONR, and NASA)

that come up from the interior of the sun and cool quickly at the surface, to be replaced by other granules coming from the interior.

In addition to the granules, the surface of the sun usually shows much larger dark, and therefore cooler, areas reaching sizes up to 90,000 miles in diameter. These are the *sunspots*. Sunspots last for periods ranging from a few weeks to several months. As they move across the disk of the sun, they give one indication of the rate of the sun's rotation.

Sunspots are an interesting though as yet mostly mysterious aspect of the sun. The number visible at any one time increases and decreases in cycles, with about 11 years elapsing between periods of maximum sunspot activity, and there are regular changes throughout a cycle. Just before the period of minimum activity, a cycle begins with a few sunspots at latitudes of about 35° north or south of the sun's equator. As the cycle progresses, their number increases and they gradually work their way toward the sun's equator. When they reach

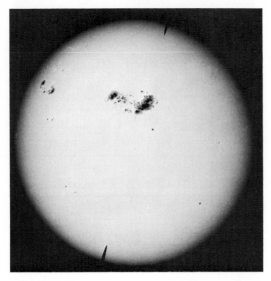

FIG. 3-3

The sun during a period of high sunspot activity, April 7, 1947. The large sunspot group in the center of the disk was one of the largest ever photographed. In addition, there is a large group rotating into view, and a number of smaller groups are visible, especially in the upper hemisphere. (Photograph from the Mount Wilson and Palomar Observatories)

lower latitudes 5 or 6 years later, their number begins to decrease until, at the end of the cycle, they reach a latitude of about

5°, where the last few sunspots of the old cycle fade. At that time a new cycle starts near the 35° latitudes again.

Generally sunspots appear in pairs consisting of a *preceding* and a *following* spot, with the preceding spot growing much larger and lasting much longer than the following spot. Zeeman-effect studies (Chap. 19) show that there are strong magnetic fields associated with sunspots, with the following and preceding spots of opposite magnetic polarity. The order of polarities persists for the entire cycle and is in the opposite direction for spots in the northern and southern solar hemispheres. Thus, if the magnetic polarity of the preceding and following spots is in the order north-south in the northern hemisphere of the sun in one cycle, in the southern hemisphere the order is south-north. Then, when a new cycle of sunspots makes its appearance after 11 years, the order is south-north in the northern hemisphere and north-south in the southern hemisphere.

What causes these reversals, the opposite polarities of preceding and following spots, the opposite polarities in the two hemispheres, the shift in location of the spots, and, finally, the 11-year cycles, is unknown.

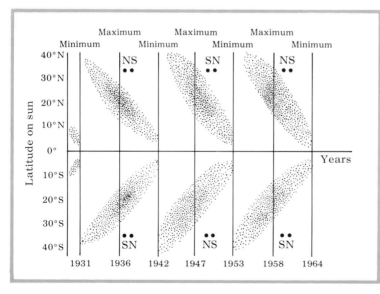

Approximate number and location of sunspots in the course of a sunspot cycle. At the beginning of the cycle, sunspots appear about 35° north and south of the solar equator. As the cycle progresses, their number increases and their location moves toward the equator until, near the end of the cycle, they appear near the equator and their number again becomes very small. Magnetic polarity of preceding and following spots is reversed in the two hemispheres and changes in each successive cycle.

FIG. 3-4

It is quite certain, however, that the cooler sunspots are brought to the surface by the turbulent motions of particles inside the sun.

THE CHROMOSPHERE
AND CORONA

During total eclipses of the sun, when the photosphere is hidden, or with an especially adapted telescope called the *coronagraph,* which blocks out the sun's brilliant disk, two other shells that surround the sun become visible. The first, stretching for about 8,000 miles beyond the photosphere, is a brightly lit band called the *chromosphere.* Beyond it, and extending as much as 14 million miles into space, is the faintly glowing, tenuous *corona.* The chromosphere and the corona are regions in which the gases are very sparse, but apparently in great turmoil. Their temperatures increase from the 4500°C of the photosphere, to tens of thousands of degrees in the chromosphere, up to a million degrees in the corona. Both the chromosphere and the corona are the source of radio signals and X radiation.

The turbulence of the outer parts of the sun produces characteristic outbursts of energy and matter which can be observed when the photosphere is blocked. At times *prominences,* huge clouds of chromospheric material, appear against the corona at distances up to a million miles above the chromosphere. Prominences differ greatly in their behavior, some hanging quietly before falling; others erupting with speeds up to 450 miles/sec; still others apparently forming high above the sun and gradually moving downward. The cause and nature of prominences are largely unknown.

Similar to prominences are *solar flares,* sudden and short-lived increases in brightness in the corona associated with sunspots. Solar flares undoubtedly result from the interaction of material erupting from the sunspot with the gases of the corona. This matter apparently continues to travel outward from the sun because solar flares are often accompanied by the appearance of northern lights, *aurora borealis,* on earth

 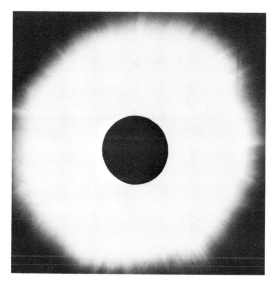

FIG. 3-5

Shape of the sun's corona. The left picture was taken at a time of minimum sunspot activity, June 18, 1918; the right picture was taken at a time of maximum sunspot activity, May 20, 1947. (Left, Photograph from the Mount Wilson and Palomar Observatories; right, Yerkes Observatory Photograph)

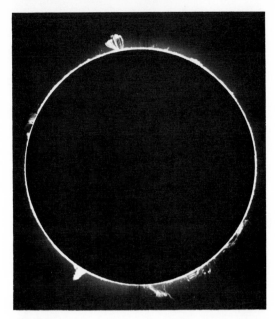

FIG. 3-6

The nearly total eclipse of the sun, December 9, 1929, during which a number of solar prominences of different shapes appeared. (Photograph from the Mount Wilson and Palomar Observatories)

and the disruption of radio communication, both of which can be traced to the arrival of solar particles high in the earth's atmosphere.

One final word about the sun. The amount of energy poured forth by it clearly is of different order of magnitude from the amount of energy we obtain from burning oil or coal, or from hydroelectric power stations. Until recently this was a mystery too, but with the discovery of "atomic energy," that mystery has been cleared up. We now know that hydrogen atoms fuse into heavier elements. The process of fusion (see Chap. 18) provides sufficient energy to keep the sun and the stars glowing brightly for billions of years in spite of their fantastic rates of energy production.

THE STARS

While it is the nearest and therefore the most accessible star for study, the sun turns out to be quite average in its properties. With modern methods of observation and the calculations of astrophysics, much more than the location of stars on the celestial sphere is known. The temperatures, both surface and interior, the dimensions, and the masses of a goodly number of stars have been studied in detail, enough to be quite certain that among those studied are representatives of all the types of stars in the universe. And among the different kinds of stars, the sun is quite ordinary, one of the more common, smaller, apparently normal stars.

The temperature of the surface of a star can be deduced directly from the spectrum of its light. Just as white-hot iron is much hotter than red-hot iron, a star which emits predominantly blue or white light is much hotter at the surface than a star that emits mostly yellow or red light. From this analysis, it has been possible to establish that the surface temperatures of stars vary from about 2000 to about 40,000°C. With an average surface temperature of 6000°, the sun is among a very large and common group of stars between the extremes.

The measurement of the amount of energy in the light which we receive from a star, when used in a calculation just like the one by which we can determine the energy radiated from the surface of the sun, gives the brightness of the star. It is necessary to distinguish between two kinds of brightness. One, the *absolute luminosity,* is the brightness at the surface of the star. The light emitted there, however, dims as it travels to the earth, to a greater extent as the distance is greater. The brightness we observe, *apparent luminosity,* thus depends on the absolute luminosity and the distance to the star. (Interstellar gas and dust between the star and the earth may also dim its light. These two are more troublesome since their presence and quantity cannot be observed and must be inferred from indirect evidence.) The brightest stars in the night sky are by no means those with the

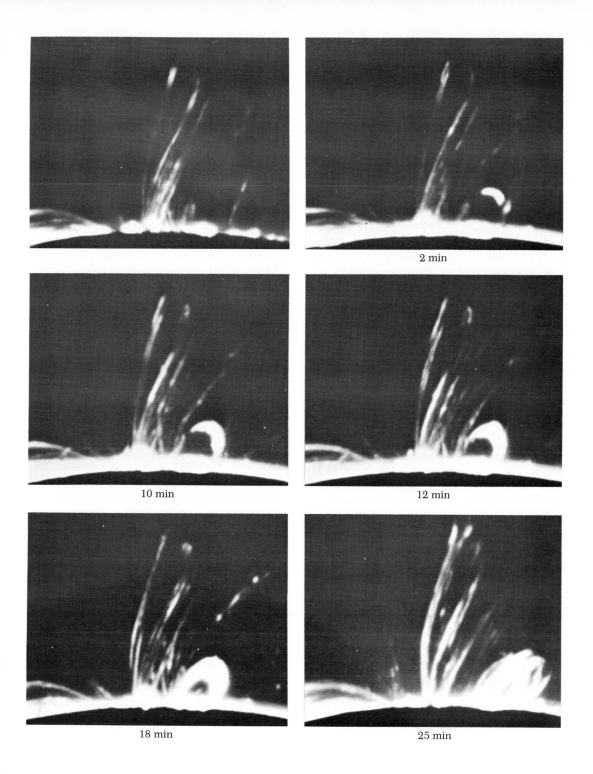

2 min

10 min

12 min

18 min

25 min

FIG. 3-7

A typical loop prominence, reaching about 100,000 miles above the chromosphere, taken on September 7, 1939. The short time interval between the pictures shows the vast and rapid changes taking place. (McMath-Hulbert Observatory, University of Michigan)

greatest absolute luminosity. They just happen to be nearby. In absolute luminosity, too, the sun is ordinary. There are stars 500,000 times as bright as the sun and others only one five-thousandth as bright.

A diagram which plots the absolute luminosity of a star against the color of its light, known as the Hertzsprung-Russell (H-R) diagram after its discoverers, the Danish astronomer Ejnar Hertzsprung (b. 1873) and the American H. N. Russell (1877–1957), shows some interesting characteristics (Fig. 3–8). Most of the stars lie on the diagonal extending from the upper left to the lower right, known as the *main sequence* of stars. Main-sequence stars increase in brightness as their surface temperature increases. They range from the dull reddish stars at the lower right to the extremely bright white stars at the upper left. Since the brightness of a star increases with the amount of surface which radiates

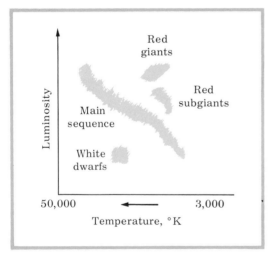

FIG. 3-8

Representation of the Hertzsprung-Russell (H–R) diagram. Most stars lie along the diagonal from upper left to lower right called the main sequence, which seems to include stars in their early and quite stable life histories. Then they probably cool and expand to become red subgiants or red giants. The white-dwarf stage represents extremely small and extremely hot stars, probably stars that are near exhaustion of their available energies and will soon become cool and dark.

(the star's size) as well as with the temperature, this means that main-sequence stars range from red dwarfs to white giants.

But there are stars that do not fit the main sequence. In the upper right are red stars that are much brighter than main-sequence stars of equal temperature. These, which must have huge surface areas to be so bright, are known as *red giants*. Some red giants are so large that they would fill the entire orbit of Mars. In the lower left are stars that are quite dim although their light is white. To emit so little light in spite of their high temperatures, these stars must be very small. They are the *white dwarfs*, some of them smaller than the earth.

The H-R diagram has given rise to some fairly well-defined notions about the life of stars. It is now thought that stars are born into the main sequence by the collection of hydrogen gas into a condensed structure large enough to begin radiating energy. Their place along the main sequence depends upon the amount of matter that congeals to form the star. The greater the amount of matter, the hotter and brighter the star when formed.

But stars do not remain forever in their original state, though their lifetimes are measured from tens of thousands of years for the very hot, rapidly burning white giants up to billions of years for ordinary stars like the sun. Since in all stars there is a balance between the energy-radiation pressure and gravity, very massive (high-gravity) stars maintain the balance by a high rate of energy production. But the energy produced consumes the hydrogen fuel of stars. Thus by shining, stars gradually spend themselves, and the bright, rapidly radiating stars spend themselves faster.

The life history of a star is approximately this. It is born into the main sequence, where it slowly and apparently without much outward change consumes a part of its hydrogen fuel. This goes on for thousands to billions of years, depending upon the mass of the star at birth. When a substantial fraction of the hydrogen has been used, the star begins to cool on its surface and to expand. It becomes redder but maintains its brightness by its larger surface area. In this process it moves off the main sequence to the right, becoming a red giant if it was originally large, or a red subgiant if it was originally smaller. Thereafter the star develops further although it is not certain how the changes take place. Most astronomers agree that in the end the star becomes highly compact and very hot, a white dwarf in the lower left-hand corner of the H-R diagram. This is the graveyard of stars because being hot, they dissipate their energy very quickly and presumably end up cold and invisible.

So much of the history of stars is accepted by most astronomers. It is an unsatisfactory picture because so many gaps are left. No account is given in it for several kinds of *variable stars,* an interesting and important group which change their light intensity at regular intervals, or for many other special kinds of stars that do not fit. Also, no account is given in it for the development that takes the cool, gigantic red giants and converts them into the hot, tiny white dwarfs. However, neither observation nor theory is adequately developed as yet to fill the vacant gaps to the satisfaction of most astronomers. The study of the creation of the heavenly bodies and of the universe is one of the liveliest and most interesting, but also one of the most difficult and undeveloped branches of science. We shall return to it at the end of the book.

VARIABLES

Several kinds of variable stars are now recognized in which some structural instability gives rise to regular pulsations, but little is known about the how or why of this strange behavior. Equally mysterious is the existence of the several different kinds. The *Cepheid variables,* so called because they are represented in the constellation Cepheus, have a special historical significance because it was among them that Miss H. Leavitt (1868–1923) of the Harvard Observatory discovered a relationship between the luminosity and the period of their variation. This discovery led to the best method now available for measuring large stellar distances and helped solve one of the most

FIG. 3-9

Nova Herculis, which burst into prominence in 1934. In the upper picture it is barely visible at the tip of the arrow despite the greater brightness of the surrounding stars, which indictates a longer exposure. In the lower picture it has increased its brightness manifold. (Yerkes Observatory Photograph)

difficult problems in astronomy. The Cepheid variables normally have periods of pulsation ranging from 1 day for dim ones to about 50 days for bright ones. In these periods they change their brightness by factors of about 2 to 5.

Study of the variable stars requires the skills and instruments of the professional astronomer. Another group of unstable stars, the *novae,* can readily be detected by the amateur. Novae, or new stars, derive their name from the fact that the earliest novae, which were discovered long before the invention of telescopes, appeared on the celestial sphere where no star had been observed before. Thus they seemed like newly born stars.

Novae are stars that suddenly increase their luminosity by factors of 10,000 or more. Consequently a star that is invisible to the naked eye may suddenly flare into a nova of great prominence, from which it fades over a period of several months. Some novae have flared more than once, though most appear once only and then fade again to relative insignificance. Novae are now thought to be stars well along in their evolutionary path which become unstable and flare while shedding a sizable fraction of their mass.

An occasional nova attains such a brightness that it is put into a distinct class, the *supernovae.* Supernovae may attain a brightness equal to that of several millions of stars. Supernovae probably represent the same sort of development as do novae, though they probably began as larger stars which reach exceptional brightness and pour exceptionally large amounts of matter into space during their explosion.

One other group of stars of special interest to the astronomer is the *binaries,* pairs of stars that are sufficiently close together to influence each other's motion. Binaries revolve around each other as the moon revolves around the earth. Periods of revolution of many binaries have been measured. They range from days to hundreds of years. Some binaries are as close

to one another as the earth is to the sun; others are farther than Pluto is from the sun. Some consist of stars of nearly equal brightness; others consist of a bright star and a dark star, recognized only by the motion of the bright companion around the other. Of major interest in the study of binaries is the fact that their masses may be calculated from their orbits around one another. From this, the relation between mass and luminosity of stars has been added to the temperature-luminosity relation of the H-R diagram. This, too, has contributed to our detailed knowledge of stars.

STELLAR DISTANCES

Mapping the universe, finding not only the direction of stars but also their distances from the solar system, is one of the most difficult tasks confronting astronomers because the distances are so fantastically large. The sun's nearest neighbor, α Centauri, is 2.5×10^{13} miles away. Given such immense distances, the astronomical unit, a mere 93 million miles, is totally inadequate and a more convenient measure of distance, the *light-year* is used. The light-year is the distance traveled by light in one year. Since the speed of light is 186,000 miles/sec, the light-year is 186,000 miles/sec $\times$ 3,600 sec/hr $\times$ 24 hr/day $\times$ 365 day/year, not quite 5.9×10^{12} miles. This places α Centauri 4.3 light-years away. What happens there today will not be known to us until 4.3 years from now, when the light reaches us to bear the message, or, to put it another way, the light of α Centauri, today, brings us a message 4.3 years old.

The only direct method for determining stellar distance is through the measurement of stellar parallax, the difference in the position of a star when viewed from one end of the earth's orbit and from the other (Fig. 3–10). When viewed from the two positions A and B, the angle of sight to the star changes slightly, compared to steadier

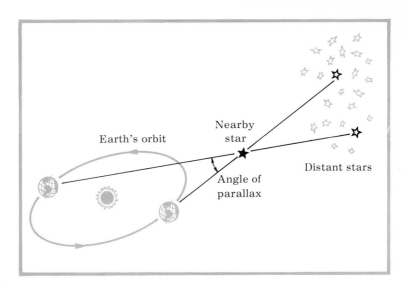

When measured against the background of distant stars at 6-month intervals, a nearby star appears slightly displaced. Knowing the angle of displacement, the stellar parallax, and the distance between the two positions from which sightings were made permits the computation of the distance to the star.

FIG. 3-10

and more distant stars; and from the measured values of the two angles *A* and *B*, and the distance between points *A* and *B*, the distance to the star may be computed. This is the surveyor's method for computing distances, although in its application in astronomy ingenious adaptations have to be used to measure the small angles of stellar parallax with sufficient accuracy. (The largest stellar parallax, that of α Centauri, is only 1.5 seconds of arc.) At this time, the distances to some 6,000 stars within 100 light-years of our sun have been measured by stellar parallax. The farthest of these has a parallax of about 0.03 second of arc, which probably is the limit of this type of measurement. For all other distance measurements indirect methods must be used.

The next most important method for obtaining stellar distances employs the difference between absolute luminosity (brightness at the star's surface) and apparent luminosity (its brightness in the telescope). This difference arises from the loss of light intensity as the light traverses space. Thus it is related to the distance of travel. The fundamental problem with this method is that only the apparent luminosity is directly measurable. Consequently the astronomer always faces

the question: Is this dim star dim because it is intrinsically dim and nearby, or because it is intrinsically very bright but very far away? To answer that question reliably, a means had to be found for estimating absolute luminosity. The method for doing this employs the period-luminosity relationship for variable stars discovered by Leavitt.

Leavitt had discovered the period-luminosity relationship by observing the variable stars in a small cluster of stars known as the Small Magellanic Cloud—now known to be about 750,000 light-years away. Since all these variable stars are in the same cluster, the distance to each is almost identically the same, and each loses the same fraction of its light intensity on its way to the telescope. This means that the *apparently dim* Small Magellanic Cloud variables are also *absolutely dim*, and the *apparently bright* Small Magellanic Cloud variables are also *absolutely bright*. Furthermore, Leavitt had discovered that the apparently but also absolutely bright variables have much longer periods of variation than the apparently but also absolutely dim ones. This was the clue needed by one of Miss Leavitt's colleagues at the Harvard Observatory, Harlow Shapley (b. 1885), to determine stellar distances.

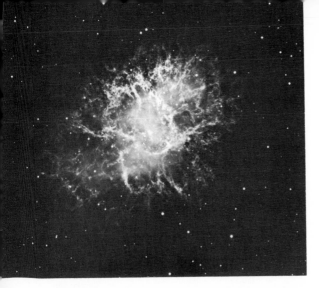

FIG. 3-11

The Crab Nebula in the constellation Taurus. It is the gases emitted by the explosion of a supernova in the year 1054, illuminated by a bright star within. (Photograph from the Mount Wilson and Palomar Observatories)

First Shapley searched for variable stars near enough so that their distances could be measured directly by stellar parallax. He found several and measured their distance. Next, with very sensitive instru-

FIG. 3-12

The Horsehead Nebula in the constellation Orion. A cloud of cool, dark gases obscures the light from brighter gases behind it. (Photograph from the Mount Wilson and Palomar Observatories)

ments, he measured the intensity of their light in the telescope—apparent luminosity. With these two measurements, Shapley could use the method we described for finding the energy output of the sun to compute the absolute luminosities of these nearby variables. Then he constructed a curve relating the absolute luminosity of the nearby variable stars to their period of variation.

When Shapley used his curve to compute the distance of the Small Magellanic Cloud variables, he found that all, whether dim or bright, fitted the curve if he made allowance for the loss in intensity appropriate for travel through a distance of 750,000 light-years. Hence, the nearby variables, adjusted for their measured distances, and the Small Magellanic Cloud variables, adjusted for 750,000 light-years, followed the same period–absolute luminosity curve. Since in at least two places in the universe, within measurable parallax of the sun and in the Small Magellanic Cloud, the same period–absolute luminosity relationship seemed to hold, Shapley then took the final logical step and suggested that his period–absolute luminosity curve holds everywhere in the universe. Then, whenever a variable star is found and its period of variation observed, the curve gives the absolute luminosity; direct measurement of brightness gives apparent luminosity; and the two are related by the light intensity lost during travel. From that loss the distance to the star can be computed. Although the method had to be modified when several kinds of variable stars were discovered, it has served as the foundation of all other distance determinations.

STELLAR MOTIONS

Already in 1718 Edmund Halley (1656–1742), for whom Halley's comet is named, had shown that certain stars described by Ptolemy were not where Ptolemy had located them but seemed to have moved in the meantime. With this recognition began the study of stellar motions. Two motions must be identified. One, across the celestial sphere, is the *proper* motion. It can be determined from photographs taken years apart that show the star in a different place in contrast to the background of other, steadier stars. A star visible only by telescope, called Barnard's star after the discoverer of its rapid proper motion, is the fastest known. It moves about 10 seconds of arc each year or a distance equal to the moon's diameter in about 175 years. Barnard's star is unusual, however. The average proper motion of the visible stars is about 0.1 second of arc per year, a distance much too small to be noticed except with the most precise instruments.

But observation of the change of a star's position on the celestial sphere gives its motion at right angles to our line of sight only. A star may also move toward or away from us without, however, changing its location on the celestial sphere. Here spectrophotometry comes into play. The spectrum of the light from a star changes toward the red if the star moves away from us and toward the blue if it is approaching (cf. Chap. 12). This type of motion is appreciable also and is shown by most stars.

STELLAR AGGREGATIONS

Soon after the invention of the telescope, astronomers became aware that there were many objects in the sky in addition to single stars. These, somewhat fuzzy in the telescope, were called *nebulae,* a name that stuck. The nebulous light sources, however, turned out to be of several different kinds. Some are simply clouds of gas illuminated by the light of some bright stars within them, such as the Crab Nebula shown in Fig. 3–11, which is the gases emitted by the explosion of a supernova. Others are the type of aggregation shown in Fig. 3–12, the Horsehead Nebula in the southern Milky Way. This nebula is a dark cloud of dust and gas obscuring the brighter background. But the "nebulae" of greatest in-

terest have turned out to be aggregations of stars. The simplest of these is the *star cluster,* a group of stars of about the same age bunched together and moving as a group. The Small Magellanic Cloud is an example of a star cluster. So are the two smaller groups of stars in Fig. 3–13. Star clusters may be part of larger aggregations or independent of them. They contain thousands to tens of thousands of stars.

Star clusters are among the least impressive celestial aggregations. They are small and show no significant internal structures. Far more interesting are the aggregations called *galaxies,* which consist of tens of millions of stars strung together in wheel-shaped groupings some ten thousands of light-years in diameter. The Great Galaxy in Andromeda (Fig. 3–13) is the nearest and most impressive example. While galaxies differ in their details (Figs. 3–14 to 3–16), presumably representing different stages in their development, they have the

FIG. 3-13

The Great Galaxy in the constellation Andromeda, the nearest galaxy to our Milky Way galaxy. The two bright spots are star clusters associated with the Great Galaxy in Andromeda, just as the two Magellanic Clouds are star clusters associated with our galaxy. (Photograph from the Mount Wilson and Palomar Observatories)

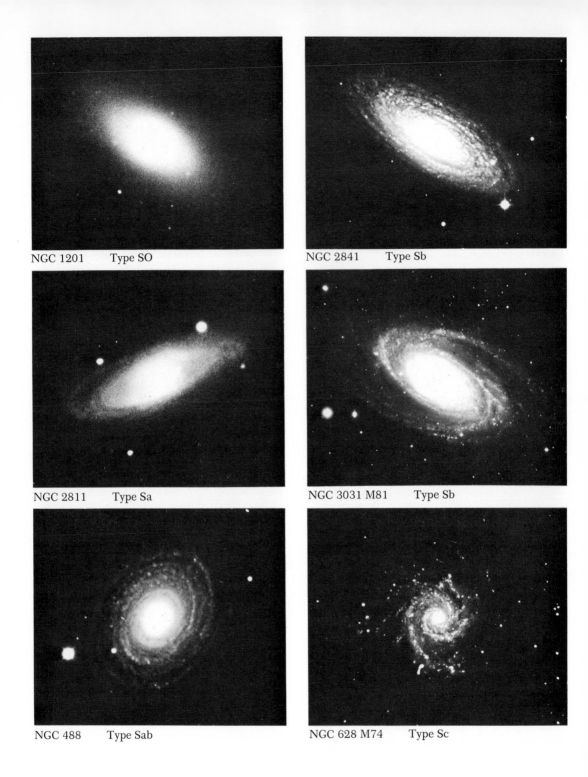

NGC 1201   Type SO

NGC 2841   Type Sb

NGC 2811   Type Sa

NGC 3031 M81   Type Sb

NGC 488   Type Sab

NGC 628 M74   Type Sc

FIG. 3-14

A group of six "normal" galaxies with different structures. Perhaps they represent a developmental sequence. Types are assigned galaxies according to their structure. NGC refers to Dryer's New General Catalogue of Galaxies; M to Messier's catalogue. (Photographs from the Mount Wilson and Palomar Observatories)

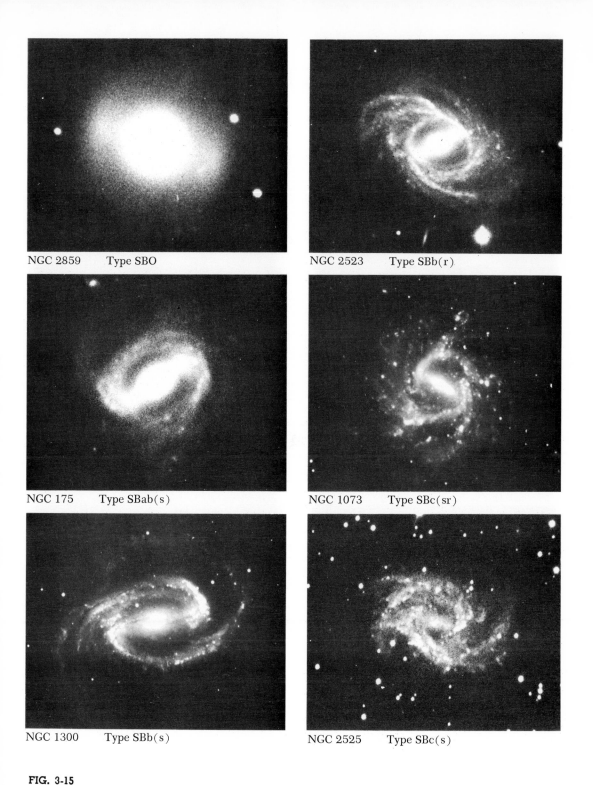

NGC 2859   Type SBO

NGC 2523   Type SBb(r)

NGC 175   Type SBab(s)

NGC 1073   Type SBc(sr)

NGC 1300   Type SBb(s)

NGC 2525   Type SBc(s)

FIG. 3-15

Another group of galaxies, called "barred" because of the pronounced bar that dissects their centers. Barred galaxies may represent a different developmental sequence. (Photographs from the Mount Wilson and Palomar Observatories)

53

FIG. 3-16

A group of galaxies in the constellation Hercules representing many types in one photograph. Many clusters of galaxies have been discovered with the 200-in. Hale telescope. (Photograph from the Mount Wilson and Palomar Observatories)

following features in common. They are disklike aggregations of tens of millions of stars, somewhere near 100,000 light-years in diameter, several thousand light-years thick at the edges, and some 15,000 to 20,000 light-years thick at the bulbous center. From this thick center portion they gradually thin toward the outside, sometimes in distinct arms, sometimes uniformly. The entire galaxy rotates slowly. Our own galaxy, for instance, makes a complete turn in about 200 million years.

The stars in a galaxy are not all of equal age. In the bulbous center and along the upper and lower surfaces of the wheel are stars that are older and further along in their evolution than those near the central plane of the disk (Fig. 3–18). Moreover, the bulbous central region is relatively dust-free, whereas the central plane of the galaxy is full of dust and cool gases. Since it is now believed that galaxies arise from the coagulation of gas and dust into stars, the parts of the galaxy with older stars have been swept dust-free. Along the central plane, on the other hand, there is still dust and new stars can and do still form.

Although galaxies have been observed wherever astronomers have looked for them, they are not scattered entirely at random throughout the universe. Each galaxy seems to be surrounded by a small number of star clusters grouped in a sphere around the nucleus. Often there are satel-

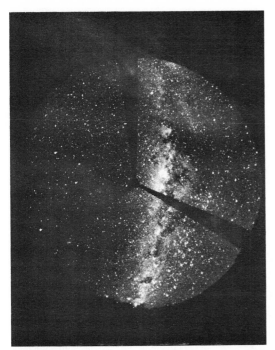

FIG. 3-17

Wide-angle photograph of the Milky Way. We are in the plane of a galaxy probably very similar to the Great Galaxy in Andromeda, looking sideways at its spiral arms. (Washburn Observatory, University of Wisconsin, Madison, Wis.; photo by Professor A. D. Code)

lite galaxies, smaller aggregations associated with the main one, such as the two satellite galaxies readily visible in the photograph of the Great Galaxy in Andromeda, or the two Magellanic Clouds, which are satellites of our own Milky Way galaxy. Then, galaxies themselves apparently are arranged into supergalaxies, consisting of tens or hundreds of galaxies grouped together. Even larger groupings are thought to occur though the observational evidence is still meager, since the more distant galaxies have only recently become distinguishable in the larger telescopes now in use. One bit of evidence concerning galaxies, however, is quite well established: the galaxies are moving away from one another and expanding into space, and they do so faster, the farther they are from us.

In this and the two preceding chapters we have raised havoc with ancient ideas. The changeless skies have been shown to be populated with moving stars, stars that are thought to be born and to die. Change, not permanence, birth and decay are the hallmarks of the heavens as well as of the earth. These ideas would have been

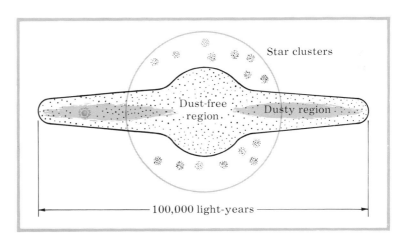

FIG. 3-18

Drawing of a sideways view of the Milky Way galaxy. It is about 100,000 light-years in diameter with a thick center and a thinning disk outward. The center and the upper and lower surfaces of the disk are relatively dust-free while the middle plane of the disk is full of dust. Surrounding the center is a group of star clusters. (George Gamow,"Matter, Earth, and Sky," © 1958. Reprinted by permission of Prentice-Hall, Inc., Englewood Cliffs, N.J.)

shattering to an Aristotle or a Copernicus, and they are not without an unsettling effect on our more modern thought. For the question of a beginning and an end to our earth and to the entire universe now takes on an observational, scientific, as well as a purely speculative meaning. "Was there a creation?" is now a scientific as well as a theological question, and so is "Will there be an end?" At the conclusion of this text we shall return to these questions. More immediately, however, we shall look at change on our own earth, for what we discover there raises the same questions of a beginning and an end.

Questions and Problems

1. List three ways in which the sun is "average" among the stars.

2. State two difficulties in determining stellar motion.

3. Give several observations which confirm the turbulence of the sun's interior.

4. Star clusters may be young or old. What kinds of evidence have we mentioned that could suggest the age of the stars in a star cluster?

5. Give the evidence which determines that (*a*) the sun is a star; (*b*) some star is a red giant; (*c*) a star has proper motion; (*d*) some stars are binaries.

6. Describe the characteristics of a main-sequence star.

7. Suggest why white dwarfs are in the "graveyard of the stars."

8. What assumption is inherent in Shapley's method for determining stellar distances?

9. Distinguish between nebulae, clusters, and galaxies.

Suggestions for Further Reading

Texts on astronomy that contain more extensive discussions of stars and galaxies are listed at the end of Chap. 1.

Books that describe the sun, stars, and galaxies include:

Baade, Walter: *Evolution of Stars and Galaxies*, Harvard University Press, Cambridge, Mass., 1963.

Bok, Bart J., and Priscilla F. Bok: *The Milky Way*, McGraw-Hill Book Company, Inc., New York, 1945.

Gamow, George: *A Star Called the Sun*, The Viking Press, New York, 1964.

Goldberg, Leo, and Lawrence Aller: *Atoms, Stars, and Nebulae*, McGraw-Hill Book Company, Inc., New York, 1943.

Menzel, Donald H.: *Our Sun*, Harvard University Press, Cambridge, Mass., 1959.

Shapley, Harlow: *Galaxies*, McGraw-Hill Book Company, Inc., New York, 1943.

Chapter 4

The Changing Earth

Change, birth, and decay in the heavens are a new idea, one which was accepted only after observations with the constantly improved astronomical instruments of the eighteenth and nineteenth centuries made the older idea of an unchanging universe completely untenable. The idea of change on earth, on the other hand, is as old as recorded history. We do not know why entirely different viewpoints prevailed to interpret evidence in the two domains. Observations alone were not the cause. Irregular changes in the heavens, like retrograde motion, were known to philosophers, and yet they extolled the perfection of the heavens. Irregular changes on earth are, of course, more widespread, and philosophers stressed the imperfection of the earth. They drew entirely different conclusions about the two realms.

Perhaps the reason for the different orientation lies in the ready availability of causal agents for changes on earth and their absence in the heavens. Change and an agent for change, a causal connection, are intimately associated in the thinking of man, whether civilized or primitive. Since philosophers could see the effects of wind and water on the soil, they could observe the changes and their agents. No similar agents could be observed or imagined in the heavens—except for the god-drawn celestial chariots of the very earliest theories. And in the absence of an agent for change, they apparently focused on order.

EROSION

Water is the immediate cause of most of the changes we observe on the surface of the earth. It freezes in the pores of rocks and splits them; it dissolves parts of important minerals and disintegrates them; it washes away loose soil. We know today that water, having carried away great quantities of topsoil on its way to the ocean, returns as rain to start the process all over again. It evaporates from the oceans, from rivers, lakes, and streams, from the soil, and from the animals and plants on it. The evaporated water condenses into clouds and comes back to the earth's surface as rain or snow to start the cycle again. The *water cycle*, powered by the earth's most important source of energy, the sun, degrades the earth's surface with each turn.

The water cycle represents new knowledge. Not until the seventeenth century, a time of great intellectual and scientific ferment, could men conceive that a few drops of rain and a few flakes of snow, falling occasionally during the year, could fill the mighty rivers all year long. Subterranean sources of water, unending in their capacity, were thought to fill the rivers. But in

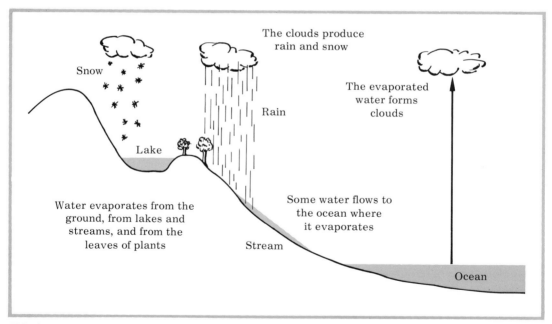

FIG. 4-1

The water cycle. Rain and snow carry water from the clouds to the earth. Much of the water evaporates immediately—from the soil, from streams and lakes, and from the leaves of plants which draw it from the soil. Some of the water, however, flows to the ocean, carrying with it large amounts of soil. Then the water evaporates from the ocean and forms clouds which bring rain and snow all over again.

1674 Pierre Perrault (1608–1680) measured the flow in the river Seine in Paris and estimated the yearly precipitation in its watershed area. His computation produced a surprise. The rainfall is not only enough to fill the Seine year-round; it produces six times as much water as is carried off by the river. The rest evaporates directly from the land or is held as groundwater in the pores of rocks or in soils. Thus the water cycle was established. From it results most of the degradation of the earth's surface, called *erosion*.

Two separate processes contribute to erosion, weathering and transportation. *Weathering* is the disintegration of rock; it is followed by *transportation* of the small particles, normally toward the sea. Water is involved in nearly every form of weathering, and it is the most important transportation medium.

Weathering processes are of two kinds, mechanical and chemical. *Mechanical weathering* results in fracture of the rock, with the fragments identical in composition to the fractured rock. Water freezing in crevices and expanding, and plant roots growing into them, are the most common causes of mechanical weathering, though in deserts or high on unprotected mountaintops rapid changes in temperature may produce uneven expansion and contraction of rocks and lead to their fracture. Also, both water and wind carry small rock particles which abrade the rocks they touch.

Chemical weathering differs from mechanical weathering by producing changes in structure and composition of the fragments in addition to the change in their size. Oxygen and carbon dioxide in the air, particularly in the presence of moisture, react with many rocks to cause their decomposition in a way similar to the rusting of iron. Or pure water may dissolve a component of a rock, or be absorbed by it, in either case causing the rock to crumble. Finally, plants take some chemicals from the ground, animals excrete some, and both decay into compounds that affect rocks. This too is an important source of chemical weathering.

It is obvious that the small loose particles formed by extensive weathering are more easily transported than the massive rock from which they originated. Yet weathering is not entirely destructive. The debris produced by weathering forms a blanket that protects the rocks underneath from further decomposition. As a covering layer, it reduces the contact between the rock and atmospheric gases; water, however, can still seep through to reach the rock. As an insulating layer, the debris moderates rapid changes in temperature and, if deep enough, keeps out frost. With time, the rock debris becomes mixed with organic material. This loose mixture of mineral and organic matter forms the *soil* in which plants grow. The plants, in turn, protect the soil against the eroding effects of wind and water. The production of rock debris and then soil, through weathering, thus first protects the rock underneath against further weathering. With time, however, this protective blanket invariably is carried away to expose the rocks once again to weathering.

Weathering is a slow process. The reduction of boulders to fine particles takes tens, hundreds, even thousands of years. Transportation, on the other hand, often takes place with dramatic suddenness. A heavy rain or a violent wind can transport thousands of tons of soil in minutes.

Two processes must be considered in the transportation of soil, picking up the particles to make them part of the transporting medium and then actually carrying them along. Particles of different sizes behave differently in these two steps.

Soil consists of many different-sized rock particles, from microscopic clays to huge boulders (Table 4–1). These are not picked up or transported with equal ease. Clays and silts are carried along most easily. Even lazy rivers and moderate breezes can carry along particles as small as clays and silts. Boulders, on the other hand, are carried only by mountain torrents or hurricane-

force winds. The particles in between behave as expected. The larger the particles,
the faster must the river flow or the wind
blow to carry them along. Otherwise the
particles settle out again.

Pickup of the load by the transporting
medium follows a perhaps unexpected pattern. Sand is most easily brought into the
suspended load, while silt and clay at one
end of the size distribution and gravel at
the other are more difficult to bring into
suspension. Consequently, when gentle rains
sweep over a landscape, little soil is picked
up and, since it is mostly sand, it is quickly
redeposited by the slowly flowing waters.
Because of their resistance to pickup, the
extremely small particles of the clays and
silts are left untouched. In contrast, a sudden downpour temporarily produces violent
surges of water. These pick up the clay and
silt particles, and when the downpour stops
and the water flow returns to normal, the
clays and silts are not again deposited. They
are carried along in streams and rivers out
toward the oceans. Thus the great damage
to land caused by violent rainstorms results
from their ability to pick up clays and silt
normally not affected by gentle rains.

One must distinguish between the kind
of suspended load, the type or size of the
material carried by the transporting medium, and the amount of suspended load.
The kind of suspended load depends almost
exclusively on the speed with which the
medium flows. The amount, on the other
hand, depends on the volume of flow. A
swift mountain stream easily carries clay,
silt, sand, pebbles, cobbles, even boulders.
But the total amount of water is small and
the total suspended load is small. A huge
lazy river, in contrast, carries an enormous
suspended load consisting, however, entirely of clay and silt.

The difference in pickup and transportation velocities for particles of different
sizes which explain many features of erosion also operate within a single stream.
Water does not flow evenly across a stream
bed. In shallower parts it flows more slowly;
in deeper channels, more rapidly. Eddies
and whirlpools produce rapid changes in
speed. And as the speed of water changes,
the kind and amount of suspended load
changes. Sand is picked up and redeposited. Clay is left at one place and eroded
a few hundred feet away. Sandbars form
that change the course of the stream and
also velocity of water flow. All these factors operate to effect a rapid and continuous interchange between the stream bed
and its suspended load. Finally, the parti-
cle-laden water rubs against the banks,
widening the stream by abrasion. Streams
constantly change their courses, their depth,
their velocity.

THE STAGES OF A STREAM VALLEY

Weathering and erosion affect all landscapes, whatever their detailed features.
Despite variations in the steepness of a terrain, the wetness of the climate, the thickness of the soil, or the hardness of the
bedrock, common characteristics appear in
the streams and rivers that drain the landscape. According to how long weathering
and erosion have operated on a landscape,

TABLE 4-1

*Classification of particle sizes**

Clay	less than $\frac{1}{256}$ mm		Pebbles	2 to 64 mm
Silt	$\frac{1}{256}$ to $\frac{1}{16}$ mm	Gravel	Cobbles	64 to 256 mm
Sand	$\frac{1}{16}$ to 2 mm		Boulders	greater than 256 mm

*After C. K. Wentworth, *Journal of Geology*, 1922, p. 381.

the stream and its valley may be classified as young, mature, or old.

How time affects the appearance of an
eroding area can be deduced in a highly
idealized manner from the factors that
govern pickup, transportation, and redeposition of the soil. Let us consider a small
landscape. It has a top, its highest ridge,
and a *base level,* a level below which erosion cannot cut. For this idealized landscape, as for the continents as a whole,
base level can be the ocean surface (Fig.
4–2). Erosion will wear this landscape
away until, ultimately, everything is at or
near base level. If the landscape were
perfectly uniform and if rainfall were
evenly distributed over it, erosion might be
fairly even. Sheets of water would flow
downhill in the direction of steepest slope.
No streams or rivers would form.

Real landscapes are not so uniform as
this. Somewhere there is a sandy patch
whose particles are picked up more easily
when the runoff sweeps the surface, or
somewhere there is a slight dip to collect
an excess of water (Fig. 4–3), or somewhere a thunderstorm strikes and washes
out a gully. This gully marks the beginning of an uneven pattern of erosion.
Because a gully has steep sides, water
falling over its entire area collects into

FIG. 4-3

*Most landscapes have uneven spots, like the
slight depression in this slope. There more
water collects and a gully forms.* (G. K. Gilbert, U.S. Geological Survey)

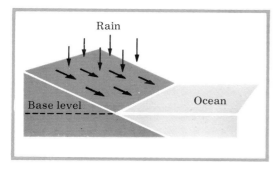

FIG. 4-2

*In an idealized picture, all landscapes can be
thought of as originating as smooth, even surfaces sloping toward a base level and being
slowly eroded by water.* (Redrawn from p. 51,
Fig. 4–13, Robert M. Garrels, "A Textbook of
Geology," Harper & Row, New York, 1951)

a channel while the surface next to it
drains evenly. This channel has more
water and is deeper than the adjoining runoff. Consequently the water runs more
quickly. More and swifter water flow means
a higher rate of erosion along the channel.
The gully is cut deeper. As the gully is cut
deeper, its sides are undercut and collapse.
This widens the gully. As it widens, its
channel collects water from a greater area.
Water flow becomes more powerful. This
deepens the channel and widens the gully
even faster. Thus the natural tendency is
for a gully to grow into a stream with
time.

A stream has one obvious requirement—
water. Hence the stream forms somewhere
on the landscape where enough water collects to produce more or less continuous
flow. Since all runoff is downward, the
farther down the landscape, the more likely
this condition is met. Let us examine a

young stream that forms somewhere below the top of the landscape.

Water flows in more or less even sheets to the stream from the areas that incline toward it. It collects them into a channel that cuts deeper and deeper into the landscape. As it cuts, its walls become steeper until, at last, the rock can no longer support them against the downward pull of gravity. The valley wall collapses in a rockslide or perhaps the soil of the valley walls merely creeps to the stream. The stream then carries the debris away. Either process leaves a valley that has a characteristic V shape with steep walls.

The young stream, as it forms, tends to cut in the direction of maximum drop of the slope until it reaches a rock formation that is especially resistant to erosion. There it may change direction abruptly to get around the obstruction to its path and to resume the shortest path down as soon as it can. Young streams tend to be straight.

Especially resistant formations also lead to rapids and waterfalls. If the rock changes from hard to soft in the downward direction, the lower rock will be eroded more quickly than the upper rock. This leads to discontinuities in the stream profile: rapids and waterfalls.

The profile of the young stream is also affected by the volume of water that reaches different parts. Lower parts receive more water which can carry away greater amounts of suspended load. Consequently, in the young stream, downstream erosion exceeds upstream erosion. The profile is steeper near the top than near the bottom. The profile of the Colorado River, a young river, illustrates this (Fig. 4–4).

Finally the area around the young stream illustrates its youth because other gullies growing into streams have probably not yet had time to form. Adjoining the young stream, typically, are more or less level areas in which runoff is still in even sheets.

Figures 4–5 to 4–7 illustrate these characteristics of young streams. Despite its mile deep gorge, the Colorado River (Fig. 4–5) is a young river with a steep-walled, V-shaped valley in a landscape in which drainage is otherwise undefined. These characteristics are more clearly shown in the photograph of one of its few tributaries (Fig. 4–6). The Yellowstone River (Fig. 4–7) shows the same features, with rapids and a magnificent waterfall besides. In its early stages of development, the *young* stream has:

1. A fairly straight course with a concave profile.

2. Rapids, waterfalls, and sharp bends.

3. V-shaped valleys with steep walls.

4. In addition, the adjoining landscape has not yet developed defined drainage channels.

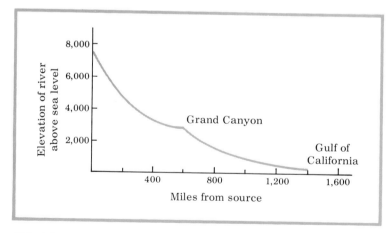

The profile of the Colorado River, a young river. Downstream erosion exceeds upstream erosion because there is greater water flow downstream. Hence there is a steeper slope headward. The break in the profile suggests that the Colorado River developed in two sections. (Redrawn from p. 60, Fig. 4–23, Robert M. Garrels, "A Textbook of Geology," Harper & Row, New York, 1951)

FIG. 4-4

FIG. 4-5

The Colorado River. It is a young river with the characteristic straight course and V-shaped valley. In the section shown, there is not a single tributary. (Spence Air Photos)

Each of the features of the young stream changes with time as erosion continues. Near base level, the stream cannot cut downward much farther. Its action there is mostly sideward. The valley widens; the stream profile flattens. As it flattens, water velocity decreases and some suspended load is deposited. This changes the stream's course somewhat more into gentle loops called *meanders* that wander across the wider valley. Additional erosion wears away previous obstacles to water flow. Waterfalls and rapids tend to disappear; sharp bends are rounded or straightened out. Upstream, further erosion has cut into the previously unchanneled landscape. The stream cuts headward and develops many tributaries. Well-defined drainage channels cover the entire landscape. Finally, additional erosion has affected the contour of the upper stream. The steeper slope there has meant

FIG. 4-6

A tributary of the Colorado River. It has the steep-walled V-shaped valley, relatively straight course, and lack of tributaries typical of a young stream. (Spence Air Photos)

FIG. 4-7

The valley of the Yellowstone River with Yellowstone Lower Falls at top. All its features point to a young river. (Yellowstone National Park Photo)

more rapid water flow and greater erosion. This has cut more deeply into headlands than near base level. The entire profile has somewhat leveled. The now mature stream shows:

1. A flattened profile without major discontinuities due to rapids or waterfalls.

2. A wider valley with a meander belt extending from side to side.

3. Many tributaries which define the drainage of the adjacent hills and valleys.

The Yakima River (Fig. 4–8) shows the wider valley and meanders of a maturing river. The development of drainage channels cutting into the entire landscape is illustrated in Fig. 4–9, which shows a portion of Madison County, Montana.

Additional erosion then converts the mature stream valley into an old stream valley. The hillsides of maturity are worn down until there is only a slight slope in the stream profile from the uplands to base

level. There is also additional sideward cutting. A very broad floodplain develops with meanders of increased width and curvature. All these factors change the stream course, and the water velocity decreases. Much additional deposition occurs, including now the smaller particles of the suspended load. As a result, the broad and lazy stream wanders back and forth across the floodplain, deposits some load and picks up other, spills over its banks and floods the adjacent area, and often changes its course. The floodplain shows the remnants of these meanderings. There are natural *levees* along its banks built from deposited load; there are cutoff meanders which have formed *oxbow lakes;* there are swamps all along. The floodplain has returned to a condition of poorly defined drainage surrounding the highly meandering stream. Now, the *old* stream shows:

1. A highly meandering course through a wide floodplain of gentle slope.

2. Oxbow lakes, swamps, and other signs of poor drainage.

Figure 4–10 shows an old stream. There are several now-abandoned meanders, remnants of a former stream course. There are at least two oxbow lakes with a third one in formation because the narrow neck between the two parts of the meander in the lower right will shortly be cut.

DEPOSITION

No matter what the stage of development of a stream or river, where it meets the ocean it deposits its suspended load. Two things coincide to cause the complete deposition. Meeting the standing water of the ocean, the river's velocity is reduced nearly to zero. All but the smallest particles, therefore, settle out because water velocity is insufficient to keep them suspended. In addition, the smallest particles which remain are affected by the high salt content of the ocean water. Salt water coagulates particles in colloidal suspension into aggregates large enough to settle out. Thus nearly all of the suspended load deposits near the river's mouth.

For most rivers and streams, the deposited load is quickly removed by wave action. But in the case of very large rivers, the rate at which material arrives is too great for reworking by the waves. Then the deposition of the load tends to build the land out into the ocean. However, the deposits also tend to block the exit channels. As one channel becomes blocked with the deposited load, the water must cut a new channel. As a result, the area where the river meets the ocean takes on a fanlike shape, the *delta,* through which new exits, the *distributaries,* are cut as old ones become filled. The Mississippi delta (Fig. 4–11) is a very good example. It shows the advance of land into the ocean, many blocked channels, and the typical "bird's-foot" pattern of the new distributaries.

EROSION BY WAVES

Waves are chiefly a surface phenomenon. They are formed by the wind ruffling the surface of the water. Initially small, wind-produced disturbances of the ocean surface, multiplied over the vast areas of the oceans, produce the waves and breakers which lead to surprisingly large erosive effects where the water meets the shore. While waves carry huge amounts of suspended load along the shorelines, because the world's shorelines are limited when compared to the expanse of the continents, the total amount of wave erosion is far less than that caused by surface waters.

Since waves are chiefly a surface phenomenon, their erosional effects are restricted to beaches and the adjoining shallower ocean bottoms. In waves, water describes small circular motions, bobbing up and forward with the wave crest and dropping backward with the wave trough. This stirs up the ocean bottom and produces some abrasion but little transport. Only inside the

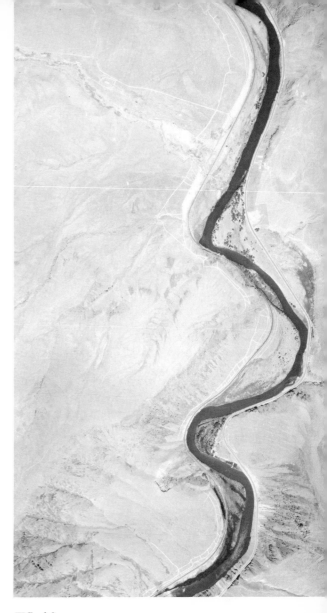

FIG. 4-8
High-altitude aerial photograph of the Yakima River. (U.S. Department of Agriculture, Agricultural Stabilization and Conservation Service)

breakers right next to the shore, where the water washes up the beach with the crest and flows back to the sea, does it carry a small amount of suspended load. In addition there is a small amount of lateral transport by *longshore* currents. But because wave action never ceases, there is an appreciable shifting of material up and down along the seacoasts.

Waves constantly cut into beaches and

65

FIG. 4-9

Aerial photograph of approximately 3 square miles of Madison County, Montana. (U.S. Department of Agriculture, Agricultural Stabilization and Conservation Service)

especially rapidly wear away headlands facing the ocean. Protruding rocks and exposed headlands are attacked most vigor-

ously because waves crash around them from all sides. They bear the brunt of the punishment. Sheltered bays behind the protruding obstacles, on the other hand, are somewhat protected from the waves and therefore attacked less vigorously. Thus waves cut at the shore unequally. Also, in sheltered bays sand tends to be deposited. In addition to gradually eroding the shoreline, a major effect of wave erosion is to straighten it.

This characteristic of wave behavior is shown by the appearance of the mouths of small streams which enter the ocean with loads small enough to be easily redistributed by the waves. Unlike the Mississippi, which carries so much suspended load that the delta builds out faster than the waves can carry it away, a small stream's load is carried away by the waves to keep the shoreline even (Fig. 4–12). Sandbars build up in front of the stream and force it

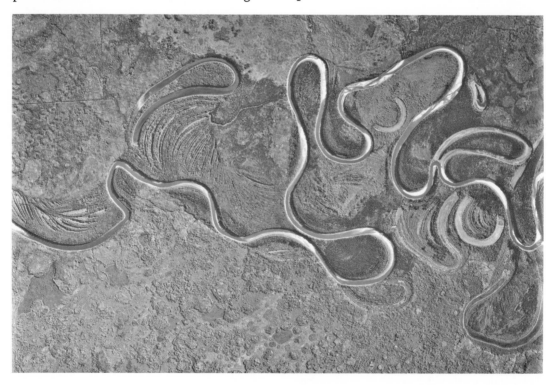

FIG. 4-10

The Hay River in northwestern Alberta, an old river meandering across a flat plain. (Department of Mines and Technical Surveys, Canada)

The Mississippi delta. Suspended load arrives faster than the waves can carry it away. Hence the land builds out into the sea. The shaded lines show old distributaries, with the heavily shaded Atchafalaya River a developing distributary that threatened to divert normal flow through the Mississippi delta until a barrier was built to prevent the diversion. (Chester R. Longwell and Richard F. Flint, "Introduction to Physical Geology," John Wiley and Sons, Inc., New York, 1962)

FIG. 4-11

to seek new egress to the ocean. The waves straighten the shoreline by redistributing its suspended load.

EROSION BY ICE—GLACIERS

At the present time ice redistributes approximately the same amount of material as do waves, but this may not have been the case at some times in the past. During the ice ages, four of which occurred within the past million years, continental ice sheets dominated the earth's surface and eroded huge quantities of the earth's rocks and soil. The results of their action still characterize much of the landscape of the northern hemisphere. Today ice erosion is limited to the much smaller *alpine* or *mountain glaciers*.

Glaciers form when large annual snowfall combines with slow rates of melting or evaporation to maintain a year-round blanket of snow. As the blanket grows in depth, pressure from the upper layers

changes the lower layers into ice. Also because of its own weight, the entire mass of snow and ice begins to creep downward and

FIG. 4-12

Outlet of the Coquille River in Oregon. (National Archives and Records Service)

FIG. 4-13

A Norwegian glacier. (Norwegian Information Service, New York)

the glacier is born. High altitudes, polar latitudes, or both are the usual conditions for glacier formation though local climate, particularly the amount of snowfall, determines whether the snow cover persists. Because there is a large amount of annual snowfall along the northwestern coast of the United States, more than melts during the summer, alpine glaciers survive at altitudes below 8,000 ft in Olympic National Park in the state of Washington. In the drier climate farther inland, there is much less snow. The entire snow cover melts each summer up to altitudes of 12,000 to 14,000 ft and no glaciers persist below those altitudes.

Glaciers cause erosion mainly because the ice mass, as it creeps downward, pushes along everything not firmly anchored in the bedrock. While the ice is soft enough to creep, it is strong enough to move huge boulders as easily as fine clay. No sorting occurs. The larger rocks apparently are tumbled about within the ice, for they emerge from the glacier scratched and scored. The sides of the glacier valleys, too, show the marks of abrasion where the glaciers' load ground against the rocks of the walls.

In contrast to water and wind, which transport relatively rapidly, glaciers move their load at speeds measured in feet per year. Yet however slowly, somewhere they reach an altitude warm enough to melt the ice as quickly as it arrives from higher places. There the glacier deposits its unsorted load, the *glacial till*, in small rounded hills stretching across the glacier valley. These rounded hills are the *terminal moraines* (Fig. 4–14). Though glaciers move slowly, the amount of material they carry may be exceedingly great. There is good evidence that Long Island, New York, and Cape Cod, Massachusetts, are terminal moraines of the continental ice sheets from the most recent ice ages. In addition, the

FIG. 4-14

Terminal moraine of the Teton Glacier, western Wyoming. Unsorted load has been deposited in an arc across the valley. (Photo by A. J. Eardley)

characteristic landscapes and soils of New England, New York, Michigan, Indiana, Wisconsin, and Minnesota suggest that the ice sheet covered these areas and left glacial till as its calling card (Fig. 4–15). Most of the fine farm soil of the Midwest was brought by ice at the expense of Canadian farmers to the north. Other characteristics

FIG. 4-15

Wisconsin landscape. The rolling terrain is part of the terminal moraine of one of the continental ice sheets. The boulders of the glacial till are clearly in evidence. (W. C. Alden, U.S. Geological Survey)

of the earlier presence of glaciers are sheltered, steep-walled bowls or *cirques,* where glacier flow began, and U-shaped valleys with abraded sides (Figs. 4–13, 5–9).

EROSION BY WIND AND GROUNDWATER

The two other agents of erosion, wind and groundwater, transport much less of the earth's surface. The action of wind is similar to that of surface water, though its effectiveness is many times smaller because both pickup and transportation require high wind velocities. Gentle breezes carry little suspended load and wind is much less effective than water in breaking apart even loosely held agglomerations of soil. The binding of clays by moisture, for instance, is sufficient to protect them from the wind. Consequently, wind erosion occurs mostly in arid regions where extremes of temperature weather the soil into a suitably fine load and where the binding moisture is absent. In the dry Southwest of the United States, the turned soil of tilled fields, which loses its moisture rapidly, often gives rise to dust storms whereas in the humid East and Southeast, soil is rarely transported by wind. Figure 4–16 shows a wind-eroded landscape with its characteristic pattern of ripples and dunes.

Groundwater, which probably should be called "underground" water, is also a special and relatively minor agent of erosion. It is effective only where there are soluble minerals and rocks, since it carries its load dissolved like sugar in coffee or salt in the ocean, not suspended like the visible soil particles of a muddy stream. Limestone is one rock that is readily attacked by groundwater because it is primarily composed of the fairly soluble mineral calcite. Consequently, limestone regions typically abound with underground caverns where groundwater has dissolved sizable amounts of the rock. Sometimes the roofs of the caverns

FIG. 4-16

Ripples and sand dunes in Death Valley National Monument, Calif. (Photo by John M. Dennison)

collapse, leaving a characteristic series of pits or *sinkholes* on the surface (Fig. 4–17).

In the caverns the solution and redeposition of the calcite by groundwater produces strikingly beautiful deposits of a variety of calcite called *travertine*. Travertine forms columns, colonnades, and towers with magnificent structural detail (Fig. 4–18), icicle-like formations hanging from the cavern roofs, *stalactites*, and pedestals rising to meet them, *stalagmites*. Often these are tinted yellow and brown by dissolved iron, which adds to the beauty of limestone caves.

SEDIMENTATION AND SEDIMENTARY ROCKS

While travertine deposits are probably the most beautiful product of an agent of erosion, the deposits from the other agents are at least as interesting and important be-

cause they can shed light on the conditions under which the sediment was eroded, how it was transported, where it was deposited,

FIG. 4-17

Sinkhole. Groundwater has washed out a cavern in limestone which collapsed, leaving a hole at the surface. (N. H. Darton, U.S. Geological Survey)

FIG. 4-18

A room in the Carlsbad Caverns of New Mexico showing stalactites hanging from the ceiling, stalagmites rising from the floor, and a massive column with colonnades. (Santa Fe Railway Photo)

and perhaps even where it came from. Wind, surface water, ice, and waves each show their own peculiarities, and the deposits they leave behind give evidence of their earlier presence.

Glacial deposition is probably easiest to identify. Glacial till is *unsorted;* it contains particles ranging in size from clays to boulders. The particles are rounded and scratched or scored. Beds of this kind of material are excellent evidence of the earlier presence of a glacier.

In contrast, wind, surface water, and waves characteristically *sort* their loads as velocities change, and *round* and *abrade* as the particles in the suspended load tumble over one another. But there are differences in the deposits that result. Wind deposits rarely contain particles larger than silt because wind is not competent to carry larger particles. Moreover, they are laid down in the absence of moisture. Wave action leaves sand deposits along the shore-

lines because particles larger than sand are ground to finer sizes by the incessant wave action while particles smaller than sand cannot settle. They are washed out to sea. Wave deposits, of course, are formed in a moist environment. Surface-water deposits, too, are formed in a moist condition and are sorted. Surface-water sediments, however, can be of sorted clays, sorted silts, sorted sand, even sorted gravel.

When the suspended load is deposited by the agents of erosion, the beds consist of loose, *unconsolidated* particles. With time, and under the pressure of successive layers, important changes take place. Water-carried sediments trap small amounts of moisture in which there are dissolved minerals. These minerals precipitate from solution and serve to bind the particles while the pressure pushes them together. Thus slowly the original unconsolidated sediments are transformed into a consolidated mass, a rock. The degree of consolidation, the

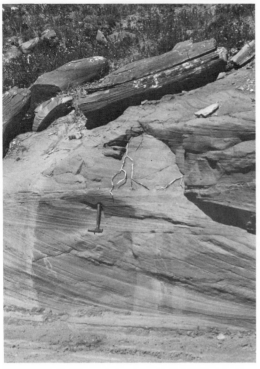

FIG. 4-19

Cross-bedding in sandstone, Hell Creek formation, east central Montana. (F. S. Jensen and the U.S. Geological Survey)

hardness of the rock formed, varies with time, circumstance, and pressure but consolidated rocks form eventually from all deposits except those carried by the wind.

Rocks that were formed from the consolidation of sediments are called, appropriately, *sedimentary rocks* (Table 4–2). Their specific names derive from the size of the particles in the original bed without regard to the chemical composition of the

TABLE 4-2

Classification of sedimentary rocks

Consolidated rock	Unconsolidated deposit	Transporting agent
Conglomerate	Gravel	Water
Sandstone	Sand	Water
Shale	Silt and clay	Water
Tillite	Glacial till	Ice

rock. *Tillite* is the consolidated remnant of glacial till. *Conglomerate* is the rock formed from gravel beds. *Sandstone* has its origin in beds of sand, and *shale* is formed from consolidated silt and clay. The material *loess* is an exception. It is the still-unconsolidated remnant of wind-blown silt which is usually classified with the consolidated sedimentary rocks.

A careful study of sedimentary rocks gives an amazing amount of information about the history of the region in which they are found. We shall return to that topic in detail in Chap. 6. Here we point only to a few of the most revealing features. The inclusion in the sedimentary rock of the remains of animals or plants, *fossils*, reveals the kind of animal and plant life that abounded at the time of deposition and suggests whether deposition occurred in oceans, in lakes, or under other circum-

FIG. 4-20

Newly formed mud cracks with footprints of birds. Such features are often preserved after the bed dries. (Photo by Walter P. Nickell)

stances. Layering within a deposit, lighter or darker strata, or finer and coarser strata, suggests seasonal or other changes during the deposition of the sediment. An unsorted layer with particles up to pebbles followed by a layer of clay and silt might perhaps suggest spring floods followed by summer droughts. Such layering is called *stratification*. It is the most important distinguishing feature of sedimentary rocks. Another feature is *cross-bedding*, structures in the rock that indicate that successive layers arrived from different directions. Cross-bedding results from changes in the direction or velocity of the prevailing transporting medium. It is found mainly in granular rocks like sandstones and is the result of changing wind or current direc-

tions. Finally, characteristic *ripple marks* and *mud cracks* retained in the sedimentary rock show the action of wind, or current, or waves, and the rapid drying of the deposit, respectively. Figures 4–5, 4–19, 4–20, and 6–2 show some of these features of sedimentary rocks.

Sedimentary rocks are at the end of a part of an important geologic cycle that begins when rocks are weathered in the mountains and in upland areas. In this chapter we have considered how these rocks are reduced in size, transported, deposited, and consolidated again into rocks. The next chapter deals with the formation of mountains, how sedimentary rocks deposited in the lowlands can be uplifted to start the erosion cycle again.

Questions and Problems

1. It has been estimated that 95 percent of the weathering that occurs is chemical. Cite examples to defend that estimate.

2. State how each agent of erosion carries out (*a*) pickup, (*b*) transportation, (*c*) sorting, (*d*) deposition.

3. How does each of the following affect weathering? (*a*) atmospheric moisture, (*b*) temperature changes, (*c*) atmospheric gases, (*d*) organic matter.

4. Some minerals in rocks do not weather chemically. Can you suggest why?

5. List some features which would designate a landscape as having been eroded by (*a*) a glacier, (*b*) wind, (*c*) groundwater, (*d*) sur-

face water for a short time, (*e*) surface water for a longer time, (*f*) surface water for a very long time.

6. List one or more depositional features that definitely suggest (*a*) stream erosion, (*b*) wind erosion, (*c*) glacier erosion, (*d*) groundwater erosion.

7. Examine a stream near your school. What kinds of rocks are left in the stream bed? What features does its valley show? In what stage of development is it?

8. Name some features in your immediate vicinity that you can definitely identify with erosion processes (for example, a moraine with a glacier; a sandbar with a longshore current).

Suggestions for Further Reading

Texts on geology that contain more complete discussions of erosion and sedimentation include:

Eardley, A. J.: *General College Geology*, Harper & Row, Publishers, New York, 1965. Chapters 2 and 3 treat sedimentary rocks; chaps. 7 to 12 treat weathering and erosion.

Garrels, Robert M.: *A Textbook of Geology*,

Harper & Row, Publishers, New York, 1951. Chapters 3 to 10.

Longwell, Chester R., and Richard F. Flint: *Introduction to Physical Geology*, 2d ed., John Wiley and Sons, Inc., New York, 1962. Chapters 7 to 17.

Strahler, Arthur N.: *The Earth Sciences*, Harper & Row, Publishers, New York, 1963. Chapters 25 to 35.

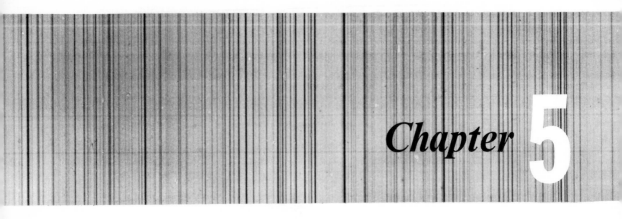

Chapter 5

Mountain Building

The degradation of the earth's surface described in the previous chapter can, in all cases, be traced back to the sun. The sun causes the evaporation of water, which begins the water cycle. Temperature and pressure differences in the air, also dependent on the sun, produce wind, which in turn produces waves. The erosive processes which turn mountaintops into ocean sediments obtain their energy from the sun. If the sun were the only source of energy of importance in geology, our planet would long ago have become worn down, covered entirely by water and ice, and inhabited by aquatic forms of life only.

It may seem ironic that the sun, which keeps us alive by providing the energy to grow our food supply, also is responsible for washing away the very soil on which these plants can grow. Fortunately, there are other sources of energy for geologic processes, much smaller than the sun's but sufficient to offset the effects of erosion. Processes occur within the earth's interior to raise the ocean bottoms up again and to fold them into mountain chains. Thanks to the upbuilding processes, *volcanism* and *diastrophism*, the earth today contains continents and mountain ranges which are probably as high and as beautiful as any that were carried to the ocean by millions of years of erosion.

VOLCANISM

Evidence that the interior of the earth is hot comes to us from many sources. Temperature readings in deep mines, hot springs, geysers, and volcanoes all testify to a hot interior of the earth, but there is no agreement about the source of the heat. An infinitely hot earth losing heat straightforwardly according to the laws of radiation would take between 20 and 40 million years to cool to the present state. Our earth is about 100 times older than that. This calculation suggests that heat must be produced in the interior, probably by radioactivity, or the earth's temperature would be uniform throughout by now. However, the calculation must make certain assumptions about the way the earth lost heat, and it could be wrong by a factor of 100. Perhaps the heat is left from the time the earth was formed as a very hot protoplanet. The source of the earth's heat is one of the puzzles of modern geology.

Hot springs and geysers are simply groundwater, heated by local subterranean hot spots, which finds an opening to the surface. In hot springs there is normal, even flow; in geysers, pockets of steam first build, which, when released, produce the characteristic sporadic geyser sprays (Fig. 5-1). The nature of volcanoes, which produce permanent changes on earth, is more complex and interesting.

FIG. 5-1

Old Faithful in Yellowstone National Park. Old Faithful is only one of many geysers in the geyser basin of Yellowstone National Park, but it is most famous because it erupts quite regularly at intervals of about 1 hr. (Yellowstone National Park Photo)

Volcanoes are probably best described through the history of one of the most recent, Parícutin, born in Mexico in 1943. In February, 1943, the area near the village of Parícutin became disturbed by a series of earthquakes which daily increased in frequency. By February 19, 300 separate tremors were counted. The next day a farmer, Dionisio Pulido, saw a small column of "smoke" rise in his field. That evening the "smoke," which actually consisted of steam mixed with gases and fine rock dust, increased in vigor and began throwing out rock fragments. By morning a cone 100 ft high had formed, spewing dust, steam, gas, and rocks of various sizes high into the air. As

FIG. 5-2

Parícutin Volcano, February 23, 1944, approximately 1 year after its birth. The eruption consists of steam, gas, dust, and molten rock. Volcanic ashes cover the landscape in the foreground. (Photo by Tad Nichols)

the rocks and dust settled on the sides of the cone, the cone grew both in height and width, rising tens of feet daily. In 2 weeks Parícutin Volcano was 500 ft high; in 3 months, 1,100 ft. While it continued to erupt with undiminished violence, its output was scattered over a larger and larger cone. Hence its upward growth slowed, but it spread over the countryside. After 1 year, Parícutin was 1,400 ft high (Fig. 5-2); after another year, only 100 ft more. Parícutin continued the violent eruption for about 10 years. Then it became quiescent.

A few days after the first "smoke" ap-

peared, a second kind of eruption began. At several places near the top of the cone, molten rock broke through to form lava flows. When it emerged, the lava was red-hot. But its surface cooled and solidified quickly while the liquid material underneath continued to flow. This broke the solid surface into big, irregular blocks between which little streams of lava gushed forth (Fig. 5-3). Lava flows occurred periodically throughout the active life of Parícutin. Ultimately the largest lava flow was a mile wide and reached a point some 6 miles from the cone. Lava flows devastated an area of many square miles and covered several villages. But a much greater cause of destruction was the fine rock particles that were blown out of the cone as part of the smoke. These, called *volcanic ashes,* covered an area 5 miles in radius to a depth of 6 in. or more and extended much farther into the countryside.

IGNEOUS ROCKS

A volcano like Parıcutin gives firsthand evidence that some of our rocks result from the solidification of molten material. The rocks formed from *lava,* molten rock above the earth's surface, and from *magma,* molten rock beneath the surface, are called *igneous* rocks because of their fiery origin. Like sedimentary rocks, igneous rocks reveal some of the circumstances of their formation and add to our knowledge of the history of the earth. But why magma forms where it forms, and how it forms, are other unsolved puzzles in geology.

Igneous rocks differ in several substantial aspects from sedimentary rocks. Since they form from the solidification of magma or or lava, the chemical composition of the magma or lava determines the kind of rock which will solidify (Table 5–1). That composition, again for unknown reasons, is quite restricted. Silica (silicon oxide) constitutes the major component of igneous rocks, varying from about 50 percent in the

FIG. 5-3

Parícutin Volcano, October 9, 1944, showing "breached" cone of Sapichu and a lava flow. (Photo by Fred M. Bullard, from "Volcanoes; in History, in Theory, in Eruption," University of Texas Press, Austin, Tex., 1961)

low-silica rocks to about 70 percent in the high-silica rocks. Besides silica, the rocks contain mainly oxides of aluminum, iron, magnesium, calcium, potassium, and sodium. However, these other oxides are distributed in quite characteristic ways. Magma that forms silica-rich rocks contains mostly aluminum, potassium, and sodium and very little iron, magnesium, and calcium. Low-silica rocks, on the other hand, contain besides aluminum, substantial amounts of iron, magnesium, and calcium, but hardly any potassium or sodium. That magmas differ in silica content is perhaps no puzzle. But why substantial amounts of iron are present only when the silica con-

TABLE 5-1

Composition of some extrusive and intrusive rocks

Extrusive rocks (fine-grained)	Intrusive rocks (coarse-grained)	COMPOSITION		
		Silica	Alumi-num	Other metals
Rhyolite	Granite	70–75%	6–7%	High: potassium, sodium Low: magnesium, iron, calcium
Trachyte	Syenite			
Andesite	Diorite			
Basalt	Gabbro	40–50%	7–9%	High: magnesium, iron, calcium Low: potassium, sodium

tent is low, or potassium only when the silica content is high, is another puzzle. Igneous rocks present all sorts of mysteries.

Only in rare cases does the molten magma solidify into a homogeneous solid. More typically, on cooling, a rock with firmly interlocked crystals of pure chemical substances forms. The silica-rich rock granite (Fig. 5–4), for instance, contains crystals of the three substances quartz (silica), feldspar, and mica (both potassium aluminum silicates). The low-silica rock basalt (Fig. 5–5) contains pyroxene and olivine (iron and magnesium silicates) but no quartz.

The substances which separate from the magma to form the igneous rocks are *minerals*. Minerals are defined as naturally occurring inorganic substances with characteristic composition and properties and a characteristic internal structure. "Naturally occurring" and "inorganic" need not concern us here except to point out that the definition excludes petroleum as a mineral because of its organic origin. "Characteristic composition and properties" are what distinguish minerals from rocks. Unlike

FIG. 5-5

Basalt, a fine-grained igneous rock. The rock has a mottled appearance, but the grains of the minerals pyroxene and olivine are too small to be distinguished. (Photo by A. J. Eardley)

sedimentary rocks, which vary in composition with the origin of the sediment and vary in properties with the extent of consolidation, and unlike the igneous rocks, which vary in composition with the composition of the magma from which they solidify and vary in structure and properties with the kind and size of the crystals, the small crystals themselves are fixed in composition and properties. Every mica crystal in granite is identical in composition and properties to the deposits of pure mica which exist, and every quartz and feldspar crystal is identical to other crystals of the same kind. This stability can be traced to composition and internal structure, which we take up again in Chap. 21. Chemically, rocks are mixtures whereas minerals are pure substances.

The size of the mineral crystals in an igneous rock plays an important role in helping to decipher the rock's past history. Experiments have shown that rapid cooling produces small crystals; large crystals form only when the hot mass is well-insulated and cools slowly. Since rocks are good insulators and air is a good coolant, this suggests that coarse-grained rocks like granite solidified from magma beneath the sur-

FIG. 5-4

Granite, a coarse-grained igneous rock. The large crystals of the individual minerals are clearly distinguishable. The light minerals are quartz and feldspar; the dark mineral is mica. (Ward's Natural Science Establishment, Inc., Rochester, N.Y.)

face of the earth. The molten magma intruded into some rocks and as it cooled slowly, the large crystals formed. Because of this, coarse-grained igneous rocks are called *intrusive* rocks. (How rocks separate to permit the intrusion of magma is another puzzle.) In contrast, fine-grained rocks formed above the earth's surface, where contact with air cooled them rapidly. In basalt, for instance, the crystals began to form but could not grow before the rock cooled and solidified; the mineral crystals are too small to be individually distinguishable. Fine-grained igneous rocks that formed after reaching the surface are called *extrusive* rocks. Finally, in obsidian (Fig. 5–6) the cooling was so rapid that crystals did not form at all. Obsidian is a glasslike solid. Examples of intrusive and extrusive rocks are given in Table 5–1.

THE ROCK RECORD

We now have several pieces of evidence with which to trace back the history of a particular section of the earth's surface. Igneous rocks reveal former volcanic activity and tell whether lava reached the surface or whether the magma cooled within

FIG. 5-6

Obsidian, an igneous rock which cooled so quickly that separate mineral crystals did not form. The magma froze into a dark, glassy mass. (Ward's Natural Science Establishment, Inc., Rochester, N.Y.)

the crust. Sediments suggest former subaqueous deposition with some further clues from shales, or sandstone, or conglomerate as to the nature of the transporting medium. Glacial till gives other evidence still, and so do the drainage pattern and the shape of valleys. They tell something about the time since the most recent major upheaval.

When all this is put together, rather surprising detail about the past emerges. The *law of superposition* states that an overlying sediment is younger than the one on which it rests. This gives a time sequence to a series of sedimentary formations. Sequence of igneous formations is suggested by the character of the rocks. Let us illustrate with a hypothetical landscape. A mature stream has exposed a valley with extrusive igneous rock along the lower valley walls and sedimentary rocks on the upper valley walls. This allows us to infer at least this much. Volcanic activity occurred before the upper wall sediments were laid down— the igneous rocks are older (law of superposition) and they formed on the surface (extrusive). In other words, sometime in the past igneous activity took place. Then the landscape sank and was covered with water; during this time the sediments were laid down. Then, some long time ago (mature stream) the area rose again for the current cycle of erosion.

A more specific example of this kind of reasoning suggests the history of a peculiar mountain in New Mexico called Ship Rock (Fig. 5–7). Ship Rock is a huge igneous rock formation, about ½ mile in diameter, from which rather thin igneous walls radiate. Ship Rock itself has all the earmarks of being a *plug*, the magma flow which closed the open cone of a long-extinct volcano. The radiating walls are *dikes*, remnants of magma flows into cracks between the rocks which existed when Ship Rock was formed. Thus, at least this much of the history is fairly well established. A volcano formed on top of earlier formations which cracked at least in some places and

FIG. 5-7

Ship Rock in New Mexico. The rock itself is probably a plug which was at the center of an extinct volcano. From it radiate dikes, flows of magma into cracks in the existing rocks. (Spence Air Photos)

permitted the formation of dikes. But this was long ago. The softer earlier rocks have since been eroded away and the more re-

FIG. 5-8

Diagram showing the structure of several kinds of igneous formations.

sistant Ship Rock now stands above them, itself showing signs of extensive erosion.

There are other igneous formations and other aspects of igneous geology which are of great importance to the geologist. Dikes formed where hot magma flowed into a break across previously existing formations. Where the magma intruded between and parallel to the earlier formations, the structure is a *sill;* where it extruded parallel to, but on top of, existing formations, it is a *flow* (Fig. 5–8). One visible distinction between a sill and a flow is the characteristics of intrusion and extrusion of the igneous rock. Other distinctions result from the changes that the hot magma produced in the appearance of rocks with which it came into contact. Thus both formations adjoining a sill will show these heat-produced changes. A formation overlying a flow, on the other hand, lacks them. These features also establish the sequence of events. The deposit overlying the flow is younger than the flow, whereas the deposit overlying a sill, with the heat-produced changes, is older than the sill.

The most puzzling igneous formation is the *batholith*, a huge structure often covering thousands of square miles of area and containing tens of thousands of cubic miles of granitic igneous rock. A batholith is essentially one continuous rock of dimensions measured in tens of miles. Yosemite Valley (Fig. 5–9) is carved into a batholith, which is exposed on its walls. Where the magma for a batholith came from, and how the batholith was formed, are some more of the puzzles of igneous geology. Presumably the batholith solidified deep in the earth's crust and slowly rose to the surface.

METAMORPHIC ROCKS

There is a third group of rocks, *metamorphic rocks*. These give evidence that dras-

tic conditions sometimes prevail after the formation of sedimentary or igneous rocks. Metamorphic rocks are formed when extreme temperature or pressure, or both, completely change the character of a previously existing rock formation without, however, melting the earlier rock. As a result, the earlier rock often is still recognizable, though the effect of the extreme conditions is also evident. Heat and/or pressure deform, fracture, or reorganize the grains of the earlier rock. They compact them into new crystal patterns. Sometimes new minerals appear. For example, the banded metamorphic rock gneiss (Fig. 5–10) shows extensive reorganization of mineral crystals. The metamorphic rock marble is an entirely new rock formed by the recrystallization of limestone; and hard coal and diamond are minerals formed from the recrystallization of soft coal.

FIG. 5-9

Yosemite Valley in California. A glacier-carved valley with the typical U shape. At left is the ½-mile-high cliff, El Capitan, and in the rear, Half Dome. The entire valley was cut into a batholith. (F. E. Matthes, U.S. Geological Survey)

FIG. 5-10

An outcrop of gneiss in Canada. Pressure and temperature have reorganized the minerals into bands. (Geological Survey of Canada)

Metamorphism does not always obliterate the features of the earlier rock. Figure 5–11 shows a metamorphic rock formed from an earlier conglomerate. The earlier pebbles are easily recognized although they have been squeezed into lenses by pressure.

Metamorphic rocks are often found adjacent to igneous formations where the magma's heat transformed the earlier deposits, or in folded strata that resulted from compression of the earth's surface. During folding, especially, stresses are extreme. To form the earliest Appalachian Mountains, for instance, it is believed that a level strip of surface 200 miles wide was compressed and folded into the narrow mountain chain which on the average is only about 40 to 50 miles wide. Layers of hard rock flowed and bent like putty, without crumbling or breaking, and under the stress the earlier sedimentary formations changed into metamorphic rock.

REALISTIC EARTH MODELS

That water can carry off whole mountains is not too difficult for us to believe because we see water chipping away rock or eroding the soil almost every day. Even ice transport seems natural. All we need to do is increase the scale of what we see around us and to extend it in time, and the erosive processes become believable. But how hard rocks can flow plastically without fracturing, how mountains can rise, and deltas sink, strains our imagination. To understand the processes that could have formed the Appalachians or the Alps from sediments, we must change our scale or frame of reference, but we must change it in a more sophisticated manner than when we add thousands of raindrops to get a river or thousands of gullies to form a mountain gorge.

The problem we face is a psychological problem. How can we accommodate our knowledge of hard rocks with their plastic folding into mountain chains? How can we

FIG. 5-11

A metamorphic rock showing the effects of pressure on what at one time were pebbles embedded in a conglomerate. (Geological Survey of Canada)

reconcile it with the flattening of the earth at the poles and the equatorial bulge? If we make a sphere of granite to represent the earth, we certainly cannot squeeze it into mountain chains or spin it to form a bulge. For that it is too rigid. This model does not behave as we know our earth to behave. The model suggests rigidity, not plasticity. But the model is highly limited as a representation of the earth. It is infinitely smaller, weighing a million million, million million times less. Nor does it rotate 1,000 mph at its surface. Although lengths are to scale in this model, velocities surely are not. The crucial question for us is whether the model, for its size, is as plastic as the earth, for its size. The evidence suggests that it is not. A *true scale model* should be made of much softer stuff.

Let us try to rationalize this as follows. Suppose we take a ½-in. ball of putty and place it on a table. The putty remains rigid and holds its form. Suppose we increase the ball to ½ ft in diameter. Now the putty cannot hold its shape, it flows and flattens. To make a rigid ½-ft ball, we could use clay. A ½-ft lump of clay retains its shape quite well. But let us increase it to 50 ft in diameter and the clay, too, begins to creep and flow. To make a rigid object 50 ft tall, we must use steel or a rock like granite. Now, does the rock remain as rigid when its dimension changes to 50 miles as in a mountain chain, or 7,900 miles as in the earth? We do not know, of course, but the line of reasoning we have pursued strongly suggests that a true scale model of the earth must allow for the flow of materials as hard as granite.

ISOSTASY

The idea of the plasticity of the rocks in the earth's crust which we tried to make plausible in the previous section is needed

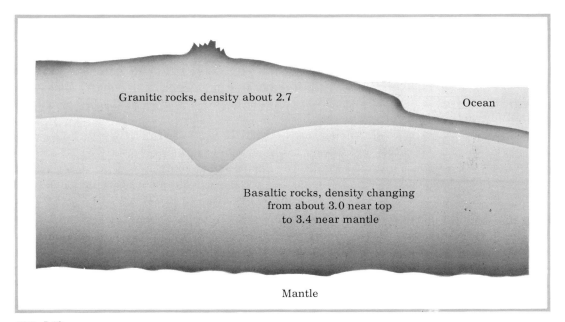

FIG. 5-12

Cross section of the earth's crust which illustrates the principle of isostasy. The total weight resting on the mantle at any point is presumed equal to the weight at all other points because the depths of the less dense granitic minerals and the more dense basaltic minerals adjust. (Adapted from "Principles of Physical Geology" by Arthur Holmes. Copyright 1945 The Ronald Press Company, New York, and Thomas Nelson and Sons, Limited, London)

to understand the evidence regarding the behavior of the earth's crust. The *crust* is the outer 20- to 25-mile shell of the planet. Extremely accurate measurements of gravity indicate that the crust is not uniform, either in thickness or in composition. As shown in Fig. 5–12, the upper layers are chiefly less dense granitic rocks which rest on much denser basaltic rocks. The crust as a whole rests on the next layer of the earth, the *mantle*, which has properties much different from those of the crust.

There appears to be a fine balance in the crust so that the total weight of material resting on the mantle is everywhere the same. Under the oceans, with their low-density water, are thick layers of the dense basaltic rocks. The continents rest on much thinner layers of the basalt, and mountain ranges have roots of granitic rock dipping into the denser basalt layer to keep the total weight about equal. The entire crust can be considered as a variety of rocks "floating" on the lower mantle under conditions of equilibrium which keep the crustal weight equal everywhere. This idea of a floating equilibrium is called the principle of *isostasy*.

Isostasy has certain consequences which can be tested. It suggests that there should be a continuous adjustment of the earth's surface as the weight of material over any one spot changes. Consider, for instance, a river delta. Dense clay, silt, and sand replace the much less dense water. The delta,

therefore, should have a tendency to sink and to push the underlying rocks downward and outward into the denser rock formations to maintain the total weight constant. This prediction is entirely borne out by the profile of the Mississippi River delta, which has been carefully studied (Fig. 5–13). Older rock formations are folded and depressed under the new deposits. Where previously a thin layer of ocean overlay the dense basaltic lower crust, there is now a thick deposit of the less dense sedimentary materials on a thinner layer of basaltic rocks. Together they maintain the "floating" isostatic equilibrium.

At the other end of the erosion process, in the mountain areas, changes must also occur because of isostasy. As the mountaintops erode away, the land should be uplifted and the less dense granitic roots of the mountains should be replaced by denser basaltic rocks. But the evidence of such changes, unlike that at river deltas, is buried so deeply under the mountains that it has never been exposed for direct study. It can only be inferred from the other evidence concerning isostasy. One thing is certain about the uplift due to isostasy: it alone cannot explain the uplift which built the mountain ranges in the first place.

MOUNTAIN BUILDING

Mountain building is a process for which there is direct evidence; yet its causes are

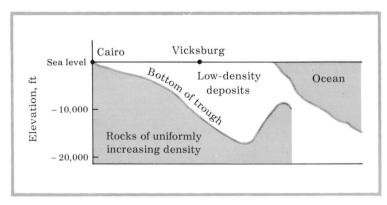

Cross section of the rocks beneath the Mississippi River delta. The deposits of low-density rock pushed the higher-density basaltic rocks downward and outward to maintain weight equilibrium. (Redrawn from Robert M. Garrels, "A Textbook of Geology," p. 339 Fig. 18–3, Harper & Row, New York, 1951)

FIG. 5-13

Convection currents in the earth. Because of hotter and cooler spots in the earth, slow convection currents of plastic rocks exist. These place the crust under tension at some places and compress it at others. The location of the hotter and cooler spots is not permanent but changes with geologic time. Thus places which today are stable may have been geologically active in the past, and today's places of greatest activity may become quiescent in the future.

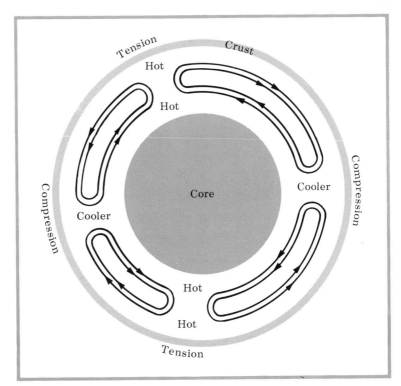

FIG. 5-14

poorly understood. There are three major ways in which the land surfaces on earth are rebuilt: volcanism, or the upward flow of molten rock, best illustrated by volcanoes; diastrophism, uplift resulting from compression and folding of surface formations; and more gentle, regional uplifts which may be accompanied by slight tilting of formations.

The cause of volcanism is probably best known of the three though, as we pointed out, the whole field of igneous geology is beset by many puzzles. Deep within the mantle of the earth there are pockets which, for somewhat uncertain reasons, are hot enough to melt rock into magma. Being deep within the earth, the magma is under considerable pressure. When a fracture occurs in the formations above, it opens up an avenue to relieve the pressure on the magma. Magma flows upward along the fracture. If the fracture reaches the surface, or if the hot magma flowing through cold rocks opens the fracture all

the way to the surface, an active volcano is formed. Thus volcanoes are mountains built as a result of an outflow of molten material which effectively relieves the pressure on pockets of magma deep within the earth's mantle.

It is much more difficult to find the causes for continental uplift, or for the folding of rock formations into mountain chains. The earliest theory of sufficient breadth to produce a plausible explanation was the theory of continuous shrinkage of the earth due to gradual cooling. It is almost certain that the earth was hot when it formed, and it cooled thereafter. Because the diameter of the earth is about 7,900 miles, a slow shrinkage of a mile or two would hardly be noticeable. Yet, such a small amount of shrinkage would be enough to form the largest mountain chains. There are few peaks on the earth over 2 miles high; even Mount Everest, the tallest mountain, is only 5 miles above sea level. Such mountains could be formed by the buckling

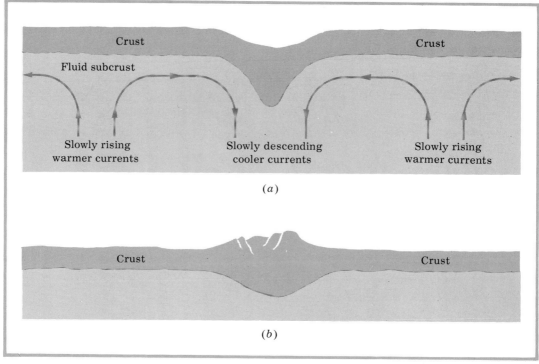

Crust

Fluid subcrust

Slowly rising warmer currents

Slowly descending cooler currents

Slowly rising warmer currents

(a)

Crust

Crust

(b)

FIG. 5-15

How convection currents form a geosyncline and a mountain range. (a) Convection currents gather crustal material at a cooler spot on the earth's surface and carry it downward to form a trough, the geosyncline. (b) Later the position of hot and cool spots shifts. There is no longer a downward current under the geosyncline, and the accumulation of crustal material rises to form a mountain range. (After David Griggs, American Journal of Science," pp. 610–650, 1939.

of the land as the earth's diameter shrank a mile or two. While the shrinkage theory provides one possible explanation for mountain building, recently a second theory concerning the origin of mountains, the convection theory, has been proposed. According to the convection theory, heat within the earth's mantle sets up convection currents in the plastic rock much as a gas burner sets up convection currents in a pot of soup, although the rate of flow of plastic rock is infinitely slower (Fig. 5–14). Because of these currents, there are regions on the earth's surface where there is compression of the crust and others where the crust is under tension. Crustal tension and crustal compression, together, can explain the evidence of mountain building one finds on earth.

While the convection theory is by no means universally accepted among geologists, it seems to describe one aspect of mountain building better than the earth-shrinkage theory. The folded strata in mountain chains show unmistakable evidence of having been, at some time in their past, submerged by oceanic waters. The fossils of aquatic animals found in the folded sedimentary strata of mountain ranges permit no other conclusion. Hence the mountain-forming process apparently begins with a period of submersion of the land, the formation of a huge trough or *geosyncline* into which are deposited thick layers of sediment. Then the sediments in the geosyncline undergo compression, which folds and uplifts them into mountain chains. Much of the present topography of the United States, for instance, can be traced back to two major geosynclines. In the East, the eventual uplift of the Appalachian geosyncline formed a mountain chain which through time was reduced to the present Appalachian Mountains. In the West, the Cordilleran geosyncline existed where now there are the Rockies.

That convection can produce first a trough and then a mountain in the same place has been established by experiments with plastic materials under conditions simulating the earth's convection currents (Fig. 5–15). At first the convection current carries the plastic mass downward at the line of compression, leaving a trough, the geosyncline. In that trough, material arriving from both sides is folded and compressed. When convection stops, the material bobs up to level the surface. In the geosyncline the same thing could happen except that the material piling up in the trough is less dense than the basaltic lower crust that is being pulled downward. When convection stops, the material bobs upward into a mountain range like a cork that has been held under water. Thus the experiments simulating convection in a plastic mass reproduce in some detail the features found in most mountain chains.

Shrinkage and convection do not exhaust the means for raising land above the oceans. The Colorado Plateau, stretching across the southwestern United States, for instance, contains clear evidence of an earlier inundated condition. It was elevated without the folding that accompanies mountain building, but how the uplift occurred is quite uncertain. The major theories of mountain building are unable to describe in detail all the various changes that have occurred on the earth's surface. Clarification of these complex and unexplained features awaits the work of future geologists.

Questions and Problems

1. Name some of the geologic features associated with volcanism; with diastrophism.

2. List two features that indicate the existence of a geosyncline where mountain chains form.

3. List and characterize several igneous formations.

4. Distinguish between the characteristics of intrusive and extrusive formations; intrusive and extrusive rocks.

5. A stream valley exposes the following: an upper horizontal sedimentary formation resting on a horizontal igneous formation, resting on another horizontal sedimentary formation, resting on some metamorphic rock; a dike from below stream level to the top of the formation. Give the stages of the valley's past. If the evidence is not clear, point to the alternatives.

6. Cite several pieces of evidence for the plasticity of rocks.

7. Distinguish between the factors that are used to classify igneous and sedimentary rocks.

8. Cite some evidence which suggests that (a) volcanism is still an active force; (b) heat produces metamorphism; (c) pressure produces metamorphism.

9. Define isostasy and cite evidence for it.

Suggestions for Further Reading

The texts listed at the end of Chap. 4 contain more extended discussions of the contents of this chapter:

Eardley, A. J.: *General College Geology*, Harper & Row, Publishers, New York, 1965. Chapters 1 and 4 to 6.

Garrels, Robert M.: *A Textbook of Geology*, Harper & Row, Publishers, New York, 1951. Chapters 11 to 13, 17, and 18; chaps. 17 and 18 deal with true scale models and theories of earth movement.

Longwell, Chester R., and Richard F. Flint:

Introduction to Physical Geology, 2d ed., John Wiley and Sons, Inc., New York, 1962. Chapters 1 to 6 and 18 to 21.

Strahler, Arthur N.: *The Earth Sciences*, Harper & Row, Publishers, New York, 1963. Chapters 19 to 23.

Another reference is:

Gilluly, James, Aaron C. Waters and A. O. Woodford: *Principles of Geology*, W. H. Freeman and Company, San Francisco, 1951. Chapter 3 treats isostasy and earth models; chap. 19, geosynclines and the convection theory.

Chapter 6

The Structure of the Earth

We have been interested in the changes produced on the surface of the earth because they help us establish its history. The careful reading of the rock record provides an insight into the past of a landscape. Sedimentary formations high in the Appalachian Mountains, for instance, unmistakably tell of a time when that region was inundated. Lava flows in eastern Canada are a record of a period of volcanic activity there. Glacial till covering much of Minnesota, the Great Lakes states, New York, and New England is evidence of the extent of the ice sheets during the ice ages.

Establishing the geologic history of a region has two purposes. The human drive for knowledge and understanding is, of course, constant and extends to our most immediate physical environment, the earth. But the commercial importance of such knowledge is not to be overlooked. Prospecting for ores in modern times is heavily dependent upon knowledge of the conditions which most favor the formation of the particular deposit sought. Petroleum fields result when muds rich in organic materials are covered and submerged by sedimentation, changed into oil by processes that presumably involve microorganisms, and gathered into pools when trapped within gentle folds of sediments (Fig. 6–1). It would be idle to prospect for petroleum in regions which lack sedimentary deposits. Deposits of other minerals like salt, potash, and borax form when inland seas dry up and leave their dissolved contents. Again a knowledge of the past helps the prospector. As a matter of fact, much of the earliest knowledge of geology was a by-product of mining, canal building, and similar practical pursuits requiring intimate knowledge of the earth's crust. Historical geology is, therefore, both a product of, and a spur to, commercial exploitation of the earth's resources.

In the systematic study of the earth's

FIG. 6-1

Petroleum is normally found in pools trapped in folds of impervious sedimentary formations. The picture shows exposed sedimentary strata gently folded into a dome with an oil well tapping the oil pool below. (M. N. Bramlette, U.S. Geological Survey)

history, the geologist does two things. One is to determine the sequence of processes that have produced the peculiar features of a given landscape. This determines the history of the particular region and may lead to discovery of valuable minerals besides. The second is to correlate the history of one region with that of all others, both nearby and far, in order to learn the changes that have followed one another over the entire surface of the earth.

THE GRAND CANYON

We shall illustrate historical geology with reference to a specific area of the United States, the Grand Canyon, a gorge 1 mile deep and over 200 miles long, carved into the surrounding Colorado Plateau by the Colorado River. To the tourist, the mile-deep gorge of the Grand Canyon is a sight of unparalleled beauty. For the geologist, its aesthetic appeal is complemented by the availability in the gorge of an exposed layer of the earth's crust 1 mile deep. Here evidence is revealed openly which elsewhere has to be pieced together from painstaking excavations and borings.

The general features of the Grand Canyon are clearly those of youth. There is the deep V-shaped valley of the Colorado River; the river has few tributaries; drainage is undefined over much of the upland plateau; and the profile of the river is characteristically concave (Figs. 4–4 to 4–6). Sometime fairly recently, probably somewhat less than 10 million years ago, the Colorado Plateau was uplifted and erosion by the Colorado River began to carve the Grand Canyon.

The uppermost 3,000 to 4,000 ft of the Grand Canyon walls expose horizontal strata of various sedimentary rocks. Clearly a long period of deposition preceded the recent uplift during which much sediment was carried to the Colorado Plateau. But the strata are readily distinguishable and, on closer analysis, reveal a number of other

FIG. 6-2

Both nearby and far away cliffs of the upper Grand Canyon clearly show numerous horizontal strata. (American Airlines)

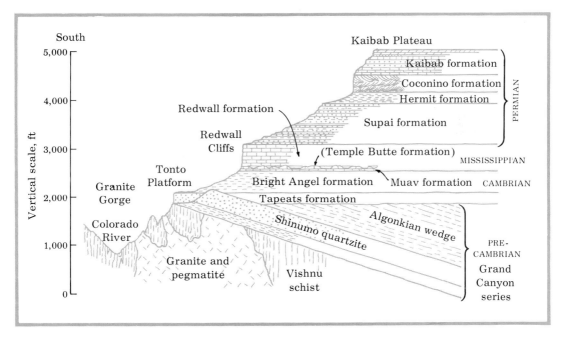

FIG. 6-3

Cross section of the north wall of the Grand Canyon, with the names of the formations and the periods of deposition.

features: the cross-bedding of wind deposition; the ripple marks of submersion; the mud cracks of a swampy period. During the period of deposition the region was not always in exactly the same state, and layer by layer, a sequence of aridity (associated with wind deposition) and total or partial submersion can be reconstructed from the characteristics of the successive strata. Thus details of the history can be established. Moreover, it is clear from the depth of the deposits and the many changes in conditions they reveal that a very long period of deposition preceded the most recent uplift.

The strata of the upper Grand Canyon are nearly horizontal, straight and even, except for the lowest layer. That one varies in thickness to fill the contours of the formations on which it rests (Fig. 6–4), and the formations below it consist of strata which are inclined. Here there is clearly

FIG. 6-4

The lowest horizontal formation fills the uneven contours of the earliest metamorphic rocks on the south rim of the Grand Canyon. Here the inclined metamorphic rocks described in the text are absent. Presumably they eroded before the deposition of the horizontal strata. The inclined formations are visible only along the north rim. (Santa Fe Railway Photo)

an abrupt change in the character of the rocks, an *unconformity*. It is unmistakable evidence that a drastic change intervened between the deposition of the rocks above and below the unconformity. The lower rocks, though also sedimentary, are tilted. This means a period of folding and uplift. Their boundaries are uneven. This means a period of erosion. Mountains existed in this region which were worn down by erosion before the upper strata were deposited. The formations below the unconformity thus suggest an earlier period of sedimentation followed by uplift and folding, erosion, and then subsidence to allow the upper deposits to form.

Another unconformity separates the lower, inclined formations from still older metamorphic rocks with igneous intrusions. The metamorphic changes are too great to allow clear deductions about these rocks at the base of the Grand Canyon although there are some indications that originally they, too, may have been sedimentary. It is clear, however, that they were intruded after the conditions that led to metamorphism. Moreover, the period of igneous activity ended before the tilted middle formations were deposited, for the intrusions stop at the lower unconformity. Since the lowest unconformity also indicates a period of erosion, the rocks at the bottom of the Grand Canyon are the remains of land that was high enough to lose soil by erosion. Only after that were the now-tilted formations deposited.

From this information the history of the Grand Canyon since the time of formation of the lowest rocks can be reconstructed. The metamorphic rocks at the base were formed a long time ago (good evidence suggests more than 600 million years ago). There followed a period of metamorphism, igneous intrusion, uplift. The uplifted region eroded and sank to start a second period of deposition. Again there was uplift and folding, though this time without igneous activity. A second period of erosion set in. The landscape sank again for a final, long period during which deposition was fairly continuous. The region was always low enough for soil to be carried to it, for there are no signs of extensive intervening erosion. Finally, the area was uplifted, but without folding, and erosion began again. Since the Colorado River valley is clearly a young valley, the last uplift occurred, geologically speaking, only a short time ago.

UNIFORMITARIANISM

The reconstruction of the history of the Grand Canyon in the previous section depends on a particularly modern point of view. We implicitly assumed that the rock record reveals a cyclic recurrence of the geologic processes of erosion, sedimentation, uplift, and subsidence. That point of view, assuming uniform behavior throughout the history of the earth, is called *uniformitarianism.*

The theory of uniformitarianism is less than 200 years old. Before it, the formation of the geologic features of the earth was ascribed to a unique event of catastrophic proportions as, for instance, the Biblical account of creation or some later fantastic tales of congealing fire and brimstone. Since the authors of these early speculations saw no evidence of uplift, they interpreted the readily observed erosive processes only as a running down of the earth. For its creation they had to assume a sudden, unique occurrence. Indeed, just prior to the general acceptance of the principle of uniformitarianism, the outstanding geologist of the time proposed a highly developed, catastrophic theory of creation which was widely acclaimed and accepted.

This last of the important catastrophic theories was proposed by Abraham Gottlob Werner (1750–1817). It derived from his study of the geology of his native Saxony. Sedimentary rocks predominate there, and Werner knew them well. Though he must have read of volcanoes, he never saw them

and apparently he dismissed them as minor aberrations. Consequently, his theory was adapted to sedimentation. In this theory an original soupy ocean, which covered the entire earth, shed its contents layer by layer and deposited all rocks, even those now known to be igneous. The ocean then receded—to where he did not say.

For a short time Werner's theory gained many adherents, although it then passed quickly from the scene. The reasons for its popularity are easy to understand. It was, first of all, a scientific theory gathered from geologic evidence, not a purely speculative one. If all we knew were the upper formations of the Grand Canyon, which for a depth of several thousand feet show layer upon layer of sediment, we might well believe that a primeval ocean had covered the 7,000--ft-high plateau and had deposited those rocks. Werner was misled here by the smallness of his sample as we should be if we looked only at the Grand Canyon. Saxony happens to be particularly uniform in its geology. But there were personal reasons for the theory's triumph as well. Werner was an outstanding field geologist and teacher. He drew to his school and on his field expeditions many of the other outstanding geologists of Europe. These men learned from the master all he had to teach, his skill as a geologist as well as his theory of creation. His personal fame as a scientific investigator, justly deserved, rubbed off on the theory, which was more questionable. While most of Werner's pupils ultimately gave up their adherence to his theory of creation when their study of Italy's volcanoes or of the igneous outcroppings in central France left them no other rational choice, they did not abandon the theory without misgivings. It was a plausible theory, within its limits, and it had been propounded by a geologist of impeccable ability and accomplishment.

The rival uniformitarian theory to which they switched had been published by the Scot James Hutton (1726–1797) at about the same time as Werner's catastrophic theory, but it took much longer to gain acceptance. Hutton found no reason to postulate a unique catastrophic occurrence. Studying uplift as well as erosion, he concluded that "the operations by which this world is continually renewed are as evident to the scientific eye, as are those in which it is necessarily destroyed." Because of this, his interpretation of the geologic evidence was the simple statement: "We find no sign of a beginning—no prospect of an end."

FOSSILS

Unconformities have been found in most places where erosion or excavations have exposed the earth's crust to a sufficient depth. With them, a local geologic history can be reconstructed. Our interest, however, extends over the entire earth. We want to know: What did New England look like when the earliest Grand Canyon rocks were eroded, and had the Alps already been formed? Were the Appalachian Mountains submerged, too, when the top of the Colorado Plateau was formed, and what did Saxony look like at that time? To tie together the history of different regions is a much more difficult task. Rock formations rarely extend over long distances. They fade away at the edges of ancient lakes or shores; they may be displaced by hundreds of feet through cracks of the crust called *faults*. Even if the deposits extend, data are rarely accessible at short enough intervals. Other means had to be found to relate deposits in different parts of a continent or the earth.

The most powerful technique to relate formations from different parts of the earth is one first used by the Englishman William Smith (1769–1839). Smith began his adult life as a surveyor, but he brought to his work a boyhood interest in fossils. Consequently, as he surveyed, he noted the fossils of the land and also studied its geology. This combination of vocational skills and avocational interests served him well. He

became a much-sought-after consultant for the building of canals because, as a geologist, he knew what other surveyors did not know: the characteristics of the rocks through which his canals led. He knew whether a formation would hold the water of the canal or allow it to leak away; whether the hills in the path of the canal would be easy to cut through or difficult. In turn, however, the excavations he planned furnished him with new evidence and new fossil specimens. At the end of his life Smith published the first complete geologic map of England, in a form that still serves as the basis for geologic mapping. It was a momentous task that took Smith nearly 20 years to complete.

As his guide for relating rocks from various parts of England, Smith used their fossil content. Fossils, as we have noted, are the remains of animals or plants preserved in rock in recognizable form. For instance, the shells of sea animals buried under ocean sediments leave their distinct imprints as the sediments turn into rocks. Or animal bones may be preserved. More rarely, plants leave their outlines within a rock, and rarer still, whole animals are preserved by unusual circumstances (Figs. 6–5 to 6–8). Since the animals that populated the earth have not been the same throughout its history, but have evolved

FIG. 6-5

Trilobite fossil. The trilobite was an aquatic animal exceedingly common in the Paleozoic era. (American Museum of Natural History, New York)

FIG. 6-6

Partly exposed fossil bones of a dinosaur from Dinosaur National Monument in Colorado. The technicians working on the bones give an indication of the size of the animal. (U.S. National Park Service)

slowly to more complex forms, the fossil content of rocks, formed at different periods in the past, differs. Conversely, rocks containing the same fossils can be assumed to have been formed at about the same time even though they may be widely separated by geography. This is the evidence Smith used. He carefully noted the fossil content of rocks in all parts of England and assumed that those rocks which contain the same fossils originated at about the same time.

As an example of this kind of work we may take the prevalence of fossils of the trilobite (Fig. 6–5), an animal of which the first traces are found in rocks about 600 million years old. Trilobites have been extinct for about 235 million years, but were very prevalent in the intervening period, a time known as the Paleozoic era. Any rock formation containing trilobite fossils is between 600 and 235 million years old. If the rock also contains fossils of early fishes, then it is no more than 500 million years old, because fishes evolved no earlier than 500 million years ago. If fish fossils are entirely absent, on the other hand, though trilobites are there, then an age of more than 500 and less than 600 million years is indicated. Thus the prevalence of certain fossils allows the approximate dating of a rock and the correlation of strata separated by geography but deposited at about the same time. (Exact dates have been supplied only recently by radioactive dating; see Chap. 18.)

The fossil record gives other valuable information about the history of a region.

FIG. 6-7

Plant fossils. Pressure and time changed these plants into carbon films which preserved much of the structural detail. (Chicago Natural History Museum)

This is illustrated in Fig. 6–9, in which the fossil content of a series of strata are plotted. Between beds *D* and *E* the abundance of fossils identical with those in bed *A* changes abruptly. Most likely, a change in the environment occurred between the deposition of beds *D* and *E* although the beds are not separated by an unconformity. The changes in the environment that occurred at that time, while substantial, were not as drastic as the changes that produce unconformities. Perhaps a million-year-long drought interrupted an otherwise moist climate; perhaps a lake formed and 100,000 years later dried again; perhaps the prevailing winds changed for some 10,000 years and steadily blew cold air into a region that previously had been hot. But there probably was no major uplift or subsidence, no folding, volcanism, or other major disturbance of the earth's crust in this region.

ERAS

With the fossil and the geologic evidence, a number of divisions in the earth's past can be established. The intervals between the major upheavals shown by unconformities are called *eras*. With the kind of additional evidence illustrated in the last paragraph, they can be divided further into smaller divisions or *periods*. But while the evidence is good, it is by no means complete, and geologists are not entirely agreed upon how to interpret unconformities and other discontinuities all over the earth, at least not in every detail. Four eras, each divided into several periods, are recognized and seem to fit most of the evidence from all parts of the earth where geologic study has been carried out. But there is some question about two Precambrian eras rather than one, and the periods particularly may not fit all parts of the earth. In other words, the same changes may not have uniformly engulfed the entire earth. The major accepted divisions in the earth's history are given in Table 6–1.

FIG. 6-8

A fly which became trapped in resin from a tree has been preserved in the hardened resin exactly as it existed millions of years ago. (Smithsonian Institution)

TABLE 6-1

Earth history

Era	Period	Duration (in millions of years)	Beginning and end (millions of years ago)	Fossil record
Cenozoic	Quaternary	...	11(?)–	First record of man
	Tertiary	70	70–?	Modern mammals
Mesozoic	Cretaceous	65	135– 70	Flowering plants, last dinosaurs
	Jurassic	45	180–135	
	Triassic	45	225–180	Birds, first mammals
Paleozoic	Permian	45	270–225	
	Carboniferous	80	350–270	Reptiles
	Devonian	50	400–350	Amphibians
	Silurian	40	440–400	
	Ordovician	60	500–440	Vertebrates
	Cambrian	100	600–500	Invertebrates
Precambrian	...	...	(?)–600	Algae near end of era

The time from the formation of the earth, presumably about 4½ billion years ago, until about 600 million years ago is called the *Precambrian* era. Very little is known about this era because it occurred so long ago and extensive metamorphic changes have occurred in its rocks. Also since Precambrian rocks are the lowest-lying formations, they are covered over by later deposits in most parts of the earth and are thus least exposed for study. However, some very large areas such as the Canadian shield consist of Precambrian rocks.

Early Precambrian rocks contain no fossils; later ones contain the fossilized remains of some simple organisms. Thus, presumably, the earth was either barren and lifeless during most of the Precambrian era or the simple one-celled animals that existed had no hard parts which could be preserved. Some geologists believe that the graphite found in some Precambrian rocks was formed from organic matter from early living things. Near the end of the era some simple life forms slowly emerged. The highly metamorphosed rocks at the base of the Grand Canyon are Precambrian rocks.

In many of the regions studied, there is evidence of a major break in the character

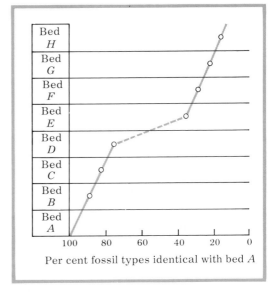

FIG. 6-9

Diagram of the hypothetical prevalence of fossils in a series of strata. If there is an abrupt change in fossil content, as between D and E, a major change in the environment probably intervened. (Redrawn from Robert M. Garrels, "A Textbook of Geology," p. 273, Fig. 14–7, Harper & Row, New York, 1951)

of the earth's surface, which occurred about 600 million years ago. There are major unconformities and distinct changes in the fossil content of rocks. Here the next era, the *Paleozoic* era, began. During the break life had evolved considerably. Fossils of many diverse marine species are prevalent in early Paleozoic rocks, though as yet no land animals or plants existed. But during the Paleozoic era, marine forms transferred to land. A great variety of early fernlike plants, some of great size, developed. Amphibians and, later, reptiles also appeared. At the end of the Paleozoic era both land and sea were populated by a variety of living forms.

There followed another major upheaval, which culminated in the beginning of the *Mesozoic* era, about 225 million years ago. The Mesozoic era extended for a little more than 150 million years. During it, the primitive ancestors of most forms of life known today evolved. Mammals, birds, and flowering plants made their appearance at this time. Dinosaurs evolved, rose to dominance, and then vanished late in the Mesozoic era. The era closed some 70 million years ago with the last major revolution, and the present era, the *Cenozoic*, began.

The Cenozoic era is marked by the ascension of mammalian forms of life, culminating about 1 million years ago in the earliest type of *Homo*, man. During the Cenozoic era, too, the flowering plants which annually shed their leaves proliferated and grew in variety. Since Cenozoic deposits have not yet been carried away by erosion, our knowledge of this era is most complete. We recognize details, such as the four ice ages which within the last million years carved the landscapes of much of North America and Europe, that are usually obscured in the record of earlier eras. Thus the closer we get to the present, the better and more extensive our evidence and the more detailed our knowledge.

THE HISTORY OF THE
NORTH AMERICAN CONTINENT

Not much is known of the state of the southern parts of the North American continent during Precambrian times. Precambrian rocks there are covered by the sediments and extrusions of later eras and are rarely exposed. Where they are exposed, as at the bottom of the Grand Canyon, they have been metamorphosed so extensively during the more than half a billion years since their formation that their earlier conditions are poorly known. However, the Canadian shield, an area of some 3 million sq miles stretching from northwestern Canada through central and eastern Canada into Greenland contains Precambrian outcrops, and from them we know that Precambrian times were by no means stable. Great upheavals, similar to those which are clearly recognizable in later eras, occurred then also. Indeed, some geologists believe there is evidence of a major unconformity that separates an earlier (Archeozoic) from a later (Proterozoic) era and prefer to divide the Precambrian era. But to relate Precambrian geologic activity for the entire continent is not possible with our present knowledge, for Precambrian times preceded the evolution of animals with bony or shell structures. Hence there are few fossil remains for correlation.

While the Canadian shield gives only meager clues about the conditions of its formation, it tells us something about the conditions there during the eras that followed. For the exposure of Precambrian rocks in the Canadian shield means that little or no sedimentation has occurred on top of it. (If there were sediments, they have eroded away.) Apparently it has not participated in the major cycles of uplift and erosion with the rest of the continent.

The first major change in the continent which has been well documented occurred early in the Paleozoic era. At its beginning the land mass extended from Canada to Central America and was bordered by two geosynclines, the Cordilleran along the west coast and the Appalachian in the east (Fig. 6–10). Then the land began to submerge from south to north. Sedimentation took place in the mid-continental areas as well.

FIG. 6-10

Appearance of North America in the early Paleozoic era. Most of the continent was above water except for two geosynclines, east and west.

FIG. 6-11

Appearance of North America in the late Paleozoic era. After nearly complete inundation, the continent emerged again and the early Appalachian Mountain chain was formed where the Appalachian geosyncline had been.

Another geosyncline formed from Oklahoma through Arkansas eastward along the Gulf Coast states. Toward the end of the Paleozoic era, the pattern began to reverse. The seas that filled the mid-continent receded southward; igneous activity and folding occurred in the geosynclines; the southern (Ouachita) geosyncline disappeared and in place of the Appalachian geosyncline a towering mountain range, the earliest Appalachian Mountains, appeared through the compression and folding of a strip of land nearly 200 miles wide (Fig. 6–11).

The Mesozoic landscape began as the Paleozoic had left off: the Appalachian Mountains in the east, a mid-continental plateau, and the Cordilleran geosyncline. Activity in the east was constant throughout the Mesozoic era: the Appalachian Mountains eroded and built the land shelf outward into the ocean and also shed much

debris westward. In the west the Cordilleran geosyncline first broadened and deepened. Then folding and igneous activity set in there while at the same time the mid-continent submerged from the Gulf of Mexico all the way to the Arctic. This was the last inundation of the continent and it lasted a short time only. The continent re-emerged toward the end of the era while at the same time the mountain building along the Cordilleran geosyncline increased in vigor and formed the Rocky Mountain range. Thus most of the major current features of the continent date to the Mesozoic era (Fig. 6–12).

The last stages in the geologic history of North America are the best known, of course, since the recency of the era and availability of data combine to give the most complete record. The history is fairly

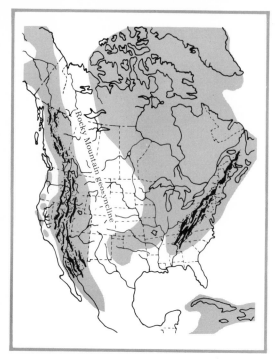

FIG. 6-12

Appearance of North America near the end of the Mesozoic era. A mountain range had formed in place of the Cordilleran geosyncline, while farther east much of the continent was submerged right up to the Arctic. Still farther east the Appalachian Mountains were slowly eroding. (Shortly after this time, the Rocky Mountains formed on the western edge of the inundation.)

unspectacular, however, in comparison to earlier eras when inundation of the continent was extensive and the great mountain chains were formed. Continuous erosion throughout the Mesozoic era had worn the Appalachian Mountains to a fairly level plain. Early in the Cenozoic, this mountain range was again uplifted, and since that time new patterns of erosion have continuously carried its rocks to the ocean. In the west, too, minor uplift and erosion were typical of the early Cenozoic era. It produced the geography shown in Fig. 6–13. But since then, the patterns in east and west have contrasted. Whereas the Appalachians have been marked by stability and the Atlantic coastal plain by gradual sub-

sidence, the Pacific coastal areas have been uplifted, new mountains have been formed, and igneous activity has become prevalent in the west. And this phase of the geologic activity of western North America has not yet ended. The frequent earthquakes in our western states, like the highly destructive earthquake in Alaska in 1964, the hot springs, mud pots, and geysers in Yellowstone and Lassen Parks, and even overt volcanic activity at Lassen Peak in California as recently as 1917 are evidence of the dynamic character of the West's geology.

PHYSICAL GEOLOGY

So far, we have been concerned chiefly with the features, past, present, and evolv-

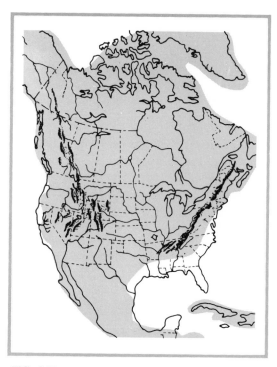

FIG. 6-13

Appearance of North America early in the Cenozoic era. Much of the continent appeared as it does today. Since that time there has been general stability in the east with the continent extending somewhat because of erosion while in the west activity built additional mountain ranges along the coast.

ing, of the earth's surface. Of interest, too, though available only through indirect evidence and ingenious interpretation, is the hidden internal structure of the earth, the part extending downward for nearly 4,000 miles from the outer mile or two which can be examined in deep mines or on ocean bottoms. We conclude our study of geology with a brief look at the current knowledge of the earth's interior.

The earth is a roughly spherical body, just about 7,900 miles in diameter, though rotation flattens it somewhat at the poles and makes the equatorial diameter 27 miles greater than the polar diameter. Recent evidence from satellites indicates that the southern hemisphere is a bit more pointed than the northern, giving the earth a somewhat pear-shaped appearance. What this shape means, and how to explain it, are as yet unsolved problems.

Surrounding the earth is a layer of gas, about 79 percent nitrogen, 20 percent oxygen, and the rest argon, carbon dioxide, water vapor, and traces of other gases. This layer, the *atmosphere*, is densest immediately on the surface of the earth and diminishes gradually and regularly upward. At a height of about 3½ miles, the density is only one-half as great as on the surface; at 12 miles, about one-tenth. How far out the atmosphere extends is a matter of definition, for the density diminishes steadily upward and fades without a break into nearly empty interplanetary space. Northern lights and shooting stars have been measured at altitudes up to about 100 miles. Since they result from the interaction of interplanetary particles with the atmospheric gases, 100 miles may be taken as the extension of the atmosphere.

Beneath the atmosphere is the earth's surface, consisting in area of about 70 percent ocean and 30 percent land. The *crust* extends downward for about 25 miles from the surface where a discontinuous change, the Mohorovicic discontinuity or *Moho* (named for Andrija Mohorovicic, a Serbian geologist, 1857–1936) occurs. The exact depth of the Moho varies from place to place in accordance with the principle of isostasy, being least under the less dense oceans, deeper under the continents with their load of rock, and deeper still under the roots of mountains.

Under the Moho and extending some 1,800 miles down is the *mantle* of the earth, a shell of denser rock that increases in density downward, presumably because of compression. Above the Moho, rock density is about 2.7 grams/cm^3 for granite and 3.0 grams/cm^3 for basalt, about the average for crustal rocks. At the Moho the density jumps to 3.3 grams/cm^3 and increases to about 5.7 grams/cm^3 at the lower boundary of the mantle. Another discontinuity marks the beginning of the *outer core,* the next shell down. The outer core contains material of density between 9.4 grams/cm^3 and 11.5 grams/cm^3, which is almost certainly in a molten state. It extends to within 800 miles of the center of the earth. Within it is the *inner core,* a region of still greater density which is probably again solid (Table 6–2).

SEISMOLOGY

The information about the inside of the earth, the different shells, the discontinuities, the density of its rocks and their state comes, in large part, from the interpretation of waves transmitted through the earth when earthquakes occur or, in more recent times, when larger nuclear explosions are set off. The study of wave transmission in the earth, *seismology,* has become highly developed. Painstaking analysis of the waves yields surprisingly much information about the hidden interior of the earth.

Earthquakes occur when rock formations break under stress and shift either horizontally, vertically, or both. This causes rapid vibrations in the affected rocks, which spread outward in the form of waves in all directions from the point of faulting (breaking). There are at least three major kinds

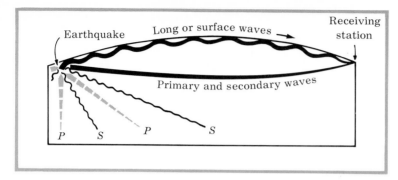

Different waves originating from an earthquake. Each kind of wave moves somewhat differently through the earth.

FIG. 6-14

of waves and several others (Fig. 6–14). P waves, or primary waves, are formed by alternate compression and decompression in the material in which they move. P waves are transmitted in any medium, solid, liquid, or gaseous. S waves, secondary waves, are transverse waves like those produced in a rope. In them there is shear up and down. S waves do not travel through liquids. Finally, L waves, the third type of wave, are propagated along the surface of

the earth only. Each of these waves travels with its own characteristic speed which is influenced by the density and the rigidity of the medium through which it travels. Like the waves of sound or light, earthquake waves bounce off surfaces that mark abrupt changes from one medium to another.

Earthquake waves are recorded on seismographs (Fig. 6–15), instruments that contain large, suspended masses which re-

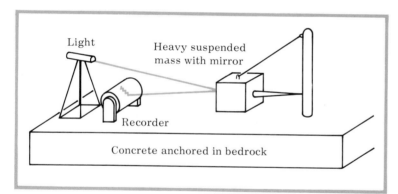

Diagram of a seismograph. The heavy mass remains stationary because of its inertia while everything anchored into bedrock vibrates with the earthquake waves.

FIG. 6-15

TABLE 6-2

The earth's interior

Name	Depth (in miles)	State	Density (in grams/cm³)
Crust	0–25	Solid	Average 2.3
Mantle	25–1,800	Solid	3.3–5.7
Outer core	1,800–3,100	Liquid	9.4–11.5
Inner core	3,100–3,960	Solid(?)	14.5–18

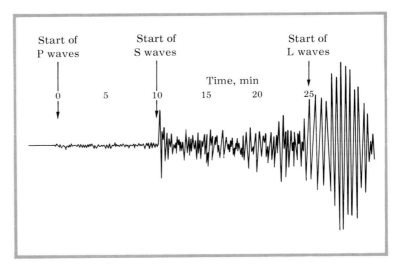

Seismograph record of an earthquake which occurred at Erzincan, Turkey, on December 26, 1929. The different times of arrival of different waves show their different transmission characteristics through the earth. (After Chester R. Longwell and Richard F. Flint," Introduction to Physical Geology," John Wiley and Sons, Inc., New York, 1962)

FIG. 6-16

main motionless during earthquakes because of their delicate suspension and large inertia. One kind has a light source anchored to the earth; this vibrates with the waves and casts a beam of light onto a mirror mounted in the stationary mass. The mirror reflects the light beam into a recording device. The beam from the vibrating source, contrasted against the stationary mirror, produces on the recorder a complex series of waves which can be resolved into types P, S, and L (Fig. 6–16) and interpreted to yield information about the interior of the earth. The nature of the interpretations is too complex to discuss here, though we can illustrate one task of seismology, locating an earthquake.

Since P and S waves travel with different speeds, the difference in their times of arrival tells the distance to their origin.

Transmission of earthquake waves. S waves cannot travel through the outer core, suggesting that it is liquid. P waves are bent by the boundary between the mantle and the outer core. This produces a shadow zone to which no waves travel directly. But the presence of weak vibrations in the shadow zone is evidence for the inner core.

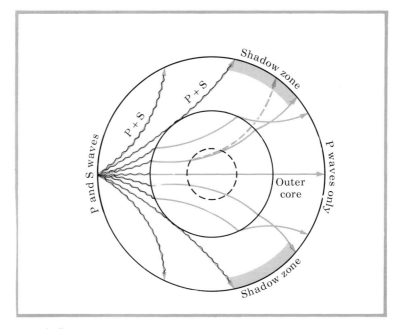

FIG. 6-17

EXAMPLE

P waves travel in the crust with a speed of 5.2 miles/sec. S waves travel at 3.0 miles/sec. The two waves arrive at a seismograph 22 sec apart. How far away was the center of the earthquake? The P wave, traveling at 5.2 miles/sec, took t sec to reach the seismograph. The S wave, traveling more slowly, took $t + 22$ sec. Since both traveled the same distance, we can express that distance mathematically in terms of either of the two waves. $d = 5.2$ miles/sec $\times t$ sec $= 3.0$ miles/sec $\times (t + 22$ sec$)$. Using only the second and third terms and multiplying, we obtain: $5.2t$ miles $= (3.0t + 66)$ miles. Rearranging this equation, we get $2.2t = 66$; $t = 30$ sec. The P wave traveled 30 sec; the S wave $30 + 22 = 52$ sec. The distance to the earthquake was 5.2 miles/sec $\times$ 30 sec $= 156$ miles (3.0 miles/sec $\times$ 52 sec $= 156$ miles).

Knowledge of the distance of an earthquake from three stations locates it. Moreover, the arrival at the same station of waves reflected from the various discontinuities (Fig. 6–17) and the time they took to reach the station add information about the depth of the discontinuity and the density and rigidity of the intervening medium. The fact that waves do not travel in straight lines through the interior of the earth suggests variations in density of the mantle and the core. The inability of the outer core to transmit S waves suggests that it must be liquid. Peculiarities in the *shadow zone,* the region of the earth which should receive no signal from the earthquake because of the bending of the waves at the discontinuity between the mantle and the outer core, suggests the existence of the inner core, and other still more sophisticated deductions have led to the rather detailed description of the interior of the earth we gave above.

Earthquake centers have been located at depths ranging from the surface to about 450 miles down, deep within the mantle. While they may occur anywhere over the entire surface of the earth, there are *earthquake belts* where their frequency has been much higher and where, consequently, there must be stresses and strains in the earth's formations which are likely to lead to future earthquakes. Not surprisingly, the earthquake belts are also regions in which there still is, or recently has been, volcanic activity. The faults produced by earthquakes provide vents through which magma can easily escape to the earth's surface. One belt of earthquake and volcanic activity rings the Pacific Ocean, from the tip of South America up its western coast, through Central America, Mexico, the western United States and Canada, Alaska, the Aleutians, Japan, Indonesia, and New Zealand (Fig. 6–18). From this "ring of fire" around the Pacific another earquake belt

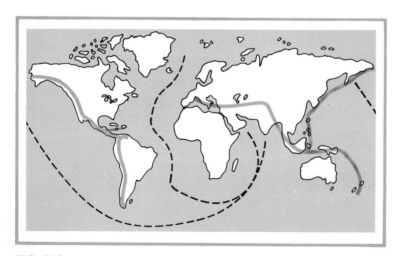

Earthquake belts. Earthquakes and volcanic activity occur chiefly along certain well-defined belts of the earth.

FIG. 6-18

branches through India and the Middle East into southern Italy. Still another earthquake belt follows the *mid-ocean ridges,* submerged mountain ranges that follow the middle of the Atlantic, Pacific, and Indian Oceans from the Arctic to near the South Pole.

With this, we leave the study of geology and turn to other aspects of our physical universe.

Questions and Problems

1. Currently geologists are reexamining uniformitarianism. Cite evidence for it. Cite evidence to the contrary, if any.

2. Consider the earth-shrinkage theory and the convection theory. Relate them to uniformitarianism; catastrophism. Do both theories require a catastrophic beginning? Is there a time limit to both theories?

3. List features that distinguish an unconformity from layering of sediments and from the appearance of an intrusive sill between sedimentary beds.

4. Which igneous formations could be interpreted as deposits of Werner's soupy ocean? Which igneous formations are definitely contradictory?

5. Why do fossils give only relative dates for the eras and periods?

6. What criteria distinguish an era from a period? Consider fossil and rock evidence.

7. Describe and date the changes that have taken place since the Paleozoic era in (*a*) the states from the Rockies west, (*b*) the states along the Eastern seaboard, (*c*) the Gulf Coast states, (*d*) the central United States, (*e*) the

area along the United States–Canadian border from the Great Lakes to the Rockies.

8. With the aid of a diagram, define shadow zone, S waves, L waves, crust, mantle, outer and inner core.

9. What evidence suggests the existence of discontinuities in the interior of the earth? What factors change abruptly at the discontinuities?

10. Can you suggest other situations in which there are waves like P waves? like S waves?

11. How far apart do S waves and P waves arrive at Hawaii if an earthquake occurs off the Aleutian Islands 2,700 miles away? Assume the velocities given in the example on page 104.

12. A geologist finds a horizontal sedimentary formation with bird fossils atop an unconformity below which there are tilted sediments. A dike passes through both formations. Give as many details of the history as you can.

13. In a series of vertical sedimentary formations, all but the easternmost and westernmost contain a certain fossil. Suggest reasons for their absence. Can you give a time sequence for the formations?

Suggestions for Further Reading

Some of the texts listed at the end of Chap. 4 devote several chapters to fossils and historical geology:

Eardley, A. J.: *General College Geology,* Harper & Row, Publishers, New York, 1965. Chapters 14 to 22.

Garrels, Robert M.: *A Textbook of Geology,* Harper & Row, Publishers, New York, 1951. Chapters 14 to 16, 21, and 22.

Strahler, Arthur N.: *The Earth Sciences,* Harper & Row, Publishers, New York, 1963. Chapters 23 and 24.

Books on historical geology include:

Dunbar, C. O.: *Historical Geology,* John Wiley and Sons, Inc., New York, 1949.

Kummel, Bernhard: *History of the Earth,* W. H. Freeman and Company, San Francisco, 1961.

Moore, Raymond C.: *Introduction to Historical Geology,* 2d ed., McGraw-Hill Book Company, Inc., New York, 1958.

Other books relating to this chapter are:

Eiby, G. A.: *About Earthquakes,* Harper & Row, Publishers, New York, 1957. Discusses earthquakes and seismology.

Moore, Ruth: *The Earth We Live On,* Alfred A. Knopf, New York, 1956. Very readable biographical essays of some of the major contributors to modern geology; semifictional.

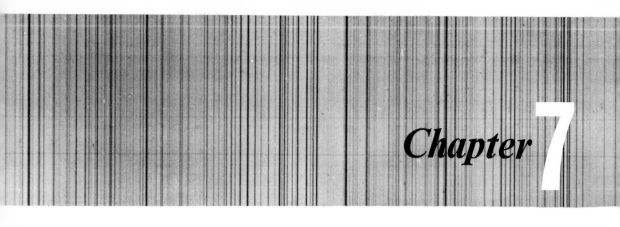

Chapter 7

The Laws of Motion

We have used geometry frequently in the foregoing six chapters. Its purpose was rather obvious. The geometric constructions represented spatial relationships and helped us visualize in simple form what would otherwise take pages of verbal description. Algebra is used in science for the same reason. It, too, describes relationships briefly and concisely. Since this is not as obvious as in the case of geometry, we shall first develop those aspects of algebra which we shall need for understanding science.

ALGEBRA IN SCIENCE

We illustrate the use of algebra in science with a familiar problem. How do we determine what mileage we are getting from an automobile? Typically, we keep track of the number of miles driven and of the amount of gasoline consumed. We might get data such as those in Table 7–1.

While this is an ordinary, everyday problem, it has all the attributes of scientific investigation. First, we assume a regularity —uniform consumption of gasoline. Second, we attempt to determine the regularity by measurement. Finally, we repeat the measurement several times to be sure that any one determination was not unusual because of uncertainties or errors in measurement, such as the incomplete filling of the gas tank.

The next step is to use the numbers obtained to establish the regularity. We could add, subtract, multiply, divide, or carry out even more complex arithmetic operations. Intuitively we know that in this case we divide miles driven by gasoline consumed since this is how we define mileage: miles driven/gasoline consumed = mileage. Let us restate this equation using symbols: m for miles driven, g for gasoline used, and K for mileage.

$$m/g = K \qquad (7\text{--}1)$$

This is the law (regularity) we are testing in three separate tests. Test 1:

$$m_1/g_1 = 176 \text{ miles}/11 \text{ gal}$$
$$= 16 \text{ miles/gal} \qquad (7\text{--}2)$$

Test 2:
$$m_2/g_2 = 237 \text{ miles}/15 \text{ gal}$$
$$= 15.8 \text{ miles/gal} \qquad (7\text{--}3)$$

Test 3:
$$m_3/g_3 = 212 \text{ miles}/13 \text{ gal}$$
$$= 16.3 \text{ miles/gal} \qquad (7\text{--}4)$$

Since each of our three tests leads to (nearly) the same result, we probably are satisfied that the car uses gasoline uniformly—that the assumed law (regularity) relating gas consumption to miles driven holds true. The car travels about 16 miles/ gal.

Let us reflect what we have done. We assumed that a law (Eq. 7–1) holds for the

TABLE 7-1

Mileage of a car

Miles driven	Gallons used	Mileage
$m_1 = 176$	$g_1 = 11$	16
$m_2 = 237$	$g_2 = 15$	15.8
$m_3 = 212$	$g_3 = 13$	16.3

car, such that m divided by g is fixed. We tested it in three instances, denoted by m_1 and g_1, m_2 and g_2, and m_3 and g_3. We found that our assumption is borne out. In each test $m/g = K$, and K has the value of 16 miles/gal (approximately). Now we are probably willing to assert that for any other measurement of m and g, call them m_x and g_x, m_x/g_x is also 16 miles/gal.

Equation 7–1 is even more general, however. If someone asked you what mileage you get with your car, you would probably answer, "About 16 miles/gal in the city, about 19 miles/gal on the highway." Something happened, because we suddenly discover that K can be 16 miles/gal or 19 miles/gal. Let us go back. Equation 7–1 when tested three times *in city traffic* led to $K = 16$ miles/gal. When tested under different conditions, on the highway, m/g produced 19 miles/gal. Under both sets of conditions the appropriate m_x was divided by g_x; however, we now see that m/g leads to uniformity only when the tests are carried out under similar conditions. With *this* car for *city driving* it leads to $K = 16$ miles/gal; with *this* car for *highway driving*, $K = 19$ miles/gal. Yet in the form $m/g = K$, Eq. 7–1 is applicable to both sets of conditions and to other cars—indeed other vehicles—and other sets of conditions as well. Reviewing our procedure step by step, we have the following:

1. The equation $m/g = K$ is general for all sets of measurements carried out under similar conditions.

2. When the conditions become specified, as for a specific car used under specific traffic conditions, the generality is reduced. K then stands for one number only. (For

this car in the city, $K = 16$ miles/gal. For another car under other conditions, say a Volkswagen on the highway, it might be 31 miles/gal.)

3. Finally, in any single measurement or test with a specific car, specific values for miles driven and gasoline used—m_x and g_x—are employed in the equation appropriate for that car. As an example, a specific application of the mileage law with the Volkswagen on the highway would have $g_x = 5$ gal, $m_x = 155$ miles, and $m_x/g_x =$ 155 miles/5 gal = 31 miles/gal.

PROPORTIONALITY CONSTANTS

There are two other aspects of Eq. 7–1 which concern us. Because of the rules of algebra, we know that $m/g = K$ is identically equal in content to $m = Kg$. Thus with algebra we can recast any equation into other forms. This is very useful because often there is unsuspected meaning in some of the new forms. A second point relates to symbols like K, which result when measurements are combined. Such symbols stand for a number that equates, algebraically, measurements that may use unrelated units. In our examples K is used to equate miles and gallons. Symbols of this kind are called *proportionality constants*. They have dimensions appropriate to complete the equality—miles per gallon, or miles/gal, in the example. (By the way, the word *per* always indicates "divide.")

Some people have difficulties with proportionality constants because they do not seem to be constant. As we have just illustrated, the mileage can have values of 16 miles/gal, 19 miles/gal, and many others. Let us see in which sense the mileage K in *Eq.* 7–1 is constant.

In a specific sense K is constant because when the conditions are specified, this car in city traffic, a fixed number like 16 miles/gal fits all pairs of measurements of m and g with that car. The constant 16 miles/gal describes the efficiency of operating a particular car and indicates how well it is

behaving. For such specified conditions K is numerically constant. But K is a constant in a general sense too. Equation 7–1 states that all cars (all gasoline-driven devices) perform in such a manner that distance and gasoline consumption stand in a fixed relationship, though the number which is inserted for K must be determined by experiment in each case. Thus K in Eq. 7–1 implies the general behavior of all gasoline engines; namely, all burn gasoline in a fixed relation to the distance they propel a vehicle.

The cost per pound, by which we buy most groceries, shows the same properties of proportionality constants. In a general sense, cost per pound means that weight purchased and price are related. The general equation is Price = $K \times$ weight. In specific instances, like apples this week at 11¢/lb, or potato chips this week at 59¢/lb, or apples last week at 13¢/lb, a fixed value of K governs all purchases. The proportionality constant thus suggests a general law governing purchases and specific price/weight relationships in specified situations.

Proportionality constants need not have neat dimensions such as cents per pound or miles per gallon. As we saw in Chap. 1, Kepler found that a regularity exists between measured quantities of planets— period of revolution and distance from sun —when the former is squared and the latter is cubed. Thus the law $T^2 = kR^3$ has a proportionality constant with dimensions, years^2/AU^3. Another example is the proportionality constant between speed and time, which has the dimensions feet/second^2. That proportionality constant, called acceleration, is fundamental to an understanding of motion, which is the purpose of this chapter. We now return to it.

UNIFORM MOTION

The measured quantities of concern in the study of motion are distance and time. We are interested in finding regularities (laws) that relate these two quantities. However, if we consider our experience with motion, say the behavior of a car, we might suspect that regularities may be hard to find. Cars go faster or slower; they have to stop for red lights. If we looked at the progress of a car minute by minute, we would certainly find that the distance covered varies considerably. But let us avoid this problem. Let us consider a car on a highway and let us look at it only every 10 min. Then we would probably find that time and distance are related quite constantly and that a statement like "I'm averaging 48 miles per hour" has considerable meaning. Specifically, if we charted the progress of such a car, we might find data like those in Table 7-2. At some point when we begin measurement, say 4:32 P.M., May 8, 1965, the car happens to pass milepost 97. Then, at 10-min intervals, when we look again, it passes mileposts 105, 113, 121, etc. The car moves 8 miles in each 10-min interval, and we would feel confident that it moves uniformly.

If we tried to use the numbers in the first two columns of Table 7-2 to express the uniform relationship between distance and time, however, we would find some difficulties. Algebraic manipulation of the numbers 4:32 P.M. and 97 miles, 4:42 P.M. and 105 miles, etc., would not immediately lead to an equation with the same proportionality constant for each set of measurements. The reasons for this are the following: Milepost 97 happens to indicate a point on the highway 97 miles from its beginning. It is not ultimately fixed in

space but was determined by the circumstances of geography and population density of the area at the time the highway was built. Some years later, perhaps, the highway will have to be extended and the mileposts renumbered. The same considerations apply to 4:32 P.M., May 8, 1965. This happens to be an agreed-upon designation for time, 1965 years and some months, days, hours, and minutes after an agreed-upon date, 0 A.D. Both of these numbers are arbitrary starting points for our measurements: reference points to which we relate all other measurements. There is nothing of interest to us about the mileposts before 97 or the time earlier than 4:32 P.M. Our experiment began only there. (If we had started 5 min later, at milepost 101, and made the same measurements, the same uniform progress would have been discovered by relating the new set of numbers to 4:37 P.M. and milepost 101.)

There are two things to be noted about the last paragraph. The first is that in measuring lengths and time, we define reference points which we most conveniently call 0 on our measurement scale and to which we refer the other measurements. The time reference point is commonly the instant we start looking at the second hand of a clock; the length reference point the place where we place one end of the measuring rod. These become the bases to which the measurements of the experiment refer.

The second relates to the manner in which we use the numbers from Table 7-2 to establish that the car is progressing at a uniform rate of 8 miles/10 min. To do this, we subtract successive measurements of distance, like 105 − 97, and successive clock readings, like 4:42 P.M. − 4:32 P.M., and then divide the distance change by the time change. Letting d_1 and d_2 represent successive distance readings and t_1 and t_2 successive time readings, we obtain the uniform rate of motion of the car by

TABLE 7-2

Progress of a car

Time	Milepost	Time interval	Distance traveled
4:32 P.M.	97	0 min	0 miles
4:42 P.M.	105	10 min	8 miles
4:52 P.M.	113	20 min	16 miles
5:02 P.M.	121	30 min	24 miles
5:12 P.M.	129	40 min	32 miles

$$\frac{d_2 - d_1}{t_2 - t_1} = 8 \text{ mile}/ 10 \text{ min}$$
$$= 0.8 \text{ mile/min} \qquad (7\text{–}5)$$

If we apply Eq. 7–5 somewhat more generally, letting the subscripts represent two different readings, though not necessarily the second and the first, we find that the equation still leads to the same uniform rate of progress for the car. For instance, readings 2 and 4 contain the numbers:

$$\frac{121 \text{ miles} - 105 \text{ miles}}{5{:}02 \text{ P.M.} - 4{:}42 \text{ P.M.}} = \frac{16 \text{ miles}}{20 \text{ min}}$$

$$= 0.8 \text{ mile/min} \qquad (7\text{–}6)$$

There are several further points of importance. Since $d_2 - d_1$ represents the change in distance during the time interval $t_2 - t_1$, we can substitute for it a notation which means change, Δ, delta. The delta is universally accepted as a symbol meaning "change of." Thus, Eq. 7–5 becomes

$$\frac{\Delta d}{\Delta t} = v \qquad \Delta d = v \, \Delta t \qquad (7\text{–}7)$$

The rate of progress which we have been discussing in this section is usually called the speed. Equation 7–7 gives a precise physical definition for speed. *Speed is the change of distance per unit time.*

Another point concerns the nature of Eq. 7–7 when we choose reference points so that measurement begins at $t = 0$ and $d = 0$. In that case, and that case only, the measured values of t_1 and d_1 are zero, and the changes in time and distance measurements equal the measured values at t_2 and d_2. For such reference points, Eq. 7–7 takes the form $d/t = v$. In most actual experiments it is convenient to adopt this reference system and to use the simplified equation.

Finally, Eq. 7–7 was used in the example in a specific sense. We found that change of distance per unit time was constant for the uniformly moving car. But Eq. 7–7 is applicable to any uniformly moving object: a plane with a speed of 10 mile/min; a bicycle with a speed of 0.2 mile/min; a man walking with a speed of 0.03 mile/min. Hence, it ex-

presses a general law, the law of uniform motion, and is called the equation of uniform motion.

We have treated motion algebraically so far. It will pay us to look at it graphically also. The data from Table 7–2 are also given in Fig. 7–1. Let us look at them in some detail.

First, we chose a convenient scale to represent distances along the vertical axis and to represent time along the horizontal axis. Each horizontal division represents 5 min, and each vertical division 5 miles. We represent each set of time-and-distance measurements by a point in the graph whose distance from the axes represents the appropriate values of d and t computed from the reference points milepost 97 and time 4:32 P.M. Note that mileposts and clock readings produce the same points as the computed elapsed-time-and-distance-traveled data. Both produce the same line to represent the equation of uniform motion. This line is straight, a characteristic of the graphic representation of uniform motion. With the line we can establish progress at intermediate points on the trip although we lack direct measurements. For instance, 12 min after the start, the car passed a point 9.6 miles from the reference milepost. We can also use the line to estimate further progress of the car, beyond the measured data, if we assume that the car continued at the same uniform speed.

We can also establish the numerical value of the speed from the graph. According to our definition, speed is the change of distance per unit time. Hence, if we take a time interval anywhere in the diagram, and measure the corresponding change in distance, we obtain the speed by dividing $\Delta d/\Delta t$. (Remember, *per* in change of distance per unit time means divide.) Thus the speed can be obtained without going back to algebra.

The importance of obtaining speed from the graph is that this method can be used in cases where the assumption of uniform motion—constant speed—does not

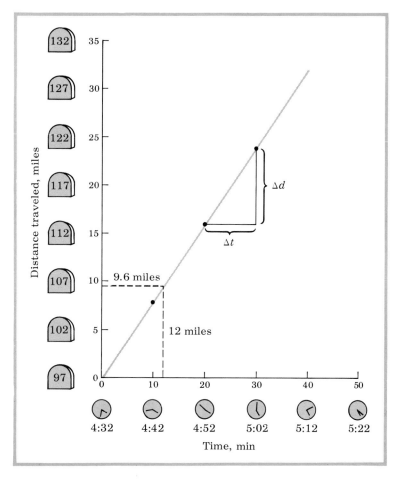

Graph describing the progress of a car. Since the graph shows the relationship between time and distance from an arbitrary point of measurement onward, the numbering of the coordinates is also arbitrary.

FIG. 7-1

hold. On a highway trip, as we pointed out before, speed remains only approximately constant. In actual fact, a car averaging 48 miles/hr no doubt slows down uphill and goes a bit faster downhill. A diagram of its progress with time would look more like Fig. 7–2, in which the speed changes almost constantly in the range 35 to 65 miles/hr. Let us use the above method for finding speed. We look at a small time interval, the corresponding change of distance, and from these compute speed. If we look at Δt_1 and the corresponding Δd_1, we obtain for the change of distance per unit time, $\Delta d_1/\Delta t_1 = 45$ miles/hr, no doubt an uphill stretch. For the next stretch, $\Delta d_2/\Delta t_2 = 50$ miles/hr. (If we don't look at such short periods of time, but look in-

stead at the average speed over both of those time intervals, that is, if we look at the average speed for the interval Δt_3, we obtain the average $\Delta d_3/\Delta t_3 = 48$ miles/hr.) Hence, we have here a way of computing speed even when the motion does not conform to the simple case we postulated in Eq. 7–7, which requires that the speed remain constant. Let us particularly note that this method leads to an *average* speed for the time interval during which the speed is not constant, and that the average depends upon the points we chose to define the intervals Δt and Δd.

(We might add one other point to this discussion. We can, following the above procedure, reduce the time interval during which the average speed is computed. The

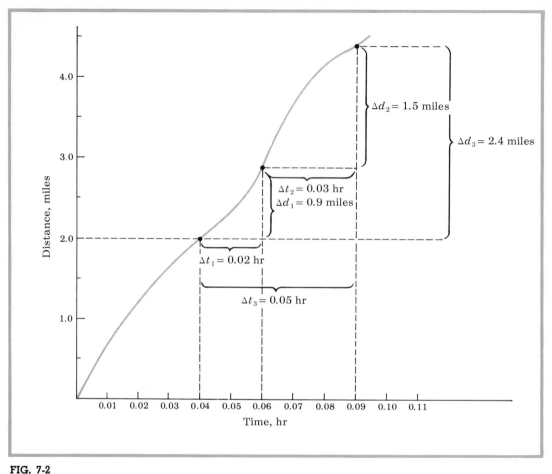

FIG. 7-2

Progress of an irregularly moving car. Average speed for any time period can be computed by dividing Δd by the corresponding Δt.

computed average speed then represents periods of smaller and smaller duration. Indeed, we can reduce the time interval to an instant and obtain the speed for that instant—the instantaneous speed. By doing this all the way along the curve, we arrive at the speed instant after instant even though the car is moving nonuniformly and its speed changes continually. This is the approach used to handle complex motion.)

UNIFORM ACCELERATION

Uniform motion is given by a simple equation but, as we saw in the previous section,

it is difficult to find objects that move with a constant speed. Uniform motion is more important for the simplicity with which it can be treated mathematically than for the frequency with which it occurs in nature. It describes an idealized situation, simple to understand but rarely found in the universe. Actual objects, like cars and bullets, change speed as they move, often in highly irregular ways. To describe them, we must use equations that take into account these changes of speed. In this book we restrict ourselves to one case of nonuniform motion: the case in which the speed changes uniformly with time and in a straight line. Such motion is called *uniformly accelerated linear motion* and follows the equation:

$$\frac{\Delta v}{\Delta t} = a \qquad \Delta v = a\,\Delta t \qquad (7\text{--}8)$$

in which Δv represents change of speed, and Δt the change in time. a is the proportionality constant which expresses the *change in speed per unit time*. In accordance with the common use of the word, a is called the *acceleration*. In uniformly accelerated linear motion, the speed increases at a constant rate while the object is in motion. For instance, in motion which starts from rest with an acceleration of 12 ft/sec² (note the dimensions), the speed is 12 ft/sec after 1 sec, 24 ft/sec after 2 sec, 60 ft/sec after 5 sec, and so forth. The acceleration may also be negative, indicating a uniform decrease of speed or stopping of motion. (Usually it is convenient to measure speed with respect to a reference system beginning with $v = 0$ at $t = 0$. Then Eq. 7–8 changes to a simpler form, $v = at$.)

Equations 7–7, $\Delta d = v\,\Delta t$, and 7–8, $\Delta v = a\,\Delta t$, both contain the symbol v although under entirely different conditions. Equation 7–7 is restricted to uniform motion; to use Eq. 7–7, speed must be *constant*. The restriction to Eq. 7–8 is that speed must *change* uniformly. Nevertheless, Eqs. 7–7 and 7–8 can be combined to give an equation relating distance and time in uniformly accelerated motion although the combination is not straightforward. To combine them, we must obtain a speed by means of Eq. 7–8 which behaves as if it were constant. Then it meets the requirement of Eq. 7–7.

In the previous section we pointed out several times that cars which change speed from instant to instant can be described by $d = vt$ by using an average speed. (We use the simpler form of the equation which requires the reference points $d = 0$ at $t = 0$.) Hence the problem of combining Eqs. 7–7 and 7–8 is to compute average speeds for the nonuniform motion governed by $v = at$. How do we usually determine our average speed as we drive down a high-

way? We look at the speedometer at equal time intervals, add the readings, and divide by their number. For instance, seven readings 1 min apart might be: 52, 55, 54, 54, 55, 50, 51. Sum = 371. $v_{av} = 371/7 = 53$. This method also works for uniformly accelerated motion, and we use it to obtain the average speed under those conditions. By means of Eq. 7–8 we calculate the speed after 1 sec, 2 sec, etc. From these separate readings we compute the average speed during the time period (Table 7–3).

If we substitute $t_0 = 0$ sec, $t_1 = 1$ sec, $t_2 = 2$ sec, etc., into Eq. 7–8, we obtain the following speeds. At the beginning of motion, t_0, $v = a \times 0$ gives 0 for the speed v_0. At $t_1 = 1$ sec, $v_1 = a \times 1$; the equation produces a speed v_1 equal to a. At $t_2 = 2$ sec, $v_2 = a \times 2 = 2a$; at $t_3 = 3$ sec, $v_3 = a \times 3 = 3a$; etc. The speeds after various elapsed times are simply a multiplied by the time.

Suppose we want to find the average speed for 1 sec of travel. We take the speed readings before we start, at t_0, and after 1 sec, at t_1, and average them. The appropriate values of the speed are 0 and a; the average speed is $(0 + a)/2 = a/2$. If we want to find the average speed for 2 sec of travel, we take the speeds at t_0, t_1, and t_2, which are 0, a, and $2a$. Their average is $(0 + a + 2a)/3 = a$. In a similar manner we generate the average speeds for longer periods of travel given in Table 7–3.

With the average speeds from Table 7–3, distance traveled can be calculated by means of Eq. 7–7 because the average speed is assumed to be uniform throughout the time interval. This is done in the last column of Table 7–3. It turns out to be interestingly uniform. For every time period, the distance traversed by the uniformly accelerated object is proportional to the length of time traveled, squared, with a proportionality constant of ½a. For uniformly accelerated motion, referred to $d = 0$ and $t = 0$.

$$d = \tfrac{1}{2}at^2 \qquad (7\text{--}9)$$

TABLE 7-3

Average speeds for uniformly accelerated motion

Time period	Readings at	Average speed for interval
0 sec	t_0	0
1 sec	t_0, t_1	$\dfrac{0+a}{2} = \dfrac{a}{2}$
2 sec	t_0, t_1, t_2	$\dfrac{0+a+2a}{3} = \dfrac{3a}{3} = \dfrac{2a}{2}$
3 sec	t_0, t_1, t_2, t_3	$\dfrac{0+a+2a+3a}{4} = \dfrac{6a}{4} = \dfrac{3a}{2}$
4 sec	t_0, t_1, t_2, t_3, t_4	$\dfrac{0+a+2a+3a+4a}{5} = \dfrac{10a}{5} = \dfrac{4a}{2}$
5 sec	$t_0, t_1, t_2, t_3, t_4, t_5$	$\dfrac{0+a+2a+3a+4a+5a}{6} = \dfrac{15a}{6} = \dfrac{5a}{2}$

This is the equation that describes uniformly accelerated linear motion.

It may be helpful to return to graphic representation to get another insight into the equations for uniform and uniformly accelerated motion. This is done in Figs. 7–3 to 7–5, which are, respectively, plots of acceleration versus time, speed versus time, and distance versus time for a car that moves as follows. It stands for 2 sec (part *A*); it then accelerates uniformly for 3 sec (part *B*); it travels with uniform speed for 5 sec (part *C*); finally it brakes (negative acceleration) uniformly to a stop (part *D*).

Part *A*. The car is stopped. No acceleration: $a = 0$; no speed: $v = 0$; no distance traveled: $d = 0$. For the first 2 sec, the values on the vertical axes of the three curves remain 0.

Part *B*. The car accelerates uniformly. For this period, by the definition of uniformly accelerated motion, a has a constant value. Under these conditions, $v = at$, that is, the speed increases in proportion to the time, starting at 0 at time = 2 and increasing for 3 sec. The distance in uniformly accelerated motion is given by $d = \frac{1}{2}at^2$. Since the square of a number increases far more rapidly than the number itself (the

squares of 1, 2, 3, and 4 are 1, 4, 9, and 16, for instance), the distance increases much more rapidly than the time. The line relating distance to time curves upward during these 3 sec.

A moment's reflection helps us to get a feel for the distance-versus-time curve during uniformly accelerated motion. This is motion in which the speed increases each second. During the first second, the speed is small, the distance covered also small. During the next second the speed has increased. Since the car is traveling at a faster rate, it covers much more distance. In the plot, distances covered each second are given by the differences between successive values: $d_4 - d_3$, $d_5 - d_4$, etc. These differences increase for each successive time interval and the line curves upward.

Part *C*. The car moves uniformly, that is, with constant speed. For this situation, $a = 0$; v has a constant value for the entire time interval, equal to the speed achieved during the period of acceleration; and $d = vt$, distance increases in proportion with time. Note especially that in this stretch of motion, the distance does not begin with a value of zero and the time does not begin with the value of zero. The car has already moved a considerable dis-

Distance according to $d = v_{av}t$
$d = \dfrac{a}{2} = \tfrac{1}{2}a \cdot 1^2$
$d = \dfrac{2a}{2} \cdot 2 = \tfrac{1}{2}a \cdot 2^2$
$d = \dfrac{3a}{2} \cdot 3 = \tfrac{1}{2}a \cdot 3^2$
$d = \dfrac{4a}{2} \cdot 4 = \tfrac{1}{2}a \cdot 4^2$
$d = \dfrac{5a}{2} \cdot 5 = \tfrac{1}{2}a \cdot 5^2$

tance and has taken some time to reach the point at which it begins its uniform motion. But from this point on, the point reached after 5 sec, additional distance covered increases proportionally with time. The differences $d_6 - d_5$, $d_7 - d_6$, etc., are equal. In this period the change of distance per unit of time is a constant.

Part D. Now the car decelerates uniformly (it has a uniform *negative* acceleration). The equation for uniform acceleration holds though the value of a is negative. $v = at$, the velocity decreases uniformly with time, starting with the value it had in part C and uniformly dropping off to zero.

Since the car does not start at zero distance as it enters the time period covered by part D, the equation for distance versus time during uniformly accelerated motion cannot be used without some modification. Instead of treating this complex case algebraically, we will describe it only qualitatively. From the speed-versus-time curve we see that the car moves more slowly with each additional second. Moving more slowly, the distance it covers in each additional second also goes down. The successive differences $d_{11} - d_{10}$, $d_{12} - d_{11}$, $d_{13} - d_{12}$, etc., become smaller for the additional time periods. Hence the line curves toward the horizontal for the period of negative acceleration.

Uniform motion and uniformly accelerated motion do not exhaust the possible kinds of motion. For instance, the acceleration can change with time, either proportionally or in a random manner. Its algebraic treatment is complex and of little further interest to us. Part E of Figs. 7–3 to 7–5 gives the graphic representation of acceleration, speed and distance when the acceleration is proportional to the time, though we shall make no further use of it. Our interest now turns to experiments in which we let nature, not a driver, determine the kind of motion. We shall look for examples in which uniform or uniformly accelerated motion occurs in nature and, from experiment, try to deduce the factors that govern motion in the universe.

MOTION IN THE UNIVERSE

The question of how things move on earth has occupied man as long as the question of how the planets move. And as in the case of the planets, earlier notions were discarded during the early seventeenth century as a result of a radical change in point of view. The new point of view was provided by the inventor of the telescope who played such an important role in the "new" astronomy, Galileo Galilei. He was not able, however, to exploit fully the new ideas he brought mankind. For that the mathematical genius of Sir Isaac Newton (1642–1727) was required. Newton brought together earlier developments and gave them structure. Though Newton alone had the skill to synthesize and clarify the ideas that had been developed by Galileo and other early experimenters, he gave them full credit for their contributions: "If I have seen further than others before me, it is only because I have stood on the shoulders of giants."

The first ideas about motion arose from the commonsense description of what we

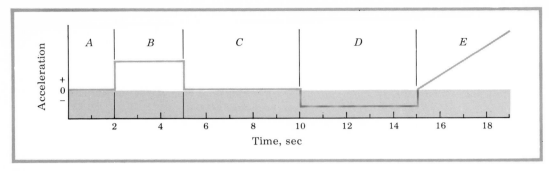

FIG. 7-3

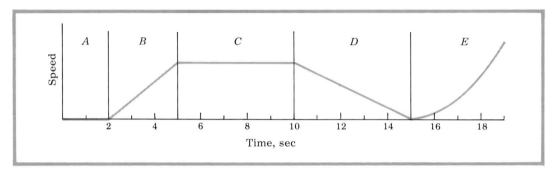

FIG. 7-4

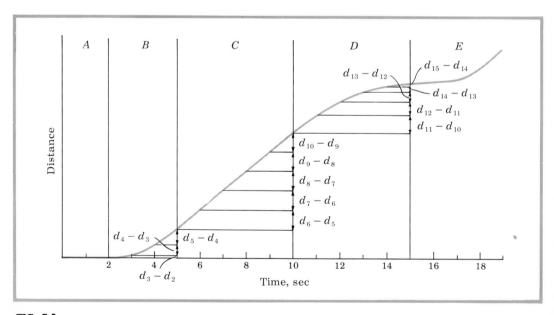

FIG. 7-5

Relation of acceleration, speed, and distance to time for different conditions of motion.

see about us. On earth things rise or fall naturally. A stone when dropped naturally falls; fire naturally rises toward the sky. Hence, vertical motion is natural motion; it was thought to occur spontaneously. Horizontal motion, on the other hand, requires a mover. A cart moves only because of the horse; when the horse stops pulling, the cart also stops. A stone that is pushed might roll a bit but soon it, too, comes to a halt; without an active pusher, the stone rests. Hence, horizontal motion on earth was considered unnatural, "impressed." It occurs only when a mover is actually in contact with the object moved. Finally, there is one kind of horizontal motion which occurs without the intercession of a mover, the horizontal motion of celestial bodies across the sky. Although this contrasts with the horizontal motion on earth, it was not hard to reconcile. The natural behavior of perfect heavenly bodies moving along perfect, circular orbits is clearly distinct from the behavior of debased earthly matter. As we saw, the heavens were in a category by themselves in early thought. That heavenly objects obeyed distinct laws was quite acceptable to early philosophers like Aristotle, whose ideas we have described in this paragraph.

These observations fitted other ideas of Aristotle quite well. His scheme was all-inclusive. It provided a complete world view. The spherical structure of the heavens, which we encountered in Chap. 1, was extended to the earth. The earth itself consisted of four spheres, each housing one of Aristotle's four terrestrial elements. The innermost sphere was that of the heaviest element, earth. Surrounding it was the sphere of the next element, water. Then came the sphere of air, and finally that of fire. Above the sphere of fire were the planetary spheres made of quintessence, the heavenly stuff.

This is a very rational scheme and follows what we know. Earth sinks through water; water falls through air though it rests on earth; air rises through water; and fire rises through the air. Hence each of these pure elements seeks its natural sphere. They move spontaneously, "naturally," in the vertical direction. No such natural urge propels them horizontally. Hence a vital mover must be provided for horizontal motion.

The fact that not all stones are in their natural sphere can be explained in two ways. First, a vital mover may have displaced them, taken them away from their natural home. Or the material at hand might not be pure but a mixture. Such a mixture would then occupy an intermediate place and return to its natural place only when unmixed. For instance, wood clearly is a mixture of fire and earth: it floats on water and sinks through air. The fact that it is a mixture is seen when it burns. Then the fire is liberated, streaming rapidly through the air to its natural sphere above it and leaving earth (ashes) behind, which sink through water to the natural sphere of earth. Not only a physics of motion but a system of chemistry is built in the four Aristotelian spheres.

But several problems were recognized with the Aristotelian system. The chief one related to artillery projectiles which, then as now, provided man with one of his chief forms of amusement. How did it happen that the stones used as ammunition in ancient Athens and Sparta did not stop their motion as soon as they left the propelling arm of the catapult? According to Aristotelian physics, if there was no mover, there was no motion. The answer provided, that a disturbance in the air propagates itself and keeps pushing the missiles, was not entirely satisfactory. For then the question arose: How does this air disturbance, and with it the missile, stop? Lacking the means or the desire to perform experiments (experiments, since they involved the use of one's hands, were considered degrading by the citizens of Greece, for whom rational thoughts alone were an occupation worthy of a free man; note the distinction in modern America) and lacking the mathe-

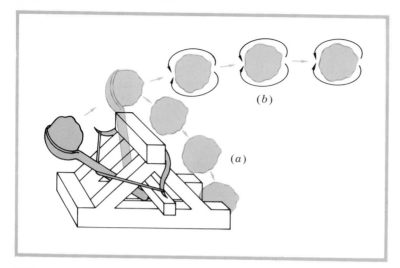

The artillery problem. (a)
Stones leaving the arm
of the catapult should
drop to earth immediately
because there is no
further impressed force.
(b) If one accepts the
alternative, that air
rushes from the front to
the rear of the stone and
pushes it, the stone
should never drop but
fly on forever.

FIG. 7-6

matical tools as well as the point of view that could give them more accurate ideas, the early philosophers seem not to have been troubled enough by these questions to challenge the explanations. Like the Ptolemaic astronomy, the entire Aristotelian physics was transmitted nearly unchanged from ancient Greece to medieval Europe and, on the word of the infallible master Aristotle, was accepted more or less in its entirety. Only in the Renaissance period, when ancient Greek sources were again examined, was the study of motion taken up again. At that time the whole Aristotelian edifice quickly tumbled and the new Newtonian physics took its place.

GALILEO AND MOTION

The rock on which the Aristotelian physics foundered was the question of natural motion. According to Aristotle, a body seeks its natural state at a rate that is proportional to its mass. A 100-lb stone falls 100 times as fast as a 1-lb stone. Now it was, and is, well known that rocks fall more rapidly than feathers; that is, that heavy objects fall more rapidly than light ones. But no one, apparently, had ever dropped a 1-lb and a 100-lb stone simultaneously. Even if

they had, it is doubtful that the experiment would have proved much. A stone dropped from shoulder height reaches the ground in about ½ sec. Only a very good clock can measure such quick action, and very good clocks were nonexistent.

Galileo, however, was bothered by Aristotle's formulation. He accepted the fact that objects of different masses fall at different rates, but he could not quite believe that Aristotle's idea was correct. He argued his case in two different ways. The first line of reasoning was simply this. Suppose we have two bricks, put them side by side, and drop them. They fall at a certain speed. Now we tie them together. Why should the addition of a little piece of string cause them to drop twice as fast? That didn't strike him as reasonable.

His second line of argument is best given in his own words. (His book, *Dialogues Concerning Two New Sciences* published early in the seventeenth century, was in the form of a conversation among friends.)

But, Simplicio, I trust you will not follow the example of others who divert the discussion from its main intent and fasten upon some statement of mine that lacks a hairbreadth of the truth, and under this hair, hide the fault of another which is as big as a ship's cable. Aristotle says that an iron ball of one hundred pounds falling from a height of one hundred cubits reaches the ground before a one-pound ball has fallen a single cubit. I say that they arrive at the same time. You find, on making the experiment, that the larger outstrips the small by two fingers breadth. . . . Now you would not hide behind these two fingers the ninety-nine cubits of Aristotle, nor would you mention my small error and at the same time pass over in silence his very large one.

From his experience, Galileo was willing to accept a small difference between the two objects. He could not, however, accept the huge one predicted by Aristotle.

By the way, it is doubtful that this experiment was ever performed by Galileo or his disciples, though legend has it that he dropped two iron balls from the top of the Leaning Tower of Pisa. How, for instance, he would have measured the two fingers' difference between the arrival of two iron balls is not known. It would require complex equipment not available until much later. But Galileo invented another device, as useful as good tools, the thought experiment. This is an experiment which is done with pencil, paper, and the mind only.

What Galileo seems to be saying to Simplicio is this: "Now, Simplicio, you and I have seen things fall and know they do not arrive at the same time. For instance, a heavy and a light stone arrive an instant apart. Let's say that a one-pound and a hundred-pound stone arrive a couple of fingerbreadths apart. But let's compare that with what Aristotle says. . . ." Likewise, in the argument that he developed with the bricks, he simply thought about the behavior of single bricks and bricks tied together. From the conclusions he reached *just thinking*, he rejected Aristotle's ideas as preposterous.

Thought experiments are extremely useful, because they are quick and cheap, and because they require that the experimenter look beyond *this* 100-lb stone or *that* brick and study behavior in general. (We used thought experiments in the early parts of **this** chapter when we generalized from *this*

car to cars *in general,* and from *specific* nearly uniform motion to *idealized* uniform motion.) But thought experiments are extremely dangerous too, unless verified by actual experiment. The entire Aristotelian scheme was a grand collection of thoughts, many of which, however, had never been put to the experimental test. As "thoughts" they were brilliant and incisive. Aristotle looked beyond the rate of drop of a feather and of a stone to rates of drop in general. But they were thoughts without experiment. Some of his *unverified* generalizations were as completely incorrect as they were completely general. Galileo, on the other hand, did not stop with the thought. He carried out actual experiments and determined that the distance of fall is proportional to the time of fall, squared. This means, as we saw in Eq. 7–9, that objects fall with uniformly accelerated motion.

The experimental test was not an easy matter. As we have already pointed out, time of fall for most objects is exceedingly small. Hence good clocks are necessary, but in the early seventeenth century clocks were hardly available, let alone good enough for measurement. Indeed, Galileo made his own clock, a water barrel with a hole in it. The rate of water issuing from the spout was his timing device, calibrated for accuracy against his pulse rate! But even this clock would not measure time of fall. To get at the time of fall, Galileo used the combination of a thought experiment with an actual experiment.

First, he recognized that balls rolling down an incline do so with measurably slow velocities. Second, he recognized that the steeper the incline, the more rapid the rate of descent. Next, he suggested that a falling ball is no more than a ball rolling down an infinitely steep incline (Fig. 7–7). Because these are all cases of the same phenomenon, the extension of rolling behavior to the infinitely steep incline gives the law of free fall. This extension represented the thought part of the experiment. Since a ball rolling down an incline does

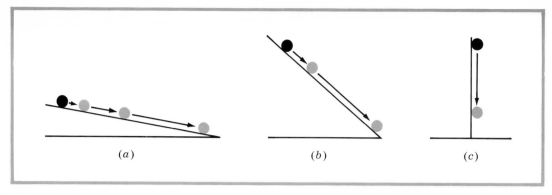

FIG. 7-7

Schematic representation of Galileo's experiments with inclines. (a) Balls rolling down an incline accelerate. (b) The acceleration is greater if the incline is steeper. (c) Free fall can be considered rolling down a vertical incline.

so slowly enough to be measured, he carried out the physical experiment on a board inclined at various angles. In each case he found that the distance increases as the square of the time. Thus Galileo discovered that falling bodies are uniformly accelerated in their fall and that all bodies accelerate in the same way, independent of their masses.

NEWTON'S LAWS OF MOTION

Galileo struck at the foundation of Aristotelian physics by overturning his laws of fall. The crack he opened in the foundation spread to other parts. If the natural tendency of earth to return to its natural sphere was not the cause of "natural" motion, if indeed, as Galileo showed, nonearthy materials fall as fast as earthy materials, then what was the cause of "natural" motion? Was the distinction between natural (vertical) and impressed (horizontal) motion tenable? The demolition of the edifice was concluded by Newton, who showed that the distinction behind natural and impressed motions was incorrect; that if one adopted a different point of view, all motion, vertical and horizontal, celestial and terrestrial, fitted the same scheme. He expressed his formulation in three laws of motion.

Newton's *first law* states (in his own words): "*Every body perseveres in its state of rest, or of uniform motion in a right line, unless it is compelled to change that state by forces impressed thereon.*" What this law implies is the following. If an object is at rest, it will not move—not even in the vertical direction—unless disturbed. On the other hand, if an object is moving, it will not stop of its own accord—even in the horizontal direction—unless disturbed. In this statement there are two implications completely contrary to Aristotelian physics. Once a body is set in motion—for instance, a stone catapulted against an enemy city—the fact that it stops must be explained rather than the fact that it keeps on moving after leaving the catapult. Also, the fact that an apple drops off a tree must be explained, for without a disturbance the apple should continue to float. Newton's first law is sometimes called the law of inertia since the resistance of an object to a disturbance of its state, whether the state be rest or motion, is the inertia of the object.

Newton's *second law* describes the way in which disturbances affect the state of objects, whether initially at rest or in motion. It is best given in mathematical form:

$$F = ma \qquad (7\text{--}10)$$

in which F is the "force impressed" on the object; a the acceleration (change in velocity per unit time) which it receives as a result of the force; and m a property of the object called the mass.

Newton's first law merely states that an object in motion or at rest does not change that state without a force. His second law then gives the mathematical description of how a given force affects the speed. Twice as large a force must be applied to change the speed of a given object in 1 sec from rest to 10 cm/sec as from rest to 5 cm/sec. Or, if a train traveling 30 miles/hr must be stopped in 2 min, three times as large a force is required than if it had been traveling only 10 miles/hr. We can measure the acceleration of a given object and with $F = ma$ compute the forces that were acting.

The direct proportionality between force and acceleration holds as long as we experiment with one object. When we compare different objects, we must also consider the property called mass. Some objects, with large m, are accelerated less by a given force than others, with small m. It turns out that the property m defined by the equation $F = ma$ and the mass which we sense when we call something heavy or light are related; that is, something we sense as being heavier is accelerated less by a given force than something we sense as being lighter. Or, if we wish to accelerate a heavier and a lighter object to the same extent, we require a larger force for the heavier object. We shall return to this point.

Finally Newton's *third law*, the law of action and reaction: *When a body* A *exerts a force on a body* B *then body* B *exerts an equal and opposite force on body* A. This is the law familiar to anyone who has ever slipped while trying to push a heavy piece of furniture.

When we push a piece of furniture, we exert a force. According to the third law, the furniture also pushes back against us. Now, these forces should propel the furniture forward and us backward. Actually

this rarely happens; one of three things typically does. Neither we nor the piece of furniture may move; or we may slip and the piece of furniture may stand still; or the furniture may move as desired while we stand still. The reason for this is that our pushing and the furniture pushing back are not the only forces acting on us or the furniture. At point O in Fig. 7–8, the man pushes and the table pushes back. At point F, however, his feet also push, against the floor, and the floor pushes back. At point G the table pushes against the floor and the floor pushes against the table. The forces at points F and G are forces of friction. If the forces at point O, where his hands push the furniture, are smaller than the frictional forces at F and G, nothing happens. His feet and the table stand still. If the forces at point O are larger than the frictional force at G but smaller than at F, the table will move while he does not. This is what we usually want. If the forces at O are larger than at F but smaller than at G, the table stands still while he slips.

In addition to showing the several points where action and reaction forces occur when we push a piece of furniture, this example illustrates two other ideas. In the first place, normally a number of forces act on an

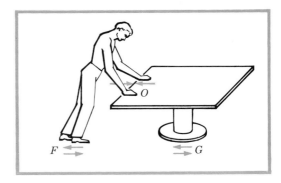

FIG. 7-8

The law of action and reaction. In pushing furniture, there are three places where forces are acting and reacting. At point O *hands push the table and the table pushes back. At point* F *feet push the floor and the floor pushes back. At point* G *the table pushes the floor and the floor pushes the table.*

object at the same time and at different points. Second, these forces lead to acceleration only if they are not in balance. Motion results only from a *net, unbalanced force,* one or more forces which do not balance acting simultaneously on an object. Thus in the first case when neither the man nor the table moves, the various forces are in balance. There is no net unbalanced force. When the table moves and the man does not, the forces on the man are in balance whereas the forces on the table are not. There is a net unbalanced force on the table that accelerates it sideways. Finally, when the man slips, the net unbalanced force is on the man while the forces on the table are in balance. (We might point out that another pair of forces involved in the diagram is that of gravity pulling downward and the floor pushing upward.)

In the light of the last paragraph, we should revise Newton's first and second laws and replace the simple word "force" by "net, unbalanced force."

MASS AND WEIGHT

In our discussion of Newton's second law, we pointed out that the mass which we describe when we call an object heavy or "massive" and the mass which appears in $F = ma$ when we push an object strongly or gently are related. Let us see how this can be explained.

When we weigh something—this is how we determine whether it is heavy or light—we let it push against a balance pan, a spring scale, or simply against our hand. Its weight is measured by the force necessary to balance the downward push. Something heavy requires a large balancing force; something light, a small balancing force. Thus weight is the force which the object exerts because gravity pulls it downward. Now this gravitational force, F_w (weight), is also given by $F_w = ma$ in which a is the acceleration due to gravity, and Galileo had already discovered all ob-

jects are accelerated equally by gravity. Hence a in the expression $F_w = ma$ is the same for all objects. With a the same, F_w—weight measured on balances—is directly proportional to m—the property that determines how easily the object is pushed.

This gives us a way to determine m—mass—without resorting to pushes and accelerations. We place two objects on the pans of a balance. If they balance, their masses are equal. If not, we can use fractions or multiples of one to determine the relationship between their masses. This is actually how mass is obtained. A platinum-iridium cylinder at Sèvres, France, serves as the international standard kilogram (kg). Other masses are compared to it, or to fractions or multiples of its mass. The most common smaller mass is the gram (sometimes abbreviated g), defined so that 1,000 grams = 1 kg. The comparisons are possible because the force of gravity acts in such a way that at any point on the surface of the earth, the weight of an object is directly proportional to the mass.

With this definition of weight, we can understand how objects change weight if transported to different parts of the earth. The acceleration due to gravity varies slightly with position on earth, being greatest near the poles, about 983 cm/sec^2, and dropping to about 978 cm/sec^2 at the equator. High above sea level, as in the mile-high city of Denver, it also has the lower value. Hence the force exerted by an object, its weight, changes accordingly. The commonly used average value, designated by g, is 980 cm/sec^2, or about 32 ft/sec^2. Weight changes also with location in the universe. On the surface of Mars, which is a much smaller planet than the earth, the acceleration is only about 390 cm/sec.^{2} The weight of a 150-lb (on earth) man would be reduced correspondingly to 60 lb. Weightlessness, in the same context, means that there is no force of gravity acting on a body. That condition does not exist anywhere in the universe.

The weightlessness of astronauts circling

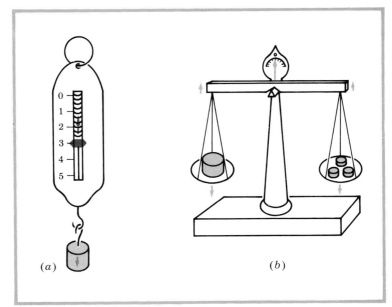

We measure weight by balancing the force of gravity on an object against (a) the force of an extended spring or (b) the force of a counterweight on a balance arm. That force is proportional to the mass of the object because gravity accelerates all objects equally.

(a)   (b)

FIG 7-9

the globe is explained in a different way. They are accelerated by gravity and, because of that acceleration, are constantly falling toward the earth. (How they are "falling" is explained in the next chapter.) But because they are free to accelerate, they do not experience the physiological effects of weight.

We can derive appropriate units for force from $F = ma$. With m in grams and a in centimeters per second, squared, force has the dimensions gram-cm/sec². That unit is usually called the *dyne*. At the surface of the earth a mass of 1 gram has a weight of 980 dynes. In the English system the unit of force is the pound (lb). A pound is a much larger unit of force than the dyne, equal to about 450,000 dynes.

Questions and Problems

1. What are the measured quantities related by the proportionality constants in the following? (*a*) batting averages, (*b*) rushing percentages in football, (*c*) rebounding in basketball, (*d*) cost of airplane tickets, (*e*) wages.

2. Write the dimensions of each proportionality constant in Question 1. See whether you can illustrate (*a*) the general application of the law, (*b*) the application of the the law to a specific set of measurements, (*c*) the application of the law to a single measurement. Can each use be illustrated for all five examples?

3. Which of the following are sets of quantities that are proportional to one another?

(*a*) Ball rolling down an incline:

Time rolling, in seconds	Distance rolled, in feet
0.5	2
1.0	8
2.0	32

(*b*) Producing hydrogen gas by reacting aluminum and hydrochloric acid:

Volume of hydrogen produced, in liters	Weight of aluminum, in grams
25	9
41.7	15
58.3	21

4. Plot the data from Question 3 on graph paper. What is the characteristic of proportional quantities?

5. Sometimes, when two quantities are not

proportional to one another, one is proportional to the square of the other. Try this with Question 3. (First square one column and plot the squares against the other. If that doesn't work, square the second.)

6. Three secretaries type student papers. Each is paid on the same basis. Find that basis.

	No. of hours	No. of papers	Pages per paper	Pay
Mary	8	3	17	$15.30
Sue	7	4	13	$15.60
Joan	7½	5	10	$15.00

7. What conditions are required for uniform motion? Is it possible to have uniform motion on the surface of the earth? in space?

8. Compute the average speed on a 200-mile journey which takes 3 hr, 20 min.

9. A driver averages 20 mph for ½ hr; then 50 mph for 1½ hr. How far does he get? What is his overall average speed?

10. A driver averages 20 mph for 5 miles, then 50 mph for 5 miles. How long does it take him? What is his average speed?

11. A stone is 16 ft above ground. How long does it take to fall? With what speed does it strike? (Use the value 32 ft/sec^2 for acceleration at the surface of the earth.)

12. Two stones are dropped simultaneously from 64 ft and 80 ft, respectively. How many seconds apart do they strike? What is their speed?

13. Compare the time interval in Question 12 with the answer to Question 11. Why the difference when both describe 16 ft of fall?

14. An automobile accelerates from standing to 44 ft/sec in 2 sec. What is the acceleration? What distance has it covered?

15. A rocket motor exerts a force of 5×10^5 dynes on a 2×10^3 gram rocket for 4 sec. What is the acceleration? What speed does the rocket reach? What distance has it traversed? (Ignore gravity, friction, etc.)

16. If the motor in Question 15 stops completely after 4 sec, how far does the rocket travel in 10 sec?

17. A 100-kg man jumps from a 250-kg boat to a dock. The boat glides away from the dock at 100 cm/sec. Why does the boat glide away? With what speed did the man jump?

18. The record for the mile run is about 3 min 50 sec. What is the average speed of the runner? The record for the 100-yd dash is about 9 sec. What is the average speed? Convert both to miles per hour and compare.

19. A certain plane weighs 50,000 kg (50 tons). It must travel 240 km/hr (150 mph) to become airborne. If it accelerates at the rate of 4 meters/sec^2, how many seconds before it can lift off? How long must the runway be? What force must the engines deliver?

20. Suggest common illustrations of each of Newton's laws of motion.

21. Relate mass and inertia.

22. Why is gravity a force?

23. Consider a tug-of-war. What forces are operative and where? When two teams of equal strength pull against each other, the team that is first pulled forward usually loses. Analyze forces to explain.

24. A ball rolling down an incline moves with a speed of 400 cm/sec. After 8 sec, how far has it rolled? What is the acceleration?

25. A stone dropped from the top of the Empire State building takes about 9.5 sec to reach the street below. How tall is the building?

Suggestions for Further Reading

Beiser, Arthur: *Basic Concepts of Physics,* Addison-Wesley Publishing Company, Reading, Mass., 1961. Chapters 1 and 2 develop the equations of motion and Newton's laws.

Holton, Gerald: *Introduction to Concepts and Theories in Physical Science,* Addison-Wesley Publishing Company, Inc., Reading, Mass., 1952. Chapter 4.

Holton, Gerald, and Duane H. D. Roller: *Foundations of Modern Physical Science,* Addison-Wesley Publishing Company, Inc., Reading, Mass., 1958. Chapters 1, 2, and 4 contain the equations of motion and the development of the ideas that led to Newton's laws.

Physical Science Study Committee: *Physics,* D. C. Heath and Company, Boston, 1960. Chapters 1 to 6 discuss the problems of measurement and the mathematical description of motion; chap. 20 deals with Newton's laws.

Rogers, Eric M.: *Physics for the Inquiring Mind,* Princeton University Press, Princeton, N. J., 1960. Chapter 1 and its appendix develop the equations of motion and discuss free fall; chap. 7 treats Newton's laws.

Chapter 8

Gravity: Falling Stones and Orbiting Planets

In the previous chapter we developed the equations for uniform linear motion and uniformly accelerated linear motion. We found that objects in the universe which follow these equations are rare. Objects that move uniformly are practically non-existent while only freely falling bodies obey the equations of uniformly accelerated motion. The most common motions in the universe are curved paths like those of baseballs or planets. Fortunately, we need not develop a new set of equations to describe curved paths. We can adapt the equations for linear motion to curved paths by means of a kind of algebra called vector algebra.

125

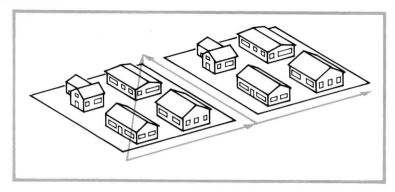

One block added to one block doesn't necessarily produce two blocks distance from the starting point. The directions of the blocks are important.

FIG. 8-1

VECTORS

We illustrate vectors with a simple problem. Suppose you need milk from the corner grocery, which is at the end of the second block from your house. How far do you have to walk? Two blocks? Well, it depends. If the grocery is two blocks down the same straight street, then clearly you have to walk two blocks. But if the second block is on a cross street, so that the grocery is one block over and one block up (Fig. 8–1) and if the neighbors don't mind your walking across their backyards, then you need to walk only about 1.4 blocks. One block distance added to one block distance does not necessarily add to two blocks distance. It depends on the direction in which the distances are measured.

Quantities like distance, whose direction as well as magnitude must be taken into account, are best represented by arrows whose lengths correspond to the magnitude and whose heads point in the appropriate direction. The arrows are called vectors, and the quantities they represent, vector quantities. Each block distance in Fig. 8–1 is shown as a vector. Addition with vectors follows a different rule. Draw the first vector. Then draw the second vector with its tail at the head of the first. Their sum is a new vector leading from the tail of the first to the head of the second. This is also shown in Fig. 8–1. Notice that for the two

possibilities there, the resulting vectors, the sum of the two distances, differ both in magnitude and in direction.

Figure 8–2 also illustrates vectors and vector addition. In it, there are three vectors: vectors representing 10 miles east, 15 miles north, and 20 miles southwest. Also in the figure is their sum, shown as a heavier line vector. As in algebra, the order in which the vectors are added does not matter. The resultant vector has the same magnitude and direction whether the order is 1, 2, 3; 2, 1, 3; or any other order.

Speed, like distance, is characterized by

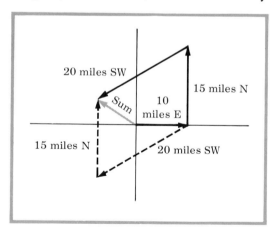

FIG. 8-2

The sum of three vectors. To add them, they are drawn tails to heads. Their sum is a vector from the tail of the first to the head of the last. Drawing the second and third vectors in reverse order (dotted lines) produces the same sum.

a direction as well as by a magnitude. This is recognized in Newton's first law, which states that motion continues "in a right line" unless changed by forces. The right (straight) line refers to the direction of the motion. The vector quantity that gives both the direction and the magnitude of the speed is called the *velocity*, and it is the velocity vector which is affected by forces. These forces may change the direction, the magnitude, or both direction and magnitude of the velocity vector. Velocity, consequently, gives more precise information than speed. It does not refer to the sort of thing we read on a speedometer, because speedometer readings remain the same whether the car goes straight or around a curve, uphill or downhill. The speedometer reads the speed which refers to a magnitude only; velocity refers to both direction and magnitude.

There is a consequence of this definition of velocity which we all have experienced many times. Constant velocity means travel at the same rate in a straight line: no acceleration, no forces. This is the sort of thing that happens in a good car on a good road; there is little, if any, sensation of

motion. On the other hand, rounding a curve even at constant speed means a change of velocity. There is deceleration and acceleration; there are forces. This is, of course, in accordance with our general experience. We feel pushed sideways whenever we are in a turning vehicle, whether it is a bicycle, a sailboat, a car, or an airplane.

Like distance and velocity, acceleration and force are also vector quantities. These are illustrated in Fig. 8-3. As the car turns the corner, its velocity in the initial direction drops to zero. A force operates in that direction to decelerate it (negative acceleration). At the same time, the car gains velocity in the new direction; a second force must operate in that direction to accelerate the car. Thus forces and accelerations operate in specific directions: they are vector quantities.

Vector mathematics is particularly important in the description of all kinds of motion which is the product of two or more separate contributions. For instance, an airplane heading due north at 120 mph when there is a 50-mph west wind actually flies toward the northeast at 130 mph. The two

FIG. 8-3

Forces operate on a car rounding a curve to decelerate it in the initial direction and to accelerate it in the new direction. (Dodge News Photo)

velocities add vectorially to produce that sum. With a head wind of 50 mph, its velocity with respect to the ground is reduced to 70 mph north; with a tail wind, it is increased to 170 mph. A boat trying to cross a river to a point directly across on the opposite shore must be headed up-river. Otherwise the current will take it to a place below its intended landing.

CURVED MOTION

With vectors one can resolve curved motion into simpler linear components. Galileo found that all objects fall toward the earth with the same acceleration. This is true whether the object is simply dropped or first thrown sideways. For instance, two balls so arranged that one is shot horizontally by a spring while the other is allowed to drop at the same instant (Fig. 8–4) reach

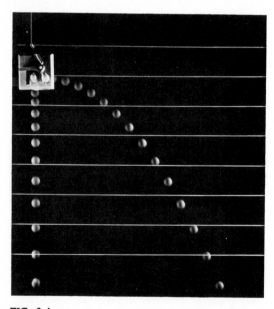

FIG. 8-4

The apparatus releases one ball and accelerates the other one horizontally. They both approach the ground at equal rates, as can be seen in this series of stroboscopic photographs in which the balls are illuminated by brief flashes of light at intervals of 1/30 sec. (From "PSSC Physics," D. C. Heath and Company, Boston, 1960)

the ground together. Their vertical progress is identical, although one, of course, also travels horizontally. This makes the description of the motion of the ball with the curved path particularly simple. Because it progresses downward exactly like the dropped ball, we can describe its vertical progress by the equations for falling objects, the equations for uniformly accelerated motion. Horizontally it experiences no force from the instant it leaves the spring until it strikes the ground. Horizontally it moves undisturbed by forces, according to the equations of uniform motion. We can combine these two aspects by adding the vectors that represent the two components of its motion. At any instant of its trajectory, the ball has a vertical component of velocity produced by its uniformly accelerated fall. It has a horizontal component of velocity produced by its uniform horizontal motion. The sum of these two velocity vectors is a vector which gives its speed and direction through space. We illustrate this with an example.

EXAMPLE

How does a stone thrown horizontally with a velocity of 45 ft/sec fall from a 256-ft-high bridge tower? Where and when does it strike the water? We solve this problem by treating horizontal and vertical motion separately, and adding the horizontal and vertical distance vectors to obtain the result (Fig. 8–5).

Horizontally the stone moves away from the bridge tower at a uniform rate of 45 ft/sec. From $d = vt$ (v is given at 45 ft/sec by the problem) its distance from the bridge is 45 ft, 90 ft, 135 ft, . . . after 1 sec, 2 sec, 3 sec, . . . respectively. Vertically the stone falls with uniform acceleration. Its vertical motion is given by $d = \frac{1}{2}gt^2$ ($g = 32$ ft/sec^2), and the distances it has fallen are 16 ft, 64 ft, 144 ft, . . . after 1 sec, 2 sec, 3 sec, . . . Now its distance from the origin atop the bridge tower can be obtained by adding corresponding vectors: 45 ft horizontal and 16 ft vertical for 1 sec; 90 ft horizontal and 64 ft vertical for 2 sec; 135 ft horizontal and 144 ft vertical for 3 sec; etc. These points describe its trajectory.

To obtain when and where the stone strikes the water, we first determine how long it takes to reach ground. According to $d = \frac{1}{2}gt^2$, a stone falls the distance of 256 ft from the top of the

Trajectory of a stone
thrown horizontally with
a velocity of 45 ft/sec
from a 256-ft-high bridge
tower. Horizontally the
stone moves at a constant
rate of 45 ft/sec because
after it is released from
the hand, no further
forces operate. Downward
the stone is accelerated
by gravity. The vertical
vectors show the distance
it falls after 1, 2, 3, and
4 sec. Its position at the
end of each second is
obtained by adding the
horizontal and vertical
distance vectors.
Connecting their sum by
a smooth curve gives the
trajectory of the stone.

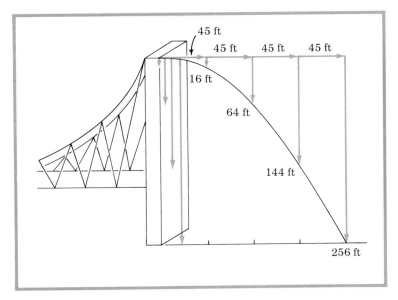

FIG. 8-5

tower in 4 sec. This is how long it falls. During that time it reaches a point 180 ft ($d = vt$ and $v = 45$ ft/sec) from the bridge. Hence it strikes 180 ft from the foot of the bridge.

There is an interesting corollary to this problem; namely, how does the trajectory of a stone dropped at the same instant compare with the trajectory we have just computed? This is analogous to the experiment shown in Fig. 8–4. For the dropped stone, we need only the vertical component of motion; only the vertical distance vectors that represent 16 ft, 64 ft, 144 ft, and 256 ft after 1, 2, 3, and 4 sec respectively. The vertical distance vectors are identical for the dropped and the thrown stones. Both stones strike the water at the same instant. Indeed, any stone thrown horizontally, whatever its horizontal velocity, has vertical distance vectors of 16 ft, 64 ft, 144 ft, and 256 ft after 1, 2, 3 and 4 sec, and it strikes the water at the same instant as any other horizontally thrown stone. All are accelerated downward by the same force. Consequently, they all achieve the same vertical velocities and travel the same vertical distances in the same periods of time.

The resolution of complex motion into simple components parallel to the rectangular axes is one of the most powerful inventions of science. With it, all sorts of simplifications can be introduced and problems can be solved which would otherwise be much too complex for either conceptual understanding or mathematical solution. Let us illustrate it with additional examples.

EXAMPLE

A baseball leaves the bat with an upward velocity of 96 ft/sec and a horizontal velocity of 16 ft/sec (Fig. 8–6). Does it leave the infield? How long is it in the air? To what height does the ball travel? Again we separate its horizontal motion from its vertical motion. Horizontally there are no forces. It moves uniformly. If we take the infield distance as the distance between home plate and second base, about 125 ft, then from the equation $d = vt$ for uniform motion with $v = 16$ ft/sec, we obtain $t = 7.8$ sec. The ball would leave the infield after about 7.8 sec. Is it in the air that long?

To determine the time it spends in the air, we use the equations of accelerated motion adjusted, however, for the fact that the ball starts off with an initial velocity. This adjustment can be introduced in several ways; we use an informal approach first. The ball starts upward with an initial velocity of 96 ft/sec. Gravity operates in the opposite direction to

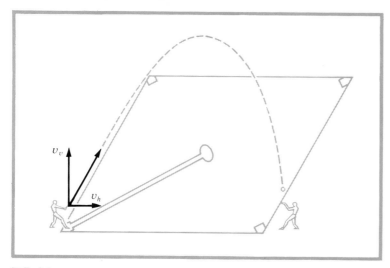

The initial motion of a baseball can be resolved into a horizontal and a vertical component. Vertically it moves under the influence of gravity with uniformly accelerated motion—with the acceleration in the direction opposite to its initial motion. Horizontally it experiences no further forces and travels uniformly with the initial velocity.

FIG. 8-6

reduce that velocity. Now the ball rises only until its upward velocity is zero. Then it starts falling. How long does it rise, and then how long does it fall? To answer the first question, how long does it rise, we must compute how long gravitational acceleration ($g = 32$ ft/sec²) must operate to reduce the initial 96 ft/sec upward velocity to zero. Another way of stating this is that we must determine how long it takes to produce a downward velocity of 96 ft/sec which exactly cancels the initial upward velocity of 96 ft/sec—and thus produces a momentarily motionless ball at the top of its path. From $v = gt$, −96 ft/sec = −32 ft/sec² × 3 sec (the minus sign indicates downward). Three seconds are needed to reduce the initial velocity to zero. This is how long the ball rises. Symmetry then suggests that it falls for 3 sec also and spends 6 sec in the air. In 6 sec it has not yet reached the outfield. It is an infield pop.

Finally, how far up does it fly? Since it travels upward and also falls in 3 sec, we can use $d = \frac{1}{2}gt^2$ with $t = 3$; it reaches a height of 144 ft.

In the solution to this example we have used a combination of intuition and informal reasoning to give us the answer. This is a good and frequently used method to simplify problems. But the method involves assumptions which must be checked. Is the path really symmetrical; that is, does the ball fall for as many seconds as it rises? Can we add the positive and negative velocities to determine the instant at which the

ball starts falling? The validity of our assumptions can be demonstrated quite exactly and rigorously if we use a form of Eqs. 7–7 to 7–9 which specifically includes the possibility that at the time we begin computations, t_0, the object moves from some distant point d_0 rather than from a zero reference point or that it accelerates at time t_0 from an initial velocity v_0 rather than from rest. The changes needed are simple; they merely add to the equation what we added by informal reasoning in solving the example. For uniform velocity,

$$d = d_0 + vt \qquad (8\text{--}1)$$

For uniformly accelerated motion:

$$v = v_0 + at \qquad (8\text{--}2)$$

$$d = d_0 + v_0t + \tfrac{1}{2}at^2 \qquad (8\text{--}3)$$

With these equations and one further caution, we can determine the vertical component of the pop-fly motion quite formally. The caution is that distance, velocity, and acceleration are vector quantities. While they act in the vertical direction, the vectors may be pointed upward and downward. As we can easily verify, an upward vector and a downward vector of equal magnitude add up to zero. They add to twice the individual value if in the same direction. Hence we need a means to keep track of the opposite directions in solving Eqs. 8–1 to 8–3. Now the minus sign does for algebraic quantities exactly what opposite directions do for vectors. A number and minus that number add up to zero; $+a - a = 0$. Hence to keep track of directions in these equations, we can use the minus sign. We call upward direction, upward velocity, and upward acceleration plus; the initial velocity v_0 is, therefore, $+96$ ft/sec. The acceleration, which is downward toward the earth, is then minus, $a = -32$ ft/sec^2. Using these numbers with Eq. 8–2 gives 3 sec as before for the point at which the ball rests, for an instant, before falling and $v = 0$. Hence, this formal method gives the same result as before.

The formal method has an advantage if we wish to determine the entire trajectory for the pop fly. Then we use Eq. 8–3 with $d_0 = 0$ (the ball starts at ground level); $v_0 = +96$ ft/sec; and $a = -32$ ft/sec^2. After 1 sec at t_1, the distance above ground is 80 ft; after 2 sec, 128 ft; after 3 sec, 144 ft; etc. These numbers give the distance from ground level as a result of the vertical component of motion. Added vectorially to the distance traveled from the origin as a result of the horizontal component of motion, they give the point the ball reaches at t_1, t_2, t_3, etc.—at 1-sec intervals in its trajectory.

EXAMPLE

A home run just clears the fence 312 ft away, exactly 3 sec after it was hit. Determine its velocity at the instant it was hit. The velocity with which the baseball left the bat was in a direction off at an angle. That velocity can be determined vectorially by finding its horizontal and vertical components. We use Eq. 8–1 for the horizontal component with $d_0 = 0$, $d = 312$ ft, and $t = 3$ sec. $v_h = 104$ ft/sec. To compute its initial vertical velocity, v_{ov}, we use Eq. 8–3 with $d_0 = 0$, $d = 0$ (when it clears the fence it is at ground level again), $t = 3$, and $a = -32$ ft/sec^2. Solution of the equation gives $v_{ov} = 48$ ft/sec. (The reader might check these results by the appropriate substitution.) The initial velocity of the baseball is the vector sum of a velocity vector of 104 ft/sec horizontally and 48 ft/sec vertically.

The vertical velocity vector could have been obtained in another way, again using intuition to help with the solution. Because of symmetry, the home run rose 1½ sec and dropped 1½ sec. Its vertical velocity is zero after 1½ sec. Then Eq. 8–2, with $v = 0$, $a = -32$ ft/sec^2, and $t = 1½$ sec, gives $v_0 = 48$ ft/sec. Of course, it is the same answer obtained above.

A consequence of the independence of horizontal and vertical motion is well known to bombardiers. A bomb released by an airplane will strike almost exactly underneath the bomber, because the bomb travels horizontally as fast as the airplane from which it was released (Fig. 8–7). It merely adds velocity in the vertical direction through the acceleration of gravity which gives it a curved path. (Actually the airfoils on the bomb increase its air friction so that this statement is only approximately true. The bomb lands a bit behind the bomber, allowing it to get out of the way of the explosion with some room to spare.)

MISSILES AND ROCKETS

The independence of the components of motion leads to two phenomena important for missile experts and rocketeers. The first relates to firing a missile either north or south. Suppose a 3,000-mile missile is test-fired from the equator due north. Will it land at a point exactly due north of the

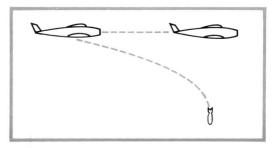

FIG. 8-7

The horizontal component of the motion of the bomb and of the bomber are identical. Except for the action of the airfoils, the bomb remains directly under the bomber.

launching pad? No. At the equator the launching pad rotates with the earth at a velocity of about 1,000 mph to the east. Therefore the missile moves with its own velocity north but also at 1,000 mph east since it maintains that velocity as a bomb maintains the velocity of the bomber. But the spot it is to hit, which is halfway to the pole, lies on a smaller latitude circle. It travels eastward with a smaller velocity. Hence the missile will strike ahead of it unless it is pointed somewhat to the west on the launching pad (Fig. 8–8). This, of course, complicates the task of the military and is one reason for the complex computers that guide military missiles.

The rocket problem is a different problem entirely. Suppose a rocket launching pad were established on top of Mount Everest for launching rockets horizontally. How far would they travel? As we pointed out in the previous section, the distance the rocket reaches depends entirely on its horizontal component of velocity. The greater the horizontal velocity, the farther away the rocket will strike. The rate and time of fall, governed by the acceleration of gravity, is the same for all rockets. But

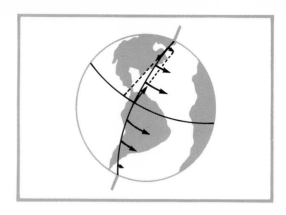

FIG. 8-8

The velocity of rotation is greatest along the equator because it has the largest radius, and smaller along the latitude circles north and south because they have smaller radii. A projectile fired from the equator is carried ahead of the points north or south; a projectile fired toward the equator is left behind.

there is a catch to this problem. For a rocket traveling horizontally with tremendous velocity, the earth cannot be considered flat. The curvature of the earth becomes important (Fig. 8–9). If the rocket strikes the ground far enough away, it falls for a somewhat longer time since it reaches

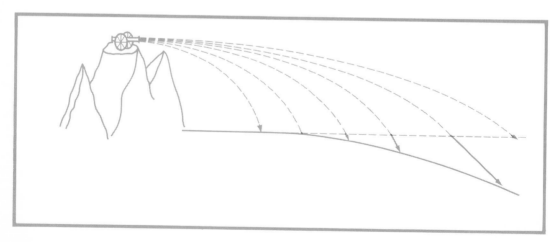

FIG. 8-9

As long as the earth can be considered flat, the time of fall of all objects is the same. But for objects that fall so far away that the curvature of the earth must be taken into account, the time of fall increases because they fall "below" the surface. An object which falls very far away may miss the surface altogether and keep on falling around the earth.

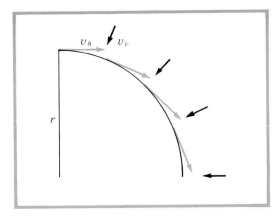

FIG. 8-10

Circular motion can be described by a series of vector pairs—one along the tangent and the other pointed toward the center of the circle.

the earth's surface "below" the plane on which a stone would strike if it could fall straight down. Now supposing the rocket starts with such great speed that it misses the earth's surface entirely, what then? Such a rocket would continue to fall but would always miss the earth. It would circle the earth, always falling toward it but always missing the "ends of the earth." It would become an artificial satellite.

The artificial satellite we launched in the last paragraph travels with uniform speed though not with uniform velocity because it is constantly under the influence of gravity and is constantly accelerated toward the center of the earth. Its motion can be analyzed in steps as follows: It begins with a horizontal velocity v_h. During the first second, it travels with the velocity v_h but is also given a vertical velocity v_v by the acceleration of gravity. Consequently at the end of 1 sec its velocity is the sum of the two vectors v_h and v_v, a velocity parallel to the tangent of the surface of the earth at that point. From here it moves with the new velocity for 1 sec, but it is also accelerated toward the earth by gravity. After the second second, therefore, its velocity is again the sum of the two and is again parallel to the surface of the earth. These processes continue and produce a circular path (Fig. 8–10).

Uniform circular motion, that is, motion which maintains constant speed along a circular path, requires an initial velocity in a direction at right angles to the line connecting the object with the center of its circular orbit and a constant acceleration toward the center. There must be a *central force,* a force directed toward the center, which pulls the object toward it. For this reason, an object moving with uniform circular motion can be considered constantly falling toward the center. The central force is called the *centripetal force.* Without it, the object flies off in a straight line.

We can quite easily determine the relationship required between the centripetal acceleration experienced by a rocket and its speed in order to circle the earth. These two must be exactly in balance, or the rocket falls to the ground or describes an elliptical path. This requirement can be stated as follows with reference to Fig. 8–11. During the time that the rocket travels the horizontal distance d_x, it must fall toward the earth exactly the distance d_y.

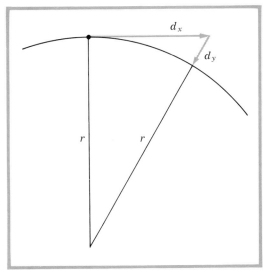

FIG. 8-11

The requirement for circular motion is that in the time it takes to travel the horizontal distance d_x, the object must also travel through the vertical distance d_y. The centripetal acceleration must be just large enough to produce that vertical motion.

From the right-triangle theorem that $a^2 + b^2 = c^2$, we can write (r = radius of the circle of motion) $r^2 + d_x^2 = (r + d_y)^2$ or, squaring the right-hand side and subtracting r^2 from both sides, $d_x^2 = 2d_yr + d_y^2$. Now d_y is a very small distance compared to r and d_x. Squaring a number less than 1 produces an even smaller number. Therefore, we may neglect d_y^2 as being too small to affect the equality. (This manner of simplifying a problem is very common in science. When an analysis of the physical situation shows that some complexing features contribute only small errors, they are neglected, at least the first time the problem is studied. However, the problem we are discussing can be solved exactly.) The equation therefore becomes

$$d_x^2 = 2d_yr \qquad (8\text{--}4)$$

d_x is a distance traveled because of an initial velocity and no further acceleration. Hence the equation of uniform motion applies, $d_x = vt$. d_y is a distance traversed because of a central force. It is an example of accelerated motion, and $d_y = \frac{1}{2}at^2$. Then, substituting these two equations into 8–4 gives

$$v^2t^2 = 2r \times \tfrac{1}{2}at^2$$
$$v^2 = ar \qquad (8\text{--}5)$$
$$a = v^2/r$$

Uniform circular motion will be described by an object if the centripetal acceleration is equal to the initial horizontal velocity, squared, divided by the radius of the orbit. If the centripetal acceleration is larger, the object falls into the center; if it is smaller, the object goes into an elliptical orbit or flies away entirely.

THE FORCE OF GRAVITY

A rocket launched from the top of Mount Everest would describe the uniform circular motion only approximately. At the height of 29,000 ft there is too much air resis-

tance, and friction would soon slow down the rocket until it fell to the ground. But the moon, 240,000 miles up, is just another "rocket" falling continually around the earth and just missing it. And from the moon's motion, Newton was able to deduce what kind of force gravity is and, what is more important, that the gravitational attraction experienced by the moon in its fall around the earth is the same as the gravitational attraction experienced by an apple falling to the ground. The moon and the apple move because of the same force, gravity.

The logical steps which led Newton to the insight into the nature of gravity are the following. The moon travels with (nearly) uniform, circular motion. (Again we simplify here because our mathematical tools are limited. The problem can be solved rigorously.) Hence, its velocity and acceleration obey the equation $a = v^2/r$. Moreover, its velocity is simply the length of its orbit (the length of a circle with radius r_m), divided by the time required for one orbit (the period of revolution, T_m). In symbols, $v = 2\pi r_m/T_m$ in which r_m is the distance moon-to-earth. Substituting the second equation into the first, we obtain

$$a = \frac{4\pi^2r_m^2}{r_mT_m^2} = \frac{4\pi^2r_m}{T_m^2} \qquad (8\text{--}6)$$

The force of gravity exerted on the moon is, like every force, equal to the mass of the moon, m_m, multiplied by the acceleration. As given in the last equation,

$$F = m_ma = \frac{4\pi^2r_mm_m}{T_m^2} \qquad (8\text{--}7)$$

But as Kepler established in his third law, the distance of an orbiting body is related to its period of revolution by $T_m^2 = Kr_m^3$. Replacing T_m^2 in Eq. 8–7 by Kr_m^3 gives

$$F = \frac{4\pi^2r_mm_m}{Kr_m^3} = \frac{4\pi^2m_m}{Kr_m^2} \qquad (8\text{--}8)$$

The force of gravity which keeps the moon falling around the earth contains some numbers, $4\pi^2/K$, and the mass of the moon, m_m, divided by the distance earth-to-moon, r_m, squared.

This solution, Eq. 8–8, is peculiar to the moon. But supposing we carried out the same mathematical steps using an artificial satellite, what changes would we have to introduce? Where the mass of the moon appears we would have to place the mass of the satellite. For the distance earth-to-moon we would have to use the distance to the satellite. Instead of m_m and r_m in Eq. 8–8, there would be m_s and r_s. In other words, any orbiting body is attracted by a force of gravity which depends on *its* mass and *its* distance to the earth. We can drop the subscripts and obtain a general equation for the force of gravity on all bodies orbiting around the earth,

$$F = \frac{4\pi^2}{K} \times \frac{m}{r^2} \qquad (8-9)$$

At this point Newton's insight added further clarification. Since for every force there is an equal and opposite force, the force of gravity attracting a heavenly body to the earth has a reaction force which equally attracts the earth to the heavenly body. Stated somewhat more accurately, they attract each other through gravity. But if the gravity experienced by the orbiting object depends on its mass, considerations of symmetry suggest that the gravity experienced by the earth should depend on the earth's mass. Equation 8–9, which expressed the mutual attraction of gravity, must contain hidden in the number $4\pi^2/K$ the mass of the earth. To extract it from that number, we replace $4\pi^2/K$ by GM_e in which G expresses what is left of $4\pi^2/K$ when M_e is extracted. Equation 8–9 then becomes $F = GM_em/r^2$. One last step. Why should the mass of the earth be peculiar? Planets orbit around the sun, presumably under the force of gravity which in that case must involve the sun's and planet's masses. We may assume that all masses attract one another, and drop the subscript that refers one mass specifically to the earth. Then the law of gravity which ex-

presses attraction of all masses in the universe to one another becomes

$$F = GMm/r^2 \qquad (8-10)$$

Two masses, M and m, attract each other with a force that is proportional (G is the proportionality constant) to the product of their masses divided by the square of the distance that separates them. Why aren't you attracted to the girl (or boy) sitting next to you? Well, you are, though because your masses are so small, the force of gravity is very feeble and can be neglected, especially compared to other attractions that may be operating. Only on a chunk of matter as large as the sun or the earth does the force of attraction become appreciable.

Now Eq. 8–10, which is a general law of attraction between masses, was obtained rigorously from the motions of the moon and then generalized. Such a generalization, which is one form of thought experiment, must be put to the test of a physical experiment. Fortunately, Newton had the data for the experiment and could check his theory.

Testing the theory is a bit roundabout. We shall use numbers derived from observations of the moon only and see whether they, the lunar numbers, produce the value of 32 ft/sec² for the acceleration of gravity on earth. If they do, Eq. 8–10 can be used for the moon and for the earth's surface and probably everywhere else too.

We begin with Eqs. 8–7 and 8–10 since both of these are equations that refer to the force exerted by the earth on the moon. Setting them equal, since they express the same force, gives

$$\frac{4\pi^2 r m_m}{T_m^2} = \frac{GM_e m_m}{r^2} \qquad (8-11)$$

We first divide by m_m, which appears on both sides of the equation. For all the remaining terms that appear in Eq. 8–11, except G and M_e, we have numbers from astronomical observations. In particular, $r = 240,000$ miles and $T = 27.3$ days. Rearranging Eq. 8–11, we obtain

$$GM_e = \frac{4\pi^2 r^3}{T_m{}^2}$$

$$= \frac{4\pi^2(240{,}000 \text{ miles} \times 5280 \text{ ft/mile})^3}{(27.3 \text{ days} \times 86{,}400 \text{ sec/day})^2}$$

$$GM_e = 1.44 \times 10^{16} \text{ ft}^3/\text{sec}^2 \qquad (8\text{–}12)$$

Now we return to earth and to the falling apple which, according to legend, inspired Newton. The apple is accelerated by gravity, which we can express by Eq. 8–10 and by Newton's second law, $F = ma$:

$$F = m_a a = \frac{GM_e m_a}{r^2} \qquad (8\text{–}13)$$

Again we divide by m_a, which appears on both sides of the equation, leaving $a = GM_e/r^2$. We computed GM_e from lunar observations in Eq. 8–12 and can put its value into the equation. The distance between the apple and center of the earth is the radius of the earth, 3,950 miles. If we place these two numbers into the equation,

$$a = \frac{GM_e}{r^2}$$

$$= \frac{1.44 \times 10^{16} \text{ ft}^3/\text{sec}^2}{(3{,}950 \text{ miles} \times 5{,}280 \text{ ft/mile})^2}$$

$$= 33.1 \text{ ft/sec}^2 \qquad (8\text{–}14)$$

Numbers obtained only from astronomical observation—the moon's distance and period of revolution in Eq. 8–12 and the earth's radius in Eq. 8–14—produce the value of 33.1 ft/sec² for the acceleration of gravity experienced by an apple on earth. This is very nearly the number obtained from direct experiments. Surely this coincidence is no accident. The law of gravity, *derived from the behavior of the moon,* also fits the attractions found on earth. Indeed, we can quite safely assume that the law, shown here to apply to two widely different situations, holds for any other masses which attract one another. Thus from the motion of the moon, checked by the behavior of falling apples, the law of gravity was established.

THE DETERMINATION OF G

In the previous calculations, we were able to compute the numerical value of GM_e but not that of either the mass of the earth, M_e, or of the proportionality constant in the law of gravity, G, separately. Determination of the value of G is important because it then permits the calculation of the mass of the earth and other computations of astronomical interest. However, unless the masses involved are very large, the measurement is very difficult because the force of gravity is exceedingly small.

The Royal Astronomer Nevil Maskelyne (1732–1811) made the first attempt to determine the value of G in 1774. He measured the deflection of a plumb bob in the vicinity of a mountain and estimated the mass of the mountain. But the deflection of the plumb bob was small, the estimate difficult to make, and his value was highly inaccurate. Not until 1798, more than 100 years after Newton published the law of gravity, was G measured successfully by the English physicist Henry Cavendish (1731–1810). Cavendish suspended a dumbbell-like rod with two balls by a fine thread (Fig. 8–12). Then he brought two heavy balls near the suspended balls as shown, carefully measuring the distance between the pairs of adjacent balls. Since each pair of balls was attracted by gravity, a slight twist was produced in the thread. Next he took the heavy balls away and determined the force required to twist the thread by the same amount. This measured force was equal to the force of gravity exerted by the two pairs of attracting masses. He now had values for the force, the masses, and the distances. Placing these into Eq. 8–10, he could calculate the value of G, the only undetermined quantity in that equation. The modern value for G, based on similar though more refined measurements, is 6.6673×10^{-8} cm³/gram-sec². This is so small a number that ordinary masses produce only negligible forces of

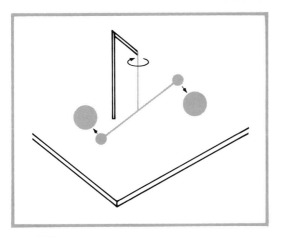

FIG. 8-12

Cavendish's determination of the gravitational constant G. The large heavy balls produced a twisting of the thread which holds the bar with the smaller balls. From the force expended in twisting the thread and the mass of the balls, G could be computed.

attraction. But the earth, whose mass can be calculated from this value of G and the value of GM_e, has a mass of 5.98×10^{27} grams. When such a large number is placed into Eq. 8–10, large forces result even though G is very small.

GRAVITATIONAL EFFECTS ON EARTH

Since the rotation of the earth flattens it at the poles and causes a bulge near the equator, different places on the earth's surface differ in their distances from the center of the earth and, therefore, differ in the gravitational attraction. Thus near the poles, where the distance to the earth's center is least, gravitational force is somewhat greater. We have already mentioned this in the previous chapter. But the difference results not only from the difference in the earth's equatorial and polar diameters but also from the fact that at the equator objects rotate with the earth at a speed of about 1,000 mph. As we saw earlier in this chapter, circular motion can be maintained

only if there is a centripetal acceleration. Hence a fraction of the gravitational force is used to keep equatorial objects whirling with the earth, and only the remainder accelerates their fall. At the poles, which are at the axis around which rotation occurs, no force is needed to maintain circular motion and all of the gravitational attraction serves to accelerate the fall of objects.

Latitude north or south of the equator is not the only factor that determines the value of the acceleration of gravity. There is a difference between sea level and mountains, and there are variations with the nature of the crust. Over dense subsurface formations, acceleration is larger than over less dense formations or over seawater.

TIDES

The effect of the gravitational attraction of the moon—and to a smaller extent of the sun—is observed in ocean tides. Since the "front" and "back" of the earth are separated by some 7,900 miles (Fig. 8–13), the near side of the earth is attracted more strongly to the moon than the far side. This difference of attraction has little effect on the land masses on earth, which are too rigid to be deformed by the moon's gravity. But the water in the oceans can follow the moon quite easily as the earth turns underneath it. The ocean level is therefore raised toward the moon, resulting in tides.

Tides occur, however, at about 12-hr. intervals, twice as frequently as one would expect from this simple picture. They occur both at the near and at the far side with respect to the moon. On the near side the explanation is the one given above. The moon's greater attraction at the near surface raises the water above its normal position. The explanation for the tide at the far side is that the moon pulls the rigid land away from under the water level. The earth's surface sinks, leaving a higher water level, a tide.

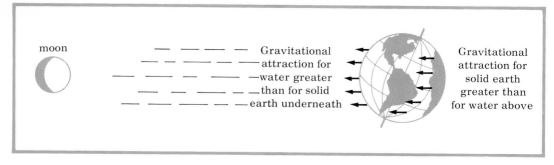

FIG. 8-13

Gravitational attraction between the moon and the earth pulls the water toward the moon on the near side and the earth from "under" the water on the far side.

While the basic cause of tides is the deformation by gravity of the nonrigid oceans, water friction, currents, and the structural features of the ocean bottom affect both the magnitude and time of the tides. Tides do not occur when the moon passes exactly overhead but follow it by regular periods that can be calculated for each shoreline. The height of the tide, too, varies for different places on the earth, ranging from normal 50-ft. tides in the Bay of Fundy, which separates Nova Scotia from New Brunswick in northeastern North America, to normal tides of a few feet only along most of the world's shorelines.

In spite of its smaller mass, the nearness of the moon makes it the chief cause of tides. But the sun's gravitational force also has an effect. The sun's influence is noticed chiefly through the more pronounced tides that occur at new moon and full moon when, because of their positions, the moon and sun act together. At other times in the month, the sun's influence becomes negligible in comparison with the moon's.

SOLAR AND STELLAR MASSES

In a previous section we saw that it is possible to compute the mass of the earth from data of the moon's orbit and the value of G, the proportionality constant in the equation for the force of gravity. By an analogous computation, one may obtain the mass of the sun from data of the orbital motion of planets; of the planets from data of the orbital motion of their satellites; and of binary stars from the motion of one star around the other. The computation of the moon's mass is more difficult because it has no satellite of its own. It has been obtained from measurements of the disturbance of the earth's orbit due to the moon's mass. Similar computations led to the discovery of Neptune and Pluto and are the means by which the mass-luminosity curves discussed in Chap. 3 were developed. As we saw there, they led in turn to our present understanding of the nature and development of stars.

Questions and Problems

1. Which of the following is a vector quantity? (*a*) weight, (*b*) distance, (*c*) force, (*d*) velocity, (*e*) mass, (*f*) acceleration.

2. Show that Eqs. 8–1 to 8–3 coincide with Eqs. 7–5 to 7–7 when at $t = 0$ there is no speed and the distance is measured from the origin.

3. Suppose the car described in Figs. 7–3 to 7–5 has attained a speed of 39 ft/sec after 5 sec and has reached a point 57½ ft from the origin. How far from the origin is it after the additional 5 sec of travel at constant speed?

4. Complete the trajectory of the pop fly in the

example on page 129, and plot your results on graph paper. Is the trajectory symmetric?

5. Draw the velocity vector at $t = 0$ for the home run in the example on page 131.

6. Muzzle velocity of a rifle bullet is approximately 1,000 ft/sec. If the rifle is fired horizontally by a man whose shoulder height is 4 ft, how far away does the bullet strike the ground?

7. If the man fires the rifle at an angle of 45°, how far away does the bullet strike the ground? (Ignore shoulder height.) How high is the bullet at its highest point? Draw its velocity vector 1 sec after firing.

8. A 500-gram stone is twirled at the end of a 50-cm-long string at a rate of 3 revolutions per second. What is the centripetal acceleration? the centripetal force?

9. If the stone in Question 8 flies away exactly horizontally at a height of 122.5 cm, how far away does it strike the ground? Draw its velocity vector, to scale, when it is released; when it strikes the ground.

10. The Mississippi delta is actually farther from the center of the earth than the Mississippi's source in Minnesota. Explain how the water flows "uphill".

11. The moon's diameter is only about one-half of the earth's. Its density is about two-thirds of the earth's. Its rate of rotation is 1/27.3 of the earth's. How does each of the factors affect the acceleration of a falling object on the moon's surface?

12. An astronaut in a capsule circling the earth is in a state of weightlessness. Explain.

13. The speed of a capsule circling the earth is slower if its orbit is farther from the earth's surface. Explain.

14. Did the two stones of 1 lb and 100 lb which Galileo supposedly dropped from the Leaning Tower of Pisa experience the same force? Explain.

15. A car traveling 60 mph (88 ft/sec) accelerates to 72 mph in 4 sec. What is its rate of acceleration? What distance did it travel in the 4 sec?

16. A kite weighing 1 lb is blown by a wind which gives it a lift equal to a force of 4 lb and a horizontal push also equal to 4 lb. What is the tension (force) on the string?

17. An airplane makes a banking turn of radius 2 miles at a speed of 300 mph. Find its angular acceleration. How does the centripetal force originate?

18. Newton proved that gravitational attraction on the moon and the earth were the same. Explain his proof.

19. What justification do astronomers have for using Eq. 8–7 to compute the masses of binary stars?

20. Use the law of gravitation and a vector diagram to show that planets accelerate as they move on their elliptical orbits nearer to the sun, and decelerate as they move farther away from the sun.

21. Use the equations of this chapter to show how the earth's acceleration toward the sun can be computed. How can the sun's mass be computed from the acceleration?

22. A pop fly hits the fielder's glove with the same speed as it leaves the bat if one neglects air friction. Explain. Does it hit the glove with the same velocity?

Suggestions for Further Reading

The texts listed at the end of Chap. 7 treat the contents of this chapter in more detail:

Holton, Gerald: *Introduction to Concepts and Theories in Physical Science*, Addison-Wesley Publishing Company, Inc., Reading, Mass., 1952. Chapter 11, universal gravitation; chaps. 12 to 14, method and structure of science.

Holton, Gerald, and Duane H. D. Roller: *Foundations of Modern Physical Science*, Addison-Wesley Publishing Company, Inc., Reading, Mass., 1958. Chapters 11 and 12, universal gravitation; chaps. 13 to 15, method and structure of science.

Physical Science Study Committee: *Physics*, D. C. Heath and Company, Boston, 1960. Chapters 21 and 22 are on Newton's work on gravity.

Rogers, Eric M.: *Physics for the Inquiring Mind*, Princeton University Press, Princeton, N. J., 1960. Chapters 2 and 3 are on vectors; chaps. 12 to 24 parallel chaps. 1, 7, and 8 of this book.

Two works by noted historians that discuss how astronomy and the study of motion led to Newton's formulation of universal laws of motion and gravity are:

Butterfield, Herbert: *The Origins of Modern Science*, Collier Books, New York, 1962 (paperback). Chapters 1 to 8.

Cohen, I. Bernard: *The Birth of a New Physics*, Anchor Books, Doubleday & Company, Inc., Garden City, N. Y., 1960 (paperback).

Chapter 9

Work, Energy, and Heat

Newton's three laws of motion form the intellectual basis for the study of mechanics, the part of physics concerned with motion. With the concepts inertia, acceleration, force, and action-and-reaction, it is possible to analyze the behavior of all moving bodies. In the previous chapter we carried through one such analysis which led from the revolution of the moon and the fall of an apple to an understanding of the nature of gravity. That analysis was due to Newton himself and has been part of our intellectual heritage since his time. Among its consequences, as we have seen, have been the discovery of two planets; elucidation of the nature of the stars and planets; and, finally, insights into the character of the universe itself.

QUANTITY OF MOTION

The laws of motion can be extended in different ways to lead to other insights concerning motion. Even before Newton, the French philosopher-mathematician-scientist René Descartes (1596–1650) had concerned himself with the apparently self-evident fact that motion leads to other motion. Consider, for instance, the sequence of motions when the ball from a wrecking crane hits the walls of an old building. The engine drives the cables which swing the ball; on impact the ball scatters bricks and beams; the bricks and beams send earth flying when they strike the ground. Descartes correctly assumed that some "quantity of motion" persists throughout this sequence of motions.

Descartes gave a formulation for the manner in which motion continues; this is now called momentum. Unfortunately, although he was a renowned mathematician, he did not formulate his principle in a mathematical form but described it by vague phrases like "quantity of motion," "proper measure of force," or "*vis viva*" (life force). These imprecise phrases did not clearly show what attribute of motion he described. Consequently a German contemporary of Newton, Gottfried Wilhelm von Leibniz (1646–1716), disputed Descartes in 1686 in a paper with the rather pointed title: "A Short Demonstration of a Remarkable Error of Descartes and Others, Concerning the Natural Law by which they think that the Creator always preserves the same quantity of Motion; by which, however, the Science of Mechanics is totally perverted." The reason for Leibniz's scorn was that he himself had discovered another principle by which "quantity of motion" was preserved. But since he also failed to use precise mathematical description, although he too was an outstanding mathematician, he did not realize that his description of "quantity of motion" referred to an attribute of moving objects different from Descartes's.

That the controversy was needless was shown with the substitution of mathematical descriptions for "quantity of motion," though this did not occur until the middle of the following century. Precision of definition is one of the chief requirements for precision of thought and clarity of understanding, and it is one of the virtues of mathematics to give such definitions by referring to unambiguous operations—multiplication, division, squaring—with measured quantities—time, distance, mass, etc. The recognition that errors of thought can creep into science because of unsuspected problems of definition is a rather late development in the history of scholarship. The importance of defining terms unambiguously was not pointed out until early in this century. No doubt, inadequately defined terms are still with us in unsuspected places.

MOMENTUM

The propagation of motion, for which Descartes and Leibniz sought a rational basis, is inherent in Newton's laws. The third law states that forces always appear in pairs, the force of action being coupled with that of reaction. From the second law we obtain that forces produce changes in motion. Thus, if one force causes a stone to stop, its reaction force causes something else to move. Motion is, in some way or other, propagated.

Descartes's formulation in quantitative form is that the product of mass and velocity, mv, called *momentum*, remains constant during collisions. Hence, the *law of conservation of momentum: the sum of the momenta of colliding objects is the same before and after collision.* If we have masses m_1, m_2, m_3, $\cdots$ each with velocity v_1, v_2, v_3, $\cdots$ before collision, and with velocities v'_1, v'_2, v'_3, $\ldots$ after collision, then

$$m_1 v_1 + m_2 v_2 + m_3 v_3 + \cdots = \\ m_1 v'_1 + m_2 v'_2 + m_3 v'_3 + \cdots$$

$$(9\text{--}1)$$

In other words: compute the momenta of the colliding objects before collision; add them; compute the momenta of the colliding objects after collision; add them. The two sums are the same. (Momenta are vector quantities; hence the summation must be done by the rules of vector addition.)

Equation 9–1 follows directly from Newton's laws of motion in a few mathematical steps. From the law of action and reaction, we get for a collision between two objects designated by the subscripts 1 and 2, $F_1 = -F_2$. (Since forces are vector quantities, the minus sign indicates the opposite direction.) Using Newton's second law, we replace F by ma, obtaining $m_1 a_1 = -m_2 a_2$. Finally, the definition of acceleration is a change of velocity (the difference in velocity before and after) per unit time which is expressed by $(v' - v)/t$ in which v' refers to the velocity after collision and v to the velocity before. Substituting this expression for acceleration into the last equation yields

$$\frac{m_1(v_1' - v_1)}{t} = -\frac{m_2(v_2' - v_2)}{t} \qquad (9\text{--}2)$$

The time during which the collision between the two objects occurs is, of course, the same for both objects. Hence t on both sides of the equation has the same value and can be eliminated. Eliminating t and multiplying out both sides of the equation, we obtain

$$m_1 v_1' - m_1 v_1 = -m_2 v_2' + m_2 v_2 \qquad (9\text{--}3)$$

Transposing the two negative terms to opposite sides of the equation gives

$$m_1 v_1' + m_2 v_2' = m_1 v_1 + m_2 v_2 \qquad (9\text{--}4)$$

Equation 9–4 is a simplified form for two objects. The same steps lead to Eq. 9–1 when more objects collide.

The importance of this principle is twofold. It is an intellectual achievement which helps us understand how the universe works. The propagation of motion we observe around us becomes intelligible through it. That a 16-lb. bowling ball is deflected by a 2-lb pin; that an infielder may be thrown

off balance by a line drive; that a small running blocker can flatten a huge standing defender are expected, not surprising, consequences of this principle. The law of conservation of momentum goes beyond this, however, and gives a precise, quantitative description of what happens. This is of utmost importance in technical applications. The thrusts of a jet and of a rocket result from conservation of momentum, for while hot gases with small mass and high velocity stream backward, momentum is conserved by the forward mv of the aircraft (Fig. 9–1). Other familiar examples are the recoil of a rifle; fire hoses and garden hoses; some automatic lawn sprinklers.

Conservation of momentum is one of the bases for considering our universe a mechanical universe, one in which future behavior is precisely predictable from known current behavior. Newton's first law describes future behavior when no forces affect the object. The law of conservation of momentum then adds its description of behavior when interactions do occur. While it does not completely specify behavior after interaction, it places important limitations on the resulting velocities by the requirement that momenta after collision must equal those before. (Additional restrictions are placed on the velocities after collision by the law of conservation of energy, which we shall discuss below and which lends further weight to the mechanical point of view.)

Whether the future of the universe can, in principle, be completely described by computation from current data is a philosophical question not resolvable by physics, although it is based on the physical principles we have discussed here. In spite of the fact that these physical laws lead to precise descriptions of future behavior in many cases, few physicists or philosophers accept the mechanical point of view of the universe because there are other events, as we shall see, not governed by this kind of law (Chap. 19).

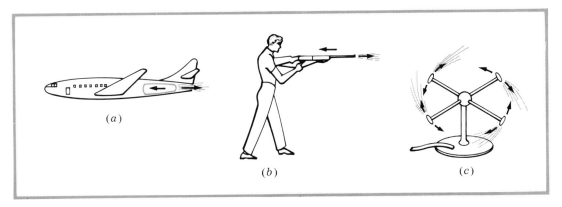

FIG. 9-1

Applications of the law of conservation of momentum. (a) The momentum of the hot gases ejected by the jet engines is equal and opposite in direction to the momentum of the airplane. (b) The momentum of the bullet is equal and opposite in direction to the momentum of the rifle stock which produces a kick against the shoulder. (c) The momentum of the ejected stream of water is equal and opposite to the momentum of the sprinkler arms, producing the rotation of the sprinkler.

In addition to the law of conservation of momentum of linear motion which we have just derived, there is a *law of conservation of angular momentum* for objects moving under the influence of a central force. It, too, follows from Newton's laws. This law states that the product mvr, in which r is the radius of the orbit, does not change. An illustration of conservation of angular momentum is the pirouettes performed by expert ice skaters. They begin by spinning slowly with outstretched arms. As they draw their arms toward the body, their rate of rotation increases greatly. The explanation for this is that with outstretched arms, the radius of curvature of their hands and forearms is quite large. mvr has a certain value. When the arms are brought close to the body, speed and radius change to v' and r'. Conservation of angular momentum requires that $mv'r'$ equal mvr. Since the mass remains the same, the decrease in r is accompanied by an increase in v, the speed of rotation.

The principle of conservation of angular momentum is of major importance in astronomy, for the sun rotates, the planets rotate and revolve, the solar system revolves around the center of the galaxy, and other galaxies and double stars rotate as well. To correspond to known physical principles, evolution of the solar system, or of the galaxies, must begin with originally rotating material since angular momentum must be preserved. This places some very definite limitations on the nature of the original material and the original processes from which the universe was created. Indeed,

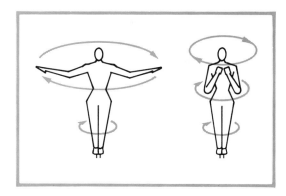

FIG. 9-2

Conservation of angular momentum. With arms outstretched, the skater's hands and arms have a large radius of curvature. When he draws them in, the radius of curvature decreases and the speed of rotation increases. Skaters always start their pirouettes with arms outstretched and then draw them in.

such misfits as Uranus, which rotates in a direction nearly at right angles to its orbit, and Pluto, with its large inclination, are difficult to place into one system. Why should these bodies have amassed all the original gases with some peculiar components of angular motion when nearly all the remaining matter in the solar system rotates and revolves in the same direction? This is a question to which no satisfactory answers have as yet been given.

KINETIC ENERGY

Momentum was Descartes's formulation for the "quantity of motion" which Leibniz ridiculed and disputed as a "remarkable error of Descartes and others." Leibniz was scornful because he approached quantity of motion from another point of view which led him to a different result. Because he had satisfied himself that his formulation was correct, he felt that Descartes's had to be incorrect. (While we may smile today with superior hindsight as we accept both formulations not as contradictory but as complementary to one another, we should not feel too proud of our greater sophistication. How often do we feel, like Leibniz, that because we are sure we are right, the other fellow must obviously be wrong?)

Leibniz derived his "quantity of motion" from the analysis of falling bodies. It seemed self-evident to him that an object of mass q falling from a height $2h$ should strike the ground with the same "quantity of motion" as a mass $2q$ falling from a height of h (Fig. 9–3). Hence, some combination of mass and velocity (expressing "quantity of motion") should produce the same number for mass q falling through distance $2h$ as for mass $2q$ falling a distance h.

First let us see whether the momentum, mv, is the proper combination. From the equations $d = \frac{1}{2}gt^2$ and $v = gt$, we can compute the velocity of a falling object. Eliminating t from the two equations produces

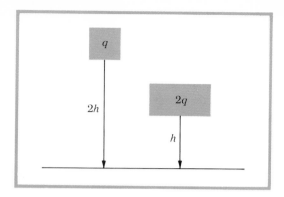

FIG. 9-3

Leibniz's conception of "quantity of motion." An object of mass q falling through a distance 2h should strike the earth with the same "quantity of motion" as an object of mass 2q falling through a distance h.

$v = \sqrt{2dg}$. The velocity of a falling object equals the square root of two times the distance of fall times the acceleration of gravity, g. Then the momentum of a falling object, mv, is given by $m\sqrt{2dg}$. With this equation we compute the momentum of the two objects studied by Leibniz:

For mass q falling a distance of $2h$:
$$m\sqrt{2dg} = q\sqrt{2 \times 2h \times g} = q\sqrt{4hg}$$

For mass $2q$ falling a distance of h:
$$m\sqrt{2dg} = 2q\sqrt{2 \times h \times g} = q\sqrt{8hg}$$

The momenta with which these objects strike the ground are not equal. Leibniz's "quantity of motion" and momentum are two different properties of moving bodies.

Let us try another combination of m and v, namely, mv^2. Again using the relation between velocity and distance for a falling object, $v = \sqrt{2dg}$, $mv^2 = 2mdg$. Now:

For mass q falling a distance of $2h$:
$$2mdg = 2 \times q \times 2h \times g = 4mhg$$

For mass $2q$ falling a distance of h:
$$2mdg = 2 \times 2q \times h \times g = 4mhg$$

The product mv^2 is equal for the two objects and represents the combination of m and v which gives Leibniz's "self-evident" equality.

The argument given in the last paragraph

indicated to Leibniz, quite correctly, that the product of mass times velocity squared, which he called *vis viva*, is an important index to express the "quantity of motion" of moving objects, though his attempt to refute the importance of momentum was needless. Both are necessary for a complete description and for the prediction of the future behavior of a system of moving particles. While our proof was limited to falling bodies, the product mv^2 multiplied by $\frac{1}{2}$ ($\frac{1}{2}mv^2$ is now called *kinetic energy*) is an important property of all moving objects and is intimately related to their behavior even when they move otherwise than under the influence of gravity.

WORK

To show the importance of the kinetic energy, we shall first reverse the process by which we arrived at $\frac{1}{2}mv^2$. (This will also indicate the reason for the multiplier $\frac{1}{2}$.) As above, we replace v^2 by g^2t^2 (from $v = gt$) in the equation $E_k = \frac{1}{2}mv_2$. This produces $E_k = \frac{1}{2}mg^2t^2 = mg \times \frac{1}{2}gt^2$. The first part—$mg$—is, from Newton's second law, the force of gravity acting on the mass m. We can replace it by F. The second part —$\frac{1}{2}gt^2$—is, from Eq. 7–9, the distance through which the mass moves while accelerated by gravity. We can replace it by d. Making these substitutions leads to $E_k = Fd$ (note that $\frac{1}{2}$ is required to establish this equality). But Fd, a force multiplied by the distance through which the force operates, is the definition of *work*. Consequently, the kinetic energy acquired by a falling object is equal to the work performed by gravity on the object during its fall.

This equality is exceedingly interesting and important and we must discuss it further. Let us review how we obtained it. Leibniz, trying to show that two balls, one twice as heavy as the other, strike the earth with the same "quantity of motion" if falling from heights in the ratio of 1 to 2,

arrived at a mathematical description of "quantity of motion" which we now call the kinetic energy, $\frac{1}{2}mv^2$. To do this, he used the familiar equations of falling objects: $d = \frac{1}{2}gt^2$ and $v = gt$. A different arrangement of the terms of the equations expresses the fall of the two balls as the work Fd done by gravity on them. The work done by the force of gravity on the two balls to set them in motion is exactly equal to the kinetic energy (energy of motion) they attain. Expressed somewhat differently, the work done by gravity has produced an equal amount of kinetic energy. This statement can be generalized one step further. *Any work performed on an object to set it in motion produces in that object a kinetic energy exactly equal to the work expended.* Here then is another conservation law, governing energies and work. For instance, kicking a football gives it a kinetic energy exactly equal to the work done by the kicker, or throwing a baseball gives the ball a kinetic energy exactly equal to the work of throwing it.

In these derivations we have again produced the results of scientific discovery without giving the reasons for proceeding in the manner we did. Indeed here, as in the formulation of the law of gravity, the reason for the intervening steps becomes clear only after the derivation is complete and the result is obtained. We shall now stop briefly to indicate why the mathematical formulation of work as Fd is intuitively reasonable. We might expect intuitively that such measurable quantities as weight (force), distance, and time (but not, for instance, area or temperature) are needed.

Let us first consider weight. Lifting a large stone quite obviously requires more work than lifting a smaller stone. Hence, intuition suggests that a quantitative expression for work contain as one of its terms the force necessary to overcome the opposing force of gravity (the weight of the object). Next, distance. Lifting a stone 200 cm obviously requires twice the work as lifting it 100 cm. Our expression should contain the distance through which we must exert force. Finally, time. Lifting a stone in 1 min or in 1 hr doesn't change what we have accomplished; the work we have done is the same (though not the rate at which we are working). The amount of work performed does not depend upon time. Indeed, as we stated and are now trying to confirm, *Fd* suffices to define work. Work is the product of a force and the distance through which the force operates. Its units of measurement are, correspondingly, dyne-cm (gram-cm²/sec²), also called *ergs*. The erg is the unit of work and energy.

Because both force and distance, the quantities one multiplies to compute work, are vector quantities, the multiplication must be carried out according to the rules of vector algebra. We do this by resolving

FIG. 9-4

Work is the product of force and distance, two vector quantities, and the multiplication must be done according to the rules of vector multiplication. Along the vertical component, the force exerted equals the weight of the book. Along the horizontal component, the book moves spontaneously (after it is initially set in motion) and requires no force. The work therefore depends entirely on the weight of the book and the vertical height.

them into components along perpendicular axes. For instance, in carrying a book up a flight of stairs, there is horizontal and vertical motion. In the vertical direction we must exert a force to counter the weight of the book. It is exerted over the vertical distance between the two floors. For a 1×10^6-dyne (about 2 lb) book between floors 350 cm (about 10 ft) apart, the work of lifting is 3.5×10^8 ergs. In the horizontal direction a very small force is needed to give the book an acceleration; thereafter it keeps moving with constant velocity without the application of additional force. The work done is very much smaller and the total work, the sum of the two, remains about 3.5×10^8 ergs. (Work is not a vector quantity, and a simple algebraic addition gives the sum.)

For the reasons implied in the last paragraph we can assert that no work is done in carrying a book or any other object horizontally (except for the small amount of work to give it an initial acceleration). While we must support the object to keep it from falling, the supporting force is exactly equal to the weight of the object. There is no net, unbalanced force to move it through a distance, and the product of $F_v d_v$ equals zero. For the same reason, the length of the stairs plays no role in determining the work done in carrying an object between two floors. Only the distance between the floors is important.

POTENTIAL ENERGY

The slight amount of work produced by the horizontal component of the force produces a velocity in the book. It is conserved as the kinetic energy of the book as it moves horizontally. But the vertical component of the force does not give the book a velocity upward; indeed, if the force stops acting, the book falls down again. The work of lifting is not conserved as kinetic energy. To maintain the general idea that work produces an equal amount of energy, it has been found desirable to define another kind of energy into which the work of lifting is converted, the *potential energy, E_p. The work of lifting an object against the force of gravity gives that object a potential energy exactly equal to the work done in lifting.*

The algebraic expression for the gravitational potential energy can be deduced from the manner in which we have just defined it. The raising of an object of weight w through a height h requires an amount of work equal to wh. On the earth's surface, the weight w equals the mass m of the object multiplied by the acceleration g of gravity. Hence,

$$E_p = mgh \qquad (9\text{-}5)$$

It is necessary in the use of Eq. 9–5 to define a reference system for height and potential energy. Consider the gravitational potential energy which is converted to electrical energy by the hydroelectric stations around Niagara Falls. The upper reservoir is approximately 6,000 cm (182 ft) above the gorge below. With respect to the gorge, 1 gram of water has a potential energy of

not quite 6×10^6 ergs. That is the maximum amount of energy which can be converted to electrical energy. But the gorge itself is approximately 12,000 cm above sea level. With respect to the sea, to which the water eventually flows, each gram in the gorge has another 1.2×10^7 ergs.

Normally, ground level serves as a convenient reference for height in the solution of problems that involve potential energy. Thus, in computing the electric potential of Niagara Falls, the height of the reservoir above the gorge is all that is needed. In the rare cases where ground level may be ambiguous, a specific zero point of height must be defined.

Work and kinetic energy are kinds of energy that relate to what an object *does.* Work is produced by a force acting over a distance; kinetic energy is the result of the motion of an object. Potential energy, on the other hand, relates to where or how an object *is.* The work of lifting becomes gravitational potential energy, a function of the height of an object. The work of compressing a spring becomes the potential energy of the coiled spring, a

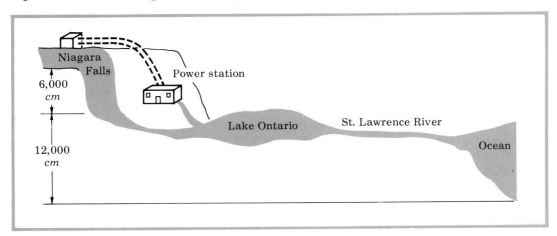

FIG. 9-5

A reference level must be established when calculating potential energy. With respect to the gorge below, each gram of water at the top of Niagara Falls has a potential energy of about 6×10^6 ergs. This is the maximum amount of electrical energy that can be produced per gram by the power stations at Niagara Falls. With respect to sea level, however, the potential energy is about 1.8×10^7 ergs. This is the net amount of work the sun has done in evaporating the seawater and bringing it back to the top of Niagara Falls as rain.

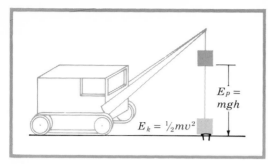

FIG. 9-6

The potential energy of a pile driver when released equals the kinetic energy with which it strikes the pile and the work it does on the pile.

function of the fact that it is compressed. The work of charging a battery becomes chemical (potential) energy, a function of the chemical state of the battery liquid. In all these transformations between work and energy of different kinds, the amount of energy of one kind which is expended is exactly equal to the amount of energy of another kind which is produced. This generalized statement is the *law of conservation of energy*.

The usefulness of the law of conservation of energy in the analysis of nature goes beyond the examples given above. It is helpful in solving some problems quickly which otherwise would require much more complex solutions. To measure the work done by a pile driver, for instance, would require a very complex experiment. But a simple analysis shows that the potential energy of the weight as it is dropped is converted into kinetic energy as it falls and expended as work as it strikes the pile. There are frictional losses as it moves through the air, but these are minor. Another question easily answered by considerations of conservation of energy is the speed with which a pendulum bob moves at its lowest point or anywhere else in its trajectory (Fig. 9–7). When it is released, it has a potential energy with respect to the lowest point equal to mgh' where h' is the height difference between the lowest point and the point of release. At the lowest

point that potential energy has been completely converted into kinetic energy and the speed can easily be computed from $E_k = \frac{1}{2}mv^2$. Similar analyses give the speed at other points of the trajectory.

THE GRAVITATIONAL FIELD

Distance above a reference surface, usually the surface of the earth, determines the gravitational potential energy of an object, as we saw in the last section. At the surface of the earth, it is given by the equation mgh because for small heights we assume the acceleration of gravity to remain constant. This assumption does not hold if we go far out into space. Then the decrease of the gravitational force with the square of the distance becomes important, and we must compute the force directly from the equation

$$F = G\,\frac{Mm}{r^2}.$$

However, the force has some interesting characteristics which lead to the concept of a gravitational field.

Let us examine the forces on a stratospheric jet of mass m_j and a weather balloon of mass m_b, both 16 miles above the

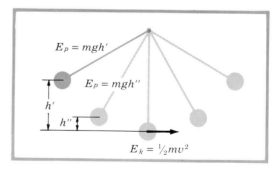

FIG. 9-7

The potential energy of the pendulum bob, with the lowest point of its swing as reference, is equal to the kinetic energy as it moves past that lowest point. At points in between, the lost potential energy has been converted into kinetic energy, and the velocity of motion at each point can thus be easily computed.

earth's surface. The forces they experience are

$$F_j = G\frac{M}{r_1^2} \times m_j$$

and

$$F_b = G\frac{M}{r_1^2} \times m_b$$

in which r_1 denotes the distance from the center of the earth, about 3,966 miles. We note that the right side of the equations can be broken into two parts. GM/r_1^2 which is characteristic of the position of the two objects, and m, which is characteristic of their masses. If we go farther out and compare the forces on the moon, F_m, and on a grain of cosmic dust, F_d, both at a distance of 240,000 miles from the earth, we obtain

$$F_m = G\frac{M}{r_2^2} \times m_m$$

and

$$F_d = G\frac{M}{r_2^2} \times m_d$$

Again the equations have two parts, a part characteristic of the position, and another, of the mass of the object. The first part, which depends only on r, is called the *gravitational intensity* or *gravitational field strength* of that point in space. When multiplied by the mass of an object, it gives the force on it.

The concept of a gravitational field is a summary description of the gravitational field strength in space around a central body like the earth. For instance, the field strength falls off with distance so that the forces experienced diminish as an object moves farther and farther away. The field strength depends only on distance and not on direction; consequently, around a single object there are spherical shells on which the field strength has the same value. These are called *equipotential surfaces*. The name equipotential surface derives from the fact that the work required to lift an object to any point on an equipotential surface is the same; therefore its potential energy

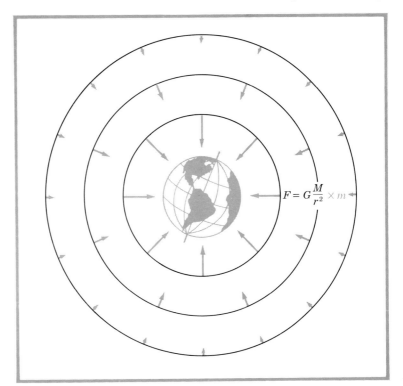

The earth's gravitational field. The force of gravity on a mass m is equal to G(M/r²) × m, in which G(M/r²) shows how the force changes with distance from the earth. It is called the field strength. The "field" describes the values of the field strength, and points in space with the same field strength define equipotential surfaces.

FIG. 9-8

anywhere on the equipotential surface is the same. Conversely, from conservation of energy it follows that moving an object between the points of an equipotential surface requires no work or the object would acquire additional potential energy. Gravitational field strength is a vector quantity because it expresses a quantity which has direction—toward the central object—as well as magnitude.

These characteristics of the gravitational field are best illustrated by the earth's gravitational field. The field strength is greatest at the surface of the earth and falls off with distance. About four thousand miles up, at twice the distance from the center of the earth, the field strength is one-fourth of its surface value of 980 dynes/gram; about 20,000 miles up, one thirty-sixth; etc., and the field strength vector points toward the center of the earth.

Except for deviations which we have discussed before, the earth's surface is taken as an equipotential surface. Consequently, potential energy can be given in terms of height above the surface, and no work is done moving horizontally across the surface of the earth. Other equipotential surfaces surrounding the earth are also spherical as long as the distance from the earth is not too great. Near the earth, the gravitational effects of other heavenly bodies are negligibly small because their field strength drops rapidly with distance. But at distances approaching the radius of the moon's orbit and in the direction toward the moon, the gravitational field strength of the moon adds to that of the earth, and the equipotential surfaces change their geometry. It is not difficult to see that on the line connecting the center of the earth with the center of the moon, there is a point at which the field strength is zero; on either side of it, it builds up toward the earth or toward the moon. An object suspended there would remain motionless and weightless, although in making this statement we are also ignoring the very small field strengths due to the sun, Jupiter, Mars,

and other heavenly bodies. Because of their distances, their contributions are negligible as a first approximation.

These are the basic characteristics of the gravitational field: a description of the gravitational forces on an object in the space surrounding another body or bodies, and their implication for energy relationships. We shall again use the concept of a field when we discuss electric charges and magnetic poles. They produce fields with the same characteristics.

HEAT AND TEMPERATURE

Nearly all the calculations we made in the last three chapters stated or implied "neglect friction" because friction is another force which affects the motion of objects. Except perhaps for the motions of the celestial bodies which move through the near total vacuum of space, all moving objects are acted on by this force; Newton's conception of uniform motion of undisturbed objects was an abstraction requiring a tremendous intellectual leap from experience. This abstraction, intellectually eliminating the effects of friction from the behavior of moving objects, was the basis of the shift from Aristotelian to modern physics and led to the clarification of motion, momentum, energy. But now we ask one question about friction. Since it reduces the velocity of objects, they lose kinetic energy. What happens to this energy? Our answer comes from our experience. Friction makes objects warmer. It produces heat. Heat is the kind of energy into which the kinetic energy is transformed. Since somewhat more than 100 years ago, when James Prescott Joule (1818–1889) began a long series of very careful experiments in each of which he found a fixed amount of heat produced whenever an erg of some other kind of energy disappeared, this question has been regarded as settled. Heat has been accepted as a form of energy. However, in the history of physics, heat and temperature had been a pair of extremely troublesome concepts, and until Joule's work they presented serious problems for the study of physics.

The first difficulty with understanding heat and temperature arose from a very common source—inadequate definition. That there is a difference between the attributes of a red-hot nail and a big pot full of hot water was recognized. Yet both were sometimes described as possessing a large "quantity of heat," a definition that fails to make the needed distinction between intensity or degree of heat—temperature—and total quantity. Moreover, until the thermometer was invented in the seventeenth century, and degree of hotness could be identified with the length of a column of some liquid in a glass tube, even distinctions between cold, cool, warm, hot, and hotter were not entirely clear. Whether a very cold object possessed more coldness or less hotness appeared an entirely reasonable question. The invention of thermometers permitted some good experiments which suggested that "less hotness" was the more reasonable explanation.

Unlike the zero mark on a meter stick, the zero point on a thermometer is arbitrary. It has been assigned by convention, to which, however, there is no universal agreement. In most scientific work the Celsius (commonly called centigrade) scale is used. In ordinary commerce and in earlier scientific work the Fahrenheit scale prevails. Both scales use water as the calibration fluid with its freezing and boiling temperatures as the major calibration points. In the Fahrenheit scale the freezing point defines $32°F$; in the Celsius scale, $0°C$. The boiling point defines $212°F$ and $100°C$, respectively. The distance between the two is divided into 180 equal divisions in the Fahrenheit scale and 100 in the Celsius, giving $1°C = 1.8°F$ and $T_F = 32 + 1.8\,T_C$.

The usual thermometric fluid is mercury, and intermediate temperatures are defined in terms of the extension of a mer-

TABLE 9-1

Some calibration points of the temperature scale

Reference substance	°C
Liquid oxygen, evaporating	−183.00
Solid carbon dioxide, evaporating	−78.51
Ice, melting	0.000
Water, boiling	100.000
Sulfur, condensing to liquid	444.60
Gold, solidifying from liquid	1063
Nickel, melting or solidifying	1452
Alumina, melting	2000
Tungsten, melting	3370±30

cury column. This distinction is needed because not all fluids expand in the same way. Thus, an alcohol thermometer (used chiefly for measuring very low temperatures at which alcohol remains fluid while mercury may freeze), calibrated exactly at $0°C$ and $100°C$ and then divided into 100 equal divisions will not read exactly $50°C$ when a mercury thermometer does because the manner of expansion of the two fluids differs slightly. Hence the need for setting mercury as the standard. Furthermore, the points at which other substances change from solid to liquid or liquid to gas have been added to those of water in order to extend the calibration points both up and down. A few other calibrating materials and their defining temperatures are given in Table 9–1.

Thermometry solved the practical problems concerning the distinction between heat and temperature. There remained the question: What is heat? To most physicists until about 150 years ago it was a subtle imponderable fluid called *caloric*, which was attracted to the particles of matter and which was squeezed from them and moved between them. In particular, friction squeezed the caloric fluid from one body into another and made caloric sensible as heat. But there were some contradictions in the supposed behavior of the caloric fluid, and as early as 1620 Francis Bacon had suggested that heat might be a kind of motion. The situation was clarified primarily by a remarkable New Englander, Benjamin Thompson (1753–1814), who was forced to flee to England because of Royalist sympathies during the Revolution. There he served King George III, who knighted him. He next moved to Germany and, as Count Rumford, became minister of war and minister of police in Bavaria.

Rumford's logic and the experiments he performed accordingly were as follows. If heat is a fluid, caloric, then whenever it appears in concentrated form, for instance, as a result of friction, it must have been lost by something else. As the Bavarian minister of war, he was charged with the supervision of the boring of cannons, during which friction produces huge quantities of heat. If this heat had been squeezed from the metal of the cannons or of the borer, Rumford reasoned, there should be a change in the caloric content of either the cannon, the scrapings which had been bored, or the borer. Yet, although he found that during ½ hr of boring enough heat had been produced to heat up a pound of brass some 65,000° (or 65,000 lb 1°),

when he examined the brass of the cannon, the scrapings, and the boring tools, he found no changes in their behavior toward heating or cooling. They behaved exactly as before the boring process. If they had lost a large amount of caloric fluid during boring, they did not seem to take up an extra amount when he heated them. This convinced him that heat was not a substance contained in the metal and squeezed from it, but was produced by the work of boring.

Rumford's experiments, only one of which is mentioned above, swung the scale toward general agreement that heat is a form of motion. The case became airtight when Joule, in a series of experiments from the 1840s until his death, showed that however he designed the experiment, the amount of energy lost against friction resulted in a proportional amount of heat produced, whether the energy were mechanical or electrical. He thus determined the *mechanical equivalent of heat*, 4.19×10^7 ergs/cal. (Heat is measured in the unit *calorie*, abbreviated cal.) One of his experiments is illustrated in Fig. 9–9. The weight falls very slowly so that its potential energy is entirely converted to heat by the friction of the paddles in the water. As a result, the

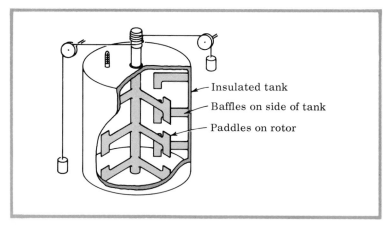

— Insulated tank

— Baffles on side of tank

— Paddles on rotor

One apparatus used by Joule to measure the mechanical equivalent of heat. The potential energy of the weight is converted into heat by the paddles that stir the water. The amount of heat produced is obtained from the increase in water temperature. (Taken from Sidney Rosen, Robert Siegfried, and John M. Dennison, "Concepts in Physical Science," p. 120, Fig. 5–12, Harper & Row, Publishers, Inc., New York, 1965)

FIG. 9-9

water warms by the amount such that for each 4.19×10^7 ergs of energy converted, the water absorbs 1 cal of heat.

Through Rumford's and Joule's experiments, heat became identified with motion.

How this is possible will be shown in Chap. 11. To understand the explanation, however, we need an understanding of the nature of matter. That is the subject of Chap. 10.

Questions and Problems

1. Combine equations $d = \frac{1}{2} gt^2$ and $v = gt$ and prove that $v = \sqrt{2dg}$.

2. Starting friction is greater than sliding friction. Explain in terms of forces involved and work needed.

3. mgh gives the potential energy on the surface of the earth but not out in space. Explain.

4. Explain why the sum of forces on a standing object must be zero. What is the sum of forces on a train moving with constant velocity?

5. List three conservation laws discussed in this chapter. Explain the meaning of "conservation." What restrictions, if any, are there to each of the conservation laws?

6. Relate conservation of momentum to Newton's laws.

7. Water at the base of a waterfall is warmer than at the top. Explain. If 1 cal heats 1 gram of water 1°C, what is the temperature increase when the waterfall is 5,000 cm high? (Assume complete conversion of other forms of energy into heat.)

8. An exploding shell sends fragments in all directions. Demonstrate that this is necessary as a consequence of conservation of momentum.

9. A bowling ball knocks a pin into the left rear corner of the alley. What happens to the velocity and trajectory of the bowling ball?

10. A 10-lb stone is raised to the top of a 6-ft wall. How much work is done? What is its potential energy? It falls and strikes a man's hip 3 ft up. With what kinetic energy did it strike?

11. 98,000,000 ergs of work were performed on a 500-gram mass. How high was it raised? What potential energy has it acquired halfway up? With what kinetic energy does it strike the ground when it is released? At what velocity does it travel three-fourths of the way to the ground?

12. An automobile traveling 60 mph has a kinetic energy of about 400,000 ft-lb. The maximum force exerted by the brake is 1,500 lb. In what distance can the car be stopped?

13. Machines conserve energy. Yet with a crowbar that has its fulcrum 5 ft from the handle and 3 in. from the load, a 50-lb child can raise a 600-lb rock. Explain.

14. The second floor of a building is 12 ft above ground level. What is the potential energy of a 100-lb crate on the second floor? In raising the crate from the delivery entrance at basement level, an elevator did 2,400 ft-lb of work. Explain. What happened to conservation of energy?

15. Discuss the values of the kinetic and potential energy in various parts of the orbit of a comet moving in the sun's gravitational field.

16. How much work is done by a 70,000-gram man climbing 400 cm between floors? How many calories of food does he require for this? (The diet watcher's Calorie equals 1,000 of the calories in mechanical equivalent of heat.) An apple supplies 150 Cal. How many flights of stairs can the man climb on one apple of energy?

17. There are two ways of reaching the rim of Yosemite Valley. One can climb one of several paths that lead almost straight up or one can walk back to the entrance of the valley and then take a road along the rim. Which requires more work? Explain.

Suggestions for Further Reading

The texts listed at the end of Chap. 7 are additional references on the conservation laws and heat:

Beiser, Arthur: *Basic Concepts of Physics*, Addison-Wesley Publishing Company, Inc., Reading, Mass., 1961. Chapters 4 and 6.

Holton, Gerald: *Introduction to Concepts and Theories in Physical Science*, Addison-Wesley

Publishing Company, Inc., Reading, Mass., 1952. Chapters 16 to 18. Includes historical development of the modern understanding of heat.

Holton, Gerald, and Duane H. D. Roller: *Foundations of Modern Physical Science,* Addison-Wesley Publishing Company, Inc., Reading, Mass., 1958, Chapters 17 to 20. Also includes a historical discussion.

Physical Science Study Committee: *Physics,* D. C. Heath and Company, Boston, 1960. Chapters 23 to 26.

Rogers, Eric M.: *Physics for the Inquiring Mind,* Princeton University Press, Princeton, N. J., 1960. Chapters 8, 26, 27, and 29.

The history of our understanding of heat is treated in detail in:

Conant, James B. (ed.): *Harvard Case Histories in Experimental Science,* vol. 1, Harvard University Press, Cambridge, Mass., 1957. Chapter 3, by Duane Roller.

Chapter 10

Matter

In the previous chapters we have been concerned with objects of two kinds: the very large—planets, stars, galaxies—and the more normal in terms of human experience—our earth and things we see on it. In the next chapters we turn our attention to the third range of dimensions, the very small. As before, focusing on motion contributes greatly to our understanding. In fact, application of the laws of motion and of conservation to the realm of the infinitesimally small, the realm of molecules, provides the basis for our understanding of the nature of matter.

When we study the behavior of the very small, we are faced, first of all, with the question of how the submicroscopic world is constituted. This is an old question which already concerned the philosophers of ancient Greece. They faced it in the

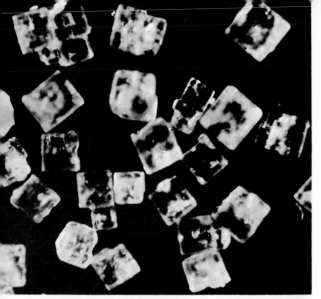

FIG. 10-1

Crystals. At the top, table salt, sodium chloride. Center, calcite, calcium carbonate. Bottom, a polished section of an iron-nickel meteorite. (Top, Morton Salt Company; others, Ward's Natural Science Establishment, Inc., Rochester, N.Y.)

following form. Suppose we take a piece of chalk and break it in two. We take one of the halves and break it also, and then break one of these halves. Can we repeat this process indefinitely without destroying the "chalkiness" of the last remaining piece? Or do we reach a smallest entity which cannot be divided further or which, if divided, loses the properties of chalk? Today we take the latter point of view. We recognize that a limit of division is reached when a smallest unit, called the molecule, appears. This view was also shared by a group of Greek philosophers the most notable of whom was Democritus. Aristotle, on the other hand, held the first view. He did not believe in molecules, for he could not imagine that the continuity of matter could be disrupted by an ultimate break into discrete particles. Aristotle reasoned that if there were smallest particles, they had to be separated by empty space, a vacuum, and this contradicted his conviction that nature abhors a vacuum. While we have become quite used to the emptiness of space today and would not reject molecules for that reason alone, we also have much additional and better evidence for accepting the existence of molecules. We shall discuss some of the evidence below.

THE STATES OF MATTER

All matter in the universe is found in one of three states: it is either solid, liquid, or gaseous. There are instances in which the division is not entirely clear-cut. Is very sticky tar still liquid or already solid? Is steam under very high pressure a gas or a liquid? These questions are somewhat troublesome, but we shall neglect them for the moment. Instead of looking for difficulties, we shall look for simple examples. Take, for instance, a few grains of salt from a saltshaker (Fig. 10–1a), or a few crystals of sugar from a sugar bowl. The outstanding characteristic of these particles, immediately apparent if looked at with even a low-power magnifying glass, is the regularity of their appearance. Their faces are square or rectangular; the edges meet at right angles. All appear nearly alike. Or look at a crystal of calcite (Fig. 10–1b). It is not cubic, like sugar or salt, but more complex in its external appearance. Yet each face is clean and sharp, separated from others by straight edges, and each face is a relatively simple, regular geometric figure. The regularity in the assembly of molecules which constitute the crystal is striking.

Not all solids reveal the regularity of their structure as clearly as the examples given in the last paragraph. Some must be etched and polished like the metal in the meteorite in Fig. 10–1c. Others must be examined with an X-ray diffraction apparatus. But when such high-powered tools are used for the examination of solid structure, the fundamental regularity reveals itself. Because of this, solids are defined as assemblies of molecules in which the constituent particles are in an ordered arrangement.

A second significant characteristic of solids is their great resistance to changes in shape. Solids are nearly incompressible, requiring pressures of thousands of pounds per square inch before even small deformations are noted. Most solids are elastic and spring back to their original shape if bent slightly. They are hard. They cannot be easily dented or scratched, though they may be broken into smaller, yet undeformed pieces. Order and stability are the chief characteristics of solids.

In some ways liquids resemble solids. They are nearly as incompressible as solids. Near the melting point, they show some regularity of structure if examined by X rays, although the order is lacking at higher temperatures. But liquids differ strikingly from solids in their structural stability. Liquids change their shape easily and spontaneously. They maintain their volume but distribute themselves to fill the lower por-

tions of containers completely. They can be displaced by solids. They even permit penetration of their volumes by molecules of another kind, dissolving other substances. If the liquid and solute are stirred, shaken, or agitated in other ways, solution is rapid and results in the complete intermingling of the two kinds of molecules. On the other hand, if the two are merely placed in contact with one another and left undisturbed, the intermingling occurs slowly by a process called *diffusion*, in which the molecules of the dissolved material slowly find their way deeper and deeper into the liquid (Fig. 10–2).

While liquids flow spontaneously, not all do so with equal ease. Some like water, alcohol, or ether spread out quickly; others like tar, honey, or motor oil flow very slowly. The internal resistance to flow is called the *viscosity* of the liquid. It depends on its constitution and on the temperature. Placing honey in hot water greatly reduces its viscosity, and it flows almost as readily as water. On the other hand, a "heavy" motor oil, which flows easily in the summer, becomes too viscous for efficient

FIG. 10-2

Diffusion. The copper sulfate crystal (left) dissolves and spontaneously diffuses throughout the entire cylinder (right). In the middle picture, solution is partial and copper sulfate has diffused through the lower half of the cylinder. (From "Everyday Problems in Science" by Beauchamp, Mayfield, and Hurd. Copyright © 1963 by Scott, Foresman and Company, Chicago)

engine lubrication in the cold winter. Change to a lighter oil is necessary in the wintertime.

While liquids are not rigid in either their external shape or their internal structure, as flow and diffusion show, they exhibit a strong cohesiveness of molecules at their surfaces. The surface of a liquid resists penetration, a phenomenon called *surface tension*. Water droplets, particularly if coated with dust, do not readily join to form larger drops. Instead, the surface of each resists being merged with that of others. Mercury droplets show this phenomenon even more strikingly because mercury has a greater surface tension. It is even possible to support an object on the surface of water if the object is carefully placed without breaking the surface (Fig. 10–3). The liquid surface tends to maintain itself unbroken and does not "wet" the paper clip, which floats on top of the surface barrier. The surface tension of water is one of its limitations as a cleaning agent. Soap must be used to lower the surface tension and allow the wetting of dirt, which can then be carried off by the water.

Gases resemble liquids in some ways just as liquids resemble solids in some ways. Like liquids, gases spread out spontan-eously, but they fill the entire volume of the container that holds them. Their flow is much more rapid; their viscosity is much lower. Gases also permit the intermingling of molecules of another kind—diffusion; the rates of diffusion are much greater than in the case of liquids. With these properties, however, the similarity ends. There are important differences. Gases are much less dense than liquids or solids. The volume of a gas depends quite significantly on the pressure exerted whereas liquids and solids are nearly incompressible. Gases expand rapidly and regularly when heated, while liquids (and solids) expand much less and much less regularly. The changes of gas volume with changes of pressure and temperature are so large and so regular that laws of gas behavior were already discovered 300 years ago.

PRESSURE

The description of gas behavior requires the precise use of the concept *pressure*. Pressure is defined as force per unit area:

$$P = \frac{F}{A} \qquad (10\text{–}1)$$

Its units are, accordingly, dynes per square centimeter ($dynes/cm^2$) or, in the English system, pounds per square inch ($lb/in.^2$). The need for the concept pressure can easily be established. Consider a cone made of lead and weighing 20 lb, resting on your hand with its base down (Fig. 10–4a). Its weight presses down on the hand. But because the force is distributed over a large portion of the hand, the hand supports the cone without damage. Now turn the cone upside down, and rest its tip on the hand (Fig. 10–4b). The force of the cone pushing downward has not changed, but the hand is much more likely to sustain injury. Why the difference? Because in one case the force is distributed over a large area and each portion of the hand supports only a small fraction of the force. The pressure,

FIG. 10-3

Surface tension prevents the paper clip from breaking the surface. Hence it floats on water.

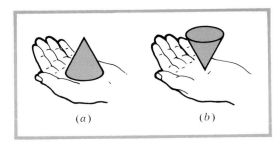

FIG. 10-4

The concept of pressure, force per unit area. (a) A given force—the weight of a lead cone —distributed over a large area exerts a small pressure. (b) The same force distributed over a small area exerts a large pressure.

force per unit area, is small. In the other case, the entire force is focused on one small point of the hand, and the pressure there is very great. Pressure describes an important property related to the concept force.

Three examples will serve to illustrate this further. The first relates to water pressures at various depths. The question here is, what is the force exerted by the water above a measuring device such as the funnel in Fig. 10–5a? It is the weight of the water above the funnel and pressing down on it. If the funnel has a wide opening, the column is wide, and the weight is large; if the funnel is small, so is the

column and its weight. But the weight of water per unit area, the water *pressure*, is the same at equal depths. Pressure turns out to be independent of the size of the measuring device (whereas force—total weight of water—does not).

Moreover, the water pressure is exerted equally in all directions. This conclusion is deduced from the following. Suppose we place a tube with a hole in its side into a tank of water (Fig. 10–5b). The water in the tank and in the tube will be at the same level; there is no net transfer of water from the tank to the tube or from the tube to the tank. What does that mean about pressures across the hole? Suppose a small amount of water is transferred from the tank to the tube. In order to make room for itself, it would have to lift the column of water in the tube, on the bottom of which there is a certain pressure. In other words, before the water could flow into the tube, it would have to exert a pressure just equal to (really an infinitesimal amount greater than) the pressure exerted downward. The analysis suggests that sideways pressure is equal to the downward pressure. Indeed, theory and experiment confirm that pressure is exerted equally in all directions.

The same point arises in connection with atmospheric pressure. The surface of

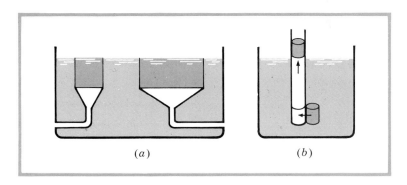

FIG. 10-5

(a) The weights of water above two funnels of unequal diameter differ. But the pressure of the water, force divided by area, is the same. (b) To move a cylinder of water from the tank into the tube, pressure is needed to make room for it. The pressure must lift the column in the tube—it must equal the pressure of the water column. Since no exchange occurs, the downward pressure of the water column in the tube and the sideways pressure are equal.

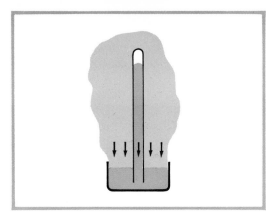

FIG. 10-6

Mercury barometer. The mercury column in the sealed tube exerts exactly the same pressure as the atmosphere outside the tube.

the earth is at the bottom of a "sea of air." A column of the atmosphere of base 1 in.² and rising to the outer reaches of the atmosphere weighs approximately 14.7 lb. Hence, atmospheric pressure is approximately 14.7 lb/in.²

Measurement of atmospheric pressure is commonly made with a mercury barometer which depends on the equality of pressure principle illustrated in the previous paragraph. The mercury barometer (Fig. 10–6) is a tube with a hole at the bottom and a sealed top. It contains a column of mercury about 30 in. long below a small evacuated space. The force exerted by this column, per square inch, equals the weight of a 30-in.-long, 1-in.²-base cylinder of mercury, or 30 in. × 1 in.² × 0.49 lb/in.³ (the density of mercury) = 14.7 lb/in.² This mercury column in the barometer is supported by the equal pressure of the atmosphere out-

side. Quite commonly gas pressures are reported directly in *inches of mercury* or *centimeters of mercury*, i.e., the height of the mercury column supported by the gas (atmospheric pressure = 30 in. = 76 cm of mercury) or in *atmospheres* (1 atm = 14.7 lb/in.²) rather than in pounds per square inch or dynes per square centimeter to which the height of the mercury column would have to be converted.

The third illustration of the usefulness of the concept, pressure, is the hydraulic jack (Fig. 10–7), a fairly common machine for increasing the force exerted by a human being. The device works as follows. Suppose a man pushes with a force of 50 lb. on a 1-in.² piston on top of a fluid. This places the fluid everywhere under a pressure of 50 lb/in.² (If the pressure were less in some portion of the fluid, fluid would immediately rush into that portion.) Suppose that at the other end the container has a second piston, 100 in.² in area. Since the pressure on the second piston is also 50 lb/in.², a force of 50 lb/in.² × 100 in.² = 5,000 lb is exerted by the large piston. A 50-lb child, by jumping on the little piston, can raise a very heavy car.

EXAMPLE

Does the hydraulic jack violate conservation of energy? To show that the hydraulic jack increases the force without, however, producing work from nowhere, we need only do a bit of bookkeeping. Suppose the small piston is depressed 1 ft (12 in.). This means that 12 in.³ of fluid flow from the small chamber to the large one (1 in.² × 12 in.). But 12 in.³ of fluid spread over the 100 in.² area in the large chamber raises the large piston only 0.12 in. (0.01 ft). Now the bookkeeping:

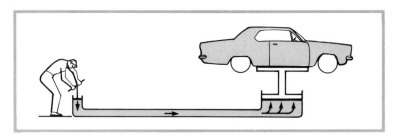

The hydraulic jack. A small force over a small area produces a sizable pressure. Because fluids are incompressible, the pressure can be exerted over a large area. That produces a large force.

FIG. 10-7

Work done by child:
$W = F \times d = 50 \text{ lb} \times 1 \text{ ft} = 50 \text{ ft-lb}$

Work done on car:
$W = F \times d = 5,000 \text{ lb} \times 0.01 \text{ ft} = 50 \text{ ft-lb}$

Energy has not been created. The machine merely enabled the weak child to lift the heavy car, though through a very small distance only.

BAROMETRY

The history of the idea of a "sea of air" is sufficiently interesting to warrant a short digression. Air is so common, so familiar to all of us that we must remind ourselves that it is there, all around us, and that it has weight and exerts pressure. Our acceptance of it is so unconscious that the remark once made about fishes—water is the last thing a fish would discover—is apt for humans and air. Familiarity may not breed contempt, but it certainly does not invite thoughtfulness.

Some of the results of atmospheric pressure were well known to early natural philosophers and artisans. It was well known, for instance, that wine would not flow from a cask unless a second opening was provided for the air to replace the wine. (This describes both the science and the habits of antiquity.) The explanation of the need for a second opening was Aristotle's dictum that "nature abhors a vacuum." (Note the connection with his views about molecules.) The suction pump (Fig. 10–8) was known for a long time, and its ability to raise water was also connected with "nature abhorring a vacuum" and filling the space beneath the piston as it was raised. While ancient well drillers knew that the suction pump can raise water only 34 ft, that if the pump is made to raise water a greater distance, nature loses her interest in "abhorring a vacuum" and does not fill the pump, this was conveniently ignored. Torricelli (1608–1647), an Italian physicist, was apparently the first to question the demise of abhorrence at the height of 34 ft. He reasoned that if air has weight,

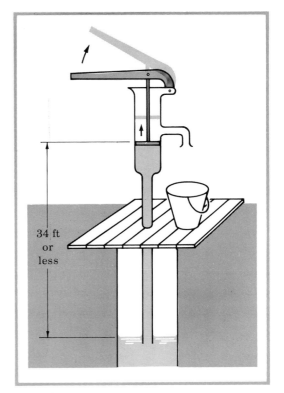

34 ft or less

FIG. 10-8

The suction pump. Water can be raised to a height of 34 ft only because it depends on air pressure to push the water up in the pipe. As the piston is raised, water rises under it and flows out of the spout. But if the pipe is longer than 34 ft, the air pressure is not large enough to push the water under the plunger and the pump runs dry.

as had been shown by Galileo, and the weight of the air supports a column of 34 ft of water in the suction pump, air should also support a column of mercury. But the mercury column should be much shorter because mercury is 13.6 times as dense as water. The length of the mercury column should be (34 ft × 12 in./ft)/13.6 or about 30 in. To test his conclusion, he sealed a glass tube, filled it with mercury, and inverted it in a pool of mercury. Thus he invented the mercury barometer.

Pascal (1623–1662), a noted French scientist, mathematician, and philosopher, learned of Torricelli's experiment and took the idea one step further. If the mercury is supported by the weight of the sea of air, then the pressure should be less at the top of a mountain, which has less air above it, than at the bottom. He asked his brother-in-law, Périer, to take a barometer to the top of the Puy de Dôme, a mountain in central France. And, indeed, Périer confirmed the deduction, though one must question whether the crude instrument he carried with him was adequate for the task. Probably, knowing what he should find influenced Périer's observations and he reported what he was "supposed to" report. The tendency of observers to find what they hope to find has been confirmed by psychologists and constitutes one of the hidden dangers in careful scientific work.

These experiments, one would think, should have convinced the natural philosophers of the time that there is a sea of air which exerts pressure. But ancient ideas die with difficulty and new ones are accepted slowly. In particular, Linus (1595–1675), an otherwise obscure scholar, suggested that not air pressure, but an invisible thread or *funiculus* holds the water in the pump and the mercury in the barometer. The funiculus is too weak to support a weight greater than that in 34 ft of water or 30 in. of mercury. While such an idea seems ridiculous to us, a clutching at a last, invisible straw, in the middle of the seventeenth century such magical solutions were taken seriously. As a matter of fact, the eminent physicist Robert Boyle (1627–1691) felt it necessary to demolish Linus's suggestion by experiment. In his descriptions of the experiments, Boyle began by stating Linus's arguments:

If you take a tube open at both ends of a good length, suppose forty inches long, and fill it with mercury, and place your finger on the top as before, taking away your lower finger, you will find the mercury to descend even to its wonted station [i.e., about 30 inches], and your finger on the top to be strongly drawn WITHIN the tube, and to stick closely unto it. Whence again it is evidently concluded that the mercury placed in its own station is not there upheld by

the external air, but suspended by a certain internal cord [the funiculus], whose upper end being fastened to the finger, draws and fastens it after this manner into the tube.

Then Boyle appealed to the principle of parsimony—do not introduce anything unnecessary into an explanation—and to experiment:

The other thing that I would have considered touching our adversary's hypothesis is that it is needless. For whereas he denies not, that the air has some weight and spring, but affirms, that it is very insufficient to perform such great matters as the counterpoising of a mercurial cylinder of 29 [now 30] inches, as we teach that it may; we shall now endeavor to manifest by experiments purposely made, that the spring of the air is capable of doing far more than it is necessary for us to ascribe to it, to solve the phaenomena of the Torricellian experiment.

The experiment which Boyle devised was simple. He bent a glass tube into the form of a J, sealed the short end, and trapped some air in it with mercury (Fig. 10–9).

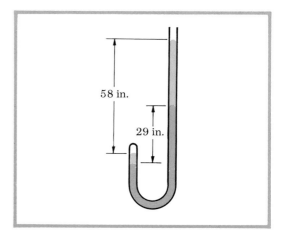

FIG. 10-9

Boyle's J tube. When he trapped air in the closed portion of the tube, Boyle found that the air would support columns of mercury much longer than the 29 (now 30) in. of mercury which Linus had said were too long for air to support. At the same time he found that the volume occupied by the air was inversely proportional to the pressure exerted by the mercury.

The results of his experiment demolished the funiculus:

It is evident, that as common air, when reduced to half its wonted extent, obtained near about twice as forcible a spring as it had before; so this thus comprest air being further thrust into half this narrow room, obtained thereby a spring about as strong again as that it last had, and consequently four times as strong as that of the common air. And there is no case to doubt, that if we had been furnished with a greater quantity of quicksilver and a very strong tube, we might, by a further compression of the included air, have made it counter balance the pressure of a far taller and heavier cylinder of mercury. For no man perhaps yet knows, how near to an infinite compression the air may be capable of, if the compressing force be competently increased. So that here our adversary may plainly see, that the spring of the air, which he makes so light of, may not only be able to resist the weight of 29 inches, but in some cases of above a hundred inches of quicksilver, and that without the assistance of his Funiculus, which in our present case has nothing to do. And to let you see, that we did not (as little above) inconsiderately mention the weight of the incumbent atmospherical cylinder as a part of the weight resisted by the imprisoned air, we will here annex, that we took care, when the mercurial cylinder in the longer leg of the pipe was about an hundred inches high, to cause one to suck at the open orifice; whereupon (as we expected) the mercury in the tube did notably ascend. Which considerable phaenomenon can not be ascribed to our examiner's Funiculus, since by his own confession that can not pull up the mercury if the mercurial cylinder be above 29 or 30 inches of mercury.

The logic of Boyle's arguments occurs in two steps. First, he shows that the spring of the air is more than great enough to support a long column of mercury (which Linus had denied) because Boyle's trapped air supported a column of 100 in. Second, by sucking at the open end, he showed that the 100-in. column could be raised. Thus the funiculus, if it were responsible for the phenomena ascribed to it, in this case did not break at 30 in.

THE GAS LAWS

These experiments, designed to disprove the existence of the funiculus, paid Boyle an important dividend. When he looked at his data quantitatively, he found that air "when reduced to half its wonted extent, obtained near about twice as forcible a spring . . . ," a relationship now known as *Boyle's law.*

It is significant that Boyle credits three of his contemporaries with having arrived at the same conclusion—Robert Hooke, Richard Townley, and Lord Brouncker. It is certainly a tribute to his integrity. In doing so, he followed the canons of the best in the scientific tradition. But it also illustrates that scientific discovery depends not only on genius but also on the appropriateness of the times. When the techniques for carrying out pressure-volume experiments had become established, following Torricelli, this relationship became amenable for discovery by thoughtful experimenters. Apparently there were four nearly simultaneous discoverers.

Boyle's law states that for a fixed sample of gas (i.e., the air trapped in his J tube) pressure times volume is constant at constant temperature. Algebraically.

$$P \times V = C \qquad (10\text{--}2)$$

The use of this law is illustrated by example.

EXAMPLE

A bicycle pump has a volume of 2 liters and contains air at atmospheric pressure. What is the pressure of the air in the pump when the piston is nine-tenths of the way down?

This problem can be solved only if the temperature of the gas does not change. Since the air is confined in the barrel of the pump, we are dealing with a fixed sample. Then, placing the numbers given into Boyle's law, we first evaluate the numerical value of the constant C.

$P \times V = 1$ atm $\times 2$ liters $= 2$ liter-atm $= C$
We know that no matter how far the piston is depressed, $P \times V = 2$ liter-atm. When the piston is nine-tenths of the way down, the volume

occupied by the gas is one-tenth its previous value, or 0.2 liter. For the depressed piston, $P \times V = 2$ liter-atm; $P \times 0.2$ liter $= 2$ liter-atm; $P = 10$ atm.

THE LAW OF CHARLES AND GAY-LUSSAC

Previously in this chapter we alluded to the fact that gases expand very regularly when heated; Fig. 10–10 illustrates this regularity. It is a bit more complex than Boyle's law.

Whenever some sample of gas at 0°C is heated, it expands by 1/273 of its volume for each degree centigrade of heating. If we call V_0 the original volume at 0°C, the change at 10°C, for instance, will be to $V_0 + 10/273V_0$. At 25°C the change is to $V_0 + 25/273V_0$. For cooling, the effect is similar though the volume becomes less. For instance, the volume at −10°C has become $V_0 − 10/273V_0$.

Now the figure has some interesting implications. If we extend the line toward

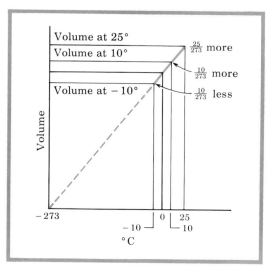

FIG. 10-10

When the volume of a gas is plotted against centigrade temperature, a straight line results that crosses the abscissa at −273°. Another temperature scale can be defined which begins with that point as the zero point. On this temperature scale, the Kelvin scale, V = kT$_k$.

lower temperatures, we find that the volume becomes zero—vanishes—at a temperature of −273°C. (This is embarrassing because of the law of conservation of matter. Fortunately, the figure is for gases and all gases liquefy before they get that cold. Hence they do not in fact vanish.) But the figure suggests that there may be something much more significant about the temperature −273°C than about the temperature 0°C, at which water happens to freeze. Indeed, from other considerations one can demonstrate that −273°C is a lower limit to temperature, and it is consequently called the *absolute zero*. Moreover, with a temperature scale based on the absolute zero, the fractions disappear in the description of gas-volume changes produced by temperature, and the equation relating gas volume to temperature becomes:

$$V = kT_k \qquad (10\text{–}3)$$

T_k refers to the temperature measured on the scale that has its zero point at the absolute zero, the freezing point of water at 273°, the boiling point of water at 373°, etc. Its temperatures are always equal to the temperature on the Celsius scale plus 273. This scale is known as the *absolute* or *Kelvin temperature* scale, after William Thomson, Lord Kelvin (1824–1907), a British physicist.

Equation 10–3 is known as *Charles's law* or the *law of Gay-Lussac*. There were again codiscoverers, Jacques Charles (1746–1823) and Joseph Louis Gay-Lussac (1778–1850).

Charles's law makes gases very handy indicators of temperature because, unlike liquids which expand each in its own way, all gases follow the same law. Fortunately the differences between the expansion of gases and other thermometric fluids are sufficiently small to ignore for all but the most precise purposes.

EXAMPLE

A J tube contains gas trapped in the closed end which, at 21°C, occupies 25 ml. The J tube is now placed in an oven and the mercury level adjusted to keep the pressure constant. The gas has expanded to 45 ml. What is the temperature in the oven?

We begin by changing 21°C to 294°K. Then, for this sample of gas, Charles's law constant k has the value:

$$k = V/T_k = 25 \text{ ml}/294°\text{K} = 0.085 \text{ ml/deg}$$

In the oven, V and T_k are related by the same constant. Therefore:

$$k = V/T_k = 0.085 \text{ ml/deg} = 45 \text{ ml}/T_k$$
$$T_k = 539°\text{K}$$

Converting back to °C, 539°K − 273 = 266°C, the temperature in the oven.

CALORIMETRY

So far in this chapter we have described solids, liquids, and gases separately and have contrasted them. Gases are characterized by a lack of innate structure; their volumes change very regularly with changes in temperature and pressure. In contrast, solids change very little with changes in temperature or pressure and their structure is quite orderly. Liquids are neither as orderly as solids, nor do they change as regularly with temperature as gases. They resemble gases in structure and solids in their resistance to compression.

While the three states of matter are distinct in their properties, they are easily converted into one another. Solids melt to liquids; liquids vaporize to gases; and even solids sublime directly to gases. These changes are closely related to heating and to changes in the temperature and must be discussed with reference to temperature and heat. But before we can study the effect of heat on changes of state, we must describe how heating affects solids, liquids, or gases without changing them into each other.

A pot of water set on a burner gradually increases its temperature. If the amount of water in the pot is large, it will "heat up" slowly; if small, more rapidly. A block of metal equal in weight to the water in the pot, if set on the same burner, will rise in temperature far more rapidly than the water. But again, a large block will increase its temperature much more slowly than a small one set on the same burner.

From these examples, we can intuitively derive the factors that relate the heat supplied by the burner to the temperature changes it brought about. We recognize, first of all, that the heat required to raise the temperature of 100 grams of water by a certain amount is twice as great as the heat required to raise the temperature of 50 grams of water by the same amount. Therefore the heat required H is proportional to the mass m of the material heated, or $H \alpha m$ (α means proportional to). Second, we recognize that to raise the water 10° requires twice as much heat as to raise the same quantity of water only 5°. Heat required is also proportional to the temperature change, or $H \alpha \Delta T$ (ΔT = change of temperature). Combining these two, we obtain $H \alpha m \Delta T$. We still need to consider the constant of proportionality.

The fact discussed above, that a given weight of metal changes its temperature more easily than an equal weight of water, suggests that the proportionality constant differs for different materials. It turns out that it must be determined separately, by experiment, for each substance, and it is called the *specific heat* of that substance. Specific heat is designated by the letter s. Inserting s into the equation gives:

$$H = sm \, \Delta T \qquad (10\text{--}4)$$

The specific heat is the quantity of heat required to raise 1 gram of a substance 1°C. If the specific heat is small, the substance is heated easily; if large, that is, if much heat is required per gram for a 1° rise in temperature, raising the temperature of the substance requires larger burners and longer time.

The unit of heat energy used is the *calorie*, which is defined as the heat required to raise 1 gram of water from 14.5 to 15.5°C. This is, of course, the specific heat of water.

EXAMPLE

A 100-gram block of aluminum, heated to 90°C, is added to 200 grams of water at 20°C in a calorimeter (an insulated box). The water and aluminum end up at 27°C each. What is the specific heat of the aluminum?

Since the aluminum and water are in an insulated box, we must assume that the heat lost by the aluminum cooling to 27°C is used to heat the water to that temperature. The heat gained by the water is

$H = sm\,\Delta T$
$H = 1$ cal/gram-deg $\times$ 200 grams $\times$ 7 deg
    $= 1400$ cal

The heat lost by the aluminum is also 1400 cal. Then, for the aluminum,

1,400 cal $= s$ cal/gram-deg $\times$ 100 grams
                $\times$ 63 deg.
$s = 1,400$ cal/6,300 gram-deg
    $= 0.22$ cal/gram-deg

the specific heat of aluminum.

CHANGES OF STATE

Equation 10–4 suggests that if some material is heated over a constant heat supply, its temperature should increase in a regular manner. This is true as long as no change in state occurs (and one neglects heat losses by the substance and a small variation of specific heat with temperature). But if the substance melts or vaporizes as it is heated, something interesting happens; heat continues to be absorbed as the state of the substance changes, but the temperature does not change. Suppose we take ice from a freezer at −20°C (approximately 0°F) and place it in a calorimeter with a small electric heater. At the beginning we should expect the ice to warm slowly and regularly. If we measured the temperature every minute, we would find that this occurs (Fig. 10–11) until the temperature reaches 0°C, the melting point of ice. At this point we would find that the temperature does not change for several minutes. Until all the ice is changed to water, the temperature in the calorimeter remains at 0°C. There is heat added to the ice without changing its temperature. This heat, which is required just to melt the ice, is called the *heat of fusion*. For ice it is 80 cal/gram, a large amount compared to the specific heat of water.

When all the ice is melted, the temperature of the water would again rise regularly

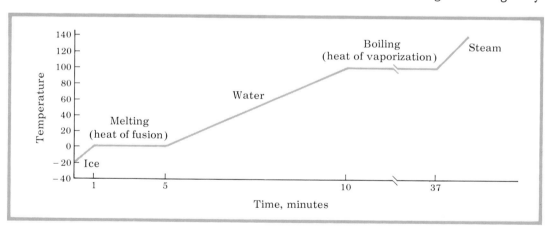

FIG. 10-11

The temperature of ice and water heated at a constant rate (approximately to scale). At first the ice increases in temperature. Then, as the ice melts, the temperature remains constant while heat of fusion is absorbed. When all the ice has melted, the water increases in temperature uniformly until the boiling point is reached. While the water changes into steam, the temperature remains constant and the heat of vaporization is absorbed. Finally, when no water remains, the steam temperature increases

until the boiling point, 100°C, is reached. Then, while the water boils away, a large amount of heat would be supplied by the heater without raising the temperature further—the *heat of vaporization*. For water the heat of vaporization is 540 cal/ gram. It is heat which merely changes the water to steam without raising its temperature. Only after all the water has boiled away would the temperature rise again as the heat supplied changes the temperature of the gaseous steam.

All substances melting absorb heat of fusion and all substances vaporizing absorb heat of vaporization. These heats are normally quite large. Much more heat is required to fuse or vaporize 1 gram of a substance than to change its temperature by 1°. When gases liquefy or liquids crystallize, these heats are given off by the substance. In this way the freezing of a lake helps to keep the water underneath somewhat warmer because a large amount of heat, 80 cal/gram, is given off by the freezing of each gram of water. Likewise, its large heat of vaporization makes steam much more dangerous than boiling water. Each gram of steam liquefying on the skin gives off 540 cal to sear the skin.

Heats of fusion and of vaporization are interesting from a number of points of view. They constitute a storage of heat without a temperature change. Not only the heat of fusion but also the heat of vaporization serves to regulate the temperature near large bodies of water. On a warm day evaporating water absorbs large quantities of heat and helps to keep the surroundings cooler. Indeed, the storage of heat in a melting solid (without change of the temperature) has been suggested as a means for regulating house temperatures. During the day the heat of the sun would be absorbed by the melting solid, keeping the house relatively cool. At night, as the melted solid recrystallized, it would give up the heat to warm the house.

EXAMPLE
Air in an average room weighs about 50 kg or 50,000 grams. Its specific heat is 0.24 cal/ gram-deg. How much sodium sulfate, which has a heat of fusion of 51.3 cal/gram, would have to solidify to raise the temperature of the air in the room by 2°C?

The heat required is $H = sm \Delta T = 0.24$ cal/ gram-deg $\times$ 50,000 grams $\times$ 2 deg = 2400 cal. To deliver this amount of heat, $H = L_f \times m$; 2400 cal = 51.3 cal/gram $\times m$ gram; $m =$ 46.8 gram of sodium sulfate. A relatively small amount will do.

Questions and Problems

1. Set up a table in which four or five properties of gases, liquids, and solids are compared.

2. To form obsidian, Fig. 5–6, magma cools so rapidly that the component particles cannot form a regular crystal structure from the melt. Obsidian is classified as a supercooled liquid, not a solid. Explain.

3. Give two common examples of (a) liquid diffusion, (b) gaseous diffusion, (c) viscosity change with temperature, (d) surface tension, (e) regular structure of solid crystals.

4. Give two common examples of (a) melting of a solid, (b) vaporization of a liquid, (c) crystallization of a liquid, (d) condensation of a gas, (e) sublimation of a solid to gas.

5. Assume that the total area of the body is 12

ft². What force does the atmosphere exert on it? What carries this force?

6. A water tank consists of a large reservoir 50 ft above ground level connected to the water mains by a pipe of exactly 1-ft² cross section. When the tank contains 3,000 ft³ of water, the water is exactly 10 ft deep in the tank. (a) What is the weight of water in the tank and the pipe? (Density 62.4 lb/ft³.) (b) What is the pressure of the water on a valve which closes the pipe exactly at ground level? Explain the difference.

7. A crate has base dimensions of 6 ft × 3 ft. It weighs 6,000 lb. What pressure does it exert on the base? Is the pressure larger or smaller than atmospheric?

8. Express the pressure in Question 7 in at-

mospheres; inches of mercury; centimeters of mercury.

9. Define heat of fusion, heat of vaporization, specific heat. Explain the statement: the calorie is the specific heat of water.

10. A hydraulic press can exert a force of 30 tons. If its piston has a 24-in² area and it is driven by a motor that produces a force of 500 lb, what is the area of the driving piston? What distance does the driving piston move to move the press ½ in.?

11. The Fahrenheit scale can be converted to increase from absolute zero. At what temperature F is the absolute zero? How many degrees above the absolute zero in the Fahrenheit scale is 70°F?

12. 100-gram blocks of each of the following metals are heated to 250°C and then placed in a large block of ice. How many calories does each lose? How many grams of ice will each melt?
Aluminum — $s = 0.22$ cal/gram
Copper — $s = 0.09$ cal/gram
Iron — $s = 0.11$ cal/gram

13. How many calories are required to raise 500 grams of water from 20°C to steam at 100°C?

14. The compressed-air tank of gas stations has a capacity of about 3 ft³ and is kept at about 11 atm of pressure. What volume of air is compressed to fill the tank? Convert 11 atm to centimeters of mercury; inches of mercury; lb/in.²

15. A certain temperature safety device keeps 100 cm³ of air, measured at 20°C, under fixed pressure. When the air expands to 125 cm³, it trips a switch which starts a bell. At what temperature does the device go off? At what volume would the device have to trip the switch if the critical temperature for safety were 79°C?

16. Compute the volume of hydrogen gas from a cylinder at 60 atm of pressure which fills a spherical balloon 10 ft in radius ($V = \frac{4}{3}\pi\ r^3$).

17. Large bodies of water tend to keep air temperature warmer in winter and colder in summer. Explain. Is your explanation still true even if the body of water freezes over completely?

Suggestions for Further Reading

More extensive discussions of the material in this chapter and in Chap. 11 are in:

Christiansen, G. S., and Paul H. Garrett: *Structure and Change*, W. H. Freeman and Company, San Francisco, 1960. Chapters 9 and 10.

Pauling, Linus: *College Chemistry*, 3d ed., W. H. Freeman and Company, San Francisco, 1964. Chapters 1 and 2.

Physical Science Study Committee: *Physics*, D. C. Heath and Company, Boston, 1960. Chapters 8 and 9.

Quagliano, James V.: *Chemistry*, 2d ed., Prentice-Hall, Inc., Englewood Cliffs, N. J., 1963. Chapters 8 to 10.

Rogers, Eric M.: *Physics for the Inquiring*

Mind, Princeton University Press, Princeton, N. J., 1960. Chapters 5, 6, 25, and 27.

Sienko, Michell J., and Robert A. Plane: *Chemistry*, 2d ed., McGraw-Hill Book Company, Inc., New York, 1961. Chapters 6 to 9.

An account of Boyle's contributions and the clarification of our understanding of gases is in:

Conant, J. B. (ed.): *Harvard Case Histories in Experimental Science*, vol. 1, Harvard University Press, Cambridge, Mass., 1957. Chapter 1, by J. B. Conant.

An extensive account of solid structure is in:

Holden, Alan, and Phylis Singer: *Crystals and Crystal Growing*, Anchor Books, Doubleday & Company, Inc., Garden City, N. Y., 1960 (paperback).

The Kinetic Molecular Theory

Table 11–1 summarizes some of the properties of gases, liquids, and solids which we discussed in the previous chapter. It is the purpose of this chapter to explain how aggregations of molecules, depending upon the conditions, show the properties of gases, liquids, or solids, and how, by heating or cooling, the states change into one another. Our explanations require a basic assumption which has already been used in Chap. 10 but for which we have not yet given any evidence:

All matter consists of small particles called molecules. In addition, our explanations draw upon information which comes from the table.

1. Depending on how much heat the molecules have, they may exist as solid, liquid, or gas. Therefore *the energy contained by the molecules is an important factor determining their state of aggregation.*

TABLE 11-1

Comparison of Some Properties of the Different States of Matter

	Density	Compressibility	Fluidity	Diffusion through state	Relative temperature at which it exists
Solid	High	Incompressible	Rigid	Very slow	Low
Liquid	High	Incompressible	Fluid	Slow	Higher
Gas	Low	Highly compressible	Very fluid	Rapid	Still higher

2. Since in liquids and solids molecules stick together, *there are forces of attraction operating between molecules.*

3. Gases and liquids flow spontaneously; even solids show "creep." Moreover, there is diffusion in both liquids and gases. Hence *molecules are in constant motion.*

4. Solids and liquids are dense; gases are much less so. Solids and liquids are nearly incompressible; gases are very readily compressible. *In solids and liquids, molecules are closely packed; in gases, they are far apart.*

The five statements in italics, with only minor modifications, suffice to provide an understanding of the phenomena described in the previous chapter. With the laws of motion we studied in Chap. 7, they produce a detailed, mathematical description of gas behavior.

THE KINETIC THEORY OF GASES

Let us first restate the problem we are about to solve and the logic we shall employ in the solution. We described a number of experimental observations concerning matter in the previous chapter: the gas laws, diffusion, viscosity, etc. We noted that gases behave in particularly regular ways, and that temperature, pressure, and volume are the important variables for describing gas behavior. It is our task now to provide an explanation for such regular behavior, starting with the picture of a gas based on the five statements with which this chapter began. In particular, our model associates

the behavior of the molecules in the gas with the behavior of the whole gas. The model we use focuses on single molecules as part of a swarm of infinitesimally small molecules, each buzzing around at relatively large distances from the others. We associate the behavior of the one molecule with the behavior of the group of molecules, and then associate the properties of the group of molecules with the observable properties of the gas. Since the molecules are moving objects, the laws of motion are one part of the bridge between the submicroscopic and the observable. We apply them. A second part of the bridge is a very special way to look at gas pressure. These two lead us to some unexpected aspects of the connection between swarming molecules and gases—new ideas about the nature of heat and temperature.

First, how do swarming molecules produce the pressure which was studied by Boyle as the "spring of the air"? Consider a single grain of buckshot. You throw it at a tin can and it bounces off with a "ping." The can stands still. Now take a handful of buckshot and throw it at one time. Perhaps if you throw hard enough, the many grains together will exert enough force on the area of the tin can to push it over. Certainly if you fire the buckshot from a shotgun, you would expect to knock over the tin can. But the force of the buckshot exerted over the area of the tin can is, by the definition of pressure, a pressure on the tin can. And gas molecules, bouncing against the walls of a container, exert a pressure in exactly the same way. *Gas pressure is the result of the collision of molecules with the walls of the container.*

To calculate the pressure exerted by the gas molecules, we need Eqs. 10–1 and 7–10, $P = F/A$ and $F = ma$. We have to know the mass of the molecules m and the acceleration they receive during the collisions a. Since the total force results from the collision of many molecules with the walls, we also need to know the number that collide with the walls each second.

The calculation of the force exerted by the gas molecules can be carried out quite rigorously. We shall use an approach with some simplifying assumptions that leads to the same result. Gas molecules swarm quite randomly, each in a different direction and with a different velocity. Moreover, they collide with each other as well as colliding with the walls. Let us assume, however, that we can divide all molecules in a gas into three groups. The members of each group move parallel to one of the three directions in space (Fig. 11–1). Let us also neglect for the moment that the molecules move with different speeds. Let us focus our attention on the average speed of all the molecules, v, and assume that each molecule travels with that speed. Also we ignore, for the moment, the collisions of molecules with each other.

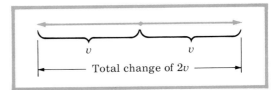

FIG. 11-2

A change of speed from magnitude v in one direction to magnitude v in the opposite direction is a change of magnitude 2v.

We describe first the motion of a single molecule of mass m as it travels between two walls of the cubic box that are separated by the length of the edge, l. This molecule travels to one wall with speed v, returns with the same speed but in the opposite direction, collides again, and travels forward with the same speed, etc. In each collision the molecule changes its speed from magnitude v in one direction to magnitude v in the opposite direction, resulting in a total change of $2v$ (Fig. 11–2).

We are interested in the force exerted on one wall. This we obtain from the acceleration at that wall which is defined as the change of velocity per second. We now know that the change per collision is $2v$. To obtain the change per second, we must find the number of collisions the molecule makes with the wall each second. Change per second equals change per collision times collisions per second.

Each molecule travels rapidly enough to make many collisions with each wall each second. Between collisions, it must travel back and forth in the box, a distance of $2l$. As Fig. 11–3 shows, traveling a distance v each second and colliding after each segment of distance $2l$ means that there are $v/2l$ collisions per second. The acceleration at one wall—change of velocity per second —computed from change per collision times collisions per second is

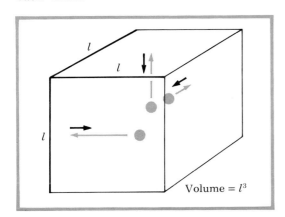

FIG. 11-1

A simplified model for a gas. The gas consists of three groups of molecules, each group moving at right angles to one pair of opposite sides and bouncing back and forth between the sides.

$$a = 2v \times \frac{v}{2l} = \frac{v^2}{l} \qquad (11\text{–}1)$$

Force is mass times acceleration. Each molecule contributes to the force

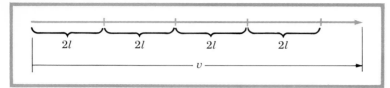

FIG. 11-3

If a distance of magnitude v *is broken into segments of magnitude* 2l, *there are* v/2l *segments.*

$$F = ma = \frac{mv^2}{l} \qquad (11\text{--}2)$$

But there is more than one molecule colliding with the wall. If there are n molecules in the box, according to the assumption we made, there are $\frac{1}{3}n$ molecules colliding with each wall. The force exerted by all of them is $\frac{1}{3}n$ times as great as the force exerted by a single molecule. The total force on the wall becomes

$$F = \tfrac{1}{3}n \times \frac{mv^2}{l} = \frac{nmv^2}{3l} \qquad (11\text{--}3)$$

Equation 11–3 gives the force exerted by the molecules on one wall, although the manner in which we derived it did not specify the wall. Any other wall is subject to the same force. The force exerted on the six walls of the cubic box, therefore, is six times as great, or $2nmv^2/l$.

To calculate the pressure, we need the equation $P = F/A$. The area of the six sides of a cubic box of length l is $6l^2$. Substituting then gives

$$P = \frac{F}{A} = \frac{2nmv^2/l}{6l^2} = \frac{1}{3}\,\frac{nmv^2}{l^3} \qquad (11\text{--}4)$$

But l^3 is the volume of a cubic box of side l, the cubic box which contains the molecules we have been studying. We replace l^3 by V, the volume, and obtain

$$P = \frac{1}{3}\,\frac{nm\bar{v}^2}{V} \qquad (11\text{--}5)$$

Equation 11–5, the gas equation, connects two measurable properties of gases, pressure and volume, with characteristics of individual molecules: their number in the box, their mass, and their average squared speed. Although we made a number of simplifying assumptions in the derivation, that all molecules move with speed v and parallel to the sides, we would have obtained the same result had we allowed the molecules to swarm at random and used the appropriate mathematics. However, we added a bar above this symbol for speed, $\bar{v}^2$, to designate that the molecules in a gas move at random and that the $\bar{v}^2$ which appears in Eq. 11–5 is the average of the square of the random velocities of the molecules.

A COMMENT ON SCIENTIFIC PROCEDURE

The derivation we have just completed may seem like magic pulled out of a hat. Let us review, therefore, the steps we have taken.

First, we surveyed the behavior of gases, liquids, and solids.

Second, we constructed a microscopic picture or model of gaseous matter—the buzzing and swarming molecules—to help us explain or understand the behavior.

Third, we used the laws of physics to derive a quantitative relationship between the pressure, a measurable quantity, and volume, another measurable quantity. The derivation began with the model. In order to calculate pressure from buzzing molecules, we first defined pressure in a particular way. Then we went back to two well-known equations, $P = F/A$ and $F = ma$, and found that a, m, and A each could be calculated from the behavior of the molecules in the model. We thus bridged the gap between the measurable quantities of the gas and the properties of the molecules.

We now shall take the last step in this

series: we shall test the derived equation to see whether it coincides with the quantitative relationships that are obtained from experiment, Boyle's and Charles's laws, for instance. If it does—and, of course, in this case it does or we would not teach it—then we can feel reassured that the model of swarming, invisible molecules is a good model, that it gives a satisfactory picture of the nature of gases. If it did not, and in the progress of scientific research many models are built which do not meet the test of agreement, or agree only partially, then we should have to look for ways of patching it up or perhaps discard it entirely in favor of new models. (One alternative model for gases that suggests itself is a spongy, elastic continuum rather than moving, discrete molecules.) Needless to say, the search for good or better models is unending. Success depends upon the imagination and intuition of the scientist, the state of progress of the field being studied, and to some extent on the good fortune of the investigator. The successful scientist is likely to have a very thorough understanding of the problem under investigation and an intuitive feeling for the order underlying apparently diverse phenomena. Then, with some good luck and much hard thinking, he is likely to devise good models.

The four steps given here are fairly typical of the manner in which scientific theories are produced and validated, though the order in which they are given by no means coincides with the order in which the active research worker encounters them. These are the textbook steps. They can be recognized after the research is completed and most of the answers are in. In the active stages of research, they occur in an order which is, to a large extent, fortuitous, and some of them are quite likely to occur simultaneously. Testing a derived equation (step 4) also brings new knowledge of the behavior of the subject under study (step 1). A new model (step 2) may point to as yet unexpected behavior (step 1 or 4) which in turn influences the derivation of

the equations (step 3). The steps thus appear in various sequences as the researcher pushes his investigations and plans and executes experiments much as an artist plans and executes his works. Only later, when the scientific creation has been successful, can the four steps be identified as inevitable parts of the logic of science.

THE GAS EQUATION AND BOYLE'S AND CHARLES'S LAWS

The most obvious test of correspondence between the derived equation, Eq. 11–5, and experimental behavior makes use of the quantities that are already given in the equation, pressure and volume. From experiment, we have Boyle's law that at constant temperature the product of pressure and volume of a fixed sample of gas is constant (Eq. 10–2). A slight rearrangement of the gas equation gives

$$PV = \tfrac{1}{3}nm\bar{v}^2 \qquad (11\text{–}6)$$

On the left-hand side of this equation is the product of pressure times volume; correspondence with Boyle's law requires that the right-hand side remain constant. On the right there are $\tfrac{1}{3}$, a fixed number; n, the number of molecules in the sample which is fixed for a fixed sample; and $m\bar{v}^2$. If PV is to be constant, $m\bar{v}^2$ must remain constant too. But Boyle's law contains the further restriction that the temperature must remain constant. This restriction suggests that we identify $m\bar{v}^2$ with the temperature of the gas. Then we obtain full agreement between the experimentally obtained Boyle's law and the derived gas equation.

The identification of the term $m\bar{v}^2$ with temperature receives further corroboration from Charles's law (Eq. 10–3) that at constant pressure the volume of a fixed sample of gas is directly proportional to the absolute temperature. To fit the gas equation to Charles's law, we again rearrange it slightly:

$$V = \frac{\frac{1}{3}nm\bar{v}^2}{P} \qquad (11\text{--}7)$$

On the left is one of the variables in Charles's law, V; on the right, $\frac{1}{3}$ and n, both of which are fixed for a fixed sample of gas, and P, which Charles's law requires to be constant too. These three can be expressed as a single constant, K, changing Eq. 11–7 into

$$V = K \cdot m\bar{v}^2 \qquad (11\text{--}8)$$

But Charles's law states that when the quantities now expressed by K are constant, the volume varies directly with the absolute temperature. Thus from Charles's law we also find that we must identify $m\bar{v}^2$ with the absolute temperature.

It remains to ascribe some familiar property of the moving molecules to $m\bar{v}^2$ so that we can gain further insight into the meaning of temperature. The kinetic energy of a moving object is given by $\frac{1}{2}m\bar{v}^2$. Multiplying Eq. 11–8 by $\frac{1}{2}$ and rearranging, we obtain

$$V = \frac{1}{2}K \cdot m\bar{v}^2 = 2K \cdot \frac{1}{2}m\bar{v}^2 \qquad (11\text{--}9)$$

and comparing the last equation with Charles's law, $V = kT_k$, we find that

$$2K \cdot \frac{1}{2}m\bar{v}^2 = kT_k$$
$$\qquad (11\text{--}10)$$
$$\frac{1}{2}m\bar{v}^2 = \left(\frac{k}{2K}\right) T_k = cT_k$$

The meaning of the last equation is simply this: absolute (Kelvin) temperature measures the average kinetic energy of the randomly moving molecules. There is a proportionality constant, c, to convert energy units (ergs) into temperature units (degrees).

HEAT AND TEMPERATURE

What kind of kinetic energy is it whose average, according to Eq. 11–10, is measured by the temperature? To answer that question, let us review the meaning of

kinetic energy and the model of a gas we have used. Kinetic energy refers to the energy of an object in motion. In the case of a gas in a cubic container (from which we derived the gas equation) neither the gas as a whole nor the container is moving. Hence the kinetic energy in whose average we are interested cannot refer to the aggregate of molecules in the box. Within the stationary box, however, the molecules are moving randomly much like bees in a swarm. As a group they get nowhere, because each upward-moving molecule has a downward-moving counterpart; each molecule moving to the left is balanced by one moving to the right. But the individual molecules in their random motions do possess kinetic energy, and it is the average of these kinetic energies—of the individual molecules in their random motions—that is expressed by the temperature. In a hot gas the molecules are moving rapidly at random. The average of the kinetic energy of these motions is great. In a cool gas the motions are slower. The average of the kinetic energy of these motions is smaller.

We need go only one step further to give a new meaning to the concept heat. We know that through the absorption of heat, a gas increases its temperature. As we have just shown, increasing the temperature means increasing the average kinetic energy of the random motions. Thus, heat is the total kinetic energy of the continuous random motions of all the molecules in the container. Both heat and temperature refer to the random motions of the gas molecules. The difference between the two is one of intensity versus quantity. *The temperature measures the intensity of the random motions by finding the average of the kinetic energy of this motion. The heat is the total of the kinetic energies of the random motions of all the molecules.* Now we can explain why 10 times as much heat is required to raise 10 grams of a gas from 10 to 20° as to raise 1 gram through the same temperature interval. In the 10-gram sample we must add to the kinetic energy of 10 times as many molecules as in the 1-gram sample. Ten times as much heat is required. Yet, the increase in the *average* kinetic energy per molecule in the two samples is the same; that is, the temperature change is the same in both since the smaller amount of heat is distributed over a correspondingly smaller number of molecules in the smaller sample.

We see, furthermore, that heat is indeed a form of energy. However, it is unlike the potential energy or the kinetic energy of a rock or a ball. When a stone rests atop a wall or flies through the air, we have no difficulty using its energy to do useful work. Heat is not like that. Because the random motions of the group of molecules are pointed in all directions at once, their energy is undirected. They cannot move levers, turn wheels, or lift weights. The kinetic energy which is heat cannot be harnessed directly. Heat energy cannot be converted, in the usual sense, into work. It is largely unavailable.

Through this analysis we can understand what happens when friction slows a moving object and dissipates its kinetic energy into heat. For instance, we know that meteors turn into shooting stars and burn themselves out when they strike the atmosphere. When traveling through the unpopulated regions of outer space, the molecules of the meteors all travel together in the same direction as a solid body. They have the directed kind of motion which is described by kinetic energy. On entering the atmosphere, this group of molecules encounters the molecules of the gaseous atmosphere. During collisions some of the kinetic energy of the group is transferred to the separate gas molecules of the atmosphere. The result of the collisions is twofold. The gas molecules gain speed in their random motions—heat up—while the group of meteor molecules add random motions within the unit to the directed motion of the whole group. Thus the kinetic energy of the entire meteor particle, all of whose molecules were moving together in the same direction, gradually changes into random motions of all molecules, meteor and gas. The kinetic energy of the meteor is gradually transformed into heat.

OTHER DEDUCTIONS FROM THE GAS EQUATION

Let us now return to the gas equation to see what other information concerning the behavior of gases we can obtain from it, for we have by no means exhausted its usefulness by finding a physical meaning for heat and temperature. Perhaps the most obvious next step is to focus on the right-hand side of Eq. 11–5 to see whether it can be used to determine experimentally the values of n, the number of molecules in the sample of gas, m, the mass of a single molecule, or $\overline{v}^2$, the average squared speed of the molecules. Of the three, speed is the most amenable to experimental study for the phenomenon of diffusion clearly involves the speed of the molecules.

Diffusion in gases is related to the speed of the molecules in a fairly complex way. Molecules of one gas do not simply fly through the vacant spaces between the molecules of the other to reach their destination in the shortest possible time. In considering diffusion we cannot, as before, neglect the fact that gas molecules collide with one another. We must explicitly recognize that they travel a short distance in one direction, then they collide with other molecules, are deflected, move ahead in the deflected direction a bit, collide and get deflected again, and thus follow a tortuous zigzag path. Hence the rate at which an odor, say of a burning roast, reaches a housewife sitting in the living room, is much smaller than the rate at which the molecules move between collisions.

The actual path of diffusing molecules cannot be photographed, of course, because gas molecules are far too small. But pollen grains suspended in water are light enough

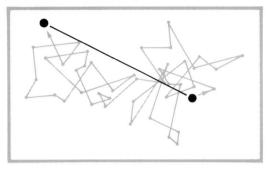

FIG. 11-4

Brownian movement. As a result of collisions with molecules of water, a tiny particle like a pollen grain is buffeted back and forth and describes a zigzag path in which it slowly moves from its point of origin. A figure like the one shown is obtained if the position of a tiny particle in water, viewed under a high-power microscope, is marked at 2-min intervals.

to be pushed around by collisions with water molecules, yet large enough to be seen under a microscope. The results of the collisions is the same zigzag motion we postulated for gas molecules. This motion was discovered already in 1828 by a Scottish botanist, Robert Brown (1773–1858), and is known as *Brownian movement* in his honor. A reproduction of Brownian movement is given in Fig. 11–4. Not only pollen grains in water but all small, suspended particles—dust in air, for instance—exhibit Brownian movement though a microscope may be needed to observe it.

In spite of the complication arising from the zigzag paths, diffusion is directly related to the molecular speed which appears in the gas equation. We will not calculate the effect of the zigzag detours in the progress of the molecules because that calculation is quite complex. We shall adopt another approach. We should expect that two gases diffusing through air should both meet the same obstacles to progress from their collisions with the air molecules. Both should be retarded to the same extent. Therefore their rates of diffusion should be proportional to the speed of the molecules between collisions. We can find the speed between

collisions from the gas equation by rearrangement.

$$v^2 = \frac{3PV}{nm} = \frac{3PV}{\mu} \tag{11–11}$$

The average squared speed equals three times the pressure multiplied by the volume of a sample and divided by the mass of the molecules in that sample (the number of molecules, n, multiplied by the mass m of each equals the mass μ of all the molecules). A heavier gas moves more slowly; a lighter gas more rapidly.

This relationship between the mass per unit volume of a gas and its rate of diffusion can be made more precise. If several gases are measured at the same pressure and volume, then, according to Eq. 11–11, the remaining variables are v^2 and μ. Weight and the average squared speed are related. Hence the rate of diffusion is inversely proportional to the square root of the weight of the sample. This is a result that was found experimentally in 1833 by Thomas Graham (1805–1869) and is known as *Graham's law of diffusion*. It is another instance in which a prediction from the derived gas equation is fully confirmed by experiment. It is illustrated in Fig. 11–5, in which the point at which dif-

FIG. 11-5

The white ring forms where ammonia molecules and hydrogen chloride molecules meet. They were released at the same time by squeezing the eyedroppers; but the much lighter ammonia molecules diffused a greater distance, and the ring is much nearer to where the hydrogen chloride molecules were released.

fusing ammonia and hydrogen chloride meet is marked by the white compound they form. Ammonia, about one-half as dense as hydrogen chloride, diffuses faster by a factor of $\sqrt{2}$, and the location where the two kinds of molecules meet is therefore much nearer to the end of the tube containing hydrogen chloride.

A more rigorous test of the predicted velocities is their direct determination. Substituting the appropriate values of P, V, and μ for the gas hydrogen, the lightest and therefore fastest-moving gas known, gives an average speed of about 1,200 meters/sec at room temperature. For oxygen at room temperature the speed is about 300 meters/sec. By comparison, a rifle bullet moves with a speed of about 500 meters/sec. Clearly, gas molecules move very rapidly. Gas velocities have been measured, but before we can turn to the experiment, we must examine more closely the concept of average speed which we have used so far in our work with the gas equation.

DISTRIBUTION OF THE SPEED OF MOLECULES

When we derived the gas equation, we assumed among other things that the molecules we studied would travel without collisions from one wall to the other. This assumption we have already found unacceptable in the discussion of diffusion and **Brownian motion, though** it does not invalidate the gas equation, which fits a number of experimental observations very nicely. The very simple model helps also with more complex situations if we make provision for the effects of collisions on the randomly moving molecules.

The number of collisions that occur in even a small sample of gas is, like the number of molecules in it, an unthinkably large number. This means that billions of collisions occur nearly simultaneously. There are so many that for every collision which has some effect on two molecules, there is another one at the same instant which has almost exactly the opposite effect on two other molecules. For every molecule that increases its speed through collision, another decreases its speed by an equal amount. For every molecule that changes direction to the left through collision, another changes direction to the right by an equal amount. While individual molecules are bumped this way or that, the gas as a whole does not change. The properties that express the average for the entire ensemble of molecules—temperature and pressure—remain constant.

On the other hand, the fact that collisions occur assures that the behavior of single molecules differs greatly throughout the ensemble and from instant to instant. Both momentum and kinetic energy are transferred during collisions, producing a wide range of speeds among the molecules, and these change all the time and after every collision. Nevertheless, because there are so many "opposite and equal" collisions, the result of the many simultaneous collisions leaves the number of very slow, slow, faster, etc., molecules unchanged regardless of what happens to the individual molecules that contribute to the average. This is a perfect case for statistical treatment. The sample is so large that one can give its group properties accurately although the individuals composing the sample behave in quite unpredictable ways. It compares to the situation from which actuaries compute insurance rates. They cannot tell who will have an accident, but with a large enough number of insured, they can predict the number involved in minor collisions, the number in major property-damage accidents, the number of personal-injury cases, etc.

The statistical treatment of speeds among the molecules leads to the results shown in Fig. 11–6, in which the fraction of molecules with a given speed are plotted against various possible speeds from zero to very large. In a given sample of gas, by far the greatest fraction of the molecules has speeds that are clustered near the average. Some few molecules show speeds that differ widely from the average, ranging from zero —a momentary pause in their motions— for a few to many times the average for

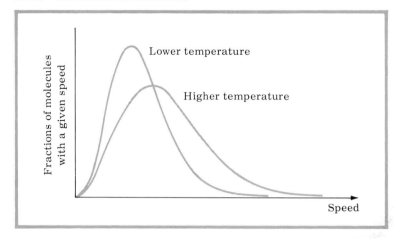

FIG. 11-6

Distribution of speeds of molecules. Molecular speeds vary from zero to very large values, with the largest fraction clustering near the average.

another few. Between the extreme values of the speed and the average, the number in each category rises gradually and smoothly, though the tail of the curve toward high speeds reaches out much farther than the low-speed tail. The figure also shows that the lower the temperature of the gas, the lower the average speed for the group and the more narrowly clustered the speeds of its molecules.

Figure 11–6 gives a calculated distribution of speeds based on a statistical model. It suggests that experiment should find molecules that have every one of the speeds given in the curve, in numbers proportional to those predicted by the curve. This experiment was first carried out by Otto Stern (b. 1888), using the apparatus shown in Fig. 11–7. The apparatus consisted of an evacuated chamber (to minimize collisions) in which there was a furnace to boil mercury. Mercury vapor served as the experimental gas. Some of the mercury molecules, those which happen to move in the direction of the opening to the furnace, escape. They are focused into a thin beam by a cold slit that catches and condenses all other molecules. The thin beam of molecules is then directed at two disks on a rotating shaft which have thin slits cut into

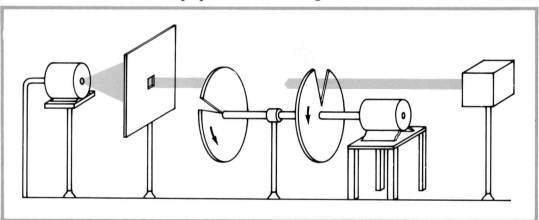

FIG. 11-7

Stern's apparatus for measuring gas speeds. Only those molecules reach the collector which have traveled between the rotating disks in exactly the time in which the second slit rotates in line with the first.

them. These slits are not in line but are slightly displaced from one another. To pass through both slits, a molecule must travel the distance between them in exactly the time it takes the second slit to rotate into the path of the beam. From the distance between slits and the rate of rotation of the disks, one can then calculate the speed of the molecules.

To collect molecules with different speeds, the rate of rotation of the disks is changed. By weighing the mercury that passes through at many different rates of rotation, one obtains the fraction of the molecules that travels with each of the many molecular speeds. This, then, gives the desired distribution. Stern's experiment confirmed the distribution curve and the average speed calculated from Eq. 11–11.

AVOGADRO'S HYPOTHESIS

One further deduction from the gas equation is of interest, particularly for our later discussion of chemistry, to which it made a major contribution. In 1811, long before the kinetic theory had been developed and its consequences worked out mathematically, the Italian physicist Amedeo Avogadro (1776–1856) suggested that *equal volumes of two gases, when measured at the same temperature and pressure, contain the same number of molecules.* This was a step toward counting molecules, immeasurably small though they are. While the hypothesis was based on experiments with the chemical reactions of gases, it is also a direct consequence of the gas equation.

Equation 11–6 was derived without reference to any specific gas. It is therefore true of all gases. If we designate by P_1, V_1, etc., the pressure, volume, etc., of one gas, and by P_2, V_2, etc., the corresponding properties of a second gas, then we can write for the two gases:

$$P_1 V_1 = \tfrac{1}{3} n_1 m_1 \bar{v}_1{}^2$$
and
$$P_2 V_2 = \tfrac{1}{3} n_2 m_2 \bar{v}_2{}^2 \qquad (11\text{--}12)$$

Avogadro's hypothesis requires equal volumes ($V_1 = V_2$) measured at equal pressures ($P_1 = P_2$). These two conditions permit us to equate

$$\tfrac{1}{3} n_1 m_1 \bar{v}_1{}^2 = \tfrac{1}{3} n_2 m_2 \bar{v}_2{}^2 \qquad (11\text{--}13)$$

Furthermore, at equal temperatures, $\tfrac{1}{2} m_1 \bar{v}_1{}^2 = \tfrac{1}{2} m_2 \bar{v}_2{}^2$. This last condition when combined with Eq. 11–13 leads to

$$n_1 = n_2 \qquad (11\text{--}14)$$

or equal numbers of molecules in the two gases. If the conditions of Avogadro's hypothesis are met, the gas equation gives the result he predicted.

NONIDEALITY

We began this chapter with a very simple model of gases and have slowly, step by step, refined it by adding more complex features. We shall continue this procedure now by correcting still another of the assumptions. This time we begin by examining the experimental data somewhat more in detail, rather than the model.

The gas equation fully corresponds with Boyle's and Charles's laws, both of which resulted from experiments. However, when Boyle (about 1660) and Charles (about 1790) made their discoveries, experimental technique was crude and limited. Their accuracy was relatively poor; really high temperatures and really high pressures were unknown and impossible to achieve in the laboratory. Hence the laws and the gas equation describe gas behavior only with limited accuracy and under a limited range of conditions. Modern accurate measurements, especially at extreme temperatures and pressures, show that there are differences between the calculated and measured properties of gases. The gas laws and the gas equation are approximately correct, and when the pressure is very low and the temperature moderate, they become almost exactly correct. The gas equation is an idealized statement based on an idealized model of gas behavior. It is therefore called the *ideal gas law*. Actual gases deviate somewhat from the calculated behavior because there are aspects of molecular interaction which were ignored when the ideal gas equation was derived from the simplified model.

A clue to the nature of the simplification that distinguishes the ideal from the real gases is the fact that the ideal gas law is approximately correct at low pressures but becomes less acceptable at higher pressures. Factors that operate at high but not at low pressures must be responsible for the deviations. The most obvious difference between the two is that at high pressures molecules are crowded together, at low pressures they are far apart. The unoccupied space between molecules, the *free volume*, shrinks as pressure pushes them together. This has an effect on the collisions molecules make with each other and with the walls.

When molecules are far apart, the free volume is large and each has nearly the entire container to itself. But when they are crowded together, much of the space is taken up by other molecules. It will appear to them as if the container had shrunk, much as a ballroom seems to shrink to the size of a postage stamp when crowded with dancers. As a result, when molecules are crowded together, the molecules near the walls are continually bounced back against the walls, far more often than predicted by the simple model of the ideal gas law. The product of *PV* is not constant, as given by Boyle's law, but becomes larger when the molecules are compressed. Another way of expressing this is to say that as the free volume decreases, the gas becomes less compressible.

A second correction to the ideal gas law arises from attractions between molecules. When we derived the ideal gas equation, we neglected attractive forces and assumed that molecules travel about the box unaware of and unimpeded by each other. But we know that molecules stick together in solids and liquids. These attractions do not disappear completely just because the molecules are far apart in the gas.

Because molecules are attracted to one another, they stick a bit whenever they happen to collide. Sticking reduces the time available for further travel and for collisions with the walls. Fewer collisions in turn mean a lower pressure. The second correction, thus, is opposite to the first. It is observed as a lower pressure and greater compressibility of the gas. The two effects do not cancel. Both are relatively unimportant, however, at very low pressures when molecules are too far apart to crowd and collisions too few to make sticking appreciable.

LIQUIDS AND SOLIDS

At low temperatures the molecules of a gas stick temporarily because of intermolecular attractive forces though the kinetic energy of random motion of the molecules is sufficiently great to break the molecules apart again. But if the gas is cooled further still, the brief but "sticky" collisions are turned into more permanent aggregations of the molecules. The gas condenses to a liquid. This argument suggests that a liquid can be thought of as a special kind of gas, one in which the molecules have insufficient kinetic energy to overcome intermolecular attractive forces although they still move about in the vicinity of one another. Their motions now resemble those of a person caught in a crowd. He moves in one direction, finds his path blocked by someone, tries another direction, perhaps is blocked again, finally sees a small hole and slips through it only to find that the hole has closed and he must again find an opening to let him progress. The molecules in a liquid, too, are caught in a loose cage formed by surrounding molecules. They, too, bounce back and forth until, by chance, a small hole has opened and they can slip into another, similar cage. Since they are still moving randomly, the ideas in terms of which we expressed heat and temperature still apply. The average of the kinetic energy of the random oscillations of the molecules expresses the temperature of the liquid. The heat which the liquid contains is the sum total of the kinetic energies of the random motions of all the molecules.

The random oscillations of the molecules within "cages" allow us to explain the observed expansion of liquids when they are heated. A higher temperature means more energetic random motions. Hence each molecule bumps its neighbors harder and provides a somewhat larger cage for itself. But larger cages mean more space between the molecules and, therefore, a greater volume occupied by the liquid as a whole. This property makes liquids useful in thermometers.

Intermolecular attractions are responsible, too, for the heat of vaporization, the fairly large amount of heat needed to convert a liquid to its vapor without changing the temperature. Energy is required to overcome the attractive forces when molecules are separated from one another. This energy serves only to pull them apart. It has no effect on the kinetic energy of their random motions. We can think of liquid molecules as links in a chain. Much energy is required to break the links. But breaking alone does not cause them to fly apart. We have to throw the links—supply more energy still—in order to give them kinetic energy. In the same way, the heat of vaporization simply separates molecules. To increase the temperature of the vapor requires more energy still. That the heat of vaporization of most liquids is fairly large indicates that the forces of attraction between molecules are generally quite strong. This heat is in turn given off when gas molecules aggregate to form liquids.

The change from liquid to solid, which occurs when a liquid is cooled below its freezing point, is similar to the change from gas to liquid. As the liquid cools, the cage surrounding each molecule draws tighter because the random motions become less energetic. Finally, on freezing, the cage becomes rigid and the molecules align themselves in the ordered, crystalline pattern. Now each molecule is definitely located at a fixed spot in the crystal lattice and its neighbors, too, occupy definite positions around it. The motions of the molecules are not stopped—there is heat in the crystal at any temperature above absolute zero—but they are now restricted to bouncing back and forth within the rigid walls formed by their neighbors. The best way to describe the motions is as vibrations about the crystal-lattice position. In solids temperature and heat are, respectively, the average kinetic energy and the sum total of the kinetic energies of the random vibrational motions of the molecules about their positions in the crystal lattice.

When a solid melts, energy is required to liberate molecules from the rigid cages of the solid into the looser, more indefinite cages of the liquid. The melting of a crystal is accompanied by the absorption of some heat, the heat of fusion, which serves to break down the crystal pattern only and does not increase the kinetic energy of random motion of the molecules. Hence, heat of fusion is absorbed without causing an increase of temperature. The reverse process, the crystallization of the liquid, liberates an equal amount of heat, also without changing the temperature.

VAPOR PRESSURE

We have treated the condensation of gases as if it were dependent only on the attractive forces between the molecules and the energy of their random motions. This is not strictly the case. The number of molecules which can easily be assembled to form a droplet affects the condensation point too. The pressure, therefore, is also involved. The lower the pressure, the lower the condensation temperature; this means that the less crowded the molecules, the more feeble their motions have to become before they stick together. Moreover, since molecular speeds are distributed over a wide range, what is true of some molecules is not true of all. Slower molecules can condense before all do; faster molecules can remain gaseous when the bulk of the molecules has condensed. The distribution of speeds enters directly into evaporation and condensation.

Let us examine in detail how a liquid changes to a gas. The liquid is an aggregation of molecules close to one another and held together by intermolecular forces of attraction. To change to the gaseous state, the molecules must have enough kinetic energy to overcome the attractive forces. Now the surface of the liquid, where evaporation occurs, consists of a large number of molecules in random but restricted motion. At any instant some of the surface molecules have kinetic energies far in excess of the average, some much less. Since there are so many on the surface, there are a number that have more than enough kinetic energy to break away from the attractions of their neighbors even before the boiling point is reached. If these molecules happen to be directed downward or sideways in their motions, they bump into neighbors and lose part of their excess energy by collision. But if they happen to be directed upward from the surface, they meet no resistance and break away from the liquid. Because there are some highly energetic molecules in the distribution at every temperature, this happens even in relatively cool liquids and among the vibrating molecules of solids. There are always some molecules breaking away from the condensed phase. It means that liquids and solids are constantly evaporating, more rapidly when hot, more slowly when cold.

The fact that during evaporation the fastest molecules leave explains how evaporating moisture cools the skin. Since the most energetic molecules leave, the average kinetic energy of those remaining is somewhat lower than before. A lower average kinetic energy is a lower temperature. The liquid has cooled. On hot days this effect cools the body through the evaporation of perspiration. It is also applied commercially to freeze some liquids.

Why, if all liquids and solids evaporate, hasn't all matter turned to gas? To some extent this happens. Water left overnight in an uncovered glass evaporates. Mothballs in clothing bags also evaporate, though it takes several months. But not all substances evaporate as quickly. In a glass of water there are several million billion billions of molecules. To evaporate overnight, about 100 billion billion of them must break away each second. That is a fairly furious pace. If only 10 broke away each second, evaporation would take about a million billion years, 100 thousand times —not just 100,000 years—longer than the earth has presumably existed. Unless evaporation occurs very rapidly, it is hardly noticed in a lifetime. But in addition, molecules do not only break away from the surface of a liquid or solid; they also settle there. Water in a covered glass does not evaporate because molecules both break away from the liquid and return.

If a liquid is kept in a totally enclosed container, the evaporated molecules cannot escape. Instead they bounce around in the vapor space above the liquid as do all gaseous molecules. They collide with one another, with the walls of the container, and sometimes with the surface of the liquid. There they are attracted by their neighbors and stick. The number that returns to the liquid depends on the number in the vapor space. If there are many molecules there, many return; if few, few return.

When a liquid is poured into a bottle and it is closed, evaporation begins. A few molecules reach the vapor state, and a small fraction returns to the liquid. With time, additional evaporation fills the vapor space with molecules and increases the number that bounce back into the liquid. Ultimately an equilibrium is set up. The

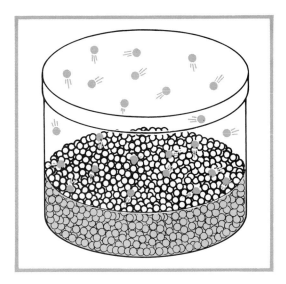

FIG. 11-8

Equilibrium between evaporation of a liquid and condensation of its vapor in a closed container. The rate at which vapor molecules bump into the liquid and settle there equals the rate at which the most energetic molecules break away from the liquid surface and enter the vapor space.

number of molecules reaching the vapor state each second is exactly equal to the number that returns to the liquid. No further net evaporation occurs. Since the number breaking away from the liquid depends on the kinetic energy to overcome attractions, the point at which equilibrium is established depends on the temperature. At a high temperature, many molecules have sufficient energy to evaporate. This means that at equilibrium the vapor space must be crowded with molecules so that many also bounce back into the liquid. At a low temperature, on the other hand, fewer molecules have enough energy to escape the liquid. At equilibrium at a lower temperature, fewer return and the vapor space contains fewer molecules.

Suppose a liquid at 40°C is in equilibrium with its vapor. A certain number of molecules escapes the liquid each second; a like number returns. Suddenly the liquid is chilled. Fewer molecules on the liquid surface are now energetic enough to escape,

but the number in the vapor space is not changed by the sudden change in temperature. The same number as before—greater than that now escaping—returns to the liquid. This depletes the number in the vapor space. As fewer molecules remain in the vapor, the rate of return to the liquid is slowed up. Thereby, the rate of return is brought back into equilibrium with the slower rate of escape at the lower temperature. In the new equilibrium, fewer molecules leave the liquid and fewer also return. The converse is the case if the liquid is suddenly heated. Then the rate of escape increases until, with the increasing number of molecules in the vapor space, the number returning again catches up with the greater number escaping. There is, at each temperature, a fixed rate of escape and return.

The equilibrium rate can be measured because the number of molecules returning is the number striking the liquid surface. According to the kinetic theory, the number of molecules striking a surface is related to the pressure on that surface. Therefore the pressure exerted by the vapor, called the *vapor pressure of the liquid*, measures the equilibrium rate of escape and return. Because for a given liquid the exchange rate between liquid and vapor depends only on the temperature, the vapor pressure also depends only on the temperature. Some typical vapor-pressure curves are shown in Fig. 11–9.

Vapor pressure is the cause of a number of familiar phenomena. Relative humidity in weather forecasting, for instance, describes the fact that air can hold only a limited amount of moisture, an amount equal to the number of molecules that exactly produce the vapor pressure of water at that temperature. Since the vapor pressure is dependent on the temperature, warm air can hold more moisture than cool air. If the temperature suddenly drops on a humid day, there may be more water molecules in the air than the number that produce the vapor pressure at the lower

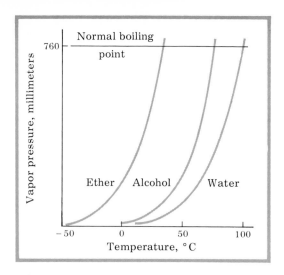

FIG. 11-9

Vapor-pressure curves for water, ethyl alcohol, and ether.

temperature. Some condense, usually as liquid droplets of fog. The equilibrium between liquid and vapor is also responsible for the greater discomfort we experience on humid days. With nearly as many molecules in the air as produce the vapor pressure, evaporation from the skin is balanced by settling on the skin. Consequently, we lose the cooling effect of rapid net evaporation.

Boiling also is related to vapor pressure. At every temperature, a liquid loses some of its molecules which exert a pressure upward equal to the vapor pressure of the downward-returning molecules. This pressure increases as the temperature of the liquid increases. When the vapor pressure of a liquid being heated becomes equal to, or just infinitesimally larger than, the pressure of the atmosphere above it, the escaping molecules sweep the air before them and rapidly escape from the liquid. In an open container the liquid is then rapidly converted into vapor and boils away. *The boiling point is the temperature at which the vapor pressure equals* (or barely exceeds) *external pressure.* Water reaches this vapor pressure (1 atm) at 100°C. Ether, which is more volatile, at 35°C;

alcohol at 78°C. But the boiling point is not constant. On the top of a high mountain, where atmospheric pressure is much less than 1 atm, water boils at a lower temperature. In a pressure cooker in which, as the name implies, the pressure is greater, the boiling point is reached at a higher temperature. This explains why foods cook more rapidly in a pressure cooker, more slowly on top of mountains. The chemical reactions which we call cooking occur much faster at higher temperatures. Foods cook more quickly in the hotter pressure cooker, more slowly in the cooler boiling water of mountain climbers (who probably would not carry pressure cookers).

FURTHER COMMENTS ON SCIENTIFIC METHOD

While we have by no means exhausted the possibilities of using the kinetic theory to explain familiar phenomena, we stop at this point with a few additional comments on the methods of explanation used in this chapter. This chapter illustrates very clearly a few of the logical steps by which man achieves an understanding of the world and which are, therefore, foundations of scientific progress. Earlier in the chapter we remarked about the role of models and deductions from models. We shall not repeat it here. But there was another logical process we followed in our explanations.

We began the chapter by assuming the simplest picture of gases we could devise: one molecule, a cubic box, and an average velocity. This simple, indeed highly oversimplified model served adequately to describe a variety of observations. But its usefulness was limited and gradually, as the occasion demanded, we added to it, made it more sophisticated. To explain diffusion, we had to consider not one but all the molecules in the box and the collisions they make with one another. To contrast real gases with the ideal gas law, we added intermolecular attractions and considered explicitly the space taken up by the little molecules and the free volume. Finally, to explain vapor pressure and boiling, we shifted attention from the average speed and treated fast and slow molecules independently. We used a very simple model at first, to become approximately familiar with the behavior of gases, then slowly added refinements as they were needed to explain more complex phenomena. We might have continued to more recent work in this field which has added further refinements in order to make the kinetic theory a still more useful tool of the understanding.

The process of approximating observed behavior with a rough explanation, one which because of its roughness has the virtue of simplicity, and then gradually refining it and making it more complex and more powerful is another foundation of scientific procedure. We have already seen it in Greek cosmology, which began with circular orbits for planets, then added epicycles, finally eccentrics. Though this avenue of refinement ultimately proved unsatisfactory, Kepler's substitution of ellipses for circles is only a different, mathematically more sophisticated refinement. We saw this process also in Galileo's work when he suggested the simple idea that bodies fall at the same rate while conceding that corrections might have to be made for friction. We shall see it again later in this book, too. But the process is not limited to the study of the physical universe. Other branches of scholarship use the same process. In economics the free market is only a rough, first approximation, as is the law of supply and demand. In psychology the stimulus-response model of learning is a first approximation only. All knowledge progresses, at times, by the slow steps of making earlier, simplified ideas successively more sophisticated and more powerful in their insight.

Questions and Problems

1. Perform the algebraic steps that lead from Eq. 11–13 to Eq. 11–14.

2. Use a model of moving molecules to explain (a) gas pressure, (b) heat, (c) temperature, (d) increase of gas pressure on heating, (e) vapor pressure, (f) heat of vaporization, (g) Brownian motion, (h) expansion of solids on heating.

3. Can the ideal gas condense to a liquid? Explain.

4. Starting with Eq. 11–5, demonstrate (a) Boyle's law, (b) Charles's law, (c) Avogadro's hypothesis, (d) Graham's law of diffusion.

5. Why are real gases less compressible than the ideal gas? Under what conditions is this important? Why are gases more compressible than the ideal gas? Under what conditions is this most important?

6. Real gases approximate ideal behavior as their pressure becomes exceedingly small. How does the condition of low pressure approach the assumption on which the ideal gas is based?

7. Describe the character of an assembly of molecules in the solid state and trace the changes that occur as heat is added and it ultimately changes into a gas.

8. When two gases are mixed, the pressure of the mixture is the sum of the pressure of each individual gas in the same container. Explain, using the model of the kinetic theory of gases.

9. If a closed vessel with water is attached to a vacuum line, the water at first appears to boil and then ice crystals form. Explain both observations.

10. A refrigerator is cooled by the evaporation of a liquid under pressure in the cooling coils. Explain.

11. The gas formed in the process described in Question 10 is compressed outside the refrigeration compartment and forms a liquid again. Explain. It becomes hot on compression and condensation. Explain.

12. Ethyl amine, which has the odor of decaying fish, travels at a rate of about 300 meters/sec. Yet if one opens a container of ethyl amine at one end of a room it does not become noticeable at the other end for several minutes. Explain.

13. Explain how mothballs evaporate without forming a liquid.

14. The weight of methane and sulfur dioxide, measured at 27°C and 1 atm pressure, are 1.26 grams/liter and 5.04 grams/liter. Which diffuses faster, and in what ratio?

15. Things cooking on a stove burn only after the pot runs dry. Explain.

16. The collision between molecules in a gas must occur without friction. What consequences can you predict if friction intervened to slow the molecules? Does it make sense to ask about friction between the molecules of a gas? Explain.

Suggestions for Further Reading

Some of the texts listed at the end of Chap. 10 also serve as references for this chapter:

Christiansen, G. S., and Paul H. Barrett: *Structure and Change*, W. H. Freeman and Company, San Francisco, 1960. Chapter 12.

Physical Science Study Committee: *Physics*, D. C. Heath and Company, Boston, 1960. Chapter 26.

Rogers, Eric M.: *Physics for the Inquiring Mind*, Princeton University Press, Princeton, N. J., 1960. Chapters 25 and 30.

Original contributions to the understanding of heat and gases are in:

Brush, Stephen G.: *Kinetic Theory*, vol. 1, *The Nature of Gases and of Heat*, Pergamon Press, New York, 1965 (paperback).

Chapter 12

Waves and Sound

The distinction between kinetic energy and heat, as we saw in the previous chapter, is the distinction between coordinated motion, all molecules moving together in the same direction, and random motion, all molecules moving individually in different directions. In the former there is net transport of matter; in the latter no net transport occurs. There is still another possibility, coordinated motion without net transport of matter, such as that which occurs in the toy called the Slinky (Fig. 12–1). The turns of the Slinky move with regularity as energy imparted at one end is carried to the other, but there is no net transport of matter because the turns wiggle back after wiggling forth, in a wavelike manner. Indeed, this is the characteristic of wave motion—transport of energy without transport of matter. Similar wavelike

FIG. 12-1

A Slinky. A group of turns can be compressed at one end and the compression made to move to the other end without a net transport of turns. (Courtesy James Industries, Inc., Hollidaysburg, Pa.)

motion of molecules, when it strikes our ears, is sensed as sound. In sound waves, molecules bounce back and forth and set up zones of compression and decompression that move outward from the source.

WAVES

Figure 12–2 shows two waves. Note that the curves represents regular and recurring displacements from some mid-value. Positive displacements are usually called *crests*;

negative displacements, *troughs*. The midpoints between the maxima, the points of zero displacement, are the *nodes*. The distance between successive crests or successive troughs is the *wavelength* of the wave, designated by the Greek letter lambda, λ. The extent of displacement of the maximum of the crest, or the minimum of the trough, is the *amplitude* of the wave.

Waves such as those in Fig. 12–2 could be the instantaneous cross section through a water wave, or a snapshot of a jerked rope or of a plucked string. In this sense they are a photographic representation of nature. It can also represent the turns of a Slinky or the molecules of air carrying sound waves. In that case, the crests represent points where the turns of the Slinky or the molecules of air are crowded together while the troughs represent points where they are spread apart. In both cases, the figure depicts the waves standing at some instant of time. Since waves carry energy through space, we must relate this standing wave to its motion.

The concept *frequency* relates the instantaneous picture of a wave to its motion. Frequency, n, is defined as the number of vibrations per second. In the case of a vibrating string, it is the number of times per second the string oscillates back and forth. In the case of water or sound waves, it is the number of complete waves which move past some point per second. The fre-

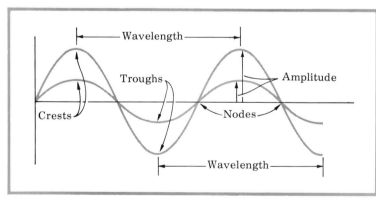

Diagram of a wave.

FIG. 12-2

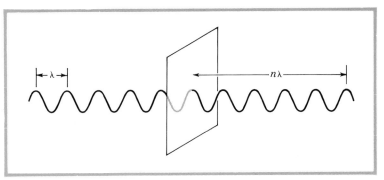

The relationship between wavelength, frequency, and wave velocity. When n waves pass a point each second—frequency equals n—and each is λ cm long, they move a distance of nλ each second. Hence their velocity v equals nλ.

FIG. 12-3

quency of a string and the frequency of the sound wave it produces are equal because each time the string vibrates forward in its oscillations, it compresses the molecules of the air, and each time it moves back, it decompresses them. A sound wave is sent out for each vibration of the string.

The velocity with which a wave travels is given by the product of the frequency and the wavelength.

$$v = n\lambda \qquad (12-1)$$

Consider the five waves in Fig. 12–3. Their length is 5λ. If they move past the screen toward the right in 1 sec, they travel a distance of 5λ in 1 sec; they have a velocity of 5λ. But 5 is the frequency of this group of waves because the five waves pass the dotted line in 1 sec. Hence the velocity of the waves is frequency λ times wavelength *n* as given by the equation.

A distinction is made between waves such as water waves, in which the water molecules travel up and down while the waves travel horizontally along the surface, and waves such as sound waves, in which the molecules travel back and forth, in the same direction as the wave as a whole. The first kind, in which the energy of the wave is transmitted in one direction while the displacements are at right angles to it, is called a *transverse* wave. A jerked rope is another illustration of a transverse wave. The second kind, in which displacements are back and forth parallel to the direction in which energy is transmitted, is called a

longitudinal wave. Sound waves and Slinky waves are longitudinal waves.

There are different requirements for the transmission of transverse and longitudinal waves. Longitudinal waves require only that the medium return to random distribution after the coordinated action of the wave passes by. Transverse waves, on the other hand, require an elastic restoring force, like surface tension or the tautness of the string, to return the displaced particles.

Few objects vibrate as simply as the wave in Fig. 12–2. Instead, they vibrate in complex patterns such as those in Fig. 12–4. Complex waves still have recurring patterns, but there is a sequence of crests and troughs of different widths and amplitudes within each recurring pattern. Fortunately for the analysis of sound, complex waves can be constructed by the addition of the positive and negative displacements of simple waves. This is indicated in Fig. 12–4*a*, which is the complex wave resulting from the addition of two waves of equal amplitude, with one wave half the wavelength of the other. The longest simple wave determines the wavelength of the recurrence of the complex pattern. It is called the *fundamental*. Fig. 12–4*b* is more complex and consists of the fundamental and many other simple waves of different wavelengths and amplitudes.

Since the wavelength of a sound wave determines the pitch we hear while the amplitude represents its strength or loudness, actual sounds consist of a mixture

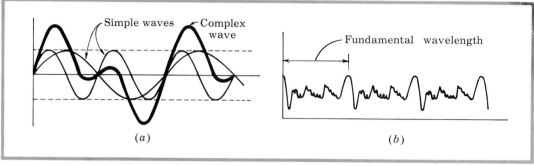

FIG. 12-4

Complex waves. (a) A complex wave that can be analyzed into two simple waves of equal amplitude, one of which has twice the wavelength of the other. (b) A complex wave consisting of many different simple waves of different frequencies and different amplitudes.

of several notes of different pitch and different loudness added together. It is easier to analyze the diagrams of waves by means of wavelength, but frequencies are more commonly used in discussing sound. The two are related by Eq. 12–1. Since all wavelengths of sound travel with the same velocity, long wavelength sounds have a low frequency while short wavelengths have higher frequencies. In a complex sound, the fundamental has the lowest frequency and the other vibrations which add to it have higher frequencies.

There are four separate aspects to the topic of sound: first, the production of sound by some vibrating medium; second, the transmission of the vibrations by means of molecules that collide with the source, where they are compressed and decompressed by its vibrations and spread its energy in waves; third, the sensing of the oscillations in the transmitting medium, usually by the ear; ultimately, the transmission of the sensation from the eardrum through the bones of the ear to the cochlea and, via the nerves, to the brain. Of these four steps, all but the last are part of the domain of physics (the last is the concern of physiology), and we shall take them up one at a time. However, we shall consider them from a physiological-psychological point of view: What sound is regarded as music and what sound as noise?

SOUND PRODUCTION

Sources that produce audible sound oscillate between about 16 and about 16,000 vibrations per second. We may notice lower-frequency vibrations through our sense of touch but not as sound; higher-frequency vibrations are too rapid for the tactile sensors or the ear, and we are unaware of the existence of the waves in the air. The upper limits of sensation of some animals are much higher. Dog whistles produce high-frequency vibrations, audible to dogs but not to man. Bats have been found to emit vibrations in the neighborhood of 50,000 vibrations/sec and to navigate by the echoes from them.

We can examine a stretched string to determine the characteristics of one common group of sound producers. First of all we note that a string can vibrate in many different ways, called *modes*. It can vibrate as a whole (Fig. 12–5a); in two parts (12–5b); three parts; etc. There is only one restriction on the number of possible modes of vibration: the ends of the string must be at a node. Normally a string vibrates in several modes simultaneously and thus vibrates in, and emits, a complex wave pattern. Which specific frequencies are produced, whether the fundamental is middle C (about 260 vibrations/sec) or A (440 vibrations/sec) depends on the length, thickness, and tension in the string. Shorter, thinner, and tighter strings produce higher sounds. But regardless of where on the scale the fundamental tone falls, the other frequencies produced are whole-number multiples of that fundamental frequency. Thus, if the string is tuned to emit middle A, 440 vibrations/sec, its other vibrations will be 880 vibrations/ sec, 1,320 vibrations/sec, 1,760 vibrations/ sec, etc. These other frequencies are called the *harmonics* of the fundamental tone.

From the point of view of music, this fact is of the utmost significance in three different senses. First, the physiology and psychology of sound and hearing are such that our brain recognizes certain *frequency ratios* as harmonious or musical. It will not be surprising that the frequency ratios which sound pleasing, the *chords* of the musical scale, include the ratios of the harmonics. Table 12–1 gives the frequencies of the notes of three octaves of the scale and the frequency ratios of the major chords. We can see that a string vibrating in its fundamental mode and harmonics contains a number of chords that give the sound a rich and pleasing character. Through the combination of these chords, in various strengths, the characteristic *timbre* of a note is produced.

Second, our ear acts very much like the string. If a pure sound of 440 vibrations/sec —produced perhaps by a tuning fork—impinges on our ear, the eardrum absorbs the energy and begins to vibrate in time with the absorbed frequency. But it vibrates not only at that frequency but also in its harmonics. Thus the harmonics of the source are produced by the ear in the process of hearing. (Our ear produces its own music.)

Finally, the manner in which the sound is excited—the skill of the violinist, for instance—produces a slightly different mixture of amplitudes of the fundamental tone and its harmonics. Slightly different positions of the bow on the string and differences in the manner of stroking change the exact character of the complex wave

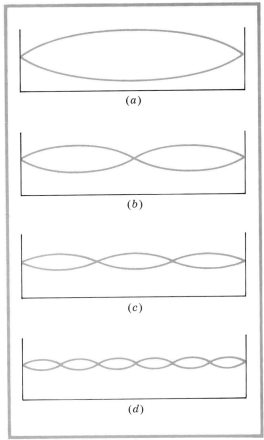

FIG. 12-5

Possible modes of vibration of a string. A string can vibrate as a whole; in two parts; three parts; etc. There is only one restriction: the ends must be at a node.

and, thereby, the relative amounts of energy emitted by the fundamental tone and its harmonics. Thus the manner of exciting the vibrations causes yet other changes in the timbre of the note.

This is the basis of the physics of music. It is determined by our psychology, which considers as "musical" sources that vibrate in a fundamental mode with whole-number multiple harmonics. Our eardrum has similar vibrational characteristics and thus helps create its own music. Differences among different musical sounds of equal pitch result chiefly from different mixtures of the fundamental mode and harmonics in the complex wave.

TABLE 12-1

Frequency ratios of notes and chords of the musical scale

	FREQUENCY RATIOS				
	To low C	To middle C	To high C	Harmonics of low C	Chords
C	8:1	4	2	*	
B	15/2	15/4	15/8		
A	20/3	10/3	5/3		
G	6:1	3	3/2	*	
F	16/3	8/3	4/3		
E	5:1	5/2	5/4	*	
D	9/2	9/4	9/8		
C	4:1	2	1	*	
B	15/4	15/8			
A	10/3	5/3			
G	3:1	3/2		*	
F	8/3	4/3			
E	5/2	5/4			
D	9/4	9/8			
C	2:1	1		*	
B	15/8				
A	5/3				
G	3/2				
F	4/3				
E	5/4				
D	9/8				
C	1			*	

Chords (grouped by braces): Octave 2:1; Major third 5:4; Fifth 3:2; Minor sixth 8:5; Minor third 6:5; Fourth 4:3; Major sixth 5:3; Twelfth 3:1.

Music is distinguished from noise by the whole-number multiple characteristic. Other sound-producing objects, like pots and pans, drums and cymbals, doors and typewriters, also vibrate in a fundamental and other modes giving rise to complex waves, but the frequencies of the noise vibrations are not whole-number multiples of one another. Their ratios are not interpreted as musical by our ears and brains.

Sound-producing objects—whether the sound is music or noise—need not be one-dimensional like strings. Drums and cymbals can be regarded as surfaces that produce a reasonably musical sound; pots are surfaces that produce noise. The music of the xylophone is produced by solid bars whereas a slamming door, another solid bar, produces noise. Of this group, the strings produce the most "musical" sounds. They are matched in musical quality by

air cavities, such as those in horns and reed instruments. In these the air in a long tube is set to vibrating with frequencies determined by the length of the tube. This arrangement, too, produces a set of frequencies which consist of a fundamental note and its harmonics.

Our discussion has been far too brief for this very interesting and culturally important topic (consider the different tonal scales of the Orient or of some primitive tribes; consider the important role of music in religion; in teen-age culture; in Indian culture; in war; etc.). Nevertheless, we shall leave the question of music versus noise at this point and turn our attention to the transmission of sound waves. Let us summarize:

1. Our ears and brain consider a set of vibrations "musical" if they consist of a fundamental frequency and its harmonics.

2. Strings and air cavities, when set in vibration, produce such musical sounds. Other vibrators produce frequencies which are not in whole-number ratios and which are sensed as noise.

3. The exact quality or timbre of a musical sound depends on the relative strength of the fundamental note and of the harmonics. The mixture of frequencies produced by any given instrument depends on the nature of the vibrating medium, the strength of the excitation, and even the exact manner of excitation.

4. Finally we should note that vibrations, after being excited, die out. The different frequencies do not do so equally rapidly. Thus the mixture of frequencies of the sound changes with time.

TRANSMISSION OF SOUND

Unless focused in some manner, sound waves travel outward in all directions from their source. It is usually convenient to think of single pencils or rays—"waves"— of sound traveling in straight lines through a uniform medium although we know that sound can travel around corners. The medium of transmission need not be air, though it must, of course, contain matter since sound transmission is through molecular compression and decompression. Indeed, sound travels much more rapidly through solids and liquids. Since in its outward travel a given amount of sound energy passes through larger and larger spheres, the intensity falls off with distance. The area over which a given number of sound waves are spread increases as r^2 since the area of a sphere is $4\pi r^2$. Hence the intensity of the sound decreases as $1/r^2$ (Fig. 12–6).

On striking objects of different material, sound waves may do one of three things: they may be reflected; they may be absorbed; or they may be transmitted by the different material, in which case, typically, their direction of propagation and speed of transmission is changed. The last phenomenon, called *refraction*, is much more easily

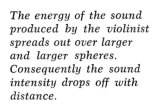

The energy of the sound produced by the violinist spreads out over larger and larger spheres. Consequently the sound intensity drops off with distance.

FIG. 12-6

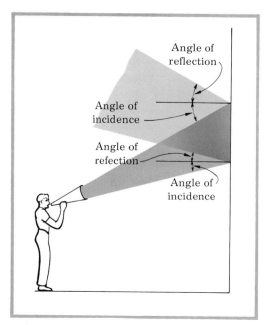

Angle of reflection

Angle of incidence

Angle of refection

Angle of incidence

FIG. 12-7

When sound is reflected from a surface, the angle of incidence equals the angle of reflection.

observed with light waves and will be discussed in that context. Absorption occurs in materials which can easily absorb and then transform and dissipate the energy of the sound waves. Porous and irregular materials tend to be good absorbers. *Reflection* of sound, best illustrated by echoes, is a phenomenon which deserves a few additional comments although it must be stressed that it is not possible to predict, on the basis of general principles, which of the three possibilities will occur in any given case. Typically, some of the sound energy is reflected when a wave strikes a different medium and some enters the new medium. There it may be refracted or simply absorbed and dissipated. The relative amounts of each must be separately determined by direct measurements.

It is a characteristic of reflection that the *angle of incidence* of the sound wave equals the *angle of reflection*, as shown in Fig. 12–7. This gives rise to a number of interesting effects. (All of these are more

familiar in the case of light, which is also energy carried by waves.)

As Fig. 12–8 shows, sound can be focused or directed by using a reflecting surface of the proper geometry; that is, using the principle that the angle of incidence equals the angle of reflection. Thus sound "mirrors" can be constructed, which act like the reflectors in automobile headlights, although this effect is rarely of practical importance and its engineering applications are few. But there are buildings whose architecture, usually without plan, has created points where sound is focused. In some restaurants certain tables are acoustically so located that even whispered conversation from some quite distant tables becomes distinct because sound waves from one happen to be focused on the other. While modern soundproofing materials have made this very rare, there are famous public buildings known for their "whispering galleries." Another sound mirror which the author has personally experienced is a telescope dome. It focuses sound so that voices inaudible on the roof next to the dome become quite distinct and audible. The many sound waves that converge because of the mirror action add to produce compressions and decompressions strong enough to be audible.

The design of auditoriums requires careful attention to the mirror effect because sounds from the stage reach the seats both directly and after reflection from the walls. It is clear that the focusing of sound at particular places in the auditorium is undesirable, especially if the focused sound comes only from particular spots on the stage. Poor design could send more than a balanced share of the drums to some seats, or the bugles could literally blast some of the audience with sound energy. On the other hand, reflection can also lead to dead spots, where parts of the orchestra are muffled by the reverse of the reinforcement of energy discussed above.

In the focusing effect, sound waves converge at a spot and the amplitudes of their

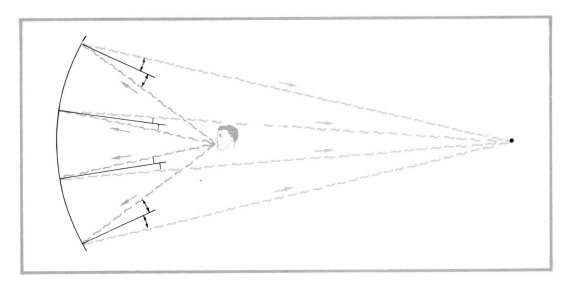

FIG. 12-8

Because the angle of incidence equals the angle of reflection when sound is reflected, certain surfaces act as sound mirrors. The sound waves spread out from the mouth and are reflected by the curved wall. Its curvature is such that the waves are then focused on a point behind the speaker where all the sound energy gathers. Hence the sound is as audible there as next to the speaker.

vibrations add to increase intensity. This requires that the waves arrive at the same time—*in phase*—such that the compression part of each wave coincides with the compressions from other waves and that the decompressions also coincide (see Fig. 12–9). Now it is entirely possible that two waves arrive *out of phase*, that the compression of one exactly meets the decompression of the other. In this case, the energy they carry acts in opposite senses; addition results in zero displacement. The two waves destroy each other and no sound arrives. This happens, for instance, if the

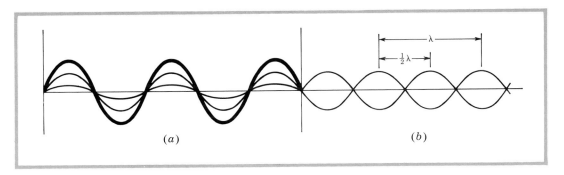

FIG. 12-9

Addition of waves. (a) If two waves are in phase so that crests coincide with crests and troughs coincide with troughs, the energy of the two waves adds to produce a wave of greater amplitude. (b) If two waves arrive out of phase so that crests and troughs do not coincide, their energies cancel. Complete destruction occurs when two waves are exactly ½λ out of phase.

paths of the two waves differ in length so that one arrives ½λ after the other. This is the cause of dead spots in an auditorium.

There is another aspect of the addition of sound waves which is quite common, important, and easily produced. Suppose two tuning forks of nearly identical frequency are struck simultaneously—say forks of 18 and 20 vibrations/sec. At the instant they are struck, both begin with a crest followed by trough in phase. Their energy reinforces as a somewhat discordant tone. But because of the slightly different frequencies, crests and troughs move out of phase (Fig. 12–10) and very quickly the sum of their displacements becomes zero. Then, again very quickly, crests begin to coincide with crests again and they again reinforce. It can be shown that reinforcement and destruction of sound energy occur for sound with different frequencies as many times per second as the difference in frequency. For tuning forks of 18 and 20 vibrations/ sec, there would be two periods of reinforcement and two periods of destruction per second; the sound would fade out and come in again twice each second.

The phenomenon described above can easily be sensed because the ear can dis-

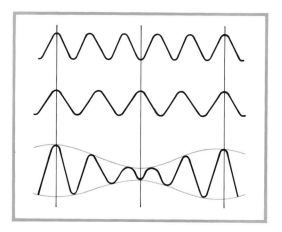

FIG. 12-10.

When two sound waves have slightly different frequencies, their energies reinforce and cancel a few times each second. Their sound is heard fading in and out, a phenomenon called beat tones.

tinguish two changes in sound intensity per second. It is a phenomenon known as *beat tones*, tones of wavering sound intensity which result from the alternate reinforcement and destruction of sound energy from two notes of nearly equal frequency. Any piano, for instance, will produce beat tones from notes in the lowest registers. Beat tones, by the way, contribute to noise. If the frequency difference becomes large enough so that the number of beat tones per second is no longer distinctly recognizable—about four per second for most ears —the alterations in sound energy still occur though the impact on our brains is no longer that of distinct fading in and out of sound. Instead, physiologically and psychologically we sense them as noise. Note also that in the harmonics, the number of beats becomes as large as the fundamental frequency and, therefore, blends in with the full sound produced.

DOPPLER EFFECT

The last significant characteristic of sound we shall discuss relates to changes in pitch, which can be observed when a source of sound moves relative to the detector. For instance, the siren of an approaching police car seems pitched higher than when it moves away. The observation is particularly striking when two trains meet with their horns or whistles blowing. There is a very noticeable drop in the pitch as one locomotive passes an observer in the other train.

A change in pitch heard by the ear means that fewer or more compressions and decompressions per second strike the eardrum than are emitted by the source. How does this happen? Consider again an observer counting (hearing) waves as they pass him by. If a source emits 20 vibrations/sec, 20 complete waves pass the point where he is counting. But now, let him move toward the source during the first

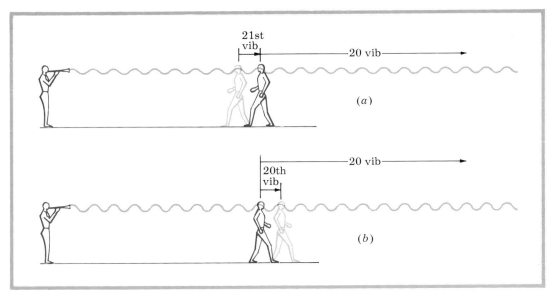

FIG. 12-11

The Doppler effect. If a source vibrates at the rate of 20 vibrations/sec, 20 complete waves pass a standing observer each second. (a) But if the observer moves toward the source, he encounters the twenty-first vibration also during that second and hears a higher frequency. (b) On the other hand, if he moves away from the source during the second, the twentieth vibration does not catch up with him. He encounters fewer than 20 vibrations and hears a lower-frequency sound.

second. He also hears the twenty-first vibration during the first second because he has moved to meet it; it did not have to travel as far to reach his ear although that same vibration still reaches the original observation post at the beginning of the second second. Hence, by moving toward the source, he meets more than 20 vibrations during the first second and he observes a higher-frequency sound. Similarly, if he moves away from the source, the twenty-first vibration which arrives at the original observation post does not find him there but must travel somewhat farther— and longer—to strike his ear. Thus the 20 vibrations preceding it take longer than 1 sec to reach his ear; he hears fewer than 20 vibrations during the first second, a lower-frequency sound. A similar effect is observed when the observer stands still and the source moves. As long as they move *relative to each other,* the observer notes a different frequency from the one emitted.

This phenomenon, which changes the pitch of the sound if source and observer move relative to one another is called the *Doppler effect* after the German physicist Christian Johann Doppler (1803–1853), who explained its cause and gave it quantitative formulation. Since the magnitude of frequency change depends on the relative velocity of observer to source, the Doppler effect can be used to estimate the velocity of a moving source of sound. This is rarely done in the case of sound waves. The Doppler effect occurs with light, too, and is the only tool available to astronomers to determine relative motions of the very distant stars and galaxies. The so-called red shift, which is a shift toward lower frequencies, suggests that a star is receding whereas the blue shift, a shift toward higher frequencies, indicates an approaching star. That the red shift is more pronounced for the more distant galaxies is the basis of the notion of an expanding universe, as we mentioned in Chap. 3; we shall refer to it again in Chap. 24.

Questions and Problems

1. In Chap. 6 we mentioned earthquake P waves and S waves; which are longitudinal and which are transverse? We also stated that P waves travel through any medium; S waves only through solids. Can you explain why?

2. What is required of the medium to transmit transverse waves? Longitudinal waves?

3. Select some chords *not* shown in Table 12–1.

4. Sound travels with a speed of 1,100 ft/sec in air. What is the wavelength of A in air? of middle C? (See page 190 for frequencies.)

5. In water the wavelength of A sharp, 466 vibrations/sec, is about 10 ft. What is the velocity of sound in water? What is the wavelength of middle C in water?

6. What happens to the energy of sound waves absorbed by curtains in a room?

7. The fifth is a chord in which the frequencies of the notes are in the ratio of 3 to 2. The major third has them in the ratio of

5 to 4. Pick the fifth and the major third of every note in the middle octave. Are these chords represented among the harmonics of a note?

8. A piano goes three octaves below middle A. What is the frequency of the lowest A? Can the ear sense the beat tones of that A and the adjacent A sharp?

9. A stone is dropped in a pond. Waves of wavelength 25 cm travel outward at a rate of 60 cm/sec. What is their frequency?

10. Two convertibles travel alongside on a turnpike. One has the radio on. Will the music sound correct or off-key to the passengers in the second?

11. A sound truck playing music is racing down a highway. Does the music sound the same to the driver as to people along the road? Explain.

12. A record player turns at 31 rpm instead of 33 rpm. How does this affect the notes?

Suggestions for Further Reading

An account of wave characteristics may be found in:

Beiser, Arthur: *Basic Concepts of Physics*, Addison-Wesley Publishing Company, Inc., Reading, Mass., 1961. Chapter 5.

Physical Science Study Committee: *Physics*, D. C. Heath and Company, Boston, 1960. Chapters 16 to 18.

Rogers, Eric M.: *Physics for the Inquiring Mind*, Princeton University Press, Princeton, N. J., 1960. Chapter 10.

Books on sound are:

Benade, Arthur H.: *Horns, Strings, and Harmony*, Anchor Books, Doubleday & Company,

Inc., Garden City, N. Y., 1960 (paperback).

A very readable book on the physics of musical instruments.

Van Bergeijk, Willem A., John R. Pierce, and Edward E. David, Jr.: *Waves and the Ear*, Anchor Books, Doubleday & Company, Inc., Garden City, N.Y., 1960 (paperback). Sound waves and how we hear.

An extensive discussion of wave phenomena is:

Kock, Winston E.: *Sound Waves and Light Waves*, Anchor Books, Doubleday & Company, Inc., Garden City, N.Y., 1965 (paperback).

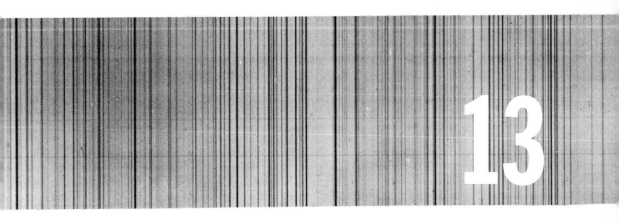

Electricity and Magnetism

In the year 1600 William Gilbert (1544–1603) published an exhaustive study, *On the Magnet,* which described magnets almost as fully as we know them today. He described their poles, their attraction and repulsion, and their alignment in the earth's magnetic field. Gilbert also recognized that static electricity, though it also produces attraction, is different from magnetism. What Gilbert did not recognize, and could not at this time, is that magnetism and electricity are related and that electricity can produce magnetism and magnetism, electricity. That came more than 200 years later, after electricity had been studied in detail. Then it took another 100 years to recognize that even so-called permanent magnets owe their properties to moving electric charges in atoms.

Chapters 13 and 14 discuss the character of electricity and magnetism, separately and then in interaction. In Chap. 19 we shall discuss the structure of atoms and show that they contain moving electric charges that produce magnetic effects.

STATIC ELECTRICITY

When we think of "static," we usually think of the almost painful sparks which fly from our hands to light switches or other metallic objects, particularly on dry winter days. Or we may think of the sparking chains dangling under oil trucks. But more interesting aspects of static electricity are seen when sparks do not fly. When a comb is run through clean, dry hair on a dry day, it can literally make the hair stand on end. It can also lift small bits of paper through a distance of 3 or 4 in. When a toy balloon is rubbed with wool, it will cling to a wall as if glued. All this is produced by static electricity. These simple effects of static electricity were known already to the ancient Greeks, who had performed experiments with rubbed amber. (The Greek word for amber, *elektron*, is the origin of the word electricity.) But understanding of static electricity remained at this rather primitive level until the early part of the eighteenth century, when experimentation in this field increased greatly along with a general spurt

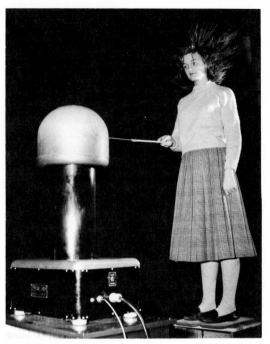

FIG. 13-2

The electric property can be transmitted over long distances provided a conducting material is used and it is insulated from the ground. The static charge of the globe which the girl is touching is transmitted through the rod and the body to the girl's hair. (Courtesy of Museum of Science, Boston)

of interest in all things scientific. Then, in fairly rapid order, it was discovered that:

1. Most materials can be electrified by rubbing; not, however, metals or moist objects.

2. The electric property can be transmitted over long distances through some materials; that is, attractions can occur a long way from the object rubbed. Not all materials conduct, however, nor does conduction occur unless the conductor is kept from contact with the ground.

3. Some electrified objects repel one another. Also, if a bit of metal or some lampblack is attracted to an electrified object, as soon as it touches, attraction changes to repulsion.

The first explanation for these observations was given by C. F. Du Fay (1698–1739), who proposed that all matter contains two

FIG. 13-1

Because of static electricity, a comb that has been rubbed will attract pieces of paper.

electric fluids that attract matter but repel one another. Through rubbing, an excess of one fluid is acquired which can then easily flow through some materials but not others. When properly extended, Du Fay's theory adequately accounts for the observations. Nevertheless it was short-lived because Benjamin Franklin (1706–1790) suggested a simpler theory a few years later. (While Franklin is usually remembered for his many other accomplishments, he was the foremost electrical scientist of his time and was recognized and honored for his work in electricity. He performed many electrical experiments in addition to the famous experiment with the kite. In that experiment he was quite lucky. The lightning bolt attracted by his kite could have killed him as lightning had killed several of his scientific contemporaries.)

Franklin's theory postulates only one electric fluid. An excess of the electric fluid, a *plus* or *positive* amount, constitutes one kind of electricity; a deficiency, a *minus* or *negative* amount, causes the other kind. A condition of balance, or electrical *neutrality,* is the normal state of matter; hence an electrified object with an excess of fluid attracts one with a deficiency of fluid, while two objects with excess fluid or two objects with a deficiency repel one another. Moreover, since the electric fluid attracts matter, an electrified body will attract an uncharged one. In these explanations Franklin anticipated much of what was later learned about electricity and laid the groundwork for what we still accept today. We still use the terms plus and minus and speak of positive and negative electricity although about 100 years after Franklin it was discovered that an electrified particle, called the *electron,* not a fluid, is transferred when static charge is produced.

Franklin's explanation and our modern acceptance of his basic terms, though with the substitution of electron for electric fluid, illustrate a number of aspects of the procedures and logic of science. In basic content and form the two explanations are identical. (Du Fay's explanation is almost identical in content also, though not in form.) If we substitute the words excess for deficiency, deficiency for excess, and negative particle for fluid, we can use Franklin's language in a modern textbook. Neither form explains more than the other about static electricity. Franklin's explanation for static electricity, his electric fluid, is quite acceptable but not unique. Nor is the current electron explanation, also acceptable, unique. It may be superseded by a new theory as the electron superseded the electric fluid. There are no unique, final explanations.

Second, the changes introduced by the modern electron theory do not make the earlier electric-fluid theory inaccurate; they merely make it less modern. Franklin's theory still explains adequately the observations of static electricity.

Third, the current acceptance of electrons as the carriers of electricity does not rest on their greater accuracy or better explication. It rests on other grounds. Electrons explain static electricity *and* some other phenomena which are not easily explained by Franklin's theory. The electron theory is preferred because of its greater universality and parsimony; it brings together into one set of explanations a greater number of phenomena. This is an important reason for accepting electrons rather than electric fluids. However, universality and parsimony, which we illustrated also in Chap. 10, are not always easy to determine and, besides, science is a human enterprise. The history of science also contains theories which were kept or discarded for reasons of pettiness, stubbornness, jealousy, or other "human" reasons.

CONDUCTION AND INDUCTION

Returning to the early observations that (1) some materials can be electrified, others not; (2) some materials conduct electricity, others do not; and (3) transmission of charge requires that the conductor be insulated from the earth, let us see how the electron theory fits them. The first point is that *all matter contains electrons,* which are highly mobile in some materials, especially metals, and highly immobile in others. The former are called *conductors* while the latter are *nonconductors* or *insulators.* Second, *electrons can be removed from materials or added to them by rubbing.* This leaves a deficiency of electrons, a positive charge, or an excess, a negative charge. (Unfortunately, objects which Franklin designated as minus or deficient in fluid are those which contain an excess of electrons. This means that electrons carry a negative charge. The fact that an *excess* of electrons produces a *minus* charge, and that a *deficiency* of electrons leaves the object with a *plus* charge, sometimes causes confusion.) Third, objects with *unlike charges attract,* those with *like charges repel.* Fourth, charge can be produced by rubbing only if the material is insulated from the earth, not *grounded,* because *the earth serves as an unlimited source or sink of electrons.* No other conductor attached to it can ever become charged because the earth replenishes any electrons that might be rubbed off, or drains away excess electrons. This explains why conducting materials held by hand cannot be electrified by rubbing. The human body is a conductor and the hand serves as a pathway to ground. Fifth, grounding explains why con-

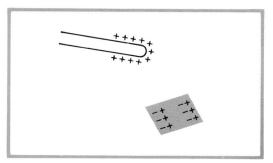

FIG. 13-4

The positive charge on the rod attracts electrons. The paper no longer has a balanced distribution of electrons and positive charges, and a slight attraction results.

duction of static electricity requires that the conductor be insulated from the earth. Otherwise the charge is immediately neutralized by contact with it.

The attraction between objects of unlike charge and the repulsion between objects of like charge are simply one of the properties of an excess or a deficiency of electrons. But we must still explain a number of phenomena in which a charged object attracts an uncharged one, like the charged comb which attracts bits of paper, or the charged balloon which clings to the wall.

The presence of a charged rod near a small piece of paper either drives electrons to the far side of the paper and leaves the near side positive—if the rod is negative —or it attracts electrons toward the rod and leaves the far side positive—if the rod is itself positive (Fig. 13–4). In either case, a separation of charge is produced in the uncharged object by the nearness of the charged rod. Furthermore, the attraction between the charged rod and the nearby surface of the paper is stronger than the repulsion between the rod and the far surface. Consequently there is a net attraction. The process of producing a charge separation in an uncharged object by means of a nearby charged object—without actual contact—is called *induction.*

Induction drives electrons away from a negatively charged rod and attracts them

FIG. 13-3

Electrons have been rubbed off one end of the ruler. Because it is not a conductor, the other end is not affected.

toward a positively charged rod. This leads to a number of interesting demonstrations. For instance, if two touching spheres are separated after a charged rod has been brought near to one (Fig. 13–5), they are found to be charged. While they were touching, the rod drove electrons from one sphere to the other, and as they were separated—by means of the insulated holders—the charge separation persisted. They are now both charged without having been rubbed or touched by a rubbed object. In these spheres, of course, the net positive charge equals the net negative charge.

It is also possible to charge a single sphere by induction (Fig. 13–6). The sphere is first grounded, then a charged rod is brought near, then the conduction to ground is interrupted before the rod is taken away. The charged rod drives electrons to ground

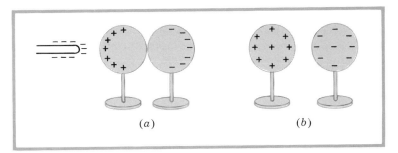

(a)   (b)

FIG. 13-5

Electrostatic induction. A hard-rubber rod which has been rubbed has an excess of electrons (negative charge). (a) These repel the electrons from the nearby conducting sphere. (b) When the two spheres are separated, one sphere remains electron-deficient and the other one maintains an excess of electrons.

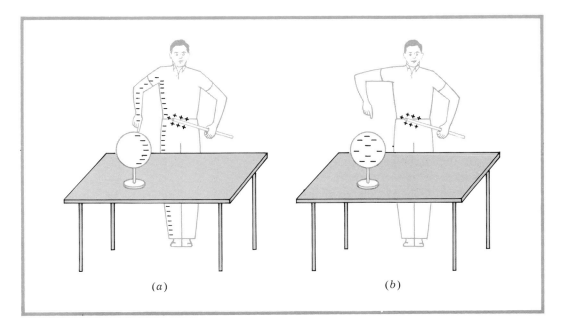

(a)   (b)

FIG. 13-6

Charging a sphere by induction. (a) The nearby positive rod attracts electrons which pass from the ground through the conductor into the sphere. (b) When the conductor is removed, the electrons remain in the sphere.

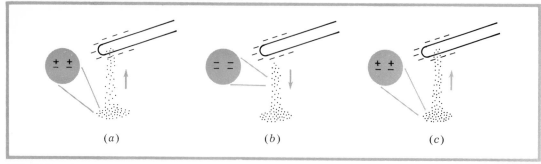

FIG. 13-7

(a) Lampblack is attracted to the charged rod by induction. (b) Upon contact, it picks up some electrons from the rod and, with the same kind of charge, is repelled. (c) In contact with the ground, the lampblack loses its excess electrons and is again attracted by induction.

—or attracts them from ground—leaving a deficiency or excess. When the conducting path to ground is broken with the rod still nearby, the sphere is left with its unbalanced charge. In this way the sphere attains a charge opposite in sign from that on the rod. An uncharged sphere can be given the same charge as a rod, of course, by direct contact.

Induction coupled with conduction explains the strange phenomenon first observed by Du Fay that a charged rod alternately attracts bits of lampblack and, after contact, strongly repels them. But as soon as they have struck the earth, they are attracted again only to be repelled again after contact (Fig. 13–7).

The charged rod attracts the lampblack by induction as the comb attracts a bit of paper. However, the lampblack contains the conductor graphite. Hence, on contact there is a rapid electron interchange. Some of the rod's charge transfers to the lampblack particle. The two then carry a charge of same sign. They repel. On contact with the ground the lampblack loses its charge and once more can be attracted to the rod by induction. Then, when it again touches the rod, it again acquires a charge of the same sign as the rod and is repelled. These processes can go through several cycles until the rod, which transfers some of its excess charge every time it touches a lampblack particle, becomes completely discharged.

APPLICATIONS OF STATIC ELECTRICITY

Electrostatic repulsion is not limited to charged objects; it extends to excess electrons in a single charged conductor. The electrons repel one another and since they are free to move, they distribute themselves in such a way as to minimize total repulsion by increasing the distance between each other. Thus in a charged conducting sphere, the electrons are uniformly distributed over the surface, none are within. This leaves the inside of the sphere free of charge and repulsion because the effects from all over the surface cancel (Fig. 13–8). In conductors with irregular shapes,

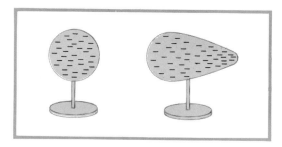

FIG. 13-8

Distribution of charge in a conductor. The electrons distribute themselves so as to minimize repulsions. This means that the excess charge is located at the surface, not the interior, of the charged conductor and tends to concentrate at points or other spots of high curvature.

likewise, electrons are located exclusively on the surface though not uniformly. They tend to concentrate at points and highly curved parts of the surface while their density is least at the least bent portions. In this case, too, electron distribution minimizes total repulsion, and there is no field within the solid. (The same principles hold, of course, for positively charged conductors with the substitution of excess positive charge for excess electrons.)

Benjamin Franklin already knew of the concentration of static charge at points and made use of it in the lightning rod, whose pointed end has the highest local concentration of charge and thus draws lightning to it. The absence of electrical attraction and repulsion within a charged solid, however, was not recognized until later. It finds one use in the Van de Graaff generator, a device for producing extremely high charges which can be released to simulate the effects of lightning (Fig. 13–9).

In the Van de Graaff generator a static charge is produced by rubbing a pointed conductor. The charge leaks off the point onto a moving, nonconducting belt. The belt moves over rollers into the inside of a large hollow metallic sphere. Because there is no repulsion inside the sphere, the charge can leak off the belt onto another set of points connected by a conducting path to the sphere. It quickly moves to the surface of the sphere because there repulsions are minimized. In this manner it is possible to produce an extremely high total charge on the sphere and to discharge it under the control of the experimenter, in one massive flash. Although the instrumentation is quite complex, this describes the essential theory. Van de Graaff generators typically are used to study the effect of the impact of high-energy electrons on various materials. For instance, the high-energy electrons will destroy bacteria and sterilize foodstuffs at room temperature. Unlike cooking, this preserves the taste of the food although the residues of electron impact may themselves alter the taste.

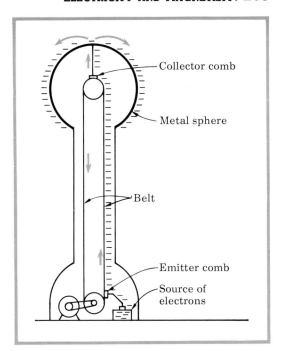

FIG. 13-9

The Van de Graaff generator. Electrostatic charge produced at the bottom flows onto a nonconducting belt which moves it into a conducting sphere. There it flows to the surface. As a result, a large amount of charge builds up.

COULOMB'S LAW

The manner in which the force of electrostatic attraction and repulsion depends upon the magnitude of charges and the distance separating the charges was investigated by Charles Augustin Coulomb (1736–1806) and is named, in his honor, Coulomb's *law of electrostatic attraction and repulsion: the attraction (or repulsion) between two charged bodies is directly proportional to the product of their charges and inversely proportional to the square of the distance separating them.* Mathematically,

$$F = \frac{q_1 q_2}{r^2} \qquad (13–1)$$

q_1 and q_2 are the magnitudes of the charges on the two objects and r is the distance between them. Notice that this law is identical in form to the law of gravitational attraction. It was determined with an apparatus very similar to the Cavendish apparatus for measuring the gravitational constant G (Fig. 8–12). When the two charges q_1 and q_2 are identical in sign, the force is repulsive. If the two charges carry opposite signs, the force is one of attraction.

In one common system of physical measurement, the unit for quantity of charge is the *electrostatic unit*, usually abbreviated *esu*. By definition the electrostatic unit is such that two charges of magnitude 1 esu each repel (or attract) each other with a force of 1 dyne when 1 cm apart.

Coulomb's law quantitatively shows how induction produces a net attraction between a charged and an uncharged object. For instance, a negative rod drives electrons to the far surface, leaving a positive charge of equal magnitude on the near surface. Then there is attraction between the rod and the induced positive charge over a small distance and repulsion between the rod and the induced negative charge over a large distance. Since electrostatic forces vary with the square of the distance, the repulsion is much smaller than the attraction. The separation of charges into positive and negative centers of equal magni-

tude within an uncharged object is called a *dipole*. In this case, there is an induced dipole.

EXAMPLE

Find the net attraction if a rod of 10-esu charge is brought to within 1 cm of a 3-cm-long object in which it induces a dipole of 2-esu charge (Fig. 13–11). The force of at-

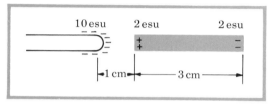

FIG. 13-11

Attraction for an induced dipole. Because the opposite charge of the induced dipole is much nearer than the charge of same sign, attraction is much greater than repulsion. (The data and drawing are highly idealized.)

traction is between the 10-esu rod and a 2-esu positive charge 1 cm away. The force of repulsion is between a 10-esu rod and a 2-esu charge 4 cm away. The net force is:

$$F = \frac{10 \text{ esu} \times 2 \text{ esu}}{(1 \text{ cm})^2} - \frac{10 \text{ esu} \times 2 \text{ esu}}{(4 \text{ cm})^2}$$
$$= 18.75 \text{ dynes} \qquad (13\text{–}2)$$

The unit dynes comes from the definition of the electrostatic unit. It is interesting that the attraction in this case is 94 percent as great as the attracton between a 10-esu rod and a 2-esu object of opposite charge 1 cm away.

Since all of space is pervaded by electrostatic forces emanating from whatever sources may be nearby (in Coulomb's law, F becomes O only when r becomes infinite), it might appear that the kind of measurement needed to establish Coulomb's law between two isolated charges would be impossible to make. Fortunately, the effect used to increase the charge in the Van de Graaff generator can be used to free small regions of space entirely of external electrostatic influence by enclosing them in a metal cage. Then the forces exerted by charges without produce a distribution of electrons in the metal of the cage such that together they leave the space within

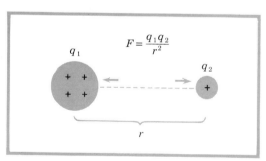

FIG. 13-10

Coulomb's law. The force between two charged objects is directly proportional to the magnitude of their charges and inversely proportional to the square of the distance between them.

the cage entirely free of net electrostatic forces. Another way of saying this is that it is possible to shield a part of space from external electrostatic influences (in contrast to gravity, against which no shielding is now thought possible). The shielding device is called a Faraday cage (Fig. 13–12).

A Faraday cage is used in the *electroscope,* a device to measure the magnitude of the force produced by a charged object (Fig. 13–13). The electroscope consists of a thin metallic leaf attached to a bar inside a solid metal case with windows (the Faraday cage). The bar extends to the outside, insulated from the metal case. When a charged object is brought near the terminal of the bar, the metal bar and leaf in the electroscope become charged by induction and separate. The extent of separation depends on the amount of charge induced in them. This, in turn, depends on the magnitude of the charge on the object that is brought near and its distance from the electroscope, according to Coulomb's law. Thus a measurement of the separation of the leaf is related to the magnitude of the electric charge.

In an alternative use, the electroscope can be charged first (by direct contact or induction) to produce a separation of the metal leaf. Bringing an object of opposite charge near the electroscope then brings the leaf closer to the bar. The magnitude of the charge can then be related to the extent to which the leaf collapses.

ELECTROSTATIC FIELDS

In view of the identity of form between the equations of force for static electricity and for gravity, it is fruitful to use the concept of an electrostatic field surrounding a charge as it was fruitful to use the concept of a gravitational field surrounding a mass. The properties of the two fields are analogous.

If we place two charges q_2 and q_3 the same

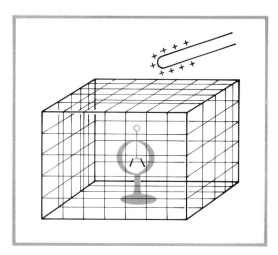

FIG. 13-12

A Faraday cage. Charges outside a metallic cage induce a distribution of electrons in the metal which counters the outside electrostatic forces. Consequently the space within the cage is left free of net electrostatic charge.

FIG. 13-13

An electroscope. A metal bar with an attached thin metallic leaf inside a Faraday cage. The bar and leaf attain a charge only by conduction from the knob. Then, because the charge is of the same sign, they repel and the leaf separates from the bar. (Central Scientific Company, Chicago, Ill.)

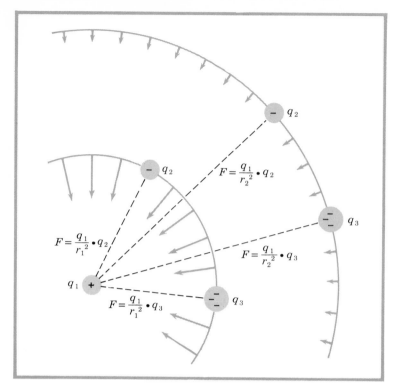

The electric field around a charge q_1. q_1/r^2 gives the field strength at a distance r.

FIG. 13-14

distance r_1 from a charge q_1, the forces on them are $F = q_1/r_1{}^2 \times q_2$ and $F = q_1/r_1{}^2 \times q_3$ (Fig. 13–14). The force exerted by q_1 is a function of position $q_1/r_1{}^2$ and the magnitude of the second charge, q_2 or q_3. A similar result is obtained if the two charges are placed at another distance, r_2, from charge q_1. Thus, we can express the force exerted by q_1 in terms of an *electrostatic field strength*, which is characteristic of the location in space, and the magnitude of the second charge. The electrostatic field is the description of the electrostatic field strength at all points in space.

The field strength is a vector quantity since it defines a direction as well as a magnitude. The direction is along the line connecting the two charges though it may point away from charge q_1 to indicate repulsion if charge q_2 has the same sign, or toward charge q_1 if q_2 has the opposite sign. The field strength has its maximum value at q_1 where $r = 0$ and F is infinite and drops off as the square of the distance.

There are many points in space at which the field strength has the same magnitude. These points define equipotential surfaces. Equipotential surfaces around an isolated charge are spherical. If there are several charges in the electrostatic field, their individual field strengths add vectorially. Then the equipotential surfaces may take on other shapes and the field-strength vector at any point is the vector sum of the contributions from the various charges in the field (Fig. 13–15).

The electrostatic potential energy of a charge q_2 is the same anywhere on an equipotential surface since the work of placing it there against the forces of the other charges in the field is the same. Also, no work is expended in moving between the points on an equipotential surface.

The field-strength vectors define the direction in which an unsupported charge would move in the field of other charges. These paths are called the *lines of force* of the field. Later in this chapter we shall

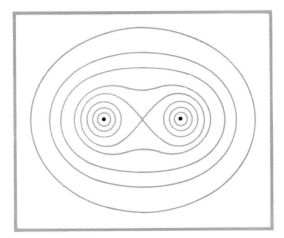

FIG. 13-15

The field around two equal charges of the same sign. The field-strength vectors due to each charge add, and equipotential surfaces connect points at which the vector sums of the field strengths are equal.

describe magnetic fields and the familiar experiment of sprinkling iron filings around magnets (Fig. 13–18). The iron filings align themselves along the lines of force of the field set up by the magnetic poles.

THE DISCOVERY OF THE ELECTRON

We have explained electrostatic phenomena in terms of an excess or deficiency of electrons although, as we pointed out, all the effects except for the discharge of the Van de Graaff generator could be explained by the absence or presence of Franklin's electric fluid or of "charge" of an unspecified character. The electron was discovered in experiments with evacuated tubes, which function somewhat like the Van de Graaff generator.

In the Van de Graaff generator, electrons jump between the terminals only because the charge is very, very high. (Electric sparks jump between our fingers and light switches because the charge is relatively high and the distance very small.) Under ordinary circumstances, air is an insulator which does not allow the passage of elec-

tric charge. In evacuated tubes, however, the flow of charge occurs more readily. This was discovered about 100 years ago when the art of glassblowing had advanced sufficiently to allow the construction of evacuated glass tubes with electrodes sealed into them. In an evacuated tube, relatively small charge differences produce a glowing beam or ray between the two electrodes similar to the static sparks. That this glow was negatively charged was demonstrated by bringing charged objects near the evacuated tube; the ray is repelled by negative charge and attracted by positive charge (Fig. 13–16). More commonly the deflection is produced by magnets (Chap. 14).

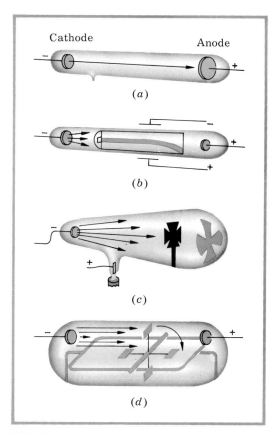

FIG. 13-16

Cathode-ray tubes. (a) Charge flows between electrodes in partially evacuated glass tubes. (b) The ray is deflected toward a positive charge. (c) The ray casts a shadow behind the positive plate. (d) The ray spins a paddle wheel toward the positive plate.

Hence in these tubes negative "charge" flows from one electrode to the other.

The direction of flow was determined by placing different objects in the path of the ray. A clear shadow of the object is cast behind the positive electrode, indicating, as would be expected of a negative ray, that it travels from the negative electrode or *cathode* to the positive electrode or *anode.* Consequently the ray was called a *cathode ray* and the tube in which it was produced, a *cathode-ray tube.*

Specific evidence of the particle character of the cathode ray came later when a paddle wheel was placed in the path of the ray. The impact of the flowing "charge" with the wheel blades sets the wheel in motion, clearly an indication of a mechanical mass in the "ray." The measurement of the actual mass of the single particles in the "ray," the mass of the electron, was the result of two famous experiments. In 1897 Sir Joseph John Thomson (1856–1940) determined the extent of deflection of the path produced by charged plates of known charge (and magnets of known strength). The deflecting acceleration depends on the electrostatic charge of the electron and the charge on the plate; the resistance to deflection depends on the mass (inertia) of the electron. Thus, through the measurement of deflection of electrons under controlled conditions, Thomson obtained the relationship between their charge and mass (see also Chap. 18). This is direct experimental verification that "charge" is not a fluid but consists of discrete particles. When the charge was measured in 1916 in the oil-drop experiment by the American Robert A. Millikan (1868–1953), the mass of the electron could be computed from Thomson's data. It is 9×10^{-28} gram.

MAGNETS

Like static electricity, magnets are well-known and need relatively little further discussion. Their general behavior is very much like that of electric charge, with a few restrictions. Whereas gravity is a property of all matter and static charge can be produced in any nongrounded material, noticeable magnetism is restricted to iron, steel, and a few special materials like the alloy *alnico*. Second, whereas there is only one polarity to mass which invariably leads to attraction, and there are two polarities to charge which may cause attraction or repulsion and which can be separated from one another, the two poles of magnets also may lead to attraction or repulsion but they always appear in pairs. All magnets have both a south and a north pole. Beyond this distinction, magnetism and electrostatics are formally identical. For instance:

1. Magnetic force can be conducted through magnetic materials.

2. Magnetism can be induced in magnetic materials without contact.

3. Magnetic materials can become permanently magnetized, though not by one simple contact with a magnet. The difference between static electricity and magnetism arises from the difference in the basic character of the two phenomena. While electricity is produced by the separation of electrons from positive charge in matter, magnetism comes about from an ordering of the atoms of magnetic materials. Each atom of magnetic materials acts like a little magnet. Normally the atoms are oriented at random and thus do not add up to a big magnet. A big magnet comes about through the realignment of the little atomic magnets, which is not as easy, energetically, as electron displacement. Hence magnetization requires more extensive contact. Moreover, a magnetized piece of iron can be demagnetized simply by heating (heat produces random motion) or by dropping, while electric charge cannot be neutralized by heat.

4. A shield can be produced by an easily magnetized screen to free portions of space from magnetic fields.

5. Magnetic force is governed by an inverse square law:

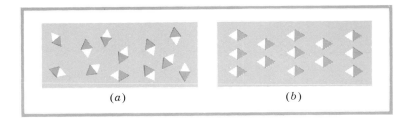

(a) (b)

FIG. 13-17

The atoms of many elements are little magnets. (a) Normally they point in all directions. (b) In some materials, like iron, the atomic magnets can line up to produce the easily recognizable properties of magnets.

$$F = p_1 p_2 / r^2 \qquad (13\text{-}3)$$

In this equation p_1 and p_2 are the pole strengths of the attracting or repelling poles. As in the electrostatic case, poles of identical polarity produce repulsion whereas poles of opposite polarity produce attraction. Unlike the electrostatic case, it is never possible to consider the influence of only one magnetic pole on another through space, because the poles are always paired. The minimum interaction involves two sets of poles producing four interactions, two of which are attractive and two repulsive.

6. While magnetic fields never have the symmetry of the fields produced by a single shielded charge (or a hypothetical separate mass), the general field concept applies to magnets as well. The familiar iron filings sprinkled over magnets, as mentioned above, align themselves along the lines of force of the magnetic field and locate the field-strength vectors. The equipotential surfaces of the magnetic field then cut the lines of force at right angles everywhere. Moreover, magnetic force, magnetic potential energy, and work done in a magnetic field are determined by position in the magnetic field as is the case in gravitational and electrostatic field.

7. As in the electrostatic case, the definition of pole strength is that two poles of unit strength (the *pole* is one commonly used measure of magnetic strength) 1 cm apart attract (or repel) with a force of 1 dyne.

THE EARTH'S MAGNETIC FIELD

Permanent or bar magnets probably derive their greatest importance from the fact that the earth is surrounded by a magnetic field in which free-swinging bar magnets align themselves parallel to the lines of force. Except for areas where deposits of magnetic rocks deflect the earth's magnetic field somewhat, the lines of force point toward spots near the geo-

The lines of force surrounding three magnets, along which the iron filings line up. Equipotential surfaces are at right angles to the lines of force. (Bell Telephone Laboratories, Incorporated)

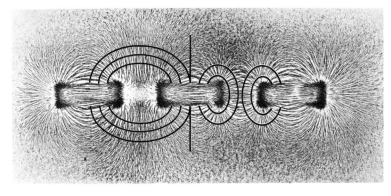

FIG. 13-18

graphic North and South Poles called the magnetic north and magnetic south poles. These free-swinging magnets, or compasses, have been used in navigation since about the fifteenth century and have played an important part in the exploration and the commerce between the East and West.

Because of their response to the earth's magnetism, magnetic poles are called north and south (rather than plus and minus), although this produces a slight difficulty. The *north* poles on compasses point to the earth's magnetic north pole— are attracted by that pole. Then since unlike poles attract, the magnetic north pole has the same character as the south poles on the compass. The converse holds for the magnetic south pole, which attracts the south poles of magnets and thus must itself be a north pole. To reduce this problem, some people prefer to call poles "north-seeking" and "south-seeking." The magnetic north pole is then a south-seeking pole, and the magnetic south pole is a north-seeking pole.

Because the earth's magnetic poles are not exactly on the geographic poles, and because of distortions of the field by deposits of magnetic materials, the earth's magnetic field is not parallel to the geographic longitude circles. Charts have been constructed that give the deviations from true north for all parts of the earth as an aid to navigators. Also, the earth's magnetic field does not follow the curvature of the surface of the earth but dips toward the surface. The extent of dip, likewise, is a

FIG. 13-19

A dip needle. A compass needle swinging on a horizontal axis shows the angle between the earth's surface and the earth's magnetic field. (Central Scientific Company, Chicago, Ill.)

characteristic of the part on the earth at which it is measured. Magnetic dip is measured with a *dip needle,* which is a compass that swings freely about a horizontal rather than a vertical axis.

While static charges and magnets produce a number of interesting effects separately, these are minor in comparison to the effects produced by electricity and magnetism combined. The electromagnetic effects discussed in the next chapter are the basis for almost all the technical developments of our current civilization.

Questions and Problems

1. Hard rubber rubbed with fur becomes negatively charged; glass rubbed with silk becomes positively charged. How would you produce a positive charge on a piece of metal insulated from ground (a) with a glass rod, (b) with a rubber rod? How would you charge it negatively?

2. Use the words "electric fluid," instead of "electrons," to explain your answer to Question 1.

3. What charge does the fur in Question 1 acquire? the silk?

4. Explain how an electron deficiency can produce positive charge; an electron excess, negative charge.

5. Du Fay's experiment with lampblack can also be carried out with bits of metal foil but not with bits of paper. Explain.

6. What properties of cathode rays are definitely demonstrated by each of the following observations? (Distinguish between proof and indication.) (*a*) They cast a shadow behind the positive electrode. (*b*) They set a paddle wheel spinning. (*c*) They flow in evacuated tubes, not in gas-filled tubes. (*d*) They are deflected by charged rods.

7. Set up a table to compare the force equation, basic units, materials affected, production of and field properties of electricity, magnetism, and gravity.

8. Compute the force, and indicate whether it is attractive or repulsive, between (*a*) is 12-esu positive charge and a 14-esu negative charge, 5 cm away; (*b*) a 7-esu negative charge and a 3-esu negative charge 7 cm away; (*c*) two magnets, each 6 cm long and with poles of strength 32, laid in one line so that the north pole of one is 2 cm from the south pole of the other.

9. An experimenter performs the following operations with an electroscope and makes the following observations. He touches the knob of the electroscope with his fingers and brings a rubber rod near. He removes his finger. Then he removes the rod. The leaf of the electroscope separates as he removes the rod. He brings the rod back and the leaf collapses. He takes it away and it separates. He touches the knob with the rod and the leaf separates and remains separated when the rod is taken away. But when it is brought near again, the leaf separates further. Explain.

10. Suggest an experiment to demonstrate that there are two kinds of electricity.

11. A piece of metal, suspended by an insulator, attracts other things. Without using a magnet or charged rods, how could you determine whether the metal is magnetized or electrified?

12. Sketch the equipotential lines around (*a*) a bar magnet 6 cm long; (*b*) the north poles of two bar magnets, 6 cm apart; (*c*) a positively charged point; (*d*) two positively charged points, 2 cm apart; (*e*) a positive point and a negative point, 2 cm apart.

Suggestions for Further Reading

Texts that serve as additional references to this chapter and Chap. 14 are:

Christiansen, G. S., and Paul H. Garrett: *Structure and Change*, W. H. Freeman and Company, San Francisco, 1960. Chapter 16.

Holton, Gerald, and Duane H. D. Roller: *Foundations of Modern Physical Science*, Addison-Wesley Publishing Company, Inc., Reading, Mass., 1958. Chapters 26 to 28. Cites the major experiments that led to the understanding of electricity and magnetism.

Physical Science Study Committee: *Physics*, D. C. Heath and Company, Boston, 1960. Chapters 27 to 30.

Rogers, Eric M.: *Physics for the Inquiring Mind*, Princeton University Press, Princeton, N.J., 1960. Chapters 33, 34, and 36.

A very readable account of many other magnetic phenomena is:

Bitter, Francis: *Magnets*, Anchor Books, Doubleday & Company, Inc., Garden City, N.Y., 1959. (paperback).

The development of ideas regarding the character of electric phenomena is in:

Conant, J. B. (ed.): *Harvard Case Histories in Experimental Science*, vol. 2, Harvard University Press, Cambridge, Mass., 1957. Chapter 8 by Duane Roller and Duane H. D. Roller.

Chapter 14

Electric Currents

Static electricity is produced by rubbing which separates electrons from positive charges under conditions that do not allow for the return of the electrons. As soon as a conducting path is provided, electrons return and the charges are neutralized. Static electricity thus leads to a brief flow of electric charge through a conductor, an electric current. When, after about 1800, other means for producing electric current were discovered or invented which, moreover, maintain the charge differential that leads to charge flow over long periods of time, the special effects of electric currents began to be studied. Steady electric current requires a continuous path of conducting material between the terminals of a source which maintains a charge difference despite the neutralizing tendency of the electron flow.

ELECTRICAL UNITS

Currents consist of charge flowing between terminals that maintain a charge difference. To measure electric currents, we need a unit that describes the amount of charge that moves and a unit that measures the charge difference on the terminals which produce charge flow. The electron, of course, has a fixed charge and would be a natural unit for measuring the amount of charge. But the electronic charge is extremely small, and large and unwieldy numbers result when the amount of charge is measured in terms of the electronic charge. Consequently the unit *coulomb*, Q, has been adopted for work with current electricity. The coulomb is the charge of 6.25×10^{18} electrons. Charge measured in coulombs leads to simple relationships between other electrical units.

Since charge flowing because of a charge difference on two terminals has electrical energy, the measure of charge difference is defined in terms of charge and energy. It is called the *voltage* or *potential difference* and is given in the unit *volt, E*. To move 1 coul of charge from the positive to the negative terminal when their potential difference is 1 volt requires 1×10^7 ergs of work. Conversely, 1 coul of charge flowing spontaneously between terminals with a potential difference of 1 volt has 1×10^7 ergs of electrical energy.

$$Q \text{ (coul)} \times E \text{ (volts)} = \text{energy} \quad (14\text{–}1)$$

In the common applications of electric currents, we are less interested in the energy of the current and the total charge which flows than in the rate at which it moves between the terminals. For instance, in describing a light bulb, our interest is with the amount of energy converted to heat and light each second since the total depends on how long the light bulb remains switched on. The rate of producing or using energy is given by the concept power. Power is energy per second, and the power of electric currents is measured in *watts, W*. One coulomb of charge flowing between a potential difference of 1 volt in 1 sec = 1 watt.

$$\frac{Q \text{ (coul)} \times E \text{ (volts)}}{t \text{ (sec)}} = W \text{ (watts)}$$

$$(14\text{–}2)$$

Again because we are usually more inter-

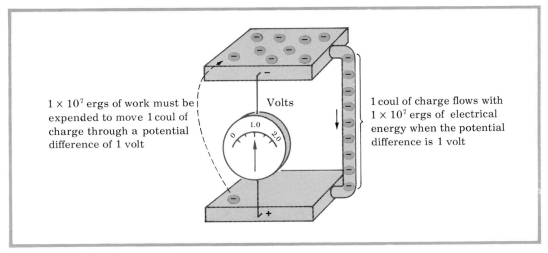

FIG. 14-1

Charge difference on terminals is defined by the energy required to move charge between them. The potential difference is 1 volt when 1×10^7 ergs of work are required to move 1 coul of charge. Conversely, 1 coul of charge flowing spontaneously has 1×10^7 ergs of electrical energy when the potential difference is 1 volt.

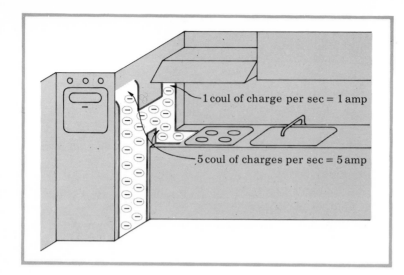

1 coul of charge per sec = 1 amp

.5 coul of charges per sec = 5 amp

Current is the rate of charge flow. When 1 coul of charge flows each second, the current is 1 amp.

FIG. 14-2

ested in the rate of charge flow than in the total charge, we also need a unit that expresses charge flow per second. Coulombs per second are measured in *amperes, I,* and are called the *current.* One coulomb flowing past a point in 1 sec is a current of 1 amp.

$$\frac{Q \text{ (coul)}}{t \text{ (sec)}} = I \text{ (amp)} \qquad (14\text{--}3)$$

Substitution in Eq. 14–2 gives the relation between volts, amperes, and watts:

$$I \text{ (amp)} \times E \text{ (volts)} = W \text{ (watts)} \qquad (14\text{--}4)$$

These are the four basic units for electric-current measurements. The volt measures the potential difference that produces charge flow. The ampere measures the current, the rate of charge flow (Eq. 14–3). Potential difference times current gives the watt, power (Eq. 14–4). Charge in coulombs times the potential difference in volts gives energy (Eq. 14–1), as does power in watts multiplied by time. The electrical units are summarized in Table 14–1.

An interesting sidelight to the definitions of the electrical units is the way we measure electrical appliances and pay for electrical energy. As we mentioned above, we classify our appliances by the rate at which they use energy. They are rated by their power consumption, in watts. The light company, on the other hand, charges for the energy supplied. Light bills are determined by the kilowatt-hours consumed, 1,000 watts used for an hour. Watts multiplied by time equals energy.

OHM'S LAW

One of the first discoveries concerning electric circuits was made by Georg Ohm (1787–1854). Ohm measured the current that flows between terminals when different conductors are used. He found that each conductor can be identified by an electric *resistance, R,* which is related to current and potential difference by *Ohm's law:*

$$R \text{ (ohms)} = \frac{E \text{ (volts)}}{I \text{ (amp)}} \qquad (14\text{--}5)$$

R is expressed in the unit *ohm.* It is defined so that a potential difference of 1 volt produces a current of 1 amp in a resistance of 1 ohm. Several examples illustrate the application of these units.

TABLE 14-1

Electrical measurements

Quantity measured	Electrical unit	Symbol	Definition	Relationship to other units
Energy	–	–	–	Wt = energy; EQ = energy
Charge	Coulomb	Q	$Q = \dfrac{6.25 \times 10^{18}}{\text{electrons}}$	
Potential difference	Volt	E	$E = \dfrac{1 \times 10^7 \text{ ergs}}{\text{coul}}$	$W = EI;\ E = IR$
Current	Ampere	I	$I = \dfrac{Q \text{ coul}}{t \text{ sec}}$	$Q = It;\ EI = W;\ E = IR$
Power	Watt	W	$W = \dfrac{Q \text{ coul} \times E \text{ volts}}{t \text{ sec}}$	$W = EI;\ W = \text{energy}/t$
Resistance	Ohm	R	$R = \dfrac{E \text{ volts}}{I \text{ amp}}$	

EXAMPLE

A resistance is rated 4 ohms. What current flows through it when it is attached to a 6-volt battery? How much power does the battery furnish? From Ohm's law we obtain 4 ohms = 6 volts/I amp. Solving the equation gives I = 1.5 amp. Then, I amp × E volts = W watts; 1.5 amp × 6 volts = 9 watts.

EXAMPLE

An automobile light bulb is rated 2.4 watts and designed for a 6-volt system. Determine its resistance. Also determine the current if it were used in a car with a 12-volt system. From I amp × E volts = W watts, we obtain I amp × 6 volts = 2.4 watts; I = 0.4 amp. Then, R ohms = E volts/I amp; R ohms = 6 volts/0.4 amp; R = 15 ohms.

To determine the current with a 12-volt system, we also use Ohm's law. R ohms = E volts/I amp; 15 ohms = 12 volts/I amp; I = 0.8 amp. Twice the current flows through the 15-ohm bulb when the voltage is doubled. Moreover, the power is then I amp × E volts = W watts; 0.8 amp × 12 volts = 9.6 watts. Under the doubled potential difference, the bulb consumes four times as much power. It would probably burn out.

We have illustrated the two most significant aspects of Ohm's law in these examples. Given a fixed potential difference to produce charge flow, the resistance of the circuit determines the current. In this way the resistance of electric circuits can be compared to water pipes. With a fixed head of water pressure, the amount of water that can flow through a pipe depends on its diameter. And just as a higher water pressure will force more water through a given pipe, a larger potential difference produces more current through a given resistance. Finally, as the smallest pipe most affects the rate of water flow in an entire waterline, so the greatest resistance most affects the current flow. In house circuits, for instance, the resistance of the wires is very small. Consequently the large resistances of electrical appliances limit the current in the entire circuit, from electric meter to the appliance back to the electric meter. The electric fuse is based on this principle. Normally, with a high-resistance light bulb or appliance in the circuit, only a small current flows through the fuse. But if a short circuit develops—a low-resistance path—the current suddenly becomes large. The large current melts the fuse, breaks the circuit at that point, and the current stops entirely.

A second point implied by Ohm's law is that the energy of the electric current is used to push the current through the resistance. The resistance converts this energy into other forms—light and heat. Thus charge which flows from the negative terminal because of a potential difference in the circuit loses its energy in the resistance (Fig. 14–3*d*). After passing the resistance,

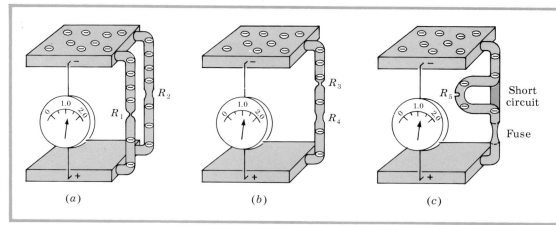

FIG. 14-3

it continues to the positive terminal though it is no longer "pushed." The loss of energy in the resistance produces a voltage drop through the resistance, usually called a *potential drop*.

When this is studied in terms of energy used per second, power, the same relationships hold. In the resistance there is a power loss equal to the rated watts of the resistance. The power loss is in turn related to current and potential drop by $W = EI$ (Eq. 14–4), and the potential drop across the resistance is related to R and current by $E = IR$ (Eq. 14–5).

CIRCUITS

In the examples we used, all the current flows through the same path; from the battery through a resistance and back to the battery. Such a circuit is called a *series* circuit. Hence, the current I is the same throughout the entire circuit although it may pass through more than one resistance (Fig. 14–4a). The resistances impede the current flow individually, each adding its own value to the total. In Fig. 14–4a the total resistance of the circuit is 40 ohms. From this we may compute the current in

the circuit. With a 12-volt source, it is 40 ohms $= 12$ volts/I amp; $I = 0.3$ amp.

The voltage in the circuit drops at each resistance and each resistance uses part of the electrical energy furnished by the battery. The potential drop between the ends of the 5-ohm resistance R_1 is 1.5 volts. The potential drop across the 10-ohm resistance R_2 is 3.0 volts, and across the 25-ohm resistance R_3 it is 7.5 volts. The energy of the current is completely transformed by the three resistances, and the sum of the potential drops equals the potential difference between the terminals of the source.

Because the current flows through all parts of the series circuit, a break in any part of the circuit stops charge flow throughout the circuit. For this reason, no current flows in our house circuits when the appliances are switched off. Appliances are wired in series with the electric meter.

Another kind of circuit (Fig. 14–4b), called a *parallel* circuit, allows for alternative paths for the current from terminal to terminal. In parallel circuits, only part of the current takes each possible path, the amount depending upon the relative magnitude of the resistance of that path. Thus a low-resistance path draws a large fraction of the current; a high-resistance path a small fraction. Potential difference for

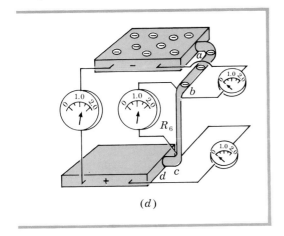

(d)

Characteristics of Ohm's law. (a) With a fixed voltage, less current flows through a large resistance R_1 than through a smaller resistance R_2. (b) When two resistances are connected in series, the largest resistance R_3 determines how much current flows in the entire circuit. (c) Normally the resistance R_5 limits the amount of current which flows in the circuit and only a small current passes through the fuse. But if a short circuit, a path with little resistance, should develop, the large current melts the fuse. (d) In the low-resistance circuit between the terminals and the resistance, from a to b and from c to d, the current flows freely and without loss of energy. The voltage at a is the same as at b, and at c the same as at d. The energy of the current is expended across the resistance and the voltage drops between b and c.

each of the possible paths is the same—equal to the voltage of the source. Again Ohm's law is applied for each resistance separately; however, the total current is the sum of the fractions passing through each part. For instance, for the circuit given in Fig. 14-4b, the voltage of the source is also 12 volts. Through R_1, 2.4 amp flow; through R_2, 1.2 amp; and through R_3, 0.48 amp. The total current flowing between the terminals of the source is the sum of the three, or 4.08 amp. (It should be noted that a break in one part of a parallel circuit does not completely stop current flow since alternative paths remain available).

Electrical devices like radios contain both parallel and series circuits, separately and in combination. This makes actual computations somewhat more tedious although, ultimately, they reduce to combinations of the two kinds illustrated here.

(a) A series circuit. All the current passes through the same path, and the potential drops across each of the resistances add to equal the potential difference between the terminals.
(b) A parallel circuit. There are several alternative paths for the current, and the potential drops across each of the resistances equal the potential difference between the terminals.

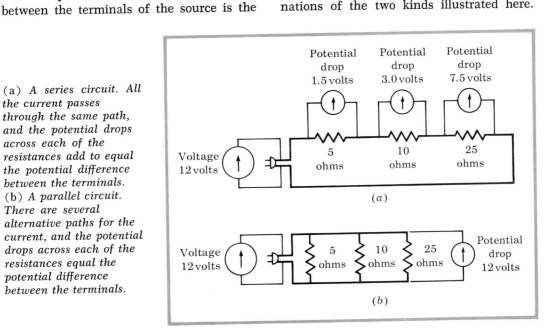

FIG. 14-4

ELECTROMAGNETISM

The next group of interesting effects accompanying an electric current occur not in but around the conductor. In 1820 Hans Christian Oersted (1777–1851) noticed that a compass needle held above a current-carrying wire becomes deflected at right angles to the wire and that the direction of deflection changes if the compass is moved from above to below the wire. If held next to the wire, the compass is not affected, but a dip needle is, and the direction in which the dip needle points also changes from the left side to the right side. The manner of deflection indicates that the field affecting the compass and dip needle is circular with the wire at its center. Its orientation is always such that if the wire were grasped by the left hand with the thumb in the direction of electron flow in the wire, the fingers would point in the direction of the north-seeking pole of the compass or dip needle. Obviously, if the direction of electron flow is reversed in the wire, so is the orientation of the magnetic field.

The discovery of the magnetic field surrounding a current-carrying wire led to many important and practical uses of electricity. Already in 1820 André Marie

Ampère (1775–1836) had discovered the electromagnet by winding wires into helical coils. This results in the vectorial addition of the fields from each turn of the wire (Fig. 14–6). Note that the addition leads to a field pointing in one direction within the helix; in the opposite direction outside the helix; and that vectorial addition of the individual contributions in the space between the separate turns leads to zero field strength there. Moreover, an iron bar inside the helix concentrates the magnetic lines of force and increases the strength of the electromagnet.

Electromagnets find almost infinite application in today's technology because they produce forces that are unique in several respects. The first is regulation of field strength and field geometry. An electromagnet's properties are determined by the number of turns in the helix and by the current flowing in them. Both of these can be precisely controlled. Furthermore, the geometry of the field can be adjusted by the iron cores which concentrate the lines of force inside the helix. Thus electromagnets produce forces that can be specified within very narrow limits, from the very small as in hearing aids and other small devices to the huge as in cyclotrons or magnetic cranes. Next is the fact that electromagnets work only if there is current

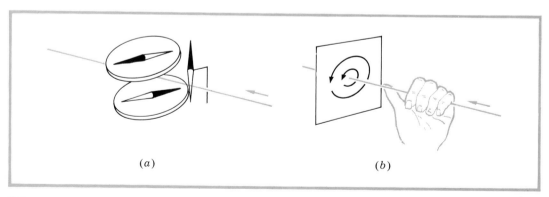

(a)   (b)

FIG. 14-5

The magnetic field around a current. A compass and a dip needle are deflected to indicate that the field surrounds the wire and points in the direction of the fingers when the thumb of the left hand points in the direction of electron flow.

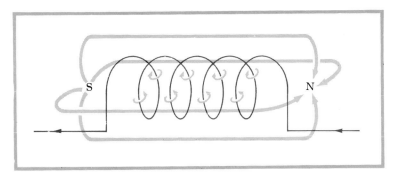

The fields surrounding each turn of a wire helix add to produce a strong electromagnet.

FIG. 14-6

in their coils. Thus switching the current on and off switches the force on and off. This principle is applied in bells, buzzers, and chimes and in magnetic valves. Finally, the strength of an electromagnet can be varied by changing the current that flows in its wires. Its chief applications are in communications. Radio speakers, for instance, produce sound because a fluctuating current in an electromagnet produces

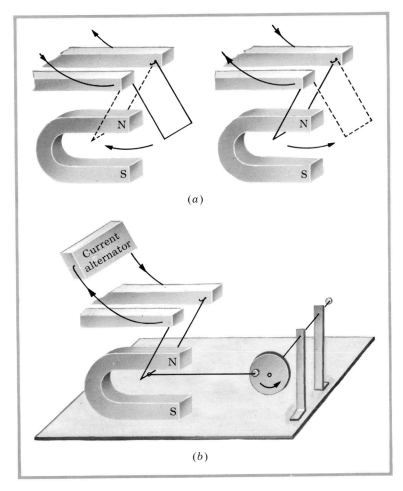

Conversion of electrical energy into mechanical energy. (a) A wire carrying current is drawn into or repelled from the poles of a horseshoe magnet. (b) If a means is found to alternate the direction of current flow and to change the back-and-forth motion into rotation, a simple electric motor results.

(a)

Current alternator

(b)

FIG. 14-7

vibrations of the proper frequencies in a diaphragm.

Perhaps a more important application of electromagnets is in the conversion of electrical to mechanical energy, in electric motors. In their magnetic effects, electromagnets and permanent magnets are indistinguishable. For instance, a current-carrying wire brought between the poles of a horseshoe magnet will be either drawn into or repelled from between the poles of the magnet, depending upon the direction of current flow. Now a number of variants of this are possible. One can, as in Fig. 14–7b, rig up the circuit to alternate the direction of current flow and then translate the back-and-forth motion of the current-carrying wire into rotational motion. This would not be a very efficient motor, but it might work.

A more efficient variant would be to suspend a loop of wire between the poles of the magnet (Fig. 14–8a). In this arrangement attraction and repulsion between the

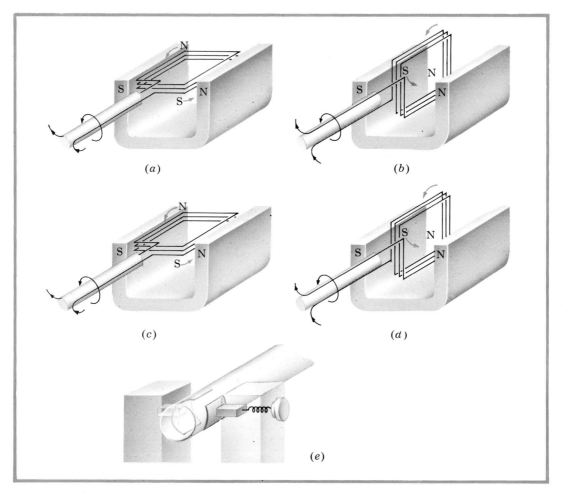

FIG. 14-8

Electric motor. (a) The field of an electromagnet suspended between the poles of a horseshoe magnet will tend to line up. (b) If the current direction is reversed, so is the polarity of the electromagnet, which continues to turn (c) in order to line up the now reversed poles. (d) Just before this occurs, the current is again reversed and the coil continues to rotate. (e) A commutator and brushes are used in motors to reverse current direction.

electromagnet and the permanent magnet produce a twisting motion of the wire loop. If, in addition, a device is introduced to alternate the direction of current flow, the twisting can be sustained and becomes rotation. For instance, the electromagnet coil in Fig. 14–8 tends to rotate in a clockwise direction until attracting poles of the two magnets face one another. Then it stops. But if, after the twisting has started with an initial current, the current is somehow reversed, what were attracting poles become repelling poles with the reversal of the current. Thus the twisting motion is reinforced and the coil continues to rotate. After another half rotation, another current reversal places repelling poles next to one another again and leads to further rotation. Repetition of this procedure then leads to continuous rotation.

This is the principle of the electric motor. Reversal of current direction is accomplished very simply by making the connection between the current source and the rotating electromagnet through a split ring called a *commutator* (Fig. 14–8e) and *brushes*. As the shaft carrying the electromagnet and the commutator rotates, alternate parts of the commutator make contact with the brushes, each time reversing the direction of current through the wire in the electromagnet. While modern direct-current motors have many technical improvements over the simple device illustrated, the basic principles involved are those sketched out here.

An alternate arrangement of the coil-within-magnet produces a measuring device for electric current called a *galvanometer* (Fig. 14–9). If the electromagnet is attached through a semirigid support like a thin wire or a quartz fiber, instead of being allowed to rotate freely as in the motor, it twists its support when current flows. Only partial rotation can occur. The extent of rotation depends on the strength of the magnetic field set up by the coil, which in turn depends on the magnitude of the current. Thus the galvanometer translates

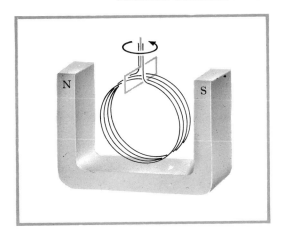

FIG. 14-9

A galvanometer. Current in the wire produces a magnetic field in the coil which causes the coil to twist. The twisting is restricted by the rigid support and depends on the amount of current in the wire. The twisting of the coil thus measures the amount of current.

current magnitude into extent of twist of the coil for measurement.

INDUCED ELECTRIC CURRENT

Oersted and Ampère found that moving electric charge sets up a circular magnetic field surrounding the flow of charge. A few years later Michael Faraday (1791–1867) in England and Joseph Henry (1797–1878) in America found that the converse is true also: a magnetic field produces current in a wire *provided* the wire moves with respect to the magnetic field. The wire must cut the lines of force or be cut by them. For instance, a wire drawn back and forth between the poles of a horseshoe magnet has, while moving relative to the magnetic field, a current flowing in it. This is easily demonstrated by connecting the ends of the wire to a galvanometer (Fig. 14–10a). It is an example of a wire cutting the lines of force. The same effect is produced by pushing a magnet into a coil of wire (Fig. 14–10b). Here the lines of force cut across the wires. Such a current, produced without physical contact to electron-defincient and electron-surplus terminals, is called an *induced* current. Electromagnetic induction ranks with direct electromagnetic effects in its importance in modern technology.

The direction of electron flow in the induced current has an interesting aspect. In the first place, the magnetic lines of force and the motion of the wire must be at an angle to one another for the production of induced current. If they are parallel, no current is induced. Then the direction of the current in the wire is at right angles to both (Fig. 14–10). What is interesting is that the direction of the induced current in the wire is such that the magnetic field it produces opposes the magnetic field through which the wire moves (and which caused the induced current in the first place).

It should be apparent that electromagnetic induction can be used to produce electric current on a large scale, as in electric generating stations, provided the technical or practical problems for maintaining the continuity of the current are solved. Consider again the electric coil inside the poles

of a magnet (Fig. 14–8). In the previous section we determined that if current is furnished by an external source, mechanical motion results. Now consider what happens if mechanical motion is furnished by an external source; for instance, if the coil is attached to a steam- or water-driven turbine. In that case, the coil is made to cut the magnetic field which induces a current. Then, if the coil is attached to an external circuit through a commutator and brushes, the current can be utilized to light lamps, heat heaters, or drive electric motors. This is the basic principle of the generator; in basic construction it is like a motor reversed, though technical details differ.

The connection via a commutator is needed in the generator for the same reason as in the motor (Fig. 14–11). During half of the rotation, the coil cuts the magnetic field in one direction—part *A* upward through the field and part *B* downward. These add to send the current in the direction indicated. But when the coil has gone through half a rotation, *A* begins to cut downward and *B* upward. Now the cur-

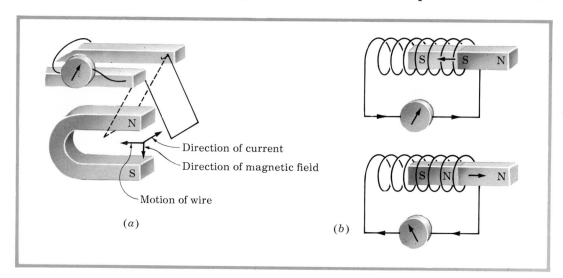

(a)

Direction of current
Direction of magnetic field
Motion of wire

(b)

FIG. 14-10

Induced current. (a) When a wire cuts across the lines of force of a magnetic field, a current is induced in the wire. Electrons flow at right angles to both the direction of the field and the motion of the wire. (b) An induced current is also produced when moving lines of force cut across a stationary wire.

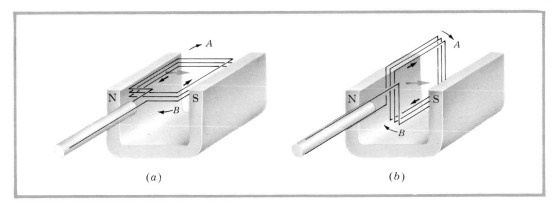

FIG. 14-11

Current reversal in a generator coil. (a) When the part of the coil labeled A moves upward through the field, electrons move from the back to the front. At the same time the part labeled B moves downward and electrons move from front to back. The direction through the coil is in the same sense. (b) One-half rotation later, A moves downward and B upward. The current in the coil reverses.

rent direction is reversed. However, the commutator halves have also moved on, each to the other brush. Thus there is a corresponding reversal at the point of contact with the external circuit which maintains a constant direction of flow. Current in which the charge always flows in the same direction is called *direct current* (abbreviated d-c).

ALTERNATING CURRENT

It should not be assumed that the principles outlined above are directly usable in commercial motors or generators without additional technical inventions. Consider some of the more obvious practical problems. Suppose that the d-c motor in Fig. 14–8 stops with the brushes touching only the insulation that separates the halves of the commutator. How does the motor get started? Or suppose the electromagnet lines up exactly opposing the magnetic field. How does one make it turn in the desired direction, instead of in the opposite direction, both of which are energetically equal? Or how does one manage to maintain the current smooth and steady in a d-c generator when, as the coil cuts near

the pole faces, it cuts a great number of lines of force which produce a greater current, whereas it cuts no lines of force a quarter of a rotation later? All these problems require careful and complex design for actual d-c motors and actual d-c generators. Some of these problems are eliminated or reduced with current that alternately flows back and forth, *alternating current* (a-c).

If the contact between the rotating coil of a generator and the external circuits is continuous rather than reversing as through a commutator, current flow through the external circuit is in one direction for half a coil rotation and in the opposite direction for the other half. Charge moves back and forth. If we plot the magnitude of the current with time, we obtain a curve as in Fig. 14–12. The broken and solid lines indicate the surges of the current that alternately move in one direction and then in the other. In ordinary a-c house current, for instance, the charge completes 60 cycles—120 individual surges—each second.

For heating and lighting and in most electromagnets, the additional effects due to current reversals of alternating current are irrelevant. The devices function almost

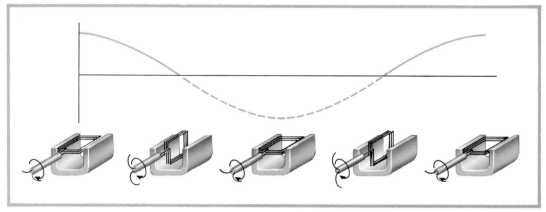

FIG. 14-12

Alternating current. The current in the rotating coil builds up when the coil cuts at right angles to the magnetic field, then drops off as one-quarter of a rotation later the coil moves parallel to the field, then builds up with electron flow in the opposite direction for the next part of the rotation, drops off again, etc. The curve indicates the magnitude and direction of the alternating current.

identically with alternating as with direct current. This does not mean that all d-c devices can be plugged into a-c outlets or vice versa, but it means that, in principle, their operation is the same. However, there are many devices which make specific use of the fact that the current builds up and collapses periodically, with the current-produced magnetic fields likewise building up and collapsing. For instance, alternating current simplifies the construction of an electric motor since a commutator is no longer needed for reversing the magnetic field of the rotating coil (called *armature* in a motor). The most serious technical problem, then, is the synchronization of the rate of rotation with the rate of current reversal. The steady motion of an electric-clock motor, for instance, depends on such perfect synchronization.

The *transformer* specifically uses the alternate buildup and collapse of the magnetic field that accompanies an a-c current. Whereas in a d-c circuit the magnetic field builds as the circuit is closed, remains unchanged while current flows, and collapses when the circuit is broken, in an a-c circuit the field builds up and collapses in one half cycle, builds up and collapses in the opposite direction in the next half

cycle, builds up and collapses again in the first direction in the next half cycle, and so on for each half cycle. Now, a building or collapsing magnetic field has lines of force cutting through space. Consequently, a second wire near the primary, a-c-carrying wire experiences a magnetic field moving relative to it. Current is induced in the second wire during each of the half cycles.

The electromotive force induced in the secondary circuit depends upon the strength of the magnetic field set up by the primary circuit and the number of times that its field cuts the secondary wire. Both of these factors can be altered by coiling both the primary and the secondary. This leads to a simple equation for the voltage change between primary and secondary circuits in a transformer:

$$E_p \, / \, E_s = \text{turns}_p \, / \, \text{turns}_s \qquad (14\text{--}6)$$

For instance, the transformers that reduce house current from a voltage of perhaps 330,000 volts with which it is carried in long-distance lines to the 110 volts of the wall socket have 3,000 turns in the long-distance circuit for each turn in the house circuit. Since energy is conserved in the transformer (except for minor heat losses; the transformer is the most efficient machine known, with an efficiency of around 99 percent), there is a corresponding change in the current between the primary and the secondary. Thus a transformer which reduces the voltage as given in the example—a *step-down* transformer—would at the same time increase the current by a factor of 3,000.

ELECTRON TUBES

While our discussion has focused entirely on current transmitted through wires, every effect we have mentioned has a parallel in cathode-ray tubes, where electrons move through space without the aid of a low-resistance conducting path. Electrons flowing in space produce effects identical with those of current carried in wires, and they are affected by similar effects. The most important interaction perhaps is with magnetic fields. In current-carrying wires this interaction produces the motor; in a stream or beam of electrons it produces deflections which are the basis of radio, TV, and communications in general. (As we briefly indicated, Thomson's measurement of the electronic charge and mass depended on the deflections of cathode rays by both magnetic fields and electric fields.)

To understand the radio tube, we need one additional discovery: electrons can be

pulled from a wire if energy is supplied to liberate them. This is easily achieved. A large potential difference can do it. More commonly the conductor is heated at the point where electron release is desired and electrons are literally boiled off. Then a much smaller positive potential attracts them away.

The simplest radio tube, a diode (two electrodes), consists merely of two wires sealed into an evacuated chamber. One wire is heated. It functions as follows (Fig. 14–14a). In the part of the a-c cycle in which the hot electrode is the cathode, negative with respect to the other electrode, the combination of heat to release the electrons and positive charge on the other electrode allows electron flow through the space between the electrodes. The circuit is complete and current flows in the attached wires also. For the half cycle during which the hot electrode is positive with respect to the cold electrode, on the other hand, no electrons are released. No current flows during this half of the a-c cycle. The diode converts alternating current into pulsed direct current. Current flows in one direction only. It is *rectified*.

While a single diode rectifier wastes half of the a-c current, the combination of two diode rectifiers with the appropriate circuitry can add successive half cycles in such a way that the resulting current is all

A transformer. (a) Alternating current in the primary wire is surrounded by an alternating magnetic field whose lines of force cut across the secondary wire and induce a current in it. (b) Voltage and current in the secondary change if the number of turns of wire differs. The iron core makes transmission of energy more efficient

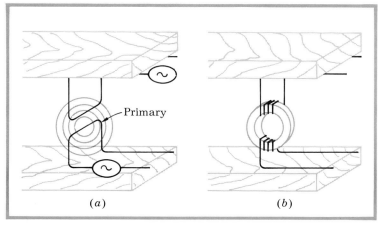

(a)   (b)

FIG. 14-13

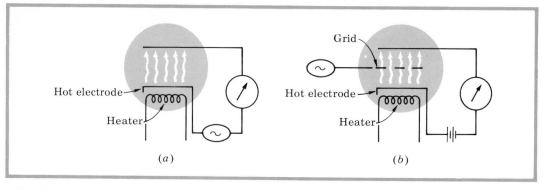

FIG. 14-14

Simple radio tubes. (a) Diode. Current flows through the evacuated tube only during that part of the a-c cycle during which the heated electrode is negative and the cold electrode positive. Current flow is in one direction only and it is interrupted. (b) Triode. The hot electrode is maintained negative and the cold electrode positive. The grid may have positive or negative charge on it from a different circuit. When the grid is positive, it aids electron flow and a strong current results. When the grid is negative, it repels electrons leaving the hot cathode and no current flows.

in the same direction. The introduction of a device called a filter, furthermore, can somewhat smooth the intermittent surges of the rectified circuit and produce a nearly constant flow of direct current.

A triode, a vacuum tube with three electrodes, performs another important function—amplification. In the amplifier triode, the main circuit is d-c, interrupted between the hot cathode and cold anode (Fig. 14–14b). Hence electron flow through the tube is always in the same direction. But between these two electrodes, there is a third electrode called the *grid*, so constructed that electrons may pass through it. The grid is powered by a second circuit, typically of varying voltage. Then, when the grid is positive with respect to the hot cathode, the positive potential on the grid adds to the positive potential on the anode to produce a strong current through the tube. If the grid potential decreases, the electric field governing electron flow through the tube also decreases, and the current in the tube decreases correspondingly. Since the grid is much closer to the hot cathode than is the anode, its contribution to the field at the cathode is much greater. Hence electron flow is influenced

to a far greater extent by the grid voltage than by the constant positive voltage at the anode. With a negative charge on the grid, it is even possible to stop electron flow through the tube despite the positive charge on the anode. It is thus possible to use a changing weak current in the grid to produce a similarly changing but much larger current through the triode.

Of course, it is possible to feed the larger triode output into the grid of another triode and amplify the current still further. Through such stages a very weak signal, such as the signal picked up by a radio antenna, can be amplified until the current which carries it is strong enough to power a radio speaker.

Radio tubes with more than three electrodes are in use. The extra electrodes, however, serve chiefly to increase the reliability in amplification and to reduce distortions of the amplified signal as compared to the weak input. These distortions, which result from the imperfect operation in practice of what in theory appears as perfect, are called, appropriately enough, *noise*. In communication theory the term noise applies generally to factors in transmission and amplification that distort the original true signal. Thus, in mouth-to-mouth communication, the embellishments of gossip constitute noise. In television transmission, fuzziness caused in both the sound and the picture would also be classed as noise.

APPLICATIONS IN COMMON DEVICES

In principle, if not in full technical detail, we can now understand the operation of many of our common household appliances. The TV tube, for instance, is only a sophisticated cross between the amplifying triode and Thomson's cathode-ray tube.

A TV picture consists of about 200,000 dots arranged in rows across the face of the tube, each dot with a brightness corresponding to the brightness of the displayed picture. These 200,000 dots are produced one at a time by electrons impinging on a coating on the tube face, with more energetic electrons producing brighter dots.

Finally, the entire set of 200,000 dots is reproduced 30 times each second, allowing for changes in brightness corresponding to motion in the picture. (The rate of change of the picture is much too fast for our visual receptors, which cannot distinguish the changes in individual dots but, instead, fill in the dark time with "visual memory.")

The technical problem, therefore, is to focus an electron beam on about 200,000 different locations within 1/30th sec and to adjust the electron energy at each location to produce spots of the desired brightness. Fortunately electrons are so small that the time scale is more than adequate to make the necessary adjustments in a focusing current and a modulating current.

The electron beam is emitted by a hot cathode toward an anode with a hole in it to allow passage of the beam (Fig. 14–15). Between the two there is a grid, charged by the amplified TV signal, to modify the energy of the electrons in the beam. Spot brightness is controlled by this grid. Spot location is obtained by sending the beam

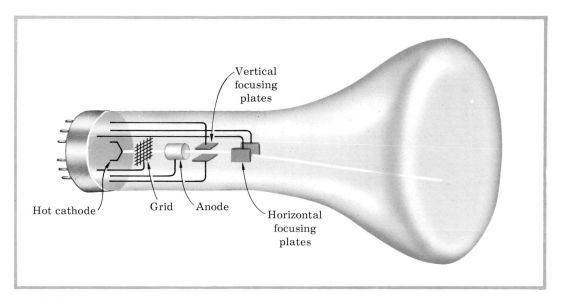

Vertical focusing plates

Hot cathode   Grid   Anode

Horizontal focusing plates

FIG. 14-15

Television tube. Electrons from the hot cathode pass through a grid which regulates their energy and through an anode with a hole in it. Then they pass between horizontal and vertical plates which bend the beam toward the appropriate spot on the face of the tube. A bright spot results from the collision of the electrons with the material that coats the face of the tube.

between a set of vertically directing plates and a set of horizontally directing plates, fed by a separate directing current. This current changes about 200,000 times for each single picture to locate the beam at the appropriate spot on the face of the tube, and repeats the process 30 times each second. Moreover, the beam is interrupted 200,000 times by the grid to produce individual dots. Finally, a timing circuit synchronizes the dot location with the location of the corresponding dot on the TV camera tube so that a signal from the upper left-hand corner of the camera appears also in the upper left-hand corner of the receiver, not halfway down the tube face.

This is the essence of the operation of the picture tube, the most important part of the receiver. At the other end, the TV camera tube contains a technically much more complex mechanism for producing the converse of the above. In 1/30 sec the camera tube produces about 200,000 separate electrical impulses, each for a part of the picture and of a current intensity that corresponds to the brightness of that part of the picture. And between camera tube and picture tube are amplification, transmitting, receiving, and more amplification.

The complexities of the design of the camera tube prevent us from discussing the mechanism for producing an electrical signal for the video component of TV. In contrast, the principle of the audio pickup is rather simple. In the microphone there is a diaphragm sensitive to the incoming frequencies and intensities. It vibrates in resonance with the incoming sound energy. The diaphragm is attached to a material whose electric resistance changes with pressure. In the earliest microphones it was a little container with granules of conducting carbon. As they were compressed, their resistance dropped. Newer microphones use other pressure-sensitive materials, the so-called *piezoelectrics*. A current of constant potential is fed through the piezoelectric material of the microphone. Since its resistance changes in resonance with the sound waves, the magnitude of the current changes similarly. Thus the sound waves are transformed into electrical impulses that vary with corresponding frequencies and intensities. This fluctuating current is then amplified and transmitted.

Sound production from the electrical signal then uses an electromagnet. In the speaker the current is fed into the coil of an electromagnet which attracts a magnet attached to another diaphragm. The variations of the sound signal current produce fluctuations in the strength of the magnet

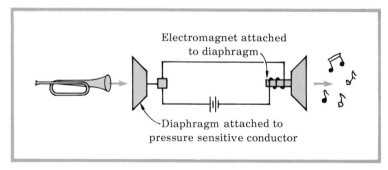

FIG. 14-16

Microphone and speaker. Incoming sound produces vibrations in a diaphragm attached to a pressure-sensitive conducting material. As the pressure on this material changes, its resistance changes and a varying current results that changes with the same frequencies as the sound. In the speaker, the current actuates an electromagnet attached to another diaphragm. As the current varies, the strength of the electromagnet changes and the diaphragm vibrates with the frequencies of the current. This vibrating diaphragm reproduces the sound.

which set the diaphragm into vibrations with the same frequencies and intensities as the variations in the signal current. The vibrating diaphragm thus produces the sound.

That outlines some of the principles behind radio and television communication, but we have said nothing about the gap between the transmitter and the antenna. We turn to it in the next chapter.

Questions and Problems

1. Draw a circuit in which two diode rectifiers produce a rectified d-c current.

2. How can a-c current be converted to d-c? In automobile radios the direct current from the battery is converted to alternating current by a vibrator that interrupts the current. How does it work?

3. Does a 1,660-watt toaster draw more current than a 60-watt lamp? Does it have a higher resistance?

4. What current flows through a 60-watt light bulb in a house circuit (110 volts)? What is its resistance? What charge does it use in 1 hr?

5. One horsepower is approximately 720×10^7 ergs. What current is required by a 1-hp motor operating on 110-volt alternating current?

6. In actual fact 110-volt alternating current flows under an average voltage of only about 70 volts. Why?

7. What happens in a wire if it is next to another wire attached to a d-c source and (a) the circuit is closed; (b) current flows in the circuit; (c) the circuit is broken?

8. A 110-volt circuit is attached to two 60-watt bulbs in parallel. What is the voltage drop across each? What is the total current in the circuit?

9. The two bulbs are then connected in series. Now what is the voltage drop across each? the total current? What happens to the power used by the circuit compared to Question 8?

10. Is your home wired in series or in parallel? Consider your answers to Questions 8 and 9 and suggest what the other wiring scheme would do to home appliances.

11. The doorbell circuit of a house is 6 volts. Compute the ratio of turns in the transformer which converts 110-volt house current to the doorbell-circuit voltage.

12. What is the charge of an electron, in coulombs? In work with particles like electrons, the unit electron-volt (ev) is used to express energy. One ev is the energy required to move one electron through a potential difference of one volt. How many ergs equal 1 ev?

13. Use the left-hand rule and the statement that the induced current produces a field that opposes the inducing field to determine the direction of induced-current flow.

14. An insulator can be considered a circuit of infinite resistance. Explain.

15. How does the power consumption of a resistance change with R? Show that $W = I^2R$.

16. Inside a toaster the wires are red-hot; outside, the wire to the wall socket stays cool. Explain.

17. Can a transformer change the frequency (cycles/sec) of an a-c current? Explain.

18. There is a potential difference between the wings of an airplane cutting through the earth's magnetic field. Explain. Could a wire be attached to the wing tips to light a bulb in the cockpit? Explain.

19. House current is sometimes brought in by a single wire and the earth is used as a second wire. Explain why the earth is needed and what it does.

20. Why did we say that the forces produced by electromagnets are unique? Contrast them with forces produced in other ways.

21. Some properties of some circuits are given below. Complete the table:

W (watts)	Q (coul)	t (sec)	R (ohms)	I (amp)	V (volts)
60	12			12	
	7	5			35
		10	12	10	
75		3	3		
	20			18	12

22. Repeat the first example on page 217 for an automobile with a 12-volt system.

23. Predict what will happen if a strongly electrified glass rod is brought near a shining light bulb; a TV tube; if a magnet is brought near them.

24. How many electrostatic units are there in 1 coul?

Suggestions for Further Reading

Electric currents are treated more fully in:

Christiansen, G. S., and Paul H. Garrett: *Structure and Change,* W. H. Freeman and Company, San Francisco, 1960. Chapter 17.

Physical Science Study Committee: *Physics,* D. C. Heath and Company, Boston, 1960. Chapter 31.

Rogers, Eric M.: *Physics for the Inquiring Mind,* Princeton University Press, Princeton, N.J., 1960. Chapters 32 and 37.

More information about electromagnetic phenomena can be found in:

Fink, Donald G., and David M. Luytens: *The Physics of Television,* Anchor Books, Doubleday & Company, Inc., Garden City, N.Y., 1960 (paperback).

Pierce, John R.: *Electrons and Waves,* Anchor Books, Doubleday & Company, Inc., Garden City, N.Y., 1964 (paperback).

Chapter 15

Electromagnetic Radiation

Radio and TV convert electric currents into radio waves which transfer the signal energy through space. The production of induced currents gives us one clue as to how this might be done. In the transformer, for instance, the energy from one circuit produces current in a second circuit without contact between them. The energy from the first circuit sets up a changing magnetic field in space, and the second circuit intercepts the magnetic field. There is no direct physical contact; nothing of a material sort passes. In this sense, even an ordinary house current transmits energy through space, however, the transmission drops off very rapidly with distance. Even a few centimeters away, the energy of a 60-cycle alternating current is barely noticeable.

The situation is entirely different with high-frequency alternating current. Currents that alternate direction 100,000 to millions of times per second transmit a major fraction of their energy into space and, furthermore, have that energy persist over long distances. In that form it is referred to as *electromagnetic radiation* or *electromagnetic energy*.

ELECTROMAGNETIC ENERGY

The efficient transmission of electrical energy through space occurs only from high-frequency a-c sources. However, under one special condition ordinary house current behaves quite similarly. Sixty-cycle alternating current flows in an interrupted circuit provided an efficient means exists to transmit the energy across the gap. Then the space of the gap becomes part of the circuit. A pair of parallel conducting plates with an insulator between (Fig. 15–1), called a *condenser*, functions in this way. Either the current of the circuit, or induction across the gap, or both, produce opposite charges on the plates of the condenser. A strong and directed electric field arises between them which carries the energy of the current.

Let us see how a condenser works in a circuit. A generator pushes electrons onto one plate while withdrawing them from the other. A field builds up in the condenser gap as charge builds up on the plates. This charge opposes further electron flow in the same direction. In a d-c circuit the condenser becomes charged and current flow stops. But in an a-c circuit the direction of current flow reverses at half-cycle intervals. Hence the accumulation of charge on the condenser plates is only temporary because in successive half cycles the current withdraws electrons from the negative plate and pushes them toward the positive plate. Plate charge and field direction in the condenser are reversed just when the accumulation of charge might prevent further electron flow. Current reversal, plate-charge reversal, and field reversal operate together to maintain efficient energy transfer through the condenser.

In a 60-cycle a-c circuit the chief concern is the efficient transmission of current through a circuit. Losses across a gap, in this case, are waste. They dissipate energy quickly over short distances and stop the current if the gap is too wide. One reason for the geometry of the condenser is to minimize such losses. With high-frequency alternating current in a radio transmitter the situation is quite different. Transmission of energy across a gap is less dependent on condenser geometry. Almost any geometrical arrangement of the gap maintains current flow although there may be considerable energy losses. However, such energy losses are desired in radio and TV transmission since that is how the signal is put into space. Thus radio and TV stations put their signals into high-frequency current because they want to radiate the signal energy, and they use antennas designed for maximum energy loss—maximum transfer of the signal energy into space.

Electromagnetic energy radiated by high-frequency sources differs somewhat from the energy carried across a condenser in 60-cycle a-c circuit. Its character can be deduced from the geometry of good transmitters. Radio signals are transmitted efficiently if the antenna consists of a straight wire with the high-frequency a-c source in the middle (Fig. 15–2). The ends of

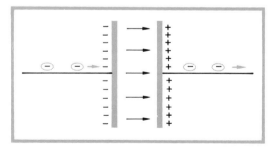

FIG. 15-1

A condenser. The buildup of charge on the plates permits the transfer of energy across the gap.

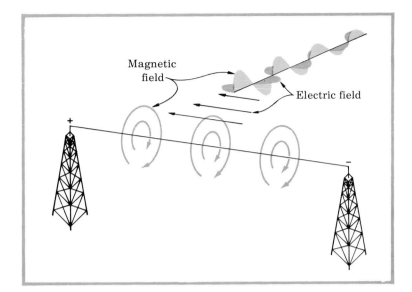

The emission of energy by a radio antenna. The electrons surge back and forth in the wire and produce a magnetic field because of their motion and an electric field because of the separation of charge.

FIG. 15-2

the antenna serve the same function as the condenser plates. In one half cycle, the source sends a surge of electrons down one half of the antenna while withdrawing them from the other. In the next half cycle, it reverses the process. This has two effects. The alternating surges of electrons through the antenna, just like the charges on the condenser plates, set up an alternating electric field. This field, however, is not focused and extends far into space. The direction of the lines of force in the field is parallel to the direction of the electron displacements, parallel to the antenna. Second, the alternating surges of electrons in the antenna also produce an alternating magnetic field whose direction is around the antenna, at right angles to the direction of the electric field. Thus the antenna radiates its energy by producing an electric and a magnetic field, electromagnetic energy. The two fields are related, of course, since they arise from the same surges of high-frequency alternating current.

The prediction and subsequent discovery of the radiation of electromagnetic energy, which ultimately led to the invention of radio and TV, is one of the most interesting chapters in the history of science. It is a clear case of a theoretical prediction of a

totally unknown phenomenon paving the way for the most practical of uses 25 years later.

The initial discoveries of Oersted and Ampère that currents produce magnetic fields, and of Faraday and Henry that relative motion between a magnetic field and a conductor produces a current, are at the beginning of this history. When these effects were formulated quantitatively by mathematical equations, the British theoretical physicist James Clerk Maxwell (1831–1879) noticed that something was missing from the equations that describe alternating electric currents and their associated magnetic fields. A gap was left in the mathematical description although the equations apply to interdependent phenomena. So he set about to modify the equations.

Maxwell was successful although to solve the problem, he had to make a strange and totally unsuspected addition to the equations. He found that electromagnetic energy had been missing from the earlier equations; electromagnetic energy is part of the relationship between currents and magnetic fields. According to his modified equations, this energy travels with the speed of light, behaves like light, and can be detected only

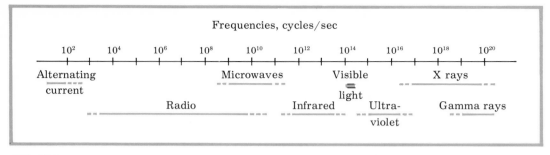

FIG. 15-3

The electromagnetic spectrum. Electromagnetic radiation consists of electric and magnetic fields that alternate hundreds to billions of billions of times each second. (Sidney Rosen, Robert Siegfried, and John M. Dennison, "Concepts in Physical Science," Harper & Row, Publishers, Inc., New York, 1965)

if of high frequency. Furthermore, his equations strongly suggested that light itself might be electromagnetic energy.

Maxwell's predictions were so astonishing that at least one of his colleagues attempted to prove his theory impossible, also on theoretical grounds. Experimental tests could not be made at the time, 1865, because sources of high-frequency current had not been designed—there was no purpose for them until Maxwell gave them one—and there were no detectors for high-frequency electromagnetic radiation either. The predictions were untested for more than 20 years. Then, in work from 1886 to 1888, a young German, Heinrich Hertz (1857–1894), devised an apparatus to produce the predicted electromagnetic radiations and to detect them a short distance away. Confirmation was unmistakable and complete. The radiation behaved like light though its frequency was lower. It could be reflected, refracted, reinforced. Later, when Hertz found a way to measure its velocity of transmission, he found, in accordance with prediction, that it was equal to the speed of light.

It was a surprise to the young Italian, Guglielmo Marconi (1874–1937), when he read of Hertz's work a short time after the latter's death in 1894, that none of the physicists who were experimenting with electromagnetic energy had considered using it for communication. While Marconi made no contributions to the theoretical understanding of electromagnetic radiation, he made discoveries necessary for its practical use. In 1896 he sent the first wireless message, in code, over a sizable distance. From that grew first radio, then radar during the wartime, then TV.

The frequencies used for communications purposes are between 10^5 and 10^9 cycles/sec. Since Marconi's time, additional electromagnetic radiations have been found to complete the *electromagnetic spectrum*, as the entire range of frequencies is called. Infrared, ultraviolet, X rays, and gamma rays have been discovered, all of them energy transmitted through space as alternating electric and magnetic fields. Figure 15–3 shows the frequencies associated with the various rays of the electromagnetic spectrum. Notice that visible light is only one of many, and that it occupies a very narrow band in the entire spectrum.

Since electromagnetic energy consists of alternating electric and magnetic fields, it is appropriate to describe it by means of waves (although we shall have to reconsider this point later). The electric and magnetic forces are exerted at right angles to the direction of wave propagation; the wave is transverse. However, the displacements in this case relate to force fields, not to the physical displacement of actual matter as in the case of earthquake and water waves (Chap. 12). Consequently it is possible to dispense with the requirement we postulated there, that an elastic restoring medium is necessary to carry transverse waves.

This point is of intense historical interest, for until a distinction was made between the nature of transverse waves carrying energy via electric and magnetic force fields and transverse waves carrying energy via actual particles, it was thought that an elastic medium, the *ether,* had to pervade all space to carry the electromagnetic energy. Physicists spent much time searching for and speculating about the ether. The ether was never found, although the famous Michelson-Morley experiment of 1887 was set up in such a manner that the ether could not have been missed had it been there. The trouble was elsewhere. In considering the character of the transverse electromagnetic energy, physicists were too strongly bound by the analogy with water waves and the actual particles of matter needed to carry them. This misled them with respect to electric and magnetic forces that, as we saw in Chap. 13, can act at a distance and through vacuum without actual physical contact through matter. Thus the analogy carried them beyond the simplest requirements of the case. Nature, of course, was and is unaware of the analogy and manages to transmit electromag-netic waves through space even without an elastic ether, which consequently has never been discovered.

THE SPEED OF LIGHT

It is convenient to think of light waves, as we thought of sound waves, in terms of single beams or rays which move outward from the source. These rays vibrate with a characteristic frequency and have a wavelength governed by the relationship between frequency, wavelength, and the velocity of light, $n\lambda = c$ in which c is the designation of the velocity of light ($186,000$ miles/sec $= 3 \times 10^{10}$ cm/sec).

In spite of its very large value, c has been known reasonably accurately for about 300 years, having been determined by an ingenious astronomical method by Olaus Roemer (1644–1710) in 1666. Galileo had discovered the satellites of Jupiter with his telescope. Thereafter their orbits around Jupiter had been computed. Now Roemer noticed that one of the satellites periodically ran ahead, and then behind, the computed position. Specifically, when the earth and Jupiter were both on the same side of the sun, the satellite ran ahead by about 660 sec. On the other hand, when the two planets were on opposite sides of the sun,

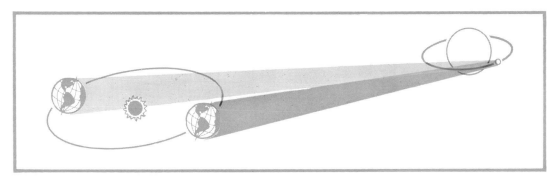

FIG. 15-4

First determination of the speed of light. When the earth is on the far side of the sun with respect to Jupiter, the satellites of Jupiter seem to lag behind in their motion, and when the earth is on the near side, they seem to run ahead. Olaus Roemer correctly assumed that the difference is due to the time it takes light to travel across the earth's orbit, and from it he calculated the speed of light.

the satellite lagged about 660 sec. In between, it was more nearly on schedule.

Roemer quite correctly reasoned that the difference could be accounted for by the time it took for the information about the satellite's position to reach the observer on earth; that is, by the speed with which light travels from Jupiter to the earth. While Roemer's value of about 140,000 miles/sec for the speed of light is only about three-fourths of today's accepted value, the velocity he determined was so very large that he was not believed. His error, by the way, resulted from poor time measurements—the value is 500 sec—and from an inadequate knowledge at that time of the diameter of the earth's orbit.

LIGHT WAVES

The frequencies represented by the visible part of the electromagnetic spectrum range from 7.5×10^{14} cycles/sec, or a wavelength of about 4×10^{-5} cm, to 4.3×10^{14} cycles/sec, or a wavelength of about 7×10^{-5} cm. The lower frequencies make up the red end of the rainbow and the higher frequencies, successively, the colors orange, yellow, green, blue, and violet. White light is a mixture of all these frequencies, black the absence of any light, and other colors and hues are sensed through the simultaneous stimulation of the eye by mixtures of frequencies.

Light waves exhibit all the phenomena we encountered with sound waves (Chap. 12). They are reflected from certain surfaces, with the angle of reflection equal to the angle of incidence. If the surface is rough, scattering and dissipation of the ray occur; if the surface is smooth as in a mirror, reflection is sharp and directed. In addition, light may be absorbed—for instance, on black surfaces—or transmitted, as through glass, water, some plastics, and other *transparent* media.

While the mechanisms differ completely because of the difference in the basic char-

acter of sound and light, all the above phenomena can be similarly described and are formally equivalent. The absorption of light energy by a black body produces heat as does the absorption of sound by soundproofing materials. This can easily be demonstrated with candle wax on a shiny can lid and on one painted black. If both are placed near a lamp, the wax on the black lid melts long before the wax on the shiny lid because of the heating due to light absorption.

Light mirrors, likewise, act like sound mirrors. They may focus light rays, as in the parabolic mirror of an automobile head lamp, or they may merely reflect them, as in the bathroom mirror. While the path of the light rays is governed by the law of reflection, equal angles of incidence and reflection, our eyes are subject to an interesting illusion because we "see" ourselves in a mirror in a position we can't possibly occupy. The actual path of the light rays emanating from a chin being shaved, for instance, is indicated in Fig. 15–7 in solid lines. Some of the rays bounce off the mirror and enter the eyes. The person shaving, however, "sees" his chin in the position sketched by the shaded lines, right in the middle of the wall, because of the way he has learned to interpret visual sensations. The eye and brain extend the

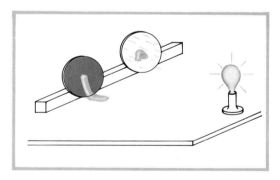

FIG. 15-5

Absorption and reflection of light. Light is absorbed and transformed into heat by black objects; it is reflected by white or silvery objects. Consequently wax melts quickly on the black lid but remains rigid on the shiny lid.

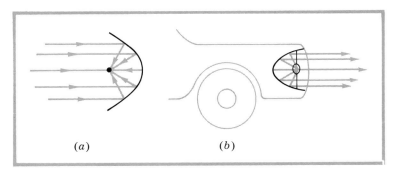

A mirror whose curvature is that of a parabola reflects parallel rays of light to focus at a point (a). In the automobile headlight a parabolic mirror (b) reflects the light coming from the lamp into beams of parallel light.

(a)   (b)

FIG. 15-6

The light rays travel from the chin to the mirror and into the eyes. The eyes and brain interpret them, however, as if they had come from the virtual image behind the mirror.

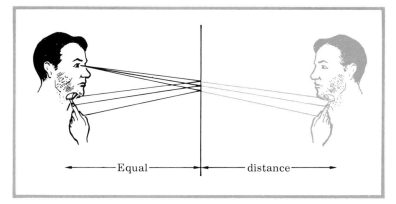

Equal ———————————— distance

FIG. 15-7

light path right into the mirror and interpret the sensation as if it had come from the *virtual* image there.

As in the case of sound, reflection of light can lead to reinforcement and interference, although because of the extremely small wavelengths of the vibrations, much smaller and more precise path differences are needed to produce them. The rainbow colors of oil spilled on the surface of water are an illustration of this effect (Fig. 15–8).

The layer of oil is a partly reflecting, partly transmitting medium, as is the water on which it floats. Hence, light rays impinging on the surface may be reflected from the top of the oil, they may pass through to be reflected by the water-oil interface, or they may pass into the water. It is evident that rays reflected by the oil-water interface must travel a slightly longer distance before they are seen than those reflected by the surface of the oil. Because of that path difference, the interface rays

may emerge in phase or out of phase with the surface rays. If the path difference is exactly one full wavelength, or two, three, four, etc., full wavelengths longer, then the two sets of rays are in phase and reinforce. For other differences in path length, partial or complete interference occurs. But the extra path length depends on two things—distance between surface and interface, and the angle at which the ray strikes. For very sharp angles of incidence the extra path is short; for slanting rays the extra path is long. This suggests that reinforcement occurs at acute angles for the short wavelength at the blue end of the spectrum and at slanting angles for the other colors. In fact, a number of bands of blue and red are seen because the depth of the oil layer is rather large compared to the wavelength of light so that reinforcement occurs at angles where the path difference is one, two, three, four, etc., wavelengths.

Since path differences of the order of 10^{-5}

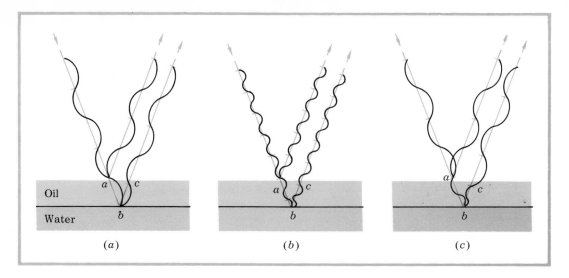

FIG. 15-8

Reinforcement and interference at an oil-water surface. Some of the light is reflected at the surface of the oil layer; some enters the oil and is reflected at the water-oil interface. If the extra path through the oil layer—a to b to c—is exactly 1 wavelength longer (a) or 2 wavelengths longer (b) or any other whole-number wavelengths longer, the two rays emerge in phase and reinforce. If the extra path is exactly ½ wavelength, or 1½, 2½, etc., wavelengths long (c), the two rays emerge out of phase and interfere.

cm are necessary to produce interference patterns in light waves and since these are rare in our usual environment, light interference is not a common phenomenon in our experience.

REFRACTION

The passage of light from one transparent medium into another gives rise to a very useful effect. Unless the ray strikes the surface at a right angle, it is bent at the interface to an extent depending upon the rate of transmission of light in the two media. In vacuum, as we indicated above, light travels at a rate of 3×10^{10} cm/sec; in air or gases, slightly slower; in all other transparent media, considerably more slowly.

In passing from one medium into another, the frequency of the light wave does not change but the wavelength does. This allows us to visualize what happens at the interface. Consider a beam of light consisting of individual rays as shown in Fig. 15–9. The lowest ray in the diagram enters the slower medium—something like glass or water—before the others. It is slowed down and its wavelength somewhat shortened. While this happens, the other rays still travel rapidly through air. The next ray, of course, is slowed down next, while the others still move as rapidly as before. Gradually, as one ray after the other enters the medium of lower velocity, it is slowed down. But the net effect of this, as the figure indicates, is that the lowest ray is delayed most and the uppermost least, bending the entire beam toward a line perpendicular to the surface, the *normal*, when the waves enter a medium of lower velocity of transmission. On emerging from the slower medium into a faster one, the entire process is reversed. At that interface the beam is bent away from the normal.

Refraction, as the bending of light rays at interfaces between media through which they travel at different rates is called, makes possible the use of lenses for focusing, enlarging, and similar tasks. These desirable effects result from the bending of light rays at the interface to gather to one point the light striking the entire surface of the lens.

Consider, for instance, the action of the convex lens in Fig. 15–10. (A *convex* lens is curved outward. It is thicker in the middle than at the ends. A *concave* lens has the opposite curvature. It is thinner in the middle than at the ends.) The light bulb in the figure sends light in all directions. Now if the lens has the appropriate geometry, all light rays from the bulb that strike the lens will be bent so that they come together again at some point on the

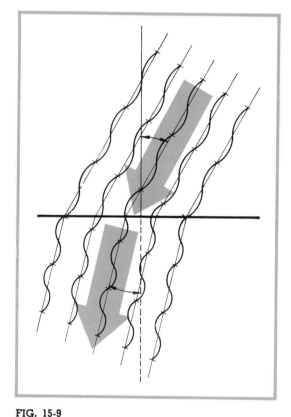

FIG. 15-9

The refraction of light. The light moves more slowly in the lower medium than in the upper. Consequently wave crests progress a shorter distance each time period, and the beam as a whole is bent toward the normal.

other side of the lens. A *real* image of the bulb is produced at that point, and the energy of the light rays can be detected there by the eye, as an image on a card, or by photographic film. Naturally, not only the light of the bulb but any light reflected by its base is focused by the lens, producing an image of the entire bulb. (The path of the rays through the lens is such that the image is inverted.)

The cornea and lens of the eye are merely such a lens system which focuses diverging rays from the objects we see onto the retina, where they produce nervous impulses that are interpreted in the brain as sight. Like all convex lenses, the cornea and lens invert the images. However, our nervous system is flexible and it reinverts the image as it interprets the sensation so that we are not conscious of the inversion. (Experiments have been carried out with people wearing additional inverting lenses. After a brief period of confusion, the brain simply flip-flopped the nerve impulses and they "saw" right side up again.) Defects in vision are due to the inability of the cornea to focus the image properly on the retina. In most cases, the addition of artificial lenses —eyeglasses—helps restore the focusing action.

The exact fate of a light ray at a lens surface depends upon the angle of incidence. How a set of rays will be focused by the lens, then, is affected by the distance of the object from the lens and by the lens curvature. Optics is a well-developed science, and algebraic equations exist by means of which the relation of object, lens, and image can be described quite precisely. We shall be satisfied with approximate answers that can be obtained by a geometric approach.

At the lens surfaces, rays emanating from each point of the object are bent, usually in such a manner that they converge and produce an image at another point. The eye may simply register the image (Fig. 15–10), or it may, as in the case of a plane mirror, imagine that the

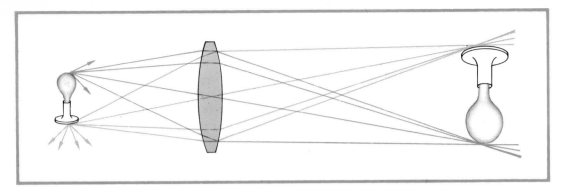

FIG. 15-10

The focusing action of a convex lens. Light is emitted by the object in all directions. The lens intercepts a fraction of the light rays and focuses them on a point. If a card is held at that point, a real image of the object appears. If the card is held elsewhere, the rays emanating from one part of the object are scattered throughout space and no image is visible.

light rays came straight through instead of having been bent (Fig. 15–7). Thus the effects of a lens can be varied. We shall illustrate this with a microscope (Fig. 15–12).

The objective lens of the microscope gathers light from the object on the stage and inverts it in a real image within the microscope. Since nothing intercepts the light rays at the point where the image is formed, they diverge again and pass on into the ocular lens, which bends them toward the eye, but in such a manner that they actually separate. The cornea of the eye then focuses these separating rays on the retina.

As far as the eye is concerned, the light rays that strike it appear to be coming from points a long distance away and, therefore, from a very large object. The eye interprets them as coming from the *virtual* image indicated in the figure. Thus the geometry of the microscope and of its lenses produces magnification.

Refracting telescopes (those with lenses) have similar magnifying systems. Reflecting telescopes (those with mirrors), on the other hand, use the optics illustrated in Fig. 15–13. In these, light is first focused by a large curved mirror before lenses produce a final small image. It should be noted that these magnifying instruments are also light-gathering instruments, for they bring together on the very small area of the eye light which would otherwise be spread over a much larger surface.

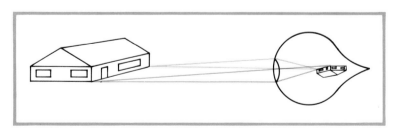

The eye. The cornea and lens serve to focus divergent rays onto the retina.

FIG. 15-11

PRISMS

The previous section sketched the use and function of lenses, though it hardly scratched the surface of the science of lens making, or the geometry of light rays. The details as usual require refinements of the basic principles. For example, refraction at interfaces is the predominant factor governing lens construction; however, the velocity of light in media such as glass is not uniform but depends somewhat on the frequency. As a result, the different colors of the spectrum are bent to slightly different

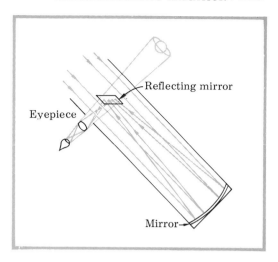

FIG. 15-13

A reflecting telescope, with a focusing design invented by Sir Isaac Newton. The light is focused by a curved mirror at the base of the telescope. A small flat mirror deflects the converging rays to the side where a lens system focuses them further for the eye.

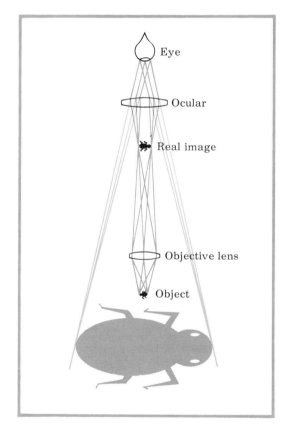

FIG. 15-12

A microscope. The objective lens inverts and focuses the light rays from the object to an image within the microscope. But the light rays pass on into the ocular lens, which focuses them again for the eye. To the eye, however, the light rays appear as if they had come from the virtual image.

extents, and various ways must be found to minimize the separation of colors in lenses due to this effect. *Chromatic aberration,* as it is called, is definitely a major problem in lens making.

The same effect can be used to advantage, however. It governs the use of prisms to separate white light into its component colors precisely because of the differences in the velocity of transmission of the various frequencies. Or, if the source emits only a limited set of frequencies, a prism can separate them into *monochromatic* lines, lines of single-frequency waves. A prism works in this way because its geometry produces additional separation at each interface rather than offsetting at one interface the effect produced at the other (Fig. 15–14).

The range of effects which can be produced with light rays and prisms is large, and they are an interesting field for amateur investigation. We shall mention only two more.

We implied when discussing the oil-on-water interference bands that rarely does

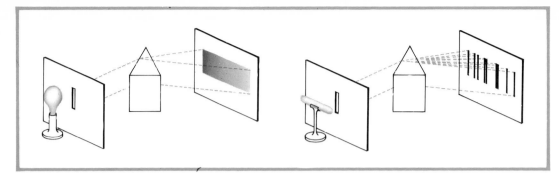

FIG. 15-14

A prism. Because of small differences in the speed of transmission of different wavelengths of light, white light is separated into different colors at both interfaces between air and a prism. If the source emits only a limited number of wavelengths, a series of monochromatic lines results.

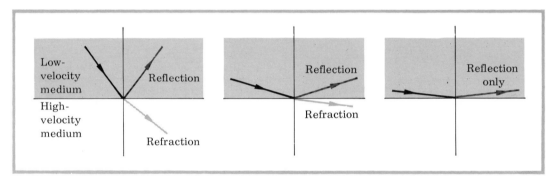

FIG. 15-15

Reflection and refraction. Normally both reflection and refraction occur at interfaces. However, rays that strike the interface from a low-velocity medium at great angles cannot emerge.

reflection, refraction, or absorption occur to the exclusion of the others, but that in most cases at least two, and possibly all three, of these effects take place at an interface. There are some exceptions.

For instance, take a ray of light emerging from a low-velocity medium into a high-velocity medium, as in Fig. 15–15. It is bent at the interface away from the normal although, typically, reflection as well as refraction occurs. Now consider what happens as the incident beam approaches the surface more and more obliquely. The emerging refracted beam, already more oblique than the incident beam, becomes more nearly parallel to the surface. Indeed,

there is a critical angle of incidence on the interface beyond which the beam cannot emerge but is totally reflected. Because of this effect, it has been found possible to send light down curved plastic tubes from which the light cannot escape because it strikes the surface everywhere at too oblique an angle.

The second interesting effect is known as *polarization*. Electromagnetic radiation consists of electric and magnetic fields oriented at right angles to the direction of light propagation. Now, in a typical light beam, there is no further orientation; the electric field may point anywhere around the direction of the ray and the magnetic field lines

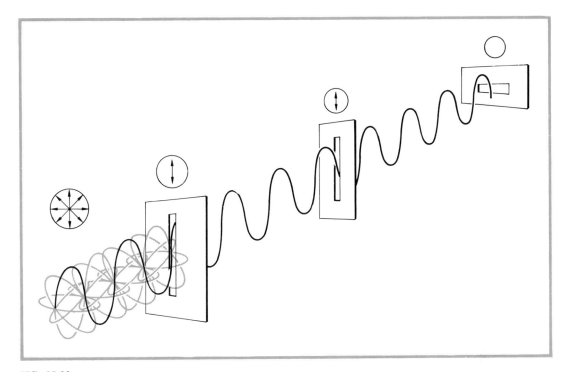

FIG. 15-16

Polarization. In ordinary light the electric and magnetic fields may be oriented in any direction around the light beam. Polarizers allow the transmission of waves which are oriented only in one specific direction. A second polarizer can stop the light beam completely.

up accordingly. But there are certain substances, *polarizers,* which are transparent to light only if its electric field is oriented in a particular direction, and which absorb all light rays with electric fields oriented differently. (The distribution of electrons and positive charge in these materials is such that they interact with and absorb electromagnetic fields except those oriented in one specific direction.) Hence, when the light beam emerges after passage through a polarizer, only that fraction of the individual waves is left whose electric and magnetic fields all vibrate in the same direction. The light is now *polarized.* Interposing a second polarizer oriented at right angles to the first then stops the polarized beam entirely. There are other substances which rotate polarized light through small angles, an effect which can be measured in a polarimeter, a device with a polarizer, a space for the rotating material, and a second polarizer. The angle of orientation between the first and second polarizers indicates the extent of *optical activity* of the rotating material. This, as we shall see, has some interesting consequences for the chemistry of life and speculations regarding the origin of the universe and evolution.

Polarization is good confirming evidence for the fact that light consists of transverse waves, because one can easily imagine a sievelike arrangement for a polarizer that allows transverse waves to pass provided they are oriented properly, while stopping those which are not so oriented. Indeed, this and refraction (it can be shown that if light consisted of particles, it should be refracted away from the normal when entering something like glass, rather than toward the normal as is found) make it very hard even to consider the possibility that light might consist not of waves but of particles. But Newton had already very firmly proposed that light consists of particles, and we now must examine this notion also.

PHOTONS

We must reexamine the idea that light consists of particles because of several experimental facts that do not fit with the wave description of electromagnetic radiation. Consider the various frequencies of the electromagnetic spectrum. It is well known that radar and radio waves have no effect upon us and that we can safely pass near a very powerful radio emitter without sensing its energy. (A few instances in which metallic tooth fillings began to sing under such conditions are known.) However, even a weak source of infrared, the next higher frequency, can be felt as heat, though without damage of any kind. Likewise, very weak light sources are sensed, have an effect on the body. Why no effect from powerful low-frequency sources when weak higher frequencies are detected? Next we turn to actually dangerous rays. Ultraviolet rays will damage the skin (sunburn) and the eyes. X rays are so powerful that they pass through the body, and they can produce damage leading to cancer when they interact with cells. Gamma rays are more dangerous still. Again, we may ask why the greater effect of small amounts of these radiations in contrast to the harmless almost continuous daily exposure to light? All our experience suggests that the damage is due to the greater energy of the brief interactions with ultraviolet rays, X rays, and gamma rays. Somehow we must tie the frequency of the radiation to its energy. This is easily done if each light ray consists of particles with an energy related to the frequency. It is very hard to do this with light rays consisting only of waves.

The notion that light consists of particles that strike objects with different energies

receives confirmation from the *photoelectric effect*. In the previous chapter we mentioned that electrons can be released at a cathode by heat or by a large potential field. There is a third way. Electromagnetic energy directed at the cathode releases electrons though not all frequencies will do so. Infrared radiation, for instance, does not release electrons from any metal. Visible light does so from a few metals. Most metals require ultraviolet radiation or X rays. If we accept that light consists of particles and that the higher-frequency radiation has more energetic particles, this is easily explained. The particles of infrared radiation are too weak to release electrons even if the source is "bright," that is, even if it emits many particles. They are like buckshot on a concrete wall. Visible light consists of somewhat more energetic particles. They release electrons from metals that hold their electrons loosely. Ultraviolet has more energetic particles still; it releases electrons from most metals. A few metals, however, hold their electrons so tightly that the still more energetic X-ray particles are required to release them. Thus, if electromagnetic radiation consists of particles with energy related to frequency, the observations are explained.

Quantitative study of the photoelectric effect confirms this. In the particle conception, a source emits particles of certain energy. A bright source emits many particles; a dim source few. Now we can reason that a minimum of energy is required to release an electron, an amount equal to the energy with which the electron is held in the metal. Then, for frequencies with lower energy than the required release energy, no photoelectric effect occurs. For the frequency which has just the right amount of energy, the electron is just released. It is free to wander off. For frequencies that have particles with more energy than the required release energy of the electron, the excess energy is imparted to the electron as kinetic energy and it goes flying off with increased speed. This is confirmed by experiment (Fig. 15–17). For each metal there are frequencies of electromagnetic radiation which fail to release electrons. There is a certain frequency, n_0, which just releases them. Higher frequencies then give the electrons additional kinetic energy—the more kinetic energy, the higher the frequency. Accordingly, the model postulates a relationship between the energy of the particles, called *photons,* and the frequency. $E = hn$. E gives the energy associated with the photons whose frequency is n. h is Planck's constant, a proportionality constant to relate energy to frequency. $h = 6.62 \times 10^{-27}$ erg-sec. Low-frequency infrared has photons of low energy; high-frequency X rays and gamma rays have photons of high energy.

In the photon model of light, the total energy of a light source depends on two things: the energy of each photon emitted and the total number of photons emitted. This furthermore suggests that the brightness of a source should affect the number of electrons released in the photoelectric effect—if any are released. This is also found by experiment. In the wave model of light, the total energy released depends only on the brightness. Thus, any bright enough source should release electrons, even if the source emits infrared, and any weak source should fail to release electrons, even if it emits gamma rays. That is contrary to experimental findings, and the wave model fails to explain the photoelectric effect.

The photon model has few common analogies and consequently is often confusing. Let us try one. Suppose a builder needs 200-lb cement bags on a platform 20 ft above ground. A weight of 200 lb is too much for one laborer to lift while going up a ladder, and two laborers cannot work together while climbing up the ladder. Indeed, no number of laborers can be used to get the cement bags up to the platform. The laborers are "photons" of too little energy. One forklift truck, on the other hand, can lift the bags, and a crane can lift them with room to spare. The laborers' energy comes in little packages, and while the contractor could hire many of them to obtain a sizable amount of total human energy, this energy is so distributed in (human) packages that they cannot ac-

The photoelectric effect. Light of frequencies below a certain minimum does not release electrons. Above that frequency electromagnetic radiation releases electrons whose kinetic energy increases as the frequency of the radiation increases.

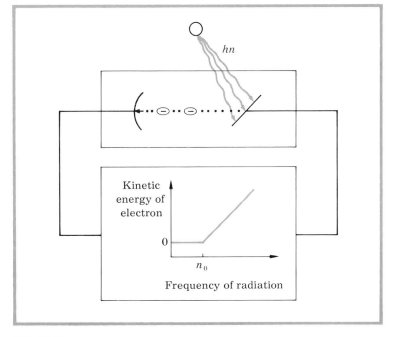

FIG. 15-17

complish a big job like lifting the cement bags. For this job the contractor needs large units of energy, like one forklift or one crane. (Of course, if he got several cranes, he would have still more total energy available.) Photons, similarly, come in packages of energy which may be small or large. While 10 photons of any one kind contain 10 times as much energy as a single photon of that kind, it is not possible in some situations, such as the photoelectric effect, to add the 10 small contributions for one large task.

The explanation of the photoelectric effect was Albert Einstein's (1879–1955) first major scientific contribution, shortly before the theory of relativity, for which he is more famous. In it he used the concept of photons, packets or particles of energy, developed earlier by Max Planck (1858–1947). The division of energy into smallest packets, *quantization* of energy, raises two very fundamental questions, one easily disposed of, the other not.

We are so used to seeing nature continuous, to thinking of drops of water of any size or of grains of sand of any weight, that ultimate particles, *quanta,* are somewhat strange to us. Yet, we accept a quantum of money—the cent—and even quanta of matter, smallest particles like atoms and electrons, give us little trouble. Only when we think of energy does the smallest-unit notion sit uncomfortably with us. Yet the evidence is there. What we generally and more easily accept in the case of matter also holds for energy. Energy comes in smallest packets, in quanta. In the case of electromagnetic radiation the quantum is called the photon. Later we shall find that other kinds of energy must be quantized. Thus, perhaps uncomfortably, we must accept the evidence concerning quantization of energy.

But there is a more serious question. How does electromagnetic radiation, which consists of fields oriented at right angles to the direction of propagation, which can be polarized, and which bends toward the normal in a medium of low velocity of transmission, end up as particles? This wave evidence is completely contradictory to the evidence we discussed in this section. These effects make no sense when discussed in terms of photons, while they are in full conformance with a wave model of radiation. How can light be particles and waves?

The answer to this paradox is troublesome because it rests upon a confession of ignorance and impotence. We do not know how the paradox can exist; we only know that it does exist. When a wave experiment like polarization is carried out, light behaves like a wave. When a particle experiment like the photoelectric effect is carried out, light behaves like particles. While we shall discuss our inability to resolve such paradoxes further in Chap. 19, and shall even embody it in a principle, we must, ultimately, accept the evidence before our senses, admit the limitations of our explanations, and accept both conceptions of light. After all, the *evidence* is not contradictory. Light itself behaves in a consistent manner. It is our *explanation* of that behavior that leads to inconsistency and contradiction. But that is a limitation of our thought processes, not of the way nature behaves.

While most physicists today accept the basic duality in the description of light, Albert Einstein was one outstanding exception. Until his death he maintained a faith that a theory would be found which would again simplify and unify the universe with only one "kind" of light.

Questions and Problems

1. Arrange the radiations of the electromagnetic spectrum in order of increasing photon energy.

2. Define, and draw a diagram to explain, refraction, reflection, interference, polarization, and photoelectric effect.

3. Draw a diagram to show the path of the light rays from a candle through a double convex lens, a double concave lens, a lens that is convex on one side and concave on the other.

4. Thunder is heard 4 sec after a lightning flash is seen. How far away was the lightning flash? (Use 1,100 ft/sec for the speed of sound.)

5. How many photons are emitted by a 1-watt radio-frequency source of 150,000 cycles/sec in 1 sec? How many photons by a 1-watt source of blue light, 7.5×10^{14} cycles/sec, in 1 sec?

6. What gives rise to polarization, chromatic aberration, a red shift in stellar light (see Chap. 12)?

7. A fish in the water appears farther away than it really is. Explain.

8. How did Roemer measure the speed of light?

9. Describe two phenomena which clearly suggest the wave nature of light. Can they be explained by the concept of light as particles?

Do the same for one that suggests the particle nature of light.

10. What is the shortest time in which we will hear via radio from an astronaut on the moon? on Venus? on Mars?

11. AM radio waves range from about 50,000 to about 160,000 cycles/sec. What are their wavelengths? FM and TV broadcasts are higher frequency. How does their wavelength compare to AM?

12. Determine the minimum difference in path length which produces interference with radio waves of 120,000 cycles/sec; with visible light of 5×10^{14} cycles/sec.

13. Distinguish between a real and a virtual image.

14. Can a d-c current emit electromagnetic radiation?

15. How long must a mirror be so that you can see yourself from head to toe? Explain. How does your answer change with distance from the mirror?

16. What purpose was served by the ether?

Suggestions for Further Reading

The properties of light and the sequence of experiments that led to the acceptance of photons are discussed in:

Christiansen, G. S., and Paul H. Garrett: *Structure and Change,* W. H. Freeman and Company, San Francisco, 1960. Chapters 25 and 26.

Holton, Gerald, and Duane H. D. Roller: *Foundations of Modern Physical Science,* Addison-Wesley Publishing Company, Inc., Reading, Mass., 1958. Chapters 29 to 31.

Physical Science Study Committee: *Physics,* D. C. Heath and Company, Boston, 1960. Chapters 11 to 19. A very extensive discussion of the behavior of light and how it can be interpreted by means of a wave or a particle theory.

Electromagnetic waves are treated extensively in:

Kock, Winston E.: *Sound Waves and Light Waves,* Anchor Books, Doubleday & Company, Inc., Garden City, N.Y., 1965 (paperback).

Pierce, John R.: *Electrons and Waves,* Anchor Books, Doubleday & Company, Inc., Garden City, N.Y., 1964 (paperback).

The determination of the speed of light and the role of the ether are described in:

Jaffe, Bernard: *Michelson and the Speed of Light,* Anchor Books, Doubleday & Company, Inc., Garden City, N.Y., 1960 (paperback).

Chapter 16

Chemistry

Matter has been part of our discussions in nearly every chapter, and we have devoted two entire chapters to it: Chap. 10, Matter, and Chap. 11, The Kinetic Molecular Theory. Yet, until now, we have ignored its most obvious characteristics: the great variety of shape, form, texture, hardness, color, taste, and many other attributes of matter. Up to this point we have considered matter largely undifferentiated. We neglected differences between steam and air and called them both gases. We ignored the differences between iron and gold and studied them both as solids, as metals, as conductors. We treated both water and alcohol as liquids and forgot about differences between them. Concern with these differences is the domain of chemistry, to which we now turn.

DALTON'S ATOMIC THEORY

As an art and a pseudoscience, chemistry is as old as astronomy. Records have been found from ancient Babylon describing early processes of pottery making, metalworking, cloth dying, and natural medicine. And there is evidence of a continuous refinement of techniques and of attempts to build a theoretical understanding of these applied chemical processes. However, unlike theoretical astronomy, which can trace a continuous thread at least to Ptolemy, modern theoretical chemistry has only feeble roots in antiquity. From classic times, when Aristotle's elements constituted a first coherent chemical theory, until the end of the eighteenth century, chemical theory was unclear and confused, muddying understanding perhaps as much as clarifying it. Much of this obscurantism was the result of confused groping in the highly complex domain of matter, which is complex exactly because it is so diverse. However, some of the obscurantism, at least in later times, appears to have been deliberate. Alchemists, who were among the most active chemical workers, were also anxious to preserve their secrets.

Although many theoretical advances were made toward the end of the eighteenth century, modern chemical theory is based on the atomic theory announced in 1803 by John Dalton (1766–1844), an Englishman. While precise terminology has changed and some of the terms used by Dalton have taken on other meanings, the essence of Dalton's atomic theory has survived.

Dalton proposed, and we still accept, that all matter consists of a number of different elements. (At the time of writing, the number is 84 natural and 19 man-made.) Each element consists of very small particles called *atoms.* The atoms of any one element are all alike; atoms of different elements differ. All matter other than the 103 elements is produced by the combination of atoms. Atoms combine into bigger particles called *molecules,* which have entirely different properties from the atoms of which they are formed. Thus the atoms of the element hydrogen—an explosive gas—joined to the atoms of the element oxygen—a gas which supports burning and explosions—produce molecules of water, which consist of atoms of both hydrogen and oxygen and which have entirely different properties. (Water, as is well known, is a liquid, is wet, and douses fires.) Dalton's atomic theory explains the variety of matter we observe by recognizing that both the number and the kinds of atoms that join can vary.

Atoms, while invisibly small, were quite real to Dalton. He invented a symbolism (Fig. 16–1) to represent them, and he joined them symbolically while requiring that they maintain their *masses* on combining. On the other hand, his theory permitted them to lose their properties on combination and to acquire new ones. This is the point at which the new chemistry departed from the old. Aristotle, too, you will recall, had elements which mixed, although Aristotle had no atoms. But the function of Aristotle's elements was to impart their *qualities* on combination. In the Aristotelian chemistry wood floats on water because it has a fair amount of fire and air in it—both quite light and imparting lightness to the wood. Some early philosophers found it possible to explain all the qualities of all

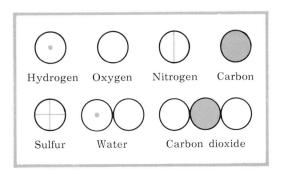

Hydrogen Oxygen Nitrogen Carbon

Sulfur Water Carbon dioxide

FIG. 16-1

The symbols invented by Dalton to represent atoms of the elements. Compounds result when atoms join.

matter by mixing the dryness and hotness of fire with the dryness and coldness of earth, the wetness and coldness of water, and the wetness and hotness of air. Appropriate mixtures of the qualities of the elements produced the qualities of the product.

While earlier views seem primitive now, they provided a rational basis for the work of the alchemists. Elements other than fire, air, water, and earth had been recognized long before Dalton's time—mercury and sulfur, for instance—but they were deemed elements because of their singular qualities rather than their unique atoms. The quest of the alchemists was nothing more than a striving to add the qualities of gold to otherwise nongolden materials. Thus one finds the alchemists trying to add the right amount of the mercurous principle, or the sulfurous principle, to iron. (Indeed, they sometimes thought they had succeeded because the union of iron and sulfur atoms produced a yellowish material, fool's gold or iron pyrites, which while not gold has one of its qualities, the yellow color.)

The transformation from the theoretical approach that focused on the stability of qualities (and paid little attention to the actual matter) to the theoretical approach that focused on the hard matter (and allowed new qualities to emerge in combinations) was slow and painful. An illustration of the semantic and conceptual hurdles that had to be overcome is in one of the earliest, almost clear statements of the nature of elements, given by Sir Robert Boyle (of Boyle's law) in 1680 in an appendix to his *Skeptical Chymist:* "To prevent mistakes, I must advertise you, that I now mean by elements, as those Chemists that speak plainest do by their principles, certain primitive and simple, or perhaps unmingled bodies; which not being made up of any other bodies, or of one another, are the ingredients of which all those called perfectly mixed bodies are immediately compounded, and into which they are ultimately resolved."

Boyle recognized elements as composed of "unmingled bodies," and yet did not clearly distinguish his "bodies" from the "principles" of the "Chemists that speak plainest." The confusion persisted for at least another 100 years.

PHLOGISTON

Before chemists settled on the "unmingled bodies" in the form of Dalton's atoms, the first chemical theory of both breadth and power was created and also overthrown. As in the case of Du Fay's and Franklin's electric fluids, it was a theory which was incorrect in its basic assumptions although adequately explanatory and identical in form to our modern understandings. Its downfall resulted, as in the electrical case, from its further implications, not from the central body of data it explained.

This early and broad theory was the *phlogiston* theory advanced by two German chemists, Becher (1635–1682) and Stahl (1660–1734), to explain combustion and combustion-related processes. According to the phlogiston theory, combustion is the liberation of the combustible principle phlogiston (note the emphasis on a quality or "principle"). Combustible materials must contain phlogiston.

The theory explains various observations. Ordinary burning is simply the liberation of phlogiston from the matter, like wood, that possesses it. Heat-requiring processes in metallurgy, which were well known because of the prevalence of a metallurgical industry, were easily accommodated. Of interest were the production of metals from their ores by heating with charcoal, and the heating of metals in air, which in many cases produces a grayish and brittle *calx* that resembles the ores. The phlogiston theory needed only to equate charcoal with purified phlogiston to incorporate these processes in its explanations.

$$\text{Ore (calx)} + \text{charcoal (phlogiston)} = \text{metal} \quad (16\text{–}1)$$

$$\text{Metal} - \text{phlogiston} = \text{calx} \quad (16\text{–}2)$$

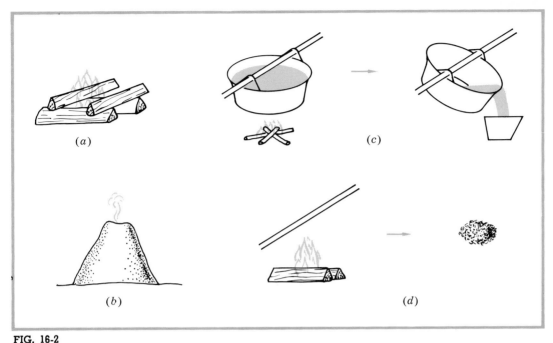

FIG. 16-2

Elements of the phlogiston theory. (a) Wood burning loses its phlogiston. (b) Charcoal which is produced when wood is heated without a flame is pure phlogiston. (c) Adding phlogiston to an ore (calx) produces a pure metal. (d) On heating, the metal loses its phlogiston and reverts to the calx.

Metals result when an ore or a calx absorbs phlogiston (from charcoal). Heating the metal then releases the phlogiston and re-forms the calx. (Note that charcoal is produced from wood. Charcoal production can be equated to phlogiston purification.)

Finally, to explain the observation that a fire goes out in an enclosed space, the phlogiston theory limited the amount of phlogiston which can be held by the air. The fact that burning stops in an enclosed vessel then shows that the air has become saturated with phlogiston.

In all these examples the phlogiston theory sufficed although its success depended in part on the poor state of observation. Gaseous products of burning that escape among the flames had simply not been discovered. Hence there was no need to account for them; the flames could be equated with escaping phlogiston.

The first challenge to phlogiston came when the chemical processes described above were accurately weighed. It was found that the metal weighed less than the ore from which it had been produced through the addition of phlogiston, and less than the calx to which it turned after losing phlogiston. This problem could be overcome by giving phlogiston a negative weight. (A subtle principle could be weightless or even negative in weight.) But the phlogiston theory could not rationalize the fact that some phlogiston-deficient calxes, when heated in closed containers, release large volumes of a gas that supports combustion much better than air. There was no rationalization for either the large volume of gas produced or its behavior toward combustion. The ultimate overthrow of the phlogiston theory, chiefly through the experiments that liberate the gas oxygen, was due to the French chemist Antoine Lavoisier (1743–1794). He replaced it by an oxygen theory of combustion in which burning is combination with oxygen, metal production the

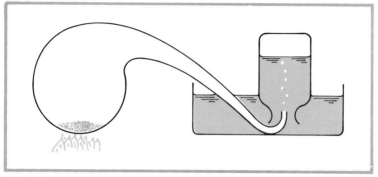

Some calxes when heated produce large amounts of a gas that strongly supports combustion. Since calxes were without phlogiston, the phlogiston theory could not account for this observation.

FIG. 16-3

removal of oxygen from an ore, and calx formation also combination with oxygen. In this work he anticipated most of the notions of chemical combination later announced by Dalton. While he did not live to witness the modern chemistry that resulted from Dalton—he lost his life in the French Revolution—he is often regarded as the father of modern chemistry.

Today the phlogiston theory has no explanatory importance and serves merely as a reminder of the character and possible fate of scientific explanations. In its time it was a theory of power and breadth that unified many of the familiar observations. But when it was put to the test of further experimentation, it failed and after about 100 years of successful application was completely discarded. There is probably no better illustration in the history of science of both the usefulness and the potential limits of a scientific theory.

ELEMENTS, COMPOUNDS, AND MIXTURES

The advance of chemical theory beyond phlogiston required, as we have noted, a shift of emphasis from qualities of matter to quantities of matter, from the conservation of "principles" or, in modern terminology, *properties,* such as color, density, or wetness, to the conservation of matter itself in the form of atoms. Historically this came

quite late. While this shift in the frame of reference may seem simple to us, it probably was difficult for the early chemists because of the great variety of matter produced by the combinations of atoms. Even today the basic simple units of chemistry are the more than 100 different atoms of the more than 100 different elements. The elements were not known to the early chemists; they had to be inferred from experimentation and intellectual analysis. They had to be found in thousands of compounds without any prior guide as to number and kind. Hence chemistry begins with an inherently complex situation. Moreover, the complexity is compounded; in addition to combinations involving different elements, there are combinations using different numbers of atoms of the same elements. For instance, millions of different chemical compounds contain only the four elements, carbon, hydrogen, oxygen, and nitrogen. In these the numbers of atoms of each vary. Consider what adding the other 99 elements can do for complexity.

Chemistry reached its modern form only because a number of profound practical and intellectual problems were resolved. One is the difficulty of establishing which kinds of matter are elemental, consisting of only one kind of atom, and which are compound. To phrase it another way, how do we know there are 103—not 110—elements? As Boyle pointed out, elements are "certain primitive and simple, or perhaps unmingled bodies." How does one find out that a body is primitive, simple, un-mingled—not mingled and complex? One tries to see whether it can be resolved. Now, if it is resolved or analyzed into simpler bodies, then it, itself, is not elemental. It is easy to determine which bodies are *not* elements. But what if resolution fails? Is it because the body is already unmingled, elemental, or is it because the experimenter is not adequately skillful? The certain iden-tification of elements was one of the great problems in Dalton's time, and while much headway had been made and continued to be made throughout the nineteenth century, it was not fully solved until 1913, when H. G. J. Moseley (1887–1915) found an-other method for characterizing elements. Water, for instance, is quite stable to fur-ther analysis and was long considered an element although it is now known to be compounded of the elements hydrogen and oxygen.

There was a second intellectual and prac-tical problem. The union of atoms leads to *molecules*, which are the ultimate or sim-plest particles of *compounds* ("mingled bodies"). But there is another way of mix-ing (mingling) atoms, or atoms and mole-cules. They can be mixed without joining. Thus the mixing of atoms of oxygen and hydrogen is perfectly possible, though highly dangerous. They may be mixed as atoms which retain their identity. The *mixture*, chemically unjoined, remains gas-eous. Hydrogen remains highly combustible and oxygen retains the property of support-ing combustion. Only when the mixture is set off by a match or a spark, and the ex-pected explosion occurs, are the mixed atoms joined as molecules of water. Hence the chemist has to distinguish between elements, compounds, and mixtures. The former two contain only identical particles, whether atoms of the same kind or mole-cules of the same kind; the latter contain different kinds of atoms or molecules. Ele-ments and compounds are *homogeneous*, alike throughout. In chemical terminology, they are *substances*. Mixtures, on the other hand, contain different kinds of uncombined atoms or molecules.

The distinction between compounds and mixtures may seem like a simple problem. In terms of definitions it is. But practically it is often very difficult to determine whether some material at hand is a sub-stance or a mixture. For example, is ho-mogenized milk, as you buy it in a store, a substance? Is air a substance? Is tea a substance? All three appear homogeneous and yet are not substances but mixtures. Mixtures present no practical problems when they are obvious like pepper and salt, or sand, or celery and nuts. But in the cases where confusion is likely, the dis-tinction is a severe practical and even theoretical problem.

To distinguish substances from mixtures, it is helpful to look at matter from two points of view that differ in regard to the size of the particles upon which attention is focused. The *microscopic* viewpoint fo-cuses on particles of atomic dimensions. Microscopically, atoms are single identical units and denote elements; molecules are units that contain several atoms linked to-gether. They occur in compounds. In sub-stances—elements or compounds—the pro-gression of units is drearily the same. They are microscopically homogeneous. In mix-tures, on the other hand, different kinds of atoms and/or different kinds of molecules follow one another. Mixtures are microscop-ically *heterogeneous*, different throughout.

Macroscopically, or from the point of view of visible or weighable amounts, no distinc-tions may be evident between elements, compounds, and even certain mixtures. Only chemical analysis can tell which of three cylinders containing colorless gases holds the element nitrogen; which the com-pound carbon dioxide; which the mixture air. All three are *macroscopically* homoge-neous, although air is microscopically het-erogeneous. Hence only nitrogen and car-bon dioxide are substances. Air is a mix-ture. Table 16–1 may help establish these definitions.

TABLE 16-1

Classification of matter

Substances			
Microscopically homogeneous	{	Elements	}
	}	Compounds	}
Mixtures	{	Solutions	} Macroscopically homogeneous
Microscopically heterogeneous	}	Mixtures	Macroscopically heterogeneous

The distinctions above suggest one further set of definitions. The change from a mixture of hydrogen and oxygen atoms to their combination into water units is relatively obvious. The macroscopically evident explosion suggests that a microscopic change also has occurred; new links or *bonds* between atoms have been formed. But what about a macroscopically less dramatic change, like the change from water to ice, or the change from sugar in the cube to sugar dissolved in tea? Are these rearrangements of the same molecules—no new bonds formed or old bonds broken—or are they like the hydrogen-oxygen explosion— new combinations of atoms? The point here is that macroscopically evident changes may be of two kinds: those involving microscopic rearrangements of the chemical bonds between atoms—*chemical changes*— and those *not* involving *microscopic* rearrangement of the bonds—*physical changes.* It is not always evident from macroscopic evidence which of the two has occurred. Freezing of water and dissolving of sugar are considered physical changes; in neither is there a major rearrangement of chemical bonds. (With these definitions we now recognize that the changes discussed in Chap. 10 were physical changes.)

LAWS OF CHEMICAL COMBINATION

Having pointed out the practical and intellectual problems that chemistry had to solve, we can return to describe the discoveries that were instrumental in solving them. Lavoisier in 1789 announced the *law of conservation of matter,* stating that in chemical reactions *the weights of reactants equal the weights of products.* It may seem like a law that should have been self-evident until we remember that an experimental advance, catching and weighing gaseous products, had to be made before the law could be discovered. Also, as we previously emphasized, the intellectual focus had to be placed on weight, rather than on other qualities.

A second discovery was perhaps more basic, for without it there would be no chemical orderliness. The *law of constant composition* states, simply, that no matter how a compound is made, and no matter where it is found in nature, *a compound always contains the same proportions by weight of its constituent elements.* Again, this seems a simple principle to us because if the proportions of the elements were to shift in water, or salt, or any other compound, how could order be established among them? Yet Berthollet (1748–1822), a French chemist famous for many other contributions, refused to accept this law. A clear intellectual distinction between compounds and mixtures had not yet been made and seems to have led him astray.

These two laws are really the basis of practical chemistry. With the law of conservation of matter, one of the most important outcomes of chemical processes, yield, can be computed in advance. Thus the heating of 100 lb of limestone, or of any other substance, can never produce more than, or less than, 100 lb of products. Moreover, because of the law of constant composition, it is possible to predict exactly that 100 lb of limestone will yield 56 lb of lime and 44 lb of carbon dioxide.

Or, to take another example that is of great industrial importance, the production of ammonia requires the mixing of 3 lb of hydrogen with 14 lb of nitrogen. It produces 17 lb of ammonia. The numbers 3 and 14, of course, depend on the constancy of composition of ammonia, which always has the two elements, hydrogen and nitrogen, in the ratio 3:14. (A further corollary, by the way, is the fact that if 7 lb of hydrogen were mixed with 14 lb of nitrogen, 4 lb of hydrogen would be left uncombined.)

The weight ratios 56:44 and 3:14 used above may appear arbitrary. They are, however, the result of experiment. But one must ask whether these ratios must be determined experimentally for each and every compound, or whether there is a connection between the weight of oxygen in water and in carbon dioxide. A further discovery just preceding Dalton's theory answered this question. It was found that the hydrogen-nitrogen ratio in ammonia, 3:14, coupled with the experimentally determined hydrogen-oxygen ratio, 3:24, allows us to predict a ratio of 14:24 for nitrogen and oxygen in a compound. The *law of equivalent proportions* states that *the proportions by weight of the various elements that combine with each other are stable regardless of the particular chemical compound which the elements form.* This law implies that the weight of all atoms of the same kind is the same, as Dalton later explicitly stated in the atomic theory. These three laws express the considerable order which had been found in chemical combinations before Dalton published the atomic theory.

AVOGADRO'S HYPOTHESIS

Dalton's recognition that weight is a characteristic property of atoms set off a search for atomic weights. The weight-in-combination mentioned in the law of equivalent proportions was not an adequate measure because it was not known whether, for instance, the ratio of 3:14 in ammonia represents a combination of one atom of hydrogen with one of nitrogen, giving atomic weights of 3 and 14, or whether, as is now known, the combination contains three atoms of hydrogen and one of nitrogen, which leads to atomic weights of 1 and 14. Weight analysis, alone, could not answer that question. Indeed, an infinite number of possibilities for the atomic weights of hydrogen and nitrogen will fit the ratio 3:14.

At this time, shortly after Dalton's theory was published, the gas laws were reexamined and helped solve the problem. Let us recall that Boyle's law and Charles's law indicate that all gases behave identically when subjected to identical temperature or pressure changes. One liter of any gas, whether nitrogen, oxygen, hydrogen, carbon dioxide, is compressed to ½ liter when the pressure is doubled. One liter of these gases expands to 2 liters when the absolute temperature is doubled. They all behave alike. But the weights of 1 liter of each of these gases are not the same. Specifically, the weights are 1.25 grams/liter for nitrogen; 1.43 grams/liter for oxygen; 0.09 gram/liter for hydrogen; and 1.96 grams/liter for carbon dioxide when measured at 0°C and 1 atm. The suggestion was therefore made that these weights reflect the atomic weights of the elements, that atoms of nitrogen weigh 14 times as much as those of hydrogen (1.25:0.09) and atoms of oxygen 16 times as much (1.43:0.09). The molecules of the compound carbon dioxide would then weigh 22 times as much (1.96:0.09) as atoms of hydrogen.

The implication of obtaining atomic weights from the weights of equal volumes of gases is that these volumes contain equal numbers of atoms or molecules. Hence the relative weights of some large number, n, in 1 liter also give the relative weights of single atoms or molecules. This is Avogadro's hypothesis, published in 1811 but ignored for more than 40 years. It states that equal volumes of gases measured under identical conditions of temperatures and pressure contain equal numbers of molecules (or atoms).

In Chap. 11 we demonstrated that Avogadro's hypothesis is a consequence of the kinetic theory of gases. It has since been confirmed by direct measurement. But without such confirmation, there is an alternative way of looking at gas volumes. They might contain unequal numbers of molecules of unequal weights. Then no deductions about atomic weights could be made. This was the position taken by Dalton and most chemists. He was led to this by two considerations. He thought that in gases the atoms or melocules touch. Since he also believed them to be of different sizes, he felt that they must occupy unequal volumes.

The second consideration which influenced Dalton was the *law of combining volumes*. In 1808 Gay-Lussac (1778–1850) had discovered that the *volumes of gases that react chemically are in simple whole-number ratios*. For instance, in the three reactions between gases given in Eqs. 16–3 to 16–5, three volumes of hydrogen combine with one volume of nitrogen; one volume of hydrogen reacts with one volume of chlorine; two volumes of hydrogen react with one volume of oxygen. The volumes are in small whole-number ratios.

Hydrogen	+ nitrogen	= ammonia
(3 volumes)	(1 volume)	(2 volumes)

$$(16\text{--}3)$$

Hydrogen	+ chlorine	= hydrogen chloride
(1 volume)	(1 volume)	(2 volumes)

$$(16\text{--}4)$$

Hydrogen	+ oxygen	= steam (water)
(2 volumes)	(1 volume)	(2 volumes)

$$(16\text{--}5)$$

The left sides of these equations seem to corroborate Avogadro's hypothesis because they suggest that three atoms of hydrogen and one atom of nitrogen combine to form ammonia; one atom of hydrogen and one atom of chlorine to form hydrogen chloride; two atoms of hydrogen and one atom of oxygen to form water. But the situation is not as simple when we look also at the right sides of the equations. The question arises, how does one atom of nitrogen form two molecules of ammonia? How do one atom of hydrogen and one atom of chlorine form two molecules of hydrogen chloride? How does one atom of oxygen form two molecules of water?

There is only one explanation possible. Somehow the nitrogen, hydrogen, chlorine, and oxygen in these reactions split in half. If both hydrogen and chlorine (Fig. 16–4) are present as molecules with two atoms joined together, they can split and recombine to form two molecules of hydrogen chloride from one molecule of each of the reactants. But this requires that hydrogen and chlorine be present as diatomic molecules, not as single atoms. Likewise nitrogen must be present as diatomic molecules that split to form ammonia; oxygen as diatomic molecules that split to form water. This idea, that elements exist as diatomic molecules, was too difficult to believe without direct evidence and created the doubts about Avogadro's hypothesis. As a result, there was no way to establish atomic weights unambiguously, and all chemical theory based on weight relationships was left without a firm foundation. Not until 1858, when Avogadro's pupil Cannizzaro (1826–1910) presented Avogadro's hypothesis again, did it find acceptance. Then atomic weights were determined unambiguously, and in a few years a number of major advances were made in chemical theory.

ATOMIC AND MOLECULAR WEIGHTS

Avogadro's hypothesis does not give the weights of single atoms or molecules; it

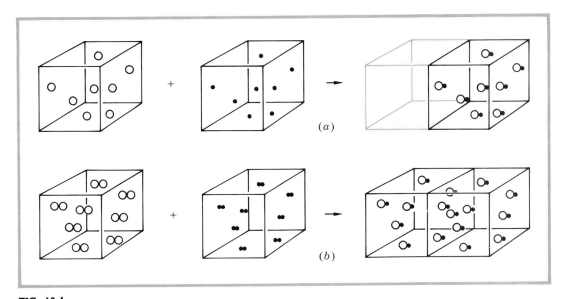

FIG. 16-4

The law of combining volumes and Avogadro's hypothesis. (a) If equal volumes of gases contain equal numbers of molecules, how can one volume of hydrogen combine with one volume of chlorine to produce two volumes of hydrogen chloride? (b) Only if the hydrogen and chlorine consist of molecules with two atoms.

merely permits their comparison, as we illustrated before. The problem of assigning a base remains. This has been solved by assigning the number 1 to hydrogen, the element with the smallest atomic weight. Then others are assigned by comparison.

Our example showed that nitrogen gas is 14 times as heavy as hydrogen; oxygen gas 16 times as heavy; carbon dioxide gas 22 times as heavy. But we also found that hydrogen, nitrogen, and oxygen consist of diatomic molecules. Then, if hydrogen atoms have an atomic weight of 1, hydrogen molecules have a molecular weight of 2. Diatomic nitrogen molecules, which are 14 times as heavy as hydrogen molecules, have a molecular weight of 28; the atomic weight of nitrogen is, consequently, 14. Diatomic oxygen molecules, which are 16 times as heavy as hydrogen molecules, have a molecular weight of 32; the atomic weight of oxygen is 16. Because of Avogadro's hypothesis, it is easy to determine atomic weights for gaseous elements. Likewise it is easy to determine the molecular weights of gaseous compounds. Carbon dioxide, for

instance, which is 22 times as heavy as gaseous hydrogen, has a molecular weight of 44.

For elements like carbon that cannot be vaporized, atomic-weight determination is more complex. Atomic weights are obtained from the molecular weight of gaseous carbon compounds. For instance, the molecular weight of carbon dioxide is 44. Moreover, chemical analysis gives for the weights of carbon and oxygen in carbon dioxide 12:32. From this we can deduce some possible atomic weights for carbon. Clearly 32 is the weight of two oxygen atoms of atomic weight 16. And 12 might be the weight of four carbon atoms of atomic weight 3; three carbon atoms of atomic weight 4; two carbon atoms of atomic weight 6; or one carbon atom of atomic weight 12. At this point we are stymied. But we can turn to other gaseous carbon compounds and repeat this analysis. We find that carbon always contributes 12 or 24 or 36 to the molecular weight of the compounds, never less. This then suggests that the atomic weight of carbon is 12, not a smaller weight, and illustrates the method used to determine the atomic weight of carbon.

THE MOLE

One problem involving atomic weights remains: that of weighing atoms individually rather than by comparison with hydrogen. Atomic weights are comparative weights. The atomic weight of 16 for oxygen means only that oxygen atoms are 16 times as heavy as hydrogen atoms. How much do they actually weigh, in grams?

This problem was solved when it became possible early in this century to count the incredibly large number of atoms in 1 gram of hydrogen, or 16 grams of oxygen. The number is 6.02×10^{23}, called *Avogadro's number*. An aggregation of 6.02×10^{23} particles has also been given a special name, the *mole*.

The mole is a very useful chemical concept because it is of a dimension which can easily be handled in the laboratory. In the first place, a mole is a measure of number. One mole of atoms is 6.02×10^{23} atoms; 1 mole of molecules is 6.02×10^{23} molecules. But it is also a measure of weight which conveniently uses the numbers of atomic and molecular weights. A mole of hydrogen atoms is 1 gram of hydrogen (whose atomic weight is 1). A mole of hydrogen molecules is 2 grams of hydrogen (whose molecular weight is 2). A mole of carbon dioxide is 44 grams (molecular weight—44). Thus the mole translates atomic and molecular weights into gram quantities. This is, of course, by design. The mole was defined to turn microscopic weights of single atoms into macroscopically convenient gram weights. This is of tremendous help in chemical work, as will become clear in the next chapter.

Questions and Problems

1. Suggest how the law of equivalent proportions implies that all atoms of the same kind have the same weight.

2. Suggest which of the following might be chemical changes and which physical changes: (*a*) heating iron until it is white-hot, (*b*) rusting of iron, (*c*) drying of paint, (*d*) baking of a cake. Defend your answers.

3. Iron oxide (Fe_2O_3) contains 70 percent iron. Ignoring any losses, how much pure iron oxide is required to produce a ton of iron? A 100-lb iron railing rusts entirely to the oxide. What weight of oxygen does it remove from the air? What volume of pure oxygen? What weight of oxide is formed?

4. Define microscopic; macroscopic. Describe several microscopic changes in your body which occur daily. Can they also be observed macroscopically?

5. Give a microscopic definition of element; a macroscopic definition. Repeat for molecule, mixture, chemical change, physical change.

6. A certain compound contains 12 grams of magnesium and 8 grams of oxygen. On the basis of this information, which of the following statements must be true, which must be false, and which are uncertain? Explain your answers based on the information in Chap. 16. (*a*) All samples contain 40 percent by weight of oxygen. (*b*) A mole of the compound contains 40 grams. (*c*) The atomic weight of magnesium is 1½ times that of oxygen. (*d*) The atomic weight of magnesium is 12. (*e*) The atomic weight of magnesium is greater than that of oxygen. (*f*) Burning of 0.9 ton of magnesium requires 0.6 ton of oxygen. (*g*) The production of 8 grams of the compound requires 4.8 grams of magnesium. (*h*) A mixture of 1.0 gram of oxygen and 1.0 gram of magnesium produces 2.0 grams of the compound.

7. Two volumes of a gas *A* decompose to produce one volume of a gas *B* and two volumes of a gas *C*. *B* and *C* are elements. Write two possible formulas for *A* as a compound of *B* and *C*.

8. The molecular weight of diphosphorus trioxide is 110. How many molecules in 27.5 grams of the compound? How many moles? What is the weight of an equal number of moles of nitrogen triiodide, mol. wt = 397? of an equal number of molecules of lithium hydride, mol. wt = 8?

Suggestions for Further Reading

The discoveries that produced the atomic theory are discussed in:

Christiansen, G. S., and Paul H. Garrett: *Structure and Change,* W. H. Freeman and Company, San Francisco, 1960. Chapters 6 and 7.

Holton, Gerald: *Introduction to Concepts and Theories in Physical Science,* Addison-Wesley Publishing Company, Inc., Reading, Mass., 1952. Chapters 19 and 20.

Holton, Gerald, and Duane H. D. Roller: *Foundations of Modern Physical Science,* Addison-Wesley Publishing Company, Inc., Reading, Mass., 1958. Chapters 21 to 24.

Conant, J. B. (ed).: *Harvard Case Histories in Experimental Science,* vol. 1, Harvard University Press, Cambridge, Mass., 1957. Chapter 4, by Leonard K. Nash. Chapter 2, by Conant, is on the history of phlogiston.

Uses of the mole in chemistry are treated in:

Kieffer, William F.: *The Mole Concept in Chemistry,* Reinhold Publishing Corporation, New York, 1962 (paperback).

Chapter 17

Characteristics of Atoms I: Group Similarities

We have commented several times already on the formidable intellectual task of creating order and understanding in chemistry with more than 100 distinct elements and billions of compounds. Fortunately the task is considerably simplified by the fact that the elements fall into groups with similar properties. In this chapter we shall orient ourselves among these groups. Before we turn to them, however, we shall adopt the system of chemical symbolism, which greatly simplifies chemical discussion.

CHEMICAL SYMBOLISM

Each element is denoted by a *symbol*, a capital letter or a capital letter followed by a lowercase letter. For instance, O is the symbol for oxygen and H the symbol for hydrogen. In most cases, the connection between the symbol and the element it represents is relatively obvious. However, difficulties arise for two reasons. For elements that were discovered before about 1800, Latin names serve as the referents. Thus Fe for iron, Au for gold, and Pb for lead come from the Latin words *ferrum, aurum,* and *plumbum.* The second difficulty arises where history or the discoverers, who have the privilege of naming new elements, have named many elements with the same initial letter. The worst offenders are elements starting with the letter *C.* No stretch of the imagination makes obvious and unique the connection between symbol and name for the elements carbon (C), calcium (Ca), and cadmium (Cd); cesium (Cs), cerium (Ce), and curium (Cm); cobalt (Co) and copper (Cu); as well as chromium (Cr), chlorine (Cl), and californium (Cf). Besides naming elements, symbols can serve many other purposes. They are used to relate compounds to their constituent elements. Thus the symbols H and Cl joined, as in HCl, give the *formula* of the compound hydrogen chloride. In this sense, the conjoined symbols name the compound and indicate that the molecules of HCl contain single atoms of the two elements. This is in distinction to molecules like NH_3 or H_2O or H_2O_2, in which, respectively, four atoms—one of nitrogen and three of hydrogen; three atoms —two of hydrogen and one of oxygen; and four atoms—two of hydrogen and two of oxygen—are joined. Thus symbols name elements. Placed together, they name compounds. And in the formula, through the use of subscript numbers, they count the number of atoms that are joined in the molecule. The absence of a subscript number after a symbol is understood to mean that the subscript is 1.

The counting of atoms in the formulas of compounds leads, immediately, to another property of chemical symbolism: it indicates weight relationships. Since atoms have unique atomic weight, one can obtain the molecular weight of the molecule represented by the chemical formula simply by adding the atomic weights of its constituent atoms. HCl has a molecular weight of $1 + 35.5 = 36.5$; NH_3 has a molecular weight of $14 + (3 \times 1) = 17$; H_2O has a molecular weight of $(2 \times 1) + 16 = 18$; and H_2O_2, $(2 \times 1) + (2 \times 16) = 34$. Thus the symbols and formulas imply a molecular weight.

Moreover, the percentages of each of the constituent elements in the compound can be computed from the atomic and molecular weights. To the molecular weight of 36.5 of HCl, 35.5 parts (97.3 percent) are contributed by the chlorine atom; only one part (2.7 percent) by the hydrogen atom. The compound, consequently, is almost all chlorine by weight (though 1:1 hydrogen-chlorine in number of atoms). Likewise, the compound NH_3 contains 82.3 percent nitrogen, 17.7 percent hydrogen by weight, although it contains three times as many hydrogen atoms as nitrogen atoms. The formulas imply weight relationships in addition to giving the numbers of atoms.

The description of chemical reactions with symbols and formulas illustrates other uses of chemical symbolism. A very simple example is the combination of hydrogen with oxygen to produce water. The simplest symbolic statement is $H + O \rightarrow H_2O$, in which the symbols and formulas serve merely to *name* the reactants and the product. Now, the symbol H would not be used in this context because, as we mentioned in the previous chapter, the species H, single atoms of hydrogen, does not occur in nature. The same holds for the symbol O, which implies single atoms. Both hydrogen and oxygen occur as diatomic molecules, H_2 and O_2. Hence the chemical equation describing the reaction would invariably be written with the natural chemical species, $H_2 + O_2 \rightarrow H_2O$.

The last equation still suffers from one defect. The symbols H_2 and O_2 indicate that two atoms of each element react; the formula H_2O indicates that the product contains two atoms of hydrogen but only one of oxygen. As written, the equation implies that an atom of oxygen has disappeared, which is contrary to the law of conservation of matter. Hence chemists *balance the equation*, fix it up to conform, symbolically, to the law of conservation of matter.

One way of fixing up the equation that suggests itself is to change H_2O to H_2O_2. That would take care of balancing very nicely, but it would change the equation in an indefensible way. H_2O_2 is not the water we drink, which is produced by exploding H_2 in O_2; H_2O_2 is hydrogen peroxide, the liquid used to bleach hair. This suggestion would balance the equation at the expense, however, of symbolizing something which does not, in fact, happen. The compound H_2O, not the compound H_2O_2, is produced. The same reasoning precludes the change to $H_2 + O \rightarrow H_2O$, which implies, also contrary to fact, that oxygen occurs as single atoms.

Another way can be found to balance the equation. Since oxygen occurs as diatomic molecules, but there is only a single atom of oxygen in the water molecule, each molecule of oxygen must produce two molecules of H_2O. This must be included in the equation. Two molecules of H_2O are represented, symbolically, by the coefficient 2, as $2H_2O$. Thus, the first step in balancing leads to $H_2 + O_2 \rightarrow 2H_2O$. But if two molecules of water are produced, a total of four atoms of hydrogen, two atoms per molecule, are needed. Two molecules of hydrogen must react to furnish four hydrogen atoms. Final balancing then yields $2H_2 + O_2 \rightarrow 2H_2O$. The final equation reads: two molecules of hydrogen (containing two atoms of hydrogen each) combine with one molecule of oxygen (consisting of two atoms of oxygen) to produce two molecules of water (which consist of two atoms of hydrogen and one of oxygen, each).

There are still other implications to the equation for, as we have already noted, symbols and formulas also imply atomic weights and molecular weights. Thus the equation can be read as: 2 moles of hy-

drogen combine with 1 mole of oxygen to produce 2 moles of water, which in view of the definition of the mole, implies that 2×2 grams of hydrogen combine with 32 grams of oxygen to produce 2×18 grams of water. Quite obviously, since the equation was balanced, the weights of the reactants equal the weight of the product.

In summary, the various levels of information given by symbols and formulas are as follows:

1. They are names.

2. They indicate the composition (kind and number of atoms) in each compound.

3. They imply atomic weights, molecular weights, and weight of the constituents in a compound.

4. In a balanced chemical equation, they give the number of molecules and/or atoms of each reactant which must combine and the number of molecules and/or atoms of each product which must be produced in accordance with the law of conservation of matter.

5. In view of the definition of the mole, they give the information necessary for weight computations.

We illustrate the levels of information by another example. In industry, two important chemicals, caustic soda (sodium hydroxide) and chlorine gas, are produced by the passage of an electric current through a solution of salt (NaCl) in water in specially constructed cells. The equation is

$$2NaCl + 2H_2O \rightarrow H_2 + Cl_2 + 2NaOH$$

$$(17–1)$$

The equation names the reactants—sodium chloride and water—and the products—hydrogen, chlorine, and sodium hydroxide. It gives the atomic constituents of each compound and, via atomic weights, their molecular weights and weight compositions. Balanced, the equation states the number of molecules of each reactant that participates in the reaction, and the number of molecules of each product. Finally, the balanced equation can be translated into 117 grams (2×58.5) of NaCl reacting with 36 grams (2×18) of water produce 2 grams of H_2, 71 grams of Cl_2, and 80 grams (2×40) of NaOH.

CHEMICAL CALCULATIONS

The last statement was based on the reaction of the quantity of salt implied by the equation, 2 moles or 117 grams. Obviously, this is an insignificant amount for commercial manufacture. Caustic soda and chlorine are tonnage, not gram, chemicals. However, the method for computing reaction needs and yield is basically the same for other weights of reactants and products. The 2 moles of NaCl and of H_2O implied by the balanced equation are not the minimum quantities (the minimum weight is the weight of two molecules of NaCl and two molecules of water) nor is there any maximum quantity.

Let us use this equation to illustrate the method for computing needed quantities when they are not the weights implied by the balanced equation.

EXAMPLE

How much NaCl is needed to produce 10 grams of NaOH? How much Cl_2 is produced at the same time? Ten grams of NaOH are 10 grams/ (40 grams/mole) = 0.25 mole of NaOH. Then, referring to the balanced equation,
NaCl needed
$$= \frac{2 \text{ moles NaCl}}{2 \text{ moles NaOH}} \times 0.25 \text{ mole NaOH produced}$$
$$\times 58.5 \text{ grams NaCl/mole}$$
$$= 14.4 \text{ grams NaCl} \qquad (17\text{–}2)$$
Cl_2 produced
$$= \frac{1 \text{ mole } Cl_2}{2 \text{ moles NaOH}} \times 0.25 \text{ mole NaOH}$$
$$\times 71 \text{ grams } Cl_2/\text{mole} = 8.9 \text{ grams } Cl_2$$
$$(17\text{–}3)$$

The logic behind the arrangement is the following. To produce 0.25 mole of NaOH requires, according to the molar relationship given by the balanced equation (2 and 2), an equal number of moles of NaCl. The first two terms of the equation tell us that 0.25 mole of NaCl is required. Multiplying this by the weight of a mole of NaCl, 58.5 grams, gives the weight of NaCl needed. Similarly, when 0.25

mole of NaOH is produced, according to the molar relationships taken from the balanced equation, only half as many (1 to 2) moles of Cl_2 are produced. The first two terms of Eq. 17–3 tell us that $\frac{1}{2} \times 0.25 = 0.125$ mole of Cl_2 results. Multiplying this by the molar weight of Cl_2, 71 grams, gives the desired answer: 8.9 grams of Cl_2 also result.

We can generalize the steps in the solution:

1. Determine the number of moles of the known reactant or product. [In the example, 10 grams/(40 grams/mole) of NaOH = 0.25 mole.]

2. From the balanced equation obtain the mole relationship between the desired and the known compounds. (In our example, 2 moles NaCl to 2 moles NaOH and 1 mole Cl_2 to 2 moles NaOH.)

3. Multiply. The number of moles of the desired compound results (0.25 mole NaCl and 0.125 mole Cl_2).

4. Multiply the number of moles of the desired compound by its mole weight (0.25 $\times$ 58.5 grams and 0.125 $\times$ 71 grams).

The method is perfectly straightforward, though the numbers need not be quite as simple as those in the example. If we had chosen 13.7 grams of NaOH as the required amount, the required moles would have been 13.7 grams/(40 grams/mole) = 0.343 mole. Thereafter the procedure would have followed exactly the same steps.

The method allows for one adaptation which is important whenever gases take part in a reaction. The volume of Cl_2 produced is usually of greater interest than its weight since volume is a more common way to measure gas quantities. To solve this problem, we refer to Avogadro's hypothesis that equal numbers of molecules occupy equal volumes under identical conditions. Since the mole always is 6.02×10^{23} molecules, we can rephrase this as equal numbers of moles of gases occupy equal volumes under identical conditions. If we measure the number of liters occupied by 1 mole of some gas, we have the number of liters occupied by 1 mole of all gases although the conditions must be specified. The measurements have been made. One mole of any gas measured at 0°C at 1 atm pressure occupies 22.4 liters. At 25°C and 1 atm, the molar volume is 24.5 liters. Hence at 25°C the chlorine gas produced under the conditions specified by the problem is 0.125 mole $Cl_2 \times 24.5$ liters/mole = 3.06 liters.

With this background in the basic system of chemical communication, we return to discuss the major findings of chemistry and their theoretical interpretations.

THE PERIODIC TABLE

Through the chemical discoveries around the turn of the nineteenth century, chiefly those of Lavoisier and Dalton, considerable order had been brought into chemistry. The myriad of separate compounds and mixtures had been reduced to combinations of about 60 different elements with their distinct atoms. While this decreased considerably the total complexity, 60 (now 103) distinct fundamental particles, each with its own characteristic properties, still constituted an uncomfortably diverse starting point. Consequently attempts were made to achieve further simplification through the grouping of elements with similar characteristics.

As early as 1817 the German Döbereiner (1780–1849) had pointed out that the three elements calcium (Ca), strontium (Sr), and barium (Ba) resemble each other chemically and show some relationship between reactivity and atomic weight. When bromine (Br) was discovered in 1826 and fitted chemically and in atomic weight between the already known elements chlorine (Cl) and iodine (I), he was quick to point to this second *triad* of related elements. However, this scheme of relating elements was primitive because it allowed grouping of only a few of the 60 known elements. Not until after Avogadro's hypothesis was generally accepted in 1860 and allowed the unambiguous assignment of atomic weights did further efforts to group elements bear

fruit. The problem of further simplification among the 60 or so known elements was then solved within 10 years.

Atomic weights were important in finding the key to the simplification of chemistry through the grouping of elements because with a characteristic number attached to each element there is an obvious way to order them. This way, arranging the elements in the order of their atomic weights, was the basis of the arrangement published by the Englishman Newlands (1836–1898) in 1864. He suggested that when the order of elements arranged according to atomic weight is interrupted after a row of seven, and the eighth element is placed under the first (Fig. 17–1), the vertical rows contain elements that are very similar in their chemical behavior. For some of his rows, this is quite true. Elements like Li, Na, and K, and Be, Mg, and Ca are, like Döbereiner's triads, chemically related. For these elements, Newlands's assertion that when the elements are arranged according to atomic weight, similar chemical properties recur at intervals of eight holds. By analogy with the recurrence of notes on the musical scale, he called his discovery the law of octaves.

But Newlands ignored the fact that the chemical similarities were less pronounced or totally absent in the other five groups. For instance, H is only approximately like F and Cl whereas Fe is completely distinct from the related O and S. Moreover, the choice of name was unfortunate, for it drew ridicule in addition to the justified criticism. When his basic idea was modified and extended in 1869 by Dmitri Mendelyeev (1834–1907) in Russia and Lothar Meyer

H	Li	Be	B	C	N	O
F	Na	Mg	Al	Si	P	S
Cl	K	Ca	Cr	Ti	Mn	Fe

FIG. 17-1

Newlands's law of octaves.

(1830–1895) in Germany, Newlands's original contribution was ignored.

Newlands's history shows the personal aspects of science. The neglect of his discovery, partial though it was, considerably embittered him, especially after the Royal Society of his own native England awarded its Davy Medal to Mendelyeev in 1882. Fortunately the story ends somewhat happily. In 1887 the importance of Newlands's first contribution was reassessed and he, too, was honored by the award of the same medal.

The greater recognition accorded Mendelyeev especially, but also Meyer, was not entirely unjustified. Newlands had forced into groups some elements whose chemical behavior did not warrant grouping. Both Mendelyeev and Meyer showed considerably better chemical judgment and avoided such unjustified grouping. They recognized that the then known chemical elements might be joined later by others that had not yet been discovered. In those places in their arrangement where the chemistry demanded it, they either left blank spaces for to-be-discovered elements, or they changed the order of atomic weights, which were not always accurately known. Through these two steps, their arrangements always listed chemi-

cally similar elements together. The recurrence of similar properties was not always at the same eight-element interval. Their arrangement is known as the *periodic table*. It follows the periodic law: *when elements are arranged* (mostly) *in order of their atomic weights, elements with similar properties appear at regularly recurring (periodic) intervals.*

An arrangement that emphasizes the periodic recurrence of similar chemical properties was contributed independently by both Mendelyeev and Meyer. Mendelyeev, however, went one step further to make perhaps the most significant contribution. He used the similarities implied by the periodic law, and a large amount of sound chemical intuition, to predict the characteristics of at least three of the elements for which he had left blank spaces in his periodic table (Fig. 17–2). The spectacular success of his predictions for the element germanium, which was discovered in 1885, 14 years after he had made them, is illustrated in Table 17–1. It demonstrated the importance and utility of the periodic table, which was quickly and firmly accepted by chemists.

Figure 17–3 gives the modern periodic table, an arrangement very similar to Men-

							H										Li					
							1										7					
							Be	B	C	N	O	F	Na								
							9.4	11	12	14	16	19	23								
							Mg	Al	Si	P	S	Cl	K	Ca			Er?	Yt?	In?	
							24	24.7	28	31	32	35.5	39	40	45	56	60	75.6	
Ti	V	Cr	Mn	Fe	NiCo	Cu	Zn			As	Se	Br	Rb	Sr	Ce	La	Dy	Th
50	51	52	55	56	59	63.4	65.2	68	70	75	79.4	80	85.4	87.6	92	94	95	118?
Zr	Nb	Mo	Rh	Ru	Pd	Ag	Cd	U	Sn	Sb	Te	I	Cs	Ba				
90	94	96	104.4	104.4	106.6	108	112	116	118	122	128?	127	133	137				
	Ta	W	Pt	Ir	Os	Hg		Au		Bi			Tl	Pb				
180	182	186	197.4	198	199	200		197?		210?			204	207				

FIG. 17-2

Mendelyeev's periodic table.

Ia																	0
1 H 1.0080	IIa											IIIa	IVa	Va	VIa	VIIa	2 He 4.0026
3 Li 6.939	4 Be 9.012											5 B 10.81	6 C 12.011	7 N 14.007	8 O 15.999	9 F 18.998	10 Ne 20.183
11 Na 22.99	12 Mg 24.31			Transition elements								13 Al 26.98	14 Si 28.09	15 P 30.974	16 S 32.06	17 Cl 35.453	18 Ar 39.948
19 K 39.102	20 Ca 40.08	21 Sc 44.96	22 Ti 47.90	23 V 50.94	24 Cr 52.00	25 Mn 54.94	26 Fe 55.85	27 Co 58.93	28 Ni 58.71	29 Cu 63.54	30 Zn 65.37	31 Ga 69.72	32 Ge 72.59	33 As 74.92	34 Se 78.96	35 Br 79.909	36 Kr 83.80
37 Rb 85.47	38 Sr 87.62	39 Y 88.90	40 Zr 91.22	41 Nb 92.91	42 Mo 95.94	43 Tc (99)	44 Ru 101.07	45 Rh 102.90	46 Pd 106.4	47 Ag 107.87	48 Cd 112.40	49 In 114.82	50 Sn 118.69	51 Sb 121.75	52 Te 127.60	53 I 126.90	54 Xe 131.30
55 Cs 132.90	56 Ba 137.34	57 La 138.91	72 Hf 178.49	73 Ta 180.95	74 W 183.85	75 Re 186.2	76 Os 190.2	77 Ir 192.2	78 Pt 195.09	79 Au 196.97	80 Hg 200.59	81 Tl 204.37	82 Pb 207.19	83 Bi 208.98	84 Po (210)	85 At (210)	86 Rn (222)
87 Fr (223)	88 Ra (226)	89 Ac (227)	104 ?														

Lanthanide elements	58 Ce 140.12	59 Pr 140.91	60 Nd 144.24	61 Pm (147)	62 Sm 150.35	63 Eu 151.96	64 Gd 157.25	65 Tb 158.92	66 Dy 162.50	67 Ho 164.93	68 Er 167.26	69 Tm 168.93	70 Yb 173.04	71 Lu 174.97
Actinide elements	90 Th 232.04	91 Pa (231)	92 U 238.03	93 Np (237)	94 Pu (244)	95 Am (243)	96 Cm (247)	97 Bk (247)	98 Cf (251)	99 Es (254)	100 Fm (253)	101 Md (256)	102 No (254)	103 Lr (257)

FIG. 17-3

A modern periodic table. For elements with no stable isotopes, the mass number of the isotope of longest half-life is given in parentheses.

delyeev's. With three exceptions, it follows the order of increasing atomic weights. In it, the triads of Döbereiner have been expanded to as many as six related elements in the vertical columns. Such related elements are called a *group* of elements. (The name family is also used at times.)

The periodic table gives the symbols of the elements, their currently accepted atomic weights, and their number in the arrangement, starting with 1 for the lightest element, hydrogen. This number is called the *atomic number*. As we shall see, it describes an important physical property. Indeed, it is the basis for the confidence we have today that if another element is to be discovered, it will fit after Lr, element 103, and not, as in Mendelyeev's times, somewhere in the body of the periodic table.

The periodic table separates the elements into four different sets. Groups Ia and IIa, at the left of the table, and the last six groups, at the right, contain elements with strong within-group resemblances and evident chemical differences between the groups. Except for the first three rows, where no elements intervene, the two sets are separated by ten groups which show some between-group similarities as well as the strong within-group resemblance. These elements are called the *transition* elements.

TABLE 17-1

Predicted and measured properties of germanium

Property	Predicted by Mendelyeev 1871	Discovered by Winkler 1885 (current values)
Name	Ekasilicon	Germanium
Atomic weight	72	72.60
Physical properties of element	Dark gray, high melting point Density: 5.5 grams/cm³	Dark gray, mp 958°C Density: 5.35 grams/cm³
Properties of oxides	Formula EsO_2; high melting point Density: 4.7 grams/cm³	GeO_2; mp 1115°C Density: 4.70 grams/cm³
Properties of chloride	Formula $EsCl_4$; boils below 100°C Density: 1.9 grams/cm³	$GeCl_4$; bp 83°C Density: 1.88 grams/cm³

The fourth set of elements is given separately at the bottom of the table and consists of the lanthanide or rare-earth elements, all of which resemble one another very strongly. They also resemble the related actinide elements. The actinides are, in addition, radioactive; unstable (except for Th and U); and from elements 93, Np, on, man-made.

SOME CHEMICAL FAMILIES

The kinds of relationships exhibited by the elements in one group are illustrated in Tables 17–2 to 17–4. The *alkali metals,* group Ia, for instance, are all metallic elements: they are silvery and conduct heat and electricity quite well. For metallic ele-

TABLE 17-2

Some properties of the alkali metals

	Li	Na	K	Rb	Cs
Metal					
Atomic weight	6.94	22.99	39.10	85.47	132.91
Melting point, °C	186	97.5	62.3	38.5	28.5
Boiling point, °C	1336	880	760	700	670
Density, grams/cm³ at 20 °C	0.53	0.97	0.86	1.53	1.87
Chloride					
Formula	LiCl	NaCl	KCl	RbCl	CsCl
Density, grams/cm³	2.07	2.17	1.94	2.76	3.97
Solubility, grams/100 cm³ water	45	35	34.7	91	186
Melting point, °C	613	801	776	715	646
Boiling point, °C	1353	1490(?)	1500(?)	1390	1290(?)
Hydroxide					
Formula	LiOH	NaOH	KOH	RbOH	CsOH
Density, grams/cm³	1.43	2.13	2.04	3.20	3.67
Solubility, grams/100 cm³ water	13	42	107	180	400
Melting point, °C	450	318	360	300	272

(?) Data not certain.

TABLE 17-3

Some properties of the alkaline-earth elements

	Be	Mg	Ca	Sr	Ba	Ra†
Metal						
Atomic weight	9.01	24.31	40.08	87.62	137.34	226.03
Melting point, °C	1280	650	810	800	850	960(?)
Boiling point, °C	1500	1100	1300(?)	1300(?)	1500(?)	1100(?)
Density, grams/cm³	1.86	1.74	1.55	2.6	3.6	5(?)
Chlorides						
Formula	$BeCl_2$	$MgCl_2$	$CaCl_2$	$SrCl_2$	$BaCl_2$	$RaCl_2$
Density, grams/cm³	1.90	2.32	2.51	3.05	3.86	4.91
Solubility, grams/100 cm³ water	vs(?)	54	59.5	43.1	31	5
Melting point, °C	440(?)	708	770	873	962	1000
Boiling point, °C	520	1412	‡1600	...	1560	
Hydroxides						
Formula	$Be(OH)_2$	$Mg(OH)_2$	$Ca(OH)_2$	$Sr(OH)_2$	$Ba(OH)_2$	$Ra(OH)_2$
Density, grams/cm³	...	2.38	2.34	3.63	4.50	
Solubility, grams/100 cm³ water	i	0.001	0.2	0.4	5.6	
Melting point, °C	d	d	d	375	78	

†Radium is radioactive; atomic weight of most common isotope.
‡Data uncertain; i—insoluble; vs—very soluble; d—decomposes.

ments, they all have surprisingly low melting points, so low that a mixture of Na and K is used as a cooling liquid in airplane valves and in experimental nuclear reactors. Their densities are also very low. All the alkali elements are extremely reactive. In air they rapidly lose their silvery luster and become coated with a gray oxide as a result of reaction with oxygen. In contact with water, all except Li react rapidly and even explosively. The product of these reactions is the strongly basic hydroxide compound, formula MOH (M here stands for any one of the alkali metals). All alkali metals form chlorides, bromides, and iodides of the formula MCl, MBr, MI. These and nearly all other compounds of the alkali metals are quite soluble in water.

Table 17-3 illustrates some of the properties of the next family, IIa, called the *alkaline earths*. They too are metals that are shiny and conduct electricity but with much higher melting points. They too react with air to form the oxides and with water

to form the hydroxides. But the hydroxides have the formula $M(OH)_2$,[1] and are produced slowly, and in the case of Be and Mg, with hot water only. Also, most of the alkaline-earth hydroxides, as most other alkaline-earth compounds, are insoluble in water. The alkaline earths also form chlorides, bromides, and iodides, but with the chemical formulas MCl_2, MBr_2, and MI_2.

Table 17-4 gives some properties of group VIIa, the *halogen* elements. The halogens are all decidedly nonmetallic. At room temperature fluorine and chlorine are yellowish gases, bromine a reddish liquid, and iodine a violet solid (with a metallic silvery luster). Astatine is not known in nature. The halogens dissolve to a small extent in water, with which they also react to a small extent (fluorine reacts strongly).

[1] The subscript 2 after the parentheses means that all elements listed in the parentheses are present twice. The reason for keeping OH together and writing $(OH)_2$ not O_2H_2 is that in hydroxides the combination OH is important as a part of the molecule. We shall meet other groupings—NO_3, SO_4, PO_4, CO_3, for instance—later.

TABLE 17-4

Some properties of the halogen elements

Property	F	Cl	Br	I
Atomic weight	19.00	35.45	79.91	126.90
Appearance	Pale yellow gas	Yellow gas	Red liquid	*Violet solid*
Melting point, °C	−223	−101.6	−7.2	113.5
Boiling point, °C	−187	−34.6	58.8	184.4
Solubility, grams/100 cm³ water	...	1	3.6	0.03

From this limited list of examples we see that the similarities among elements in a single group extend to four sets of characteristics. There are, first of all, the appearance, color, state, melting and boiling points, the *physical* properties of the elements. Then there are the reactivities of the elements toward other substances, like air, water, the halogens, etc. These are their *chemical* properties. Third, the similarities extend to appearance, solubility, density, and other physical properties of the compounds derived from the elements. Finally, the chemical composition, stability, and reactivity, the chemical properties of the compounds of elements from one group are similar. Indeed, position in the periodic table implies much of the chemistry of an element, and the full interpretation of the periodic table is the most important theoretical aid for the chemist. An excellent illustration of this point is, of course, the use made of it by Mendelyeev to predict the properties of as yet unknown elements.

THE TRANSITION ELEMENTS

In some contrast to the elements of the "a" groups, the transition elements resemble each other as well as showing the more typical group similarities. For instance, all are metallic with reasonably similar, high melting points (except Zn, Cd, and Hg) and high electrical and heat conductivities. Nearly all are relatively inert to oxygen at room temperature although this varies from the rapid combustion in air of red-hot iron, for instance, or hot cadmium, zinc, or titanium to the almost total inertness of gold or platinum even in pure oxygen. All are insoluble and fail to react with cold water. Many have oxides of formula MO, and nearly all also form several oxides with different formulas. For iron these are FeO and Fe_2O_3; for copper, Cu_2O and CuO; for titanium, TiO, Ti_2O_3, and TiO_2. But the within-group resemblances are greater. The other members of the iron family, ruthenium and osmium, resemble iron more than they do the other 27 transition elements; silver and gold resemble copper more; and rhenium resembles manganese more. Technitium is unknown in nature.

One other group requires some attention: the elements of the last row, group 0. This is a group of gases which are almost completely unreactive. With the exception of a small number of relatively unstable compounds of Kr and Xe that have been produced only since 1962, these elements do not enter into combinations with other elements. They are called the *noble* or inert (this name is no longer entirely tenable) gases. The stability or nonreactivity of these elements is of great interest in the development of chemical theory, as we shall see later.

VALENCE

In the partial list of characteristics of elements given above, we mentioned that the alkali metals form chlorides, bromides, and iodides of formula MCl, MBr, and MI, whereas the comparable alkaline-earth compounds have formulas MCl_2, MBr_2, and MI_2. We might suspect immediately, and we will confirm in Chap. 19, that the group number has something to do with this difference. Atoms of group Ia elements combine with single atoms of Cl or Br or I; atoms of group IIa elements combine with two atoms. A further inference to which our suspicion might lead us is that the compound of aluminum with chlorine should have the formula $AlCl_3$; the iodide of germanium GeI_4; the bromide of phosphorus PBr_5; and so forth. Our inferences would be correct. The number of the family indicates how the elements combine, a property called the chemical combining power or *valence*. The valence of an element is determined by how many atoms either of hydrogen or of a halogen it combines with. According to our above illustrations, and especially for groups Ia to IVa, the valence equals the group number. Group Ia members combine with one atom of the halogen elements; group IIa members with two halogen atoms; group IIIa members with three halogen atoms; and group IVa members with four.

Groups Va, VIa, and VIIa give some trouble. As indicated by the examples, the valence of phosphorus is 5; the compound PBr_5 has one atom of phosphorus combining with five bromine atoms, but there are also the compounds PBr_3 and NH_3, which suggest a valence of 3. Actually group Va elements show both valences, with 3 more common than 5. Among group VIa elements there are only a few compounds indicating a valence of 6. SF_6 is known, and so are SeF_6 and TeF_6. But there are no compounds of oxygen with six halogen atoms nor any of sulfur, selenium, or tellurium with six chlorines, six bromines, or six iodines. On the other hand, H_2O, H_2S, OF_2, Cl_2O, SCl_2, $TeCl_2$, and many other compounds of this type suggest a valence of 2 for this group. Finally, among the compounds of the halogens, there is

IF_7 to represent the valence of 7. But HF, HCl, HBr, and HI all indicate the more prevalent valence of 1 for this group.

The valences of the transition elements, like those of the other metallic elements, can be derived from their halogen compounds. We have already noted that the transition elements form several oxides. The same holds true for the fluorides, chlorides, bromides, and iodides. We can illustrate with $FeCl_2$ and $FeCl_3$; CuI and CuI_2; and $TiCl_2$, $TiCl_3$, and $TiCl_4$. The variety is great. Most of the transition elements show the valence 2; many show 3; most show other valences as well.

In general, but recognizing that there are exceptions:

1. Groups Ia to IVa show valences given by the group numbers.

2. Groups Va to VIIa also show valences given by the group numbers, but in most of their compounds the valences are 3 for group Va, 2 for group VIa, and 1 for group VIIa.

3. The transition elements show several valences, usually including valence 2 or 3.

So far we have used the experimentally determined compositions of known compounds to establish the valence of elements. The importance of the concept valence is, however, that we can reverse the process to predict the probable composition of compounds by means of valences. The rule for prediction is that in a compound that contains the atoms of two elements, the valence numbers must be equal. For instance, from the valence of 1 for all halogens and the valence of 4 sometimes shown by osmium, Os, we can predict that four atoms of chlorine combine with one of osmium, and the compound formed has the formula $OsCl_4$. We arrive at this by:

Os, transition element,
  variable valence given here as   4
Cl, group VIIa, valence 1;
  use four atoms to give 4×1 = 4

By the same reasoning we predict the compound OsO_2:

Os, as above   4

O, group VIa, valence 2;

     use two atoms to give 2×2 $= 4$

The compound Mg and N is Mg_3N_2. It follows the rule:

Mg, group IIa, valence 2;

     use three atoms to give 3×2 $= 6$

N, group Va, valence 3;

     use two atoms to give 2×3 $= 6$

In each of the above compounds, valence numbers are equated by using more than one atom of one or both elements to achieve the match. In cases like HCl, NaCl, BaO, SrS, AlN, BN, and SiC, of course, the match is achieved without any further computations.

NAMING

We have now surveyed the major observations that serve as the basis for chemical theory, and we have developed a fairly extensive chemical vocabulary. We need only some rules for the naming of compounds to tackle basic chemical theory and the problems of interest in current chemical research.

With so many possible chemical compounds, the rules for naming must be highly precise, simple, and suggestive of the chemical compositions. A basic convention has been agreed on that accomplishes this with perhaps two exceptions. One exception is the millions of compounds of the elements carbon and hydrogen. For these, the compounds of organic chemistry, a special naming convention is needed. We shall look at it, briefly, in Chap. 22. The second exception is the small number of compounds which have kept the names given them in earlier times. Water is an excellent example; its name should be hydrogen oxide. Other exceptions are ammonia, nitric oxide, etc. These illustrate chemical names in common use which do not follow the naming convention currently accepted by the International Union of Pure

and Applied Chemistry (IUPAC), which, among its other functions, passes on naming conventions, best values for atomic weights, and other matters to maintain unity in chemical research throughout the world.

Compounds between two elements only, *binary* compounds, are written with the metallic element first and the nonmetallic element second. They are named by the name of the first element followed by the name of the second element modified with the suffix *ide*. Thus the compounds, $MgCl_2$, Ca_3N_2, PbS, Na_2O are magnesium chlor*ide*, calcium nitr*ide*, lead sulf*ide*, and sodium ox*ide*. (While they may contain more than two atoms joined together in the molecules, they are all binary—containing the atoms of two elements only.) The suffix *ide* is reserved for binary compounds.

For binary compounds of the transition elements, provision is made to indicate valence by giving it in Roman numerals after naming the metal. Fe_2O_3, in which iron shows the valence 3, is written "iron (III) oxide" and read "iron-three-oxide." OsF_6, in which osmium has the valence 6 is written "osmium (VI) fluoride" and read "osmium-six-fluoride." While there is no need to write sodium (I) sulfide for Na_2S because Na, a member of group Ia, has an unambiguous valence, it would not be entirely wrong.

Finally, many group Va, VIa, and VIIa elements, which as we saw can take on at least two valences, produce more than one compound. Perhaps the most diverse are the oxides of nitrogen, of which there are six: N_2O, NO, N_2O_3, NO_2, N_2O_4, and N_2O_5. For these, the convention is to use Greek-number prefixes to indicate the number of atoms. Dinitrogen monoxide, mononitrogen monoxide, dinitrogen trioxide, mononitrogen dioxide, dinitrogen tetroxide, and dinitrogen pentoxide are the names of the six nitrogen oxides, although in common usage among chemists, the prefix *mono* is often omitted. (Indeed, chemists frequently retain archaic nonsystematic names which are shorter.) The compound SF_6 is monosulfur hexafluoride, and IF_7 is monoiodine pentafluoride.

In summary, binary compounds name the metallic element first, the nonmetallic element with the suffix *ide* second. In the case of the transition elements, all of which are metals, valence is indicated by a Roman numeral following the metal. For compounds among the elements of groups Va, VIa, and VIIa, Greek-number prefixes show the number of atoms in the molecule.

Most compounds of more than two elements contain subgroups of special stability. We referred to this briefly when we pointed out that $Ca(OH)_2$, not CaO_2H_2, is the way to write the formula of calcium hydroxide. This subgroup, OH, is not a complete chemical entity; it is always joined to a metallic element in a compound, as in $Mg(OH)_2$ or $Fe(OH)_3$. The stability of the subgroup is reflected in a special name. OH is the hydroxide group and the two compounds are magnesium hydroxide

and iron (III) hydroxide. (The hydroxide group, by the way, is the only exception to the rule that *ide* compounds are binary.)

From the way the hydroxide subgroup combines with metal atoms, in compounds, it can be seen that its valence is 1. The subgroup, as a whole, has that valence. Other common subgroups are SO_4, sulfate, valence 2; NO_3, nitrate, valence 1; CO_3, carbonate, valence 2; PO_4, phosphate, valence 3. Names of compounds with these subgroups follow the rule for binary compounds; the subgroup name follows the name of the metal. Na_2SO_4 is sodium sulfate; $Al(NO_3)_3$—the entire NO_3 group is taken three times—is aluminum nitrate; $Y_2(CO_3)_3$ is yttrium (III) carbonate; $Mg_3(PO_4)_2$ is magnesium phosphate.

One other subgroup of elements is rather common, the NH_4 or ammonium group, valence 1. It, however, is a group that appears like a metal in compounds and is therefore listed first. NH_4Cl is ammonium chloride; $(NH_4)_3PO_4$ is ammonium phosphate.

Questions and Problems

1. Write the symbols of the following elements: chlorine, sodium, potassium, oxygen, lead, iron, copper, zinc, tin, mercury, nitrogen, carbon.

2. What are the names of the elements whose symbols are I, O, Ca, Mg, Al, P, Ni, Co, Cr?

3. Name the following compounds:

(a) $Mg_3(PO_4)_2$ (e) Fe_2O_3 (i) IF_5
(b) $CaSO_4$ (f) $Ni(NO_3)_2$ (j) $CrCl_3$
(c) HCl (g) P_2O_3 (k) SnI_4
(d) $(NH_4)_2S$ (h) S_2O_7 (l) $CoBr_2$

4. Write formulas for (a) copper (I) iodide, (b) ammonium phosphate, (c) barium hydroxide, (d) aluminum sulfate, (e) chromium (II) iodide, (f) sodium nitrate, (g) dinitrogen tetroxide, (h) monophosphorus pentaiodide, (i) calcium nitride, (j) monocarbon monoxide.

5. Compute the percentage composition of the compounds in Questions 3d, 3h, 4d, 4h.

6. Determine molecular weights of the compounds in Questions 3b, 3k, 4b, 4i.

7. Compute the number of moles of Li_2SO_4 in

33 grams of the compound. How many molecules? How many atoms of Li? of S? of O?

8. How many moles, molecules, and atoms in 31 grams of ethylene glycol, $C_2H_6O_2$?

9. Balance the following equations:
(a) $FeO + Al \longrightarrow Al_2O_3 + Fe$
(b) $P_4 + Cl_2 \longrightarrow PCl_3$
(c) $NH_3 + O_2 \longrightarrow NO + H_2O$
(d) $C_4H_{10} + O_2 \longrightarrow H_2O + CO_2$
(e) $Al + HNO_3 \longrightarrow Al(NO_3)_3 + H_2$

10. A chemist requires 2 moles of phosphorus trichloride (Question 9b). How many moles of chlorine gas must he react? What weight? How many molecules? How many atoms? How many liters of chlorine at 25°C and 1 atm?

11. Compute the number of moles, molecules, and liters of each reactant and product when 8.5 grams of NH_3 react according to the equation in Question 9c.

12. Determine the valence of the italicized element in each of the following compounds:
(a) $CuCl_2$ (d) Mn_2O_7 (g) Au_2O_3
(b) AsH_3 (e) IBr_3 (h) $PtCl_4$
(c) TiO_2 (f) AgI (i) UCl_5

Suggestions for Further Reading

Texts that discuss basic chemical theory include:

Christiansen, G. S. and Paul H. Garrett: *Structure and Change*, W. H. Freeman and Company, San Francisco, 1960. Chapters 7 and 8.

Pauling, Linus: *College Chemistry*, 3d ed., W. H. Freeman and Company, San Francisco, 1964. Chapters 4, 5, and 7.

Quagliano, James V.: *Chemistry*, 2d ed., Prentice-Hall, Inc., Englewood Cliffs, N.J., 1963. Chapters 2, 4, 5, and 12.

Sisler, Harry H., Calvin A. Vander Werf, and Arthur W. Davidson: *College Chemistry*, 2d ed., The Macmillan Company, New York, 1961. Chapters 4 to 6.

Chapter 18

Characteristics of Atoms II: Nuclear Structure

The past chapters have given some of the properties of the atoms of the 103 known elements—atomic weight, valence, periodicity. The elements are unlike in many respects but with one hint of relatedness: similar properties recur at periodic intervals. Now we face the question: Is matter really so complex, composed of 103 entirely different building blocks, or are there more fundamental similarities? Are atoms the ultimate particles or are there other, more elementary particles which give a common structure to atoms?

We have one piece of evidence that atoms are not, as Dalton suggested, indivisible. We know from our previous work that electricity is associated with all atoms. We know that all metals conduct electric current and that a current consists of a stream of electrons. We know that non-conductors can be given a static charge and that this too involves the transfer of electrons from one material to another. Since electrons seem to be involved in all atoms, perhaps electrons can give us a clue about how atoms are alike (although we must then establish also how they differ). In doing this, we are appealing to the principle of parsimony. We look for a few rules to explain similarities and differences among atoms rather than looking for 103 entirely and basically different particles.

THE ELECTRICAL NATURE OF MATTER

The conviction that electrons must be basic constituents of all atoms comes from static electricity (Chap. 13) and experiments with cathode rays. Particularly, work with the latter led to the discoveries which made the notion almost inescapable that all atoms contain electrons and positive charges and

therefore have a further structure into which they can be subdivided.

A cathode-ray tube contains two electrodes sealed into a partially evacuated glass chamber. When a fairly high voltage is applied to the electrodes, a stream of cathode rays or electrons flows from the negative cathode to the positive anode. Since this works with all metals, it demonstrates that electrons flow easily through all metals and are probably part of them.

In 1886 the German physicist Eugen Goldstein (1850–1930) used a cathode-ray tube which had a perforated rather than a solid cathode. To his surprise, he found that a second group of rays appeared behind the cathode (Fig. 18–1). Evidently, positive particles had been formed in the cathode-ray tube, had been attracted toward the cathode, and had traveled through the holes to the other side. Appropriately, he called these rays *positive rays*. Further study showed them to be associated with the gas that remains in the partially evacuated cathode-ray tube.

The simplest explanation for positive rays

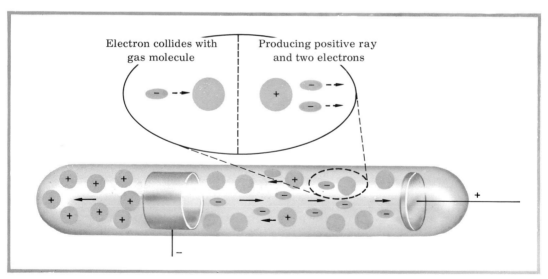

FIG. 18-1

Positive-ray tube. In addition to the negative cathode rays, positively charged particles exist in evacuated tubes when a potential is applied across the electrodes. The positive particles result from collisions between the electrons of the cathode rays and the residual gas molecules in the tube in which additional electrons are knocked off the gas molecules.

involves electrons as part of the residual gas in the tube. If gas molecules consist of something positive and something negative as static-electricity experiments already had indicated, then it is entirely reasonable to assume that occasionally, when a cathode ray—an electron—collides with a gas molecule, the molecule breaks apart during the collision. The remnants from the collision are the positive-ray particle and the "something negative" which joins the cathode rays and travels toward the anode. So far, whenever we have encountered "something negative," it has always been an electron. It is therefore most reasonable to suppose that this experiment too shows that matter —the gas in the cathode-ray tube in this case—contains electrons.

Another outgrowth of experiments with cathode-ray tubes was the discovery of X rays, which in turn led to further confirmation of the electrical nature of matter. In 1895 Wilhelm Roentgen (1845–1923) noted that a fluorescent material in his laboratory glowed every time he turned on a cathode-ray tube. Closer investigation showed that a highly energetic and penetrating form of electromagnetic radiation was generated in the cathode-ray tube and caused the fluorescence. Roentgen had discovered X rays.

X rays interact with gases to produce positive particles similar to positive rays, and negative particles that have the same properties as electrons. Since there are no electrons in the gas before irradiation with X rays, the electrons must have separated from the gas itself. This is further evidence that electrons are part of all matter.

The mechanism for this effect is similar to the mechanism for producing positive rays in the cathode-ray tubes and the photoelectric effect (Chap. 15). X-ray photons, colliding with the gas molecules, break them into electrons and positive remnants. From these and other experiments, evidence began to pile up that electrons hold the key to the structure of atoms and that this key in turn would open the door to understanding the chemical behavior of the elements.

RADIOACTIVITY

Before we can turn to the experiments which showed how electrons fit into atoms, we must describe one other discovery that occurred almost at the same time. It made possible the crucial experiment on atomic structure.

In 1896 the French physicist Henri Becquerel (1852–1908) noted that an undeveloped photographic plate which he had accidentally left near a sample of uranium had been exposed even though the plate had been tightly wrapped in black paper. Here was something as penetrating as X rays although not produced by cathode-ray tubes. Becquerel called this spontaneous emission by uranium *radioactivity*. A search for the cause of the penetrating emission led to the discovery that the ore pitchblende, which contains only small amounts of uranium, shows far greater radioactivity. Marie (1867–1934) and Pierre (1859–1906) Curie set about to isolate the powerful source of radiation in pitchblende.

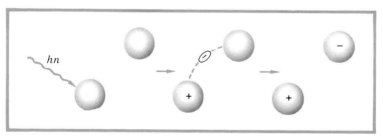

X-ray photons colliding with gas molecules release electrons from them. The electrons may collide with other molecules and attach themselves.

FIG. 18-2

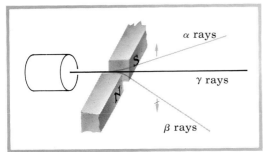

FIG. 18-3

The emission from radioactive materials consists of three distinct rays: positive α rays, negative β rays, and uncharged γ rays.

After 2 years of painstaking work, they discovered a new element, radium, the source of the radioactivity in pitchblende. They were awarded the Nobel Prize for this research.

Study of the characteristics of the radioactive emission from radium and uranium showed that it consists of three separate rays. The experimental setup is basically simple (Fig. 18–3). The sample of radium is placed in a block of lead—lead is used because high-atomic-weight elements are the best absorbers of radiation—in which a hole is bored. Radioactive rays leave only through the hole as a fine stream of radiation. When this stream is passed between the pole faces of a magnet, it separates into three distinct rays. One ray is bent in a direction showing that it consists of positive particles, called alpha particles. Another ray is bent in the opposite direction, indicating that it consists of negative particles. These are called beta particles. The third ray is unbent by the magnet, showing it to be electrically uncharged. This third ray consists of gamma rays, a true electromagnetic radiation of extremely high-energy photons. Later work with α and β particles and γ rays showed that α particles are positively charged helium atoms and that β particles are electrons. But at the time they were discovered and named, these connections were unknown and the names have persisted to this day. (Note that electrons discovered in three different kinds of experiments gave them three names: electron, cathode ray, and β ray.)

It should be clear by now that scientific progress is not an orderly matter, in which one discovery logically leads to another. Instead, many things are discovered at one time, some of them leading to new discoveries in new and different fields, others converging into a single field. Thus cathode rays, positive rays, X rays, and radioactivity all were discovered in a relatively short period of time. Each led to a new field of research of its own: cathode rays to radio and TV tubes; positive rays to the mass spectrometer; X rays to crystallography; and radioactivity to nuclear fission and fusion. But all also contributed to the elucidation of the structure of atoms, with which we are most concerned in this chapter. Therefore we leave the topic of radioactivity for a short time here and return to the main stream of our discussion, the nature of atoms. Before we do so, however, we must mention one other property of radioactive emissions. Like X rays and cathode rays, α, β, and γ rays are able to knock electrons from uncharged molecules and thus produce charged particles. The process of producing charged particles is called *ionization,* and the charged particles, *ions.*

STRUCTURE OF ATOMS

We have seen the accumulation of evidence that atoms contain electrons. Since the atom itself is electrically neutral, this means, immediately, that atoms contain some positive entity as well. What kind of positive entity? The first thoughts concerning the internal structure of atoms were that atoms consisted of jellylike positive matter in which the electrons were embedded. This idea explains the electrical nature of atoms and the space which atoms take up. How the electrons fitted into the positive jelly or what it was like, was not clear. But no alternative model suggested

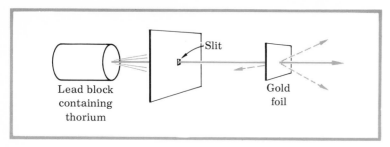

FIG. 18-4

The Rutherford experiment. When a stream of α particles was directed at gold foil, most of the α particles passed through, a few were deflected through small angles, and an occasional α particle rebounded toward the source.

itself until the English physicist, Ernest Rutherford (1871–1937), performed a now-famous experiment.

Lord Rutherford took a thin leaf of gold only a few thousandths of an inch thick. To this he directed a stream of α particles from the radioactive element thorium (Fig. 18–4). Because of the thinness of the gold leaf and the high energy of the α particles, he was not surprised that most of the α particles acted as if the gold leaf were not there; they passed right through it without any sign of interaction. That a small fraction of them were somewhat deflected was also not surprising because they had passed through a thin wall of matter. But the discovery that one α particle in about 20,000 was repelled completely by the gold foil and returned toward the source was difficult to comprehend. Rutherford has been described as saying, "It was as if a 15-lb cannon had been fired at tissue paper and the cannon ball had bounced back."

On further reflection, the results of this experiment suggested two conclusions. First, there must be much empty space in the atom to allow most of the α particles to pass through without hindrance or deflection. Second, somewhere in the atom there is the cause for the complete repulsion of the one α particle in 20,000. From these two conclusions, Lord Rutherford constructed the model of the atom we now accept.

Since α particles are positively charged, the most likely cause for repulsion is encounter with another small, positively

charged entity. Indeed, the manner in which the α particles recoiled allowed the estimation of the charge which has to reside on the repelling entity. It was a positive charge about 80 times as great as the charge on an electron. Hence, somewhere within the gold atoms there must be a small, highly charged entity, now called the *nucleus* of the atom. Surrounding the nucleus are the electrons, equal in number to the charge carried by the nucleus in order to keep the atom as a whole electrically neutral. Furthermore, the electrons and nucleus must be so arranged that much empty space remains between them. This model of an atom, illustrated in Fig. 18–5,

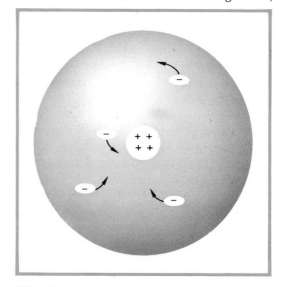

FIG. 18-5

Current model of the atom. The positive charge resides in a small nucleus around which the electrons move.

is the currently accepted model. Measurements have shown that the diameter of the nucleus is only about 10^{-13} cm, or about one hundred-thousandth of the diameter of the entire atom. The remaining space is filled with electrons which, though they are small themselves, manage to keep other atoms from penetrating that space. Since both nucleus and electrons are very small, the atom is in a sense largely empty space, although under ordinary circumstances, the empty space is reserved for the electrons associated with the nucleus. It can be entered only by high-energy particles like the α particles from thorium. All other matter is repelled and excluded.

We can now reinterpret Rutherford's experiment. Most of the α particles pass far away from the small nuclei in the gold foil. While they may collide with electrons, these are too small and too light to seriously disturb the path of the α particles which simply knock the electrons out of the way and continue undisturbed. A few α particles come close enough to nuclei to be somewhat deflected in their paths. However, one α particle in about 20,000 meets a gold nucleus in a near head-on collision. This kind of collision results in the deflection of the α particle through an angle of more than 90°.

This experiment was later repeated with other elements, and similar results were obtained. The chief variation noted was in the charge carried by nuclei of different elements. While the experiments were not sufficiently precise to allow the exact determination of the magnitude of the charge carried by each nucleus, it was found that the nuclear charge increases with atomic weight. It follows the order of elements in the periodic table.

DETECTORS

The Rutherford experiment depends on instruments that detect α particles. Several devices for this measurement are available.

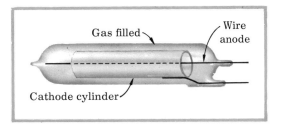

FIG. 18-6

Geiger counter. The tube contains charged electrodes and a gas at sufficiently high pressure to prevent spontaneous flow of electrons. When a particle enters and ionizes the gas, current flows through the tube and is recorded in attached electronic counting equipment.

Fluorescent materials glow when α particles strike them just as they glow when struck by X rays. Indeed, they show single flashes of light when struck by single particles. The famous Geiger counter, named after Rutherford's student and collaborator Hans Geiger (1882–1945), is another device for detecting radiation (Fig. 18–6). It depends on the fact that high-energy particles ionize a gas by knocking electrons away from nuclei. The electrically charged ions carry an electric current for a short period of time (until electrons and ions recombine) and the surge of current is recorded. Each current pulse is the product of the passage of a high-energy particle through the Geiger tube. But it is usually desirable to measure more than just the incidence of a high-energy particle. One may wish to measure its path or how it behaves in a magnetic field. For such information it is necessary to have a record of a section of the path of the high-energy particle.

Three methods can be used to track particles. If the particle happens to travel through the emulsion on a photographic plate, it will "expose" the emulsion along its path. When developed, the plate then gives evidence of the passage of the particle. But if the plate does not lie exactly in the path of the particle, it will be missed. Moreover, one cannot tell whether a particle has struck the photographic emulsion until the plate is developed. By ingenious triggering mechanisms, it has been possible in recent years to overcome this limitation, and the photographic plate is now one of the most important tools of nuclear research.

There is another device, invented in 1915 by the English physicist C. T. R. Wilson (1869–1959), which gives a trace of the passage of a high-energy particle. The cloud chamber has the advantage of covering a volume rather than just an area like the photographic plate, and giving visible tracks. It consists of a dust-free air chamber saturated with water vapor and fitted with a piston. When the piston is suddenly raised, the gas expands and cools, and water vapor begins to condense. The

FIG. 18-8

Bubble chamber and associated equipment at Brookhaven National Laboratory. The chamber itself is only 20 in. high. (Brookhaven National Laboratory)

mechanism of condensation is such that it occurs first around ions which may exist in the gas. Thus, if a high-energy particle has just passed through the cloud chamber leaving behind a trail of ions, water droplets form around those ions. The track of the high-energy particle is thus visible to the eye and can be photographed for a permanent record.

Recently an adaptation of the cloud chamber called the bubble chamber (Fig. 18–8) has been developed. It is a chamber filled with liquid hydrogen at very low temperature in which the passage of high-energy particles starts evaporation of the liquid hydrogen along their path. Thus the particle path is marked by small gas bubbles which are photographed immediately after the passage of the particle.

FIG. 18-7

Photograph of the tracks produced by particles that resulted from the collision of a high-energy photon with the gas in a cloud chamber. The photon produced electrons and positrons at the top. These collided further and produced additional electrons and positrons. The horizontal lines are metal plates which slow down the particles. (H. C. DeStaebler, Jr., and H. S. Bridge, Massachusetts Institute of Technology)

PROTONS, NEUTRONS, AND NUCLEI

The spectacular results of Rutherford's experiment led to the bombardment of other elements by α particles. When the lighter elements were used as targets, peculiar things happened. In particular, the bombardment of nitrogen gas gave rise to tracks such as the one shown in Fig. 18–9. At left center, an α particle track stops and in its place two new tracks, one short and heavy, the other long and thin, arise. Apparently, the α particle collided with a nitrogen atom and caused an explosion during collisions. Examination of the thin track indicated that it is formed by a particle about as heavy as a hydrogen atom and with a positive charge equal in magnitude to that on the electron. This particle, called the *proton*, was identified independently by Rutherford and J. Chadwick, and

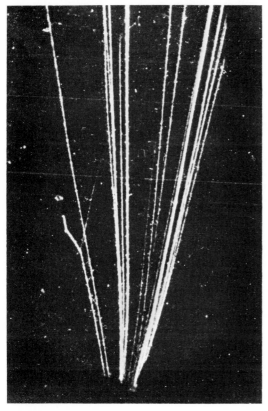

FIG. 18-9

Cloud chamber photograph by P. M. S. Blackett in 1925 in which the formation of a proton was identified. The fanlike tracks are α-particle tracks. At left center is a collision between an α particle and a nitrogen nucleus from which the thin track of a proton and the heavy track of an oxygen nucleus emerge. (Professor P. M. S. Blackett and the Royal Society)

by P. M. S. Blackett in England, and by W. D. Harkins in America. On the scale of atomic dimensions, it carries a mass of 1.00727 and a charge of +1. The proton is the nucleus of a hydrogen atom.

Similar experiments soon led to discovery of another particle, called the *neutron,* which has nearly the same mass as the proton, but which is uncharged. This discovery is shared by J. Chadwick, Frédéric and Irène Joliot-Curie, son-in-law and daughter of Pierre and Marie Curie, and the German physicists W. Bothe and H. Becker. Since protons or neutrons may appear when nuclei are bombarded by α particles, it was suggested that all atomic nuclei contain protons and neutrons, and that nuclear reactions with α particles simply release them from the nuclei. With protons and neutrons in the nucleus, the charge of the nucleus equals the number of protons in it. The mass of the nucleus equals the sum of the protons and neutrons. Since electrons contain only about one two-thousandths of the mass of protons or neutrons, they contribute next to no mass to atoms. The mass of the atom is essentially the mass of the nucleus. Table 18–1 gives a summary of the particles with their masses on the atomic-mass scale.

The discovery of protons and neutrons in the 1920s and early 1930s gave physical meaning to the atomic number. In Mendelyeev's table the atomic numbers were merely the ordinal numbers when the elements were arranged in order of increasing atomic weight. But experiments with the properties of nuclei led to the realization that the atomic number gives the charge of the nucleus of an element. Elements differ because the nuclei of their atoms have different charges. With nuclei made up of neutrons and protons, this means that elements differ in the number of protons in the nuclei.

We may now summarize the structure of atoms:

1. Atoms consist of a small positively charged nucleus which contains nearly all

TABLE 18-1

Elementary particles

	Mass, atomic scale	Mass number	Charge, electronic units	Symbol
Electron	0.00055	0	−1	e^-, $_{-1}e^0$, β
Positron	0.00055	0	+1	e^+, $_{+1}e^0$
Proton	1.00727	1	+1	p, $_1H^1$
Neutron	1.00867	1	neutral	n, $_0n^1$
α particle	4.00260	4	+2	α, $_2He^4$

of the mass of the atom and which is surrounded by electrons.

2. The nucleus is composed of protons and neutrons.

3. The atomic number gives the total charge on the nucleus which is equal to the number of protons in the nucleus.

4. The mass of the atom comes from the protons and neutrons. Therefore, the number of neutrons equals the atomic weight less the atomic number.

5. Since the atom is electrically neutral, atomic number also gives the number of electrons surrounding the nucleus.

NUCLEAR EQUATIONS AND SYMBOLS

When working with nuclei and small particles, it is convenient to adopt a system of notation which keeps track of nuclear charge and approximate nuclear mass. For reasons we shall discuss later, the masses of nuclei are not exactly whole numbers, but they differ from whole numbers only slightly. For most purposes, it is convenient to neglect such small differences and to use the integer nearest the true mass. This number is called the *mass number*. The mass number of the electron, mass 0.00055, is 0; the mass number of the proton, mass 1.00727, is 1. The common symbolism uses a subscript numeral before the symbol of the element to denote the nuclear charge; a superscript numeral following the symbol

denotes the mass number. Nitrogen, the element that led to the discovery of the proton, is written $_7N^{14}$. The 7 equals the atomic number, which equals the number of protons. The 14 gives the mass number, which also equals the number of protons and neutrons. In the same system of notation, the proton (hydrogen nucleus) is written $_1H^1$; the neutron $_0n^1$; the electron $_{-1}e^0$.

With this notation, we can now assess what happened during the nuclear transformation that led to the discovery of the proton. It involved the bombardment of nitrogen with α particles. Written as an equation, the process involved:

$$_2He^4 + {_7N^{14}} = {_1H^1} + \text{?} \qquad (18\text{--}1)$$

The α particle is a helium nucleus (the two electrons are missing). Helium, atomic number 2, has two protons in the nucleus; the nuclear mass of 4 requires that there be two neutrons as well. Nitrogen nuclei contain seven protons and seven neutrons. One result of this reaction is a single proton; conservation then requires that the other resulting particle must contain eight protons and nine neutrons. It is, therefore, the nucleus of the element with atomic number 8, oxygen, and has a mass number of 17. The equation can now be completed

$$_2He^4 + {_7N^{14}} = {_1H^1} + {_8O^{17}}$$

Protons:	2 + 7	=	1 + 8
Neutrons:	2 + 7		9

$$(18\text{--}2)$$

In the same notation, the radioactive disintegration of radium (atomic number 88; mass number 226) which emits an α particle is given by

$$_{88}Ra^{226} = {}_2He^4 + {}_{86}Rn^{222}$$

Protons:	88	=	2	+	86
Neutrons:	138	=	2	+	136

$$(18-3)$$

Radioactive elements actually disappear during radioactive decay. They are transformed into new, "daughter elements."

In considering the changes that occur in nuclei during processes such as the two illustrated above, the electrons that accompany the nuclei are generally ignored. There are several reasons for this. The electronic mass is negligibly small. Compared to the energies involved in nuclear processes, the energies required for ionization are negligibly small. From the point of view of both mass and energy, the electrons contribute little to the reactions. Also, electrons are relatively mobile, and, as we have already indicated in Chap. 13, the earth can be considered as either a sink or a source of electrons. From this source electrons are available to assure that after the reaction is complete, each product of a nuclear reaction can obtain the right number of electrons for electroneutrality.

ISOTOPES

Equation 18–2 involves an atom of the element oxygen which differs from those shown in the periodic table. In the table the atomic weight of oxygen is given as 16.00, indicating that the nucleus contains eight protons and eight neutrons. The oxygen nucleus formed in the nuclear reaction, on the other hand, contains nine neutrons. The difference between these two oxygen atoms is by no means an isolated case. All elements have some nuclei that differ from one another in the number of neutrons. Such nuclei are called *isotopes*. Isotopes also differ from one another in mass number. The fractional atomic weights given in the periodic chart arise, in part, because most elements in nature consist of mixtures of several of their isotopes. Hydrogen, for instance, is a mixture of 99.98 percent $_1H^1$ and not quite 0.02 percent $_1H^2$. The latter is called deuterium. Since about 1940 it has gained importance in various applications, most of which relate to the production of nuclear energy or nuclear bombs. Oxygen also consists of three isotopes: 99.76 percent $_8O^{16}$, 0.04 percent $_8O^{17}$, and 0.20 percent $_8O^{18}$. Chlorine contains approximately three parts of $_{17}Cl^{35}$ and one part $_{17}Cl^{37}$. The weighted average of these two isotopes leads to the atomic weight of 35.5.

Because of the existence of isotopes, elements can no longer be defined as having all atoms alike. Instead, one must resort to the atomic number, the number of protons in the nucleus, for an unambiguous definition of element. An element is a substance all atoms of which contain the same number of protons in the nucleus. Different numbers of neutrons then give rise to different isotopes of that element.

Isotopes were recognized somewhat before the discovery of nuclear reactions from experiments with modified cathode-ray tubes. Positive rays are the ions formed from the residual gas in cathode-ray tubes. Since they are moving charges, they can be deflected by electric or magnetic fields. Using the same basic design he used in his apparatus to measure the charge-mass ratio for the electron (Chap. 13), J. J. Thomson extended the evacuated space behind the cathode and deflected the emerging positive rays by placing charged plates and a magnet at right angles to their path (Fig. 18–10). With neon gas in the tube, he found not one, but two positive-ray beams emerging—the isotopes $_{10}Ne^{20}$ and $_{10}Ne^{22}$.

In principle Thomson's apparatus works as follows. Both the electric and the magnetic fields deflect the ions. The extent of deflection depends, among other factors, on

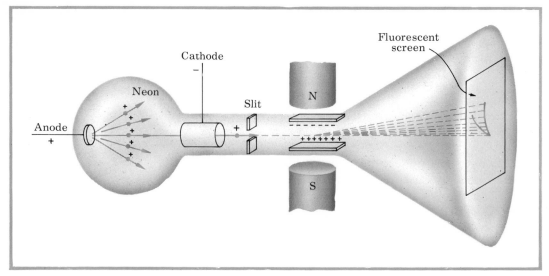

FIG. 18-10

J. J. Thomson's mass spectrograph. Positive rays are focused into a beam by the cathode and the slit. A magnet deflects them horizontally and a pair of charged plates deflects them vertically. The extent of deflection depends on the velocity of the particles and on their mass. The two lines on the fluorescent screen indicate the presence of two isotopes.

the mass of the ion, for the heavier it is, the greater is its inertial resistance to deflection. Hence, with the appropriate design one can separate particles of different masses and measure the mass of the ions in the deflected beam.

Modern devices based on Thomson's early prototype are called *mass spectrometers*. Of course they embody many refinements in design to allow very accurate work. They have found considerable use in the determination of exact isotopic masses to many decimal places and in the analysis of chemical mixtures.

HIGH-ENERGY MACHINES

When two molecules of nitrogen gas collide in the gas, they bounce off one another and continue on their way. When the gas helium is kept in a golden vessel, its molecules collide with the walls and bounce off, thus producing the pressure on the walls of the vessel. Yet, when α particles—helium nuclei—are directed at nitrogen, they fuse

with the nitrogen nuclei and produce a reaction; when they are shot at gold, they pass through the atoms. Why?

The chief distinction between α particles and helium gas molecules is the great energy of the α particles. When they are ejected from the nucleus of a radioactive element, they travel so fast, with so much kinetic energy, that they can pass through obstacles that ordinary atoms and molecules find insurmountable. Yet even here there are distinctions. The α particle from thorium is energetic enough to enter the nucleus of nitrogen. Yet, as the Rutherford experiment showed, it is repelled by the far more highly charged gold nucleus. The promise that high-energy particles would yield more information about the nucleus led physicists to build machines which take ordinary particles, protons or electrons, and hurl them at tremendous velocities at target nuclei. Several different machines can do this: the Van de Graaff generator (Chap. 13), linear accelerators, cyclotrons, and various adaptations of the cyclotron known as synchrotrons, betatrons, and cosmotrons. In all of them small charged particles are accelerated electrically and directed at some target.

The *linear accelerator* consists of a long evacuated tube—in 1966, a 2-mile-long linear accelerator was put in operation at Stanford University in California—in which there are small sections of metallic pipe. The particles travel inside the pipes (Fig. 18–11). Alternate pieces of pipe are connected to one another by wire, and both sets are connected to a source of alternating electric charge. The particle, say a proton, is fed into the first pipe, which is charged negatively while the second pipe is positively charged. Inside the pipe, because of the Faraday cage effect (Chap. 13), there is no electric field. The particle experiences no attraction or repulsion. The a-c source is so synchronized with the progress of the charged particle that the polarity changes while the particle is in the first pipe. As it leaves the first pipe, it is repelled by the now positively charged first pipe and attracted by the now negatively charged second pipe. The particle is therefore accelerated as it passes the gap between the pipes. While it is in the second pipe, the a-c source again changes cycle. Now the second pipe becomes positive and the

third negative. Thus while the particle is in the gap between the second and third pipes, it is again accelerated. The same thing continues as the particle passes through each pipe; the alternating source of charge changes cycle and provides for acceleration across each gap. The successive small accelerations add to give the particle enormous velocity before it leaves the accelerator tube and enters the target chamber at the end. The Stanford accelerator was designed to deliver the same energy as is imparted to an electron by a potential difference of over 30 billion volts. Only one other basic principle is involved. Since the particle is accelerated at each step, it travels faster on entering successive pipes. These are therefore made successively longer so that the particle spends an equal time in each of the pipes. In this way, the alternating source of power can keep up with the accelerating particle.

The *cyclotron* differs in principle from the linear accelerator in one important respect only: the accelerated particles are bent into a spiral path by means of a strong magnetic field. This is accomplished by placing the entire machine between the pole faces of two huge magnets, and pro-

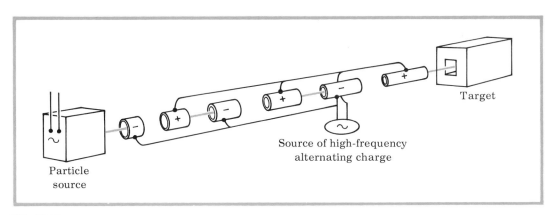

FIG. 18-11

Diagram of a linear accelerator. The particle is attracted into the first pipe. While inside, the polarity of the charge changes, and on emerging the particle is attracted into the second pipe. It gains velocity. While it is inside the second pipe, polarity changes again, and on emerging it is attracted again and increases velocity. This continues down the length of the accelerator. To keep the times spent within each pipe equal, the pipes become longer as the particle moves more rapidly.

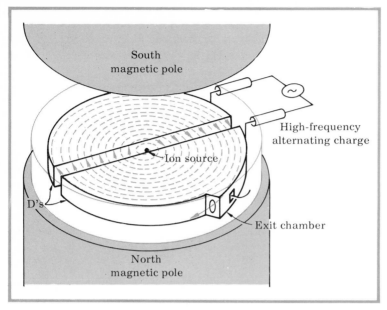

FIG. 18-12

Diagram of a cyclotron. Ions from the ion source at the center are attracted into one of the D's. They describe a circular path because of the magnetic field. By the time they emerge from the D, the polarity of charge on the D's has changed and they are accelerated across the gap. In the other D, they move more rapidly in a larger circular path. Their time of travel, therefore, is the same. When they emerge again, they are again accelerated because the polarity of the D's has changed. After thousands of such accelerations, they reach the outside of the D and are drawn into the exit chamber.

viding two semicircular, evacuated shells, the D's, for the particle track. The D's are connected to an alternating source of charge as shown in Fig. 18–12, which depicts the simplest of the cyclotron-type accelerators. (Major modifications have been made in design, though not in basic principle, in later and more powerful machines.) Charged particles are fed into the machine by the ion source in the center. The ions are attracted toward the D of opposite charge and repelled by the D of like charge, providing an initial acceleration into one of the D's. Because of the magnetic field, the ions travel in a circular path inside the D, where they do not experience electric forces. While they complete half of their circular path, the power source changes cycle. Hence, when the particles emerge from the first D, they are accelerated across the gap. They enter the second D with a

greater velocity and follow a somewhat larger, semicircular path. While they are in the second D, the cycle changes again so that on emerging into the gap between the D's, the particles are again accelerated. This process is repeated until the particles have received thousands of small accelerations and are traveling at very high speeds near the outside of the D. Now a charge is placed on a plate near the outside of the D to draw the particles from their curved path, into the exit chamber, and at the target. While with each successive acceleration the particle travels more rapidly, it also describes a larger semicircular path. These two balance exactly so that the time spent per half revolution does not change during the trip. The time a particle spends in the machine, from ion source to exit chamber, depends entirely on the particular design. In the alternating-gradient synchrotron, an accelerator of considerably more advanced design, protons complete about 300,000 revolutions in less than 1 sec.

NUCLEAR REACTIONS

One result of the studies with particle accelerators has been the production of some elements not found in nature and of radioactive isotopes of all elements. As we saw before, the collision of an α particle with a nitrogen nucleus leads to the formation of the oxygen isotope $_8O^{17}$. The high-energy machines make it possible to use other projectiles or to accelerate α particles to greater velocities than one finds in radioactive decay. Hence many more nuclear reactions can be produced. Actually these machines can be designed to accelerate nearly any charged particle. To date, this has included protons, deuterons (deuterium nuclei), electrons, and the nuclei of the lighter elements up to nitrogen. It should be noted that neutrons, too, have been used as projectiles though they must be used as they happen to appear in atomic reactors. Because they are electrically neutral, they cannot be accelerated; however, since they are uncharged, they can enter nuclei at lower velocities than charged projectiles.

So many transformations have been carried out with nuclear particles that only a few examples can be given. In general, nuclear reactions involve the absorption of the particle by the target nucleus, followed by a rearrangement to a new nucleus, the emission of different particles and often of radiation.

Projectile	Target nucleus	New nucleus	Emitted particle
$_1D^2$	$+ \ _{52}Te^{124}$	$= \ _{53}I^{*125}$	$+ \ _0n^1$
$_1H^1$	$+ \ _9F^{19}$	$= \ _8O^{16}$	$+ \ _2He^4$
$_2He^4$	$+ \ _{92}U^{235}$	$= \ _{94}Pu^{*238}$	$+ \ _0n^1$

(18–4)

In this list the first is an example of the formation of a radioactive isotope of the element iodine (the asterisk denotes a radioactive nucleus); the second, the production of a stable isotope of oxygen; the third, the production of an element which does not occur in nature.

OTHER NUCLEAR PARTICLES

Also, with the aid of these machines, the world of the nucleus has been opened to study and found to be a fairly complex world populated by a number of particles that behave in as yet largely mysterious ways. In the target chambers appear short-lived particles with or without charge, apparently created when high-energy projectiles strike target nuclei. There are positrons—electrons with a positive charge, $_{+1}e^0$; muons and mesons—positive, negative, or uncharged with masses intermediate between the electron and the proton; baryons—like mesons but heavier than protons; and neutrinos—massless and chargeless, yet not electromagnetic radiation. Exactly where they come from and why, what function they have there, and how they relate to one another are the subject of current research in high-energy physics. To date, the circumstances of their appearance and disappearance have been fairly well established. Their lifetimes are known although the most stable exist for a few millionths of a second only. Somehow these particles, which together with protons, neutrons, and electrons are called *elementary particles,* are the ultimate building blocks of matter and the glue that keeps nuclei together. But the theoretical understanding of how they function must be greatly extended. Some probably are truly elementary; others may turn out to be "mingled" bodies. The physicist, in a sense, is where the chemist was 200 years ago before elements and compounds had been clearly differentiated.

The nucleus bombarded by high-energy projectiles or neutrons is a tiny laboratory in which the conversion of mass into energy and energy into mass, predicted by Einstein in 1905, is being demonstrated. From entirely different considerations Einstein had derived an equation relating energy to mass:

$$E = mc^2 \qquad (18\text{–}5)$$

in which E is the energy, m the mass, and c the velocity of light, 3×10^{10} cm/sec. Because c is such a large number and appears as a squared term, the amounts of energy produced by mass, or required to create mass, are formidable. One proton, about 1.6×10^{-24} gram, produces 0.0015 erg; one uranium atom about ½ erg; a gram of matter 9×10^{20} ergs, nearly 25 million kilowatt-hours of energy. However, tests of the equation were not possible until the 1930s. Dimensions and energies of nuclear size, apparently, were needed to produce the mass-energy interconversions and the tools of modern physics were needed to observe them.

Nuclei—except radioactive ones—are stable aggregates of neutrons and protons which are kept stably next to one another despite the high coulombic repulsions at the nuclear distances of 10^{-13} cm. Somehow the energies of the elementary particles are involved. When a nucleus is then struck by a high-energy projectile, an elementary particle may appear. This particle undergoes further interactions with particles or nuclei.

Among the nuclear reactions that have been firmly established, there are some that totally annihilate matter. The collision of an electron with a positron produces only electromagnetic energy.

$$_{+1}e^0 + {}_{-1}e^0 \longrightarrow \gamma \text{ rays} \qquad (18\text{–}6)$$

This process may be reversed and mass created from energy if γ-ray photons meet.

$$\gamma \text{ rays} \longrightarrow {}_{+1}e^0 + {}_{-1}e^0 \qquad (18\text{–}7)$$

Reactions that are particularly important to explain radioactivity include the neutron decay, which produces a β ray (electron).

$$_0n^1 \longrightarrow {}_1H^1 + {}_{-1}e^0 + \text{neutrinos} \quad (18\text{–}8)$$

In this reaction, charge is conserved by the opposite charges of the proton and the electron. Mass is conserved, however, only by the kinetic energies with which the elementary particles fly apart. Reaction 18–8 apparently occurs within the nuclei of β-emitting radioactive nuclei. Since a proton results, the daughter nucleus is of the element with an atomic number 1 higher. Another reaction which occurs in radioactive decay, though only with artificially produced radioactive elements, is positron emission, apparently resulting from

$$_1H^1 \longrightarrow {}_0n^1 + {}_1e^0 + \text{neutrino} \qquad (18\text{–}9)$$

This produces a daughter nucleus of the element of atomic number 1 less than the positron emitter.

RADIOACTIVE SERIES

Mass-energy conversions are involved in the rearrangements of nuclei that produce radioactivity, as well as in reactions caused by particles. All radioactive elements are energetically unstable; their atoms seek stability through the loss of energy and particles. The extent of instability, however, differs for different radioactive nuclei. Most of a gram of $_{92}U^{*238}$ remains undecayed for millions of years; most of a gram of the radioactive $_{91}Pa^{*234}$ is gone in a day.

While the rate of decay differs for different radioactive nuclei, it is quite fixed for nuclei of one kind. For instance, if of 1,000 radioactive nuclei of a certain kind, 100 or 10 percent decay during the first hour, then 10 percent of the remaining 900, or 90, decay during the second hour; 10 percent of the then remaining 810, or 81, decay during the third hour; and so forth. The law of disintegration follows this very precise scheme for all radioactive materials. They differ from one another only in the time it takes for 10 percent of the nuclei to decay. Thus, it takes about 150 million years for 10 percent of $_{92}U^{*238}$ nuclei to decay; 10 percent of $_{91}Pa^{*234}$ nuclei disintegrate in about 12 min; 10 percent of $_{88}Ra^{*222}$ nuclei are gone in just over a second.

The law of radioactive decay is applicable only with groups of atoms large enough so that statistical averages are followed exactly. It is impossible to specify which specific nuclei will decay—which are part of the disintegrating 10 percent and which part of the remaining 90 percent of our examples above. But it is quite definite that, in a large group of atoms, the law of radioactive decay is followed and that exactly 10 percent of $_{88}Ra^{*222}$ nuclei disintegrate within just over 1 sec. Since the mole is 6.02×10^{23} atoms, small fractions of a mole contain enough atoms to obey these statistical laws of radioactive decay. Normally the rate of decay of radioactive elements is given by the time for half of the atoms to disintegrate, the *half-life* of the species. Half-lives of the known isotopes of uranium are given in Table 18–2. They are longer, of course, than the one-tenth-lives calculated in the last paragraph; it takes longer for half the atoms to disintegrate. For uranium isotopes, the half-lives vary from 9.3 min to 4.5×10^9 years.

Becquerel and the Curies found several radioactive elements in nature, and others have been discovered since. They belong to three series (Table 18–3), each element in the series being produced when the one before it disintegrates, with the successive radioactive disintegrations stopping when a stable isotope of the element lead is formed. Since radioactivity is a sign of relative instability, we can view the radioactive steps as a set of rearrangements of nuclei in the direction of greater stability.

We can illustrate what happens in a radioactive series with the $_{92}U^{*238}$ series. $_{92}U^{*238}$ is a quite stable element—it has a half-life of 4.5×10^9 years—which emits an α particle when it disintegrates. Loss of an α particle means the loss of two protons and two neutrons. α-particle emission, therefore, produces a nucleus of the element with two fewer protons and a mass number reduced by 4, $_{90}Th^{*234}$.

$_{90}Th^{*234}$, the daughter nucleus, is itself radioactive with a much shorter half-life of 24 days. The $_{90}Th^{*234}$ nuclei produced by the decay of U^{238} disappear very rapidly after being formed. Th^{234} is a β-particle (electron) emitter. Since the β particle comes from the nucleus of Th^{234}, not the surrounding electrons, it is produced by a rearrangement in the nucleus according to Eq. 18–8; a neutron transmutes into a proton and the β particle. Hence the daughter nucleus of Th^{234} contains one more proton and has the same mass number. It is $_{91}Pa^{*234}$. β emission produces a nucleus of atomic number 1 greater and the same mass number.

Pa^{234} is itself a β emitter with a 6.7-hr half-life. Its daughter nucleus is an isotope of uranium, $_{92}U^{*234}$. As the table shows, unstable daughter nuclei continue to be formed after the further decay of U^{234}, each with the emission of energy and either an α or a β particle, and each with its own half-life until, finally, the stable isotope of

TABLE 18-2

Half-lives of the isotopes of uranium

Isotope	Half-life	Isotope	Half-life
$_{92}U^{228}$	9.3 min	$_{92}U^{234}$	2.4×10^5 years
$_{92}U^{229}$	58 min	$_{92}U^{235}$	8.91×10^8 years
$_{92}U^{230}$	20.8 days	$_{92}U^{237}$	6.8 days
$_{92}U^{231}$	4.2 days	$_{92}U^{238}$	4.5×10^9 years
$_{92}U^{232}$	70 years	$_{92}U^{239}$	23 min
$_{92}U^{233}$	1.6×10^5 years		

TABLE 18-3

Radioactive decay series

$_{92}U^{*238} \xrightarrow[4.5 \times 10^9 \text{ yr}]{\alpha} {}_{90}Th^{*234} \xrightarrow[24 \text{ da}]{\beta} {}_{91}Pa^{*234} \xrightarrow[6.7 \text{ hr}]{\beta} {}_{92}U^{*234} \xrightarrow[2.4 \times 10^5 \text{ yr}]{\alpha} {}_{90}Th^{*230} \xrightarrow[8 \times 10^4 \text{ yr}]{\alpha}$

$_{88}Ra^{*226} \xrightarrow[1.6 \times 10^3 \text{ yr}]{\alpha} {}_{86}Rn^{*222} \xrightarrow[3.8 \text{ da}]{\alpha} {}_{84}Po^{*218} \xrightarrow[3 \text{ min}]{\alpha} {}_{82}Pb^{*214} \xrightarrow[27 \text{ min}]{\beta}$

$_{83}Bi^{*214} \xrightarrow[19.7 \text{ min}]{\beta} {}_{84}Po^{*214}$; $_{83}Bi^{*214} \xrightarrow{\alpha} {}_{81}Tl^{*210} \xrightarrow[1.32 \text{ min}]{\beta}$; $_{84}Po^{*214} \xrightarrow[1.5 \times 10^{-4} \text{ sec}]{\alpha} {}_{82}Pb^{*210} \xrightarrow[22 \text{ yr}]{\beta} {}_{83}Bi^{*210} \xrightarrow[5 \text{ da}]{\beta}$

$_{84}Po^{*210} \xrightarrow[140 \text{ da}]{\alpha} {}_{82}Pb^{206}$

$_{92}U^{*235} \xrightarrow[9 \times 10^8 \text{ yr}]{\alpha} {}_{90}Th^{*231} \xrightarrow[25 \text{ hr}]{\beta} {}_{91}Pa^{*231} \xrightarrow[3 \times 10^4 \text{ yr}]{\alpha} {}_{89}Ac^{*227} \xrightarrow[20 \text{ yr}]{\beta} {}_{90}Th^{*227} \xrightarrow[19 \text{ da}]{\alpha}$

$_{88}Ra^{*223} \xrightarrow[11.2 \text{ da}]{\alpha} {}_{86}Rn^{*219} \xrightarrow[3.9 \text{ sec}]{\alpha} {}_{84}Po^{*215} \xrightarrow[1.8 \times 10^{-3} \text{ sec}]{\alpha} {}_{82}Pb^{*211} \xrightarrow[36 \text{ min}]{\beta}$

$_{83}Bi^{*211} \xrightarrow[2.2 \text{ min}]{\alpha} {}_{81}Tl^{*207} \xrightarrow[4.8 \text{ min}]{\beta} {}_{82}Pb^{207}$; $_{83}Bi^{*211} \xrightarrow[2.2 \text{ min}]{\beta} {}_{84}Po^{*211} \xrightarrow[5 \times 10^{-3} \text{ sec}]{\alpha} {}_{82}Pb^{207}$

$_{90}Th^{*232} \xrightarrow[1.4 \times 10^{10} \text{ yr}]{\alpha} {}_{88}Ra^{*228} \xrightarrow[6.7 \text{ yr}]{\beta} {}_{89}Ac^{*228} \xrightarrow[6 \text{ hr}]{\beta} {}_{90}Th^{*228} \xrightarrow[1.9 \text{ yr}]{\alpha} {}_{88}Ra^{*224} \xrightarrow[3.6 \text{ da}]{\alpha}$

$_{86}Rn^{*220} \xrightarrow[55 \text{ sec}]{\alpha} {}_{84}Po^{*216} \xrightarrow[0.16 \text{ sec}]{\alpha} {}_{82}Pb^{*212} \xrightarrow[10.6 \text{ hr}]{\beta}$

$_{83}Bi^{*212} \xrightarrow[1 \text{ hr}]{\alpha} {}_{81}Tl^{*208} \xrightarrow[3 \text{ min}]{\beta} {}_{82}Pb^{208}$; $_{83}Bi^{*212} \xrightarrow[1 \text{ hr}]{\beta} {}_{84}Po^{*212} \xrightarrow[4 \times 10^{-6} \text{ sec}]{\alpha} {}_{82}Pb^{208}$

lead, $_{82}Pb^{206}$, is produced. Because the length of time during which a particular kind of nucleus in the series exists depends on its half-life, the nuclei in the series that have short half-lives are present in very small amounts, and those with longer half-lives are present in larger quantities.

Since α emission reduces the mass number by 4 while the β emission does not change the mass number, all the daughter atoms of the U^{238} series differ in mass number from 238 by 4 or multiples of 4. Another way of saying this is that their mass numbers can be expressed by $4n + 2$, in which n equals 59 for uranium and decreases by 1 every time an α particle is emitted. The other two series also decay by α and β emission only. They constitute the series of mass numbers $4n + 3$ and $4n$. Missing in nature are nuclei with the only other possible set of mass numbers, those expressed by $4n + 1$. The suggestion has

been made that the members of this series, which have been produced artificially by accelerators and have relatively short half-lives, existed when the earth was formed, but that they have decayed completely since that time. Only the stable last member, an isotope of bismuth, $_{83}Bi^{209}$, remains. The other artificially produced elements, the actinides, all of which have short half-lives compared to geologic time, may also have existed and decayed into daughter nuclei which are members of one of the four radioactive series.

The decay of radioactive materials can be used as a means for determining the age of rocks and other geologic formations whose period of existence is too long for other methods of dating. In the $_{92}U^{*238}$ series, all daughter atoms have half-lives that are very much shorter than that of the parent. Consequently, in just over 4.5 billion years, half of an original deposit of

$_{92}U^{*238}$ will end up as $_{82}Pb^{206}$. Thus the ratio of lead formed to uranium still present gives an estimate of the length of time since the uranium first became part of the rock. While there are a number of assumptions involved in this method of dating— no $_{82}Pb^{206}$ present at the beginning, for instance—the results are consistent with estimates of geologic time obtained by other methods and have found considerable use. Adaptation of the principle to radioactive carbon ($_6C^{*14}$, half-life 5×10^3 years) has provided a means for dating materials which are only 2,000 to 10,000 years old and has proved a valuable aid to historical research.

ARTIFICIALLY PRODUCED RADIOACTIVE ELEMENTS

In addition to age determination, radioactive isotopes have found many uses in medicine, research, and industry. The emission of high-energy particles is easily detected. By looking for the emitted particles, one can trace the path of the element in various situations. Or the energy liberated by the transformation may be used directly. In medical and biological research, for example, radioisotopes have been used to trace the course of various nutrients throughout the body, or to destroy cancerous tissues by radiation. In genetics research they have been used to cause mutations in plants. Radioisotopes power small batteries which are used in space research and are also available commercially. In industry they have been used to provide the energy for luminous watch dials and to trace the progress of oil through pipelines. These are a few examples of literally thousands of applications of radioisotopes, most of which have been developed only in the last 20 years when artificially produced radioisotopes became available on a large scale. The necessary condition for the large-scale production of radioisotopes has been the development of *atomic reactors,* in which

large quantities of neutrons are available for research or other purposes.

Because the neutron carries no charge, it cannot be accelerated or deflected by electric or magnetic fields. Hence it cannot easily be handled experimentally. For the same reason, however, it is not repelled by the charged nuclei and easily fuses with them. This makes it one of the most interesting particles in nuclear physics.

The neutron interacts with other nuclei just like the charged high-energy particles. The equations given before showed that the neutron is often a product of a nuclear reaction. Below are examples of reactions in which the neutron is the projectile.

$$_0n^1 + {}_7N^{14} = {}_6C^{*14} + {}_1H^1$$
$$_0n^1 + {}_{92}U^{*238} = {}_{92}U^{*239} \qquad (18\text{--}10)$$

When fusing with a nucleus, it may produce stable or radioactive isotopes of naturally occurring elements, or new elements. Hundreds of radioisotopes of the stable elements have been produced by neutron reactions or in high-energy machines. They emit only β particles or positrons and γ radiation by reactions like:

$$_6C^{*14} \longrightarrow {}_7N^{14} + {}_{-1}e^0$$
$$_{15}P^{*30} \longrightarrow {}_{14}Si^{30} + {}_{+1}e^0 \qquad (18\text{--}11)$$

ATOMIC ENERGY

There is one additional neutron reaction which has led not only to a rearrangement of a nucleus but to some major rearrangements in the thinking of all people on the earth. In 1939, near the outbreak of World War II, two German chemists, Hahn and Strassman, noted that when U^{235} was bombarded with neutrons, instead of rearranging to a new nucleus and emitting another kind of particle as had been observed for previous nuclear reactions, it broke apart into two smaller elements and at the same time emitted several neutrons. As usual, considerable energy was liberated in this nuclear reaction. The splitting of one nucleus into two or more smaller nuclei is

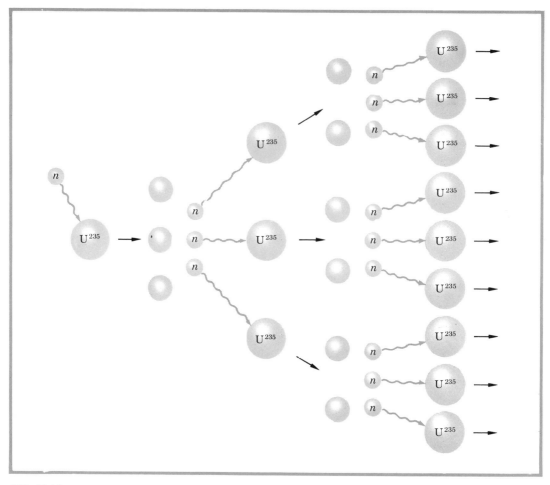

FIG. 18-13

Chain reaction of U²³⁵. The reaction between a neutron and U²³⁵ produces two smaller nuclei and two or three neutrons. These can react with other U²³⁵ nuclei to produce more small nuclei and more neutrons. The reaction thus rapidly grows into many simultaneous fission reactions with the liberation of much energy.

called *fission*. A number of scientists around the world realized that this result had interesting possibilities. For if one uranium nucleus reacts with one neutron and gives back three neutrons, these three can now react with three uranium nuclei and give back nine neutrons; the nine neutrons can react with nine nuclei and produce twenty-seven neutrons, which can react with twenty-seven nuclei to. . . . Since these reactions occur very rapidly, in fractions of microseconds, and produce tremendous amounts of energy, they appeared to be of military interest. Einstein communicated

these conclusions to President Roosevelt for himself and other scientists. The idea was accepted, and a sizable fraction of the country's scientific talent was recruited to make the process, which looks so simple on paper, a reality. The rest is history. In 1942 a group headed by Enrico Fermi produced the first self-sustaining chain reaction in a squash court at the University of Chicago. In 1944 the first atomic bomb was exploded over New Mexico in a test. It had been developed at Los Alamos, New Mexico, in a laboratory headed by Robert Oppenheimer. Early in 1945 two operational models were dropped over Japan. Since that time four other nations have developed atomic bombs of a size and power to make the early models look puny (several more are probably close to it), and many nations have used the same reaction for peaceful purposes.

The problems involved in producing the atomic bomb were many; there are at least as many in keeping the fission reaction in a nuclear reactor under control. Here we shall mention only three. First, only the isotope of uranium of mass number 235 sets off the chain reaction. U^{238}, as Eq. 18–10 shows, serves to absorb neutrons and thus stop the fission chain. But natural uranium contains only about 0.7 percent U^{235}. A means had to be found to separate this isotope from the bulk of the material. Two methods were explored to accomplish separation. An adaptation of the mass spectrometer was found to yield too little material to be efficient. On the other hand, the rate of diffusion of gases depends on their mass, and there is a difference of three mass units between U^{235} and the bulk of uranium, U^{238}. Moreover, the compound UF_6 is a gas. While the difference in mass is slight, by cascading many stages of separation, essentially pure U^{235} is obtained.

FIG. 18-14

Model of the research reactor at Brookhaven National Laboratory. Uranium fuel is loaded through the holes in the face at right; the holes in the face at left are exit ports for neutrons used in research. The reactor is graphite-moderated and enclosed in 5 ft of concrete. (Brookhaven National Laboratory)

A second problem involved in controlling a nuclear reactor is that the neutrons are emitted in the fission reaction with tremendous velocities, too high to be effective for the next fission stage. They must be slowed down. This is accomplished by a *moderator,* some material composed of light atoms with which the high-energy neutrons collide without absorption and to which they transfer some of their energy during collision. Good moderators are deuterium oxide and graphite.

Finally, a means had to be devised to control the reaction should it get out of hand. For this, the element cadmium is used. Like U^{238}, cadmium absorbs neutrons without producing other particles. Thus it serves as a neutron trap in case the reactor should "run away." Nuclear reactors contain *control rods* of cadmium which can be dropped in whenever the neutron flux gets too high.

While U^{238} serves as a neutron trap, and thus is useless to produce energy in a reactor, its presence is not a total loss. For the absorption of a neutron by U^{238} leading to U^{239} is only a first step. U^{239} is radioactive, a β emitter, with a short half-life; its daughter Np^{239} also emits an electron to form Pu^{239}. And Pu^{239}, which is a fairly long-lived element (half-life 2.4×10^4 years), has the same property as U^{235}. It undergoes fission with the emission of several neutrons and can maintain the chain reaction. Thus U^{238} in a reactor serves as a means to replenish nuclear fuel, to breed a new fissionable species. Reactors have been designed to capitalize on this reaction. They are called *breeder reactors* because they produce new fuel while also producing some power.

NUCLEAR STABILITY

The reason that uranium fission is such a good means to produce energy lies not only in the favorable aspects of the chain reaction but also in the greater stability of the nuclei in the middle of the periodic table, into which U^{235} splits during fission. So far in this chapter we have neglected small differences between the mass number of a nucleus and its exact mass. But this difference is the key to nuclear stability; small mass losses provide the energy to hold protons and neutrons together.

Consider the helium atom. Its weight should be the weight of two protons, two neutrons, and two electrons.

The mass of the helium atom should therefore be:

2 protons:	$2 \times 1.00727 =$	2.01454
2 neutrons:	$2 \times 1.00867 =$	2.01734
2 electrons:	$2 \times .00055 =$	.00110
		4.03298

But the mass of a helium atom, when measured on a mass spectrometer, is only 4.00260. Obviously, the fusion of the four nuclear particles has been accompanied by a loss of mass or, because of $E = mc^2$, by the loss of a large amount of energy. To allow the particles to separate again, the same amount of energy would have to be supplied. It is this energy which binds the protons in the nucleus and prevents them from flying apart because of repulsion.

One way to consider the loss of mass or energy in helium is to say that each of the four nuclear particles is bound by $\dfrac{(4.03298 - 4.00260)}{4}$ or 0.0076 mass units converted to energy. This gives an estimate of the stability of each of the four nuclear particles in the helium nucleus. Similarly in $_6C^{12}$, the binding energy is the mass of six protons (6.04362) plus the mass of six neutrons (6.05202) less the mass of the nucleus, 12.00052. Per particle this is 0.0079 mass units. When similar calculations are made for all elements, it is found that the elements in the middle of the periodic table, the elements between Si, mass number 28, and Ce, mass number 140, have the greatest binding energy per nuclear particle (Fig. 18–15). Converting uranium, which lies near one end of

Binding energy per particle of the elements. The binding energy per particle rises rapidly from He to around Ne (mass number 20). It then increases slowly to about Ni or Co (mass number near 60). Then the binding energy per particle decreases slowly toward larger nuclei.

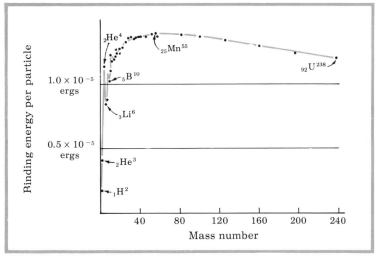

FIG. 18-15

the chart, into two smaller elements near the middle makes available large amounts of binding energy per nuclear particle. This is the chief source of energy in nuclear fission. Much smaller amounts of binding energy are liberated if elements near the middle are converted into one another.

FUSION

Uranium or plutonium fission produces large amounts of energy by moving from the less stable elements at one end of the periodic chart to more stable ones near the middle. Can similar large amounts be obtained by combining the light nuclei at the other end into heavier ones? *Fusion* of light nuclei seemed the obvious next problem to be tackled after fission energy became a reality, and it is a problem which is being actively attacked by many scientists both in this country and abroad. In two different senses the answer is already yes. The hydrogen bomb, more powerful than the uranium or plutonium bomb, makes use of the fusion of small particles into heavier nuclei. Also, the energy poured out by stars almost certainly is the result of the fusion of hydrogen atoms. But controlled fusion under conditions which will

make the energy available for other than destructive purposes on earth seems still some way off, although research is full of unsuspected surprises, both favorable and unfavorable. Prediction here is hazardous.

In its essence, the reaction to be carried out is

$$4_1H^1 = {}_2He^4 + 2_{+1}e^0 \qquad (18\text{--}12)$$

Undoubtedly the reaction does not proceed in this way but takes place by steps which fuse two protons, then add a third, etc. It is a reaction which, to be self-sustaining, requires extremely high temperatures, since the kinetic energies of the particles must be great enough to fuse them rather than repelling. There is no doubt that the reaction is possible. Not only does it occur in hydrogen bombs and probably in stars; it has been carried out in the laboratory, though only for minute fractions of a second at a time.

One major problem is the container for the reaction in which the particles reach millions of degrees. This is no problem on a star which is that hot throughout. But no material on earth can remain in contact with such a temperature without disintegrating. The experiments which have produced the fusion reaction under controlled conditions for fractions of seconds used the interaction of magnetic fields with moving protons to contain the reaction. They were carried out, literally, in magnetic bottles. But the steps between a tiny reaction lasting a few milliseconds and controlled nuclear fusion on a scale large enough to produce usable energy are such that fusion energy is probably a long way off. Some scientists feel that more efficient harnessing of solar energy is a more promising approach to meet the world's energy needs, at least in the foreseeable future.

Questions and Problems

1. Complete the following table:

Atomic No.	Mass No.	Protons	Neutrons	Element	Symbol
22	48				
	119				
				Tin	
					$_{17}Cl^{38}$
		15	16		
41			50		
	56	26			
	40		21		

2. Give the mass number, charge, and symbol, if any, for each of the following: α particle, β particle, positron, neutron, electron, X ray, cathode ray, γ ray.

3. Describe the basic principles behind each of the following machines, and give their use: (a) Van de Graaff generator, (b) cyclotron, (c) bubble chamber, (d) mass spectrograph, (e) linear accelerator, (f) atomic reactor, (g) cloud chamber, (h) breeder reactor, (i) Geiger counter.

4. Define radioactivity, nucleus, mass number, isotope, half-life, radioactivity series, elementary particles, fission, fusion.

5. Describe the Rutherford α particle scattering experiment and defend its conclusions.

6. Which nucleus in the radioactive decay series of U^{238} is present in the smallest quantity in any ore? In the series for Th^{232}, arrange the nuclei between Ra^{228} and Rn^{220} in order of decreasing amounts.

7. The following statements are evidence for one or more major ideas about the structure of matter and/or the nature of energy. Give at least one major idea for each statement: (a) α-particle tracks through gases or thin metal foil are straight. (b) a neutral meson may decay into two γ rays. (c) The decay of one kind of neutral meson produces a positive and a negative meson. (d) α-particle emission produces an element of atomic number 2 less. (e) α-particle tracks on photographic plates sometimes stop, and a short heavy track and a long thin track begin where the α-particle track stopped.

8. Balance each of the following equations and describe what they represent.

(a) $_1H^1 + _{52}Te^{130} \rightarrow _{53}I^{*130} + ($ $)$
(b) $_0n^1 + _{92}U^{*235} \rightarrow 3_0n^1 + _{56}Ba^{*142}$
    $+ ($ $)$
(c) $_0n^1 + ($ $) \rightarrow _{11}Na^{*24} + _2He^4$
(d) $_2He^4 + _{13}Al^{27} \rightarrow ($ $) + _0n^1$
(e) $_1H_2 + _{29}Cu^{63} \rightarrow _{29}Cu^{*64} + ($ $)$
(f) $_{94}Pu^{*232} \rightarrow _{92}U^{*228} + ($ $)$
(g) $_{49}In^{*112} \rightarrow ($ $) + _{+1}e^0$
(h) $($ $) \rightarrow _{36}Kr^{*85} + _{-1}e^0$

9. Compute the binding energy per particle in the deuterium nucleus, mass 2.00142.

10. The half-life of $_{53}I^{*131}$ is 8 days. A patient is given a dose of I^{131} for thyroid treatment. What fraction of the I^{131} remains after 16 days? How long until he has less than 6.25 percent of the original amount?

11. Write the equation for (a) α emission by At^{217}, (b) β emission by O^{19}, (c) neutron absorption by U^{238}, (d) positron emission by C^{11}, (e) neutron absorption by Be^5, which produces an α particle.

Suggestions for Further Reading

Some parts of this chapter are treated in the following texts:

Christiansen, G. S., and Paul H. Garrett: *Structure and Change*, W. H. Freeman and Company, San Francisco, 1960. Electrons (chap. 18); radioactivity and the nucleus (chap. 27); nuclear reactions, accelerators, and fission (chap. 30).

Holton, Gerald, and Duane H. D. Roller: *Foundations of Modern Physical Science*, Addison-

Wesley Publishing Company, Inc., Reading, Mass., 1958. Radioactivity (chap. 36); isotopes (chap. 37); nuclear physics (chaps. 38 and 39).

Pauling, Linus: *College Chemistry*, 3d ed., W. H. Freeman and Company, San Francisco, 1964. Electrons and the nucleus (chap. 3); elementary particles (chap. 29); radioactivity (chap. 30).

Physical Science Study Committee: *Physics*, D. C. Heath and Company, Boston, 1960. Rutherford's experiment (chap. 32).

Rogers, Eric M.: *Physics for the Inquiring Mind*, Princeton University Press, Princeton, N.J., 1960. Electrons (chap. 36); the nucleus (chaps. 38 and 40); radioactivity (chap. 39); accelerators (chap. 42); nuclear physics (chaps. 43 and 44).

Books that deal with selected topics from this chapter include:

Andrade, E. N. da Costa: *Rutherford and the Nature of the Atom*, Anchor Books, Doubleday & Company, Inc., Garden City, N.Y., 1964 (paperback). An account of Rutherford's monumental contributions to nuclear physics.

Ford, Kenneth W.: *The World of Elementary Particles*, McGraw-Hill Book Company, Inc., New York, 1963. Known particles and the current status of theory in high energy physics.

Frisch, Otto R.: *Atomic Physics Today*, Basic Books, Inc., New York, 1961. A nontechnical account of modern atomic and nuclear physics.

Heisenberg, W.: *Nuclear Physics*, Philosophical Library, New York, 1953. A very readable, brief book by one of the major contributors to modern physics.

Hughes, Donald J., *The Neutron Story*, Anchor Books, Doubleday & Company, Inc., Garden City, N.Y., 1959 (paperback). A very readable book on the behavior and uses of the neutron.

Romer, Alfred: *The Restless Atom*, Anchor Books, Doubleday & Company, Inc., Garden City, N.Y., 1960 (paperback). A short history of the experiments which produced modern nuclear physics.

Wilson, Robert R., and Raphael Littauer: *Accelerators*, Anchor Books, Doubleday & Company, Inc., Garden City, N.Y., 1960. Describes various high-energy machines and how they operate (paperback).

A very comprehensive source on most aspects of atomic and nuclear physics is:

Glasstone, Samuel: *Sourcebook on Atomic Energy*, 2d ed., D. Van Nostrand Company, Inc., Princeton, N.J., 1958.

Chapter 19

Characteristics of Atoms III: Electronic Structure

When Rutherford proposed the nuclear atom, a number of problems immediately presented themselves to the structure he suggested. How can electrons remain outside the nucleus when there must be a very strong attraction between its large positive charge and the negative charges carried by the electrons? One possible answer is that electrons travel around the nucleus in orbits much as the planets revolve around the sun. The electrostatic attraction then serves the same function that gravity does in the solar system and keeps the moving electrons from flying off into space. This is a sensible suggestion, but it raises a second, more serious objection. Oscillating charges emit electromagnetic energy. The rapidly revolving electrons should, therefore, emit energy constantly. Since this energy must come from their kinetic energy of revolution (conservation of energy), they should lose energy gradually and slowly spiral into the nucleus. The atom should be unstable! and all existing atoms should radiate energy which gradually decreases in frequency as the electrons' motions become more feeble. None of this is found, of course. Atoms are stable. Normally, they do not radiate. And when atoms do emit energy, the electromagnetic radiation is not continuous and changing in frequency but appears as a few sharp, well-defined spectral lines. To overcome the objections which classical theory presents against moving electrons, several revolutionary conceptions had to be developed. Most of the renowned physicists of modern times contributed to this development, which has taken place during the last 50 years.

THE UNCERTAINTY PRINCIPLE

Philosophically, the breakthrough came from the realization that when applied to very small particles at very small distances, the laws of physics take on a different form and have to be modified to fit these conditions. In the micro world, micro factors operate that are too small to be noticed in our common experience with much larger objects. There they are obscured by the large effects we have been studying. These micro factors may seem strange because we are not accustomed to them. Already when we studied light and nuclear phenomena, we found that convenient distinctions from the macro world disappear. Experiments do not confirm whether light is a particle or a wave, and matter produces energy and energy, matter. There is no final answer to "what light really is" or "what a particle really is." Under one set of experimental conditions it is one; under another set, another of the two possibilities. And just as we had to accept the complementarity of wave-photon and matter-energy there, we must be satisfied with a less clear-cut con-

ception of the "real" nature of things when we move to the next range of dimensions, atomic size.

The difference between large objects and small particles, and the cause for the indefiniteness of our descriptions, are best understood if we consider how we obtain experimental information about these two classes of objects. Consider first a macro experiment; an athletic contest, a race. How is the speed of the runners timed? The runners wait at the starting line; the starter fires a gun, starting sound waves; the sound waves strike the runners' ears and they leap ahead. At the same time a stopwatch is started. At the end of the race there is a tape. The first runner to arrive breaks the tape and stops the watch. d/t gives his speed.

Now suppose we wish to time an "electron race." The electrons are poised; the starter fires the gun; sound waves (energy transmitted by means of alternate compressions and decompressions of the air molecules) travel to the electrons. The electrons . . . oops! An energetic air molecule bumps into an electron and sends it flying off the racetrack. Therein lies the problem. Small particles interact with the means of measuring them. If light is used to observe an electron, the light photon transfers energy to the electron and changes its behavior. We cannot, therefore, observe how the electron would-have-behaved-had-it-not-absorbed-the-photon for without the light, there is no observation, and with the light, the electron's condition is upset. For this reason, we cannot observe all properties of a small particle in its undisturbed state. If we locate an electron exactly, the act of locating disturbs its momentum. If we measure its momentum exactly, the act of measuring changes its location. This limitation to experiment was stated more elegantly by the German physicist Werner Heisenberg in the *uncertainty principle: we cannot determine simultaneously both the position and the momentum of small particles.*

For electrons in atoms, the implication of the uncertainty principle is this: the questions asked at the beginning of this chapter about the electrons' location in the atom and their motion around the nucleus cannot be answered by experiment. We cannot observe both simultaneously. We must be satisfied to squeeze out as much information as possible from observations that can be made, and we must reconcile ourselves to the fact that some aspects of the electronic motions around the nucleus remain unspecified. Our model of the atom cannot have neat little electrons running around the nucleus like the planets of the solar system; instead it has fuzzy electrons moving somehow, somewhere in the neighborhood of the nucleus.

ABSORPTION AND EMISSION SPECTRA

Like the information about nuclei, information about electrons comes from their interaction with energy. Since electrons are much less tightly bound than are nuclear particles, the intensity of the energy involved, the frequency of the interacting electromagnetic radiation, is much smaller. Visible light, ultraviolet, and soft X rays are sufficient to affect the electrons in atoms.

The interaction of radiation with electrons can occur in one of two ways. If the atoms, usually as a gas, are placed between a source of radiation emitting all frequencies and a detector, it is found that the atoms absorb a select number of frequencies and let the rest pass through. The spectrum then appears in the detector as a continuum with a number of dark lines (Fig. 19–1). The missing spectral lines are called the *absorption spectrum* of the element whose atoms are studied. How many dark lines, and the frequencies at which they appear, depend on the element in the apparatus. Each element has a characteristic absorption spectrum by which it can be identified. The dark lines in the sun's spectrum, the *Fraunhofer lines*, are absorption lines that serve to identify the composition of the sun's corona through which the light from the chromosphere passes before it reaches the earth (Fig. 19–2).

The second type of interaction of atoms with radiation is the reverse of absorption. If the atoms are heated to a very high temperature, or energy is added in some other way, the atoms emit radiation of some discrete frequencies. The lines of the *emission spectrum* coincide exactly with the dark lines of the absorption spectrum. The

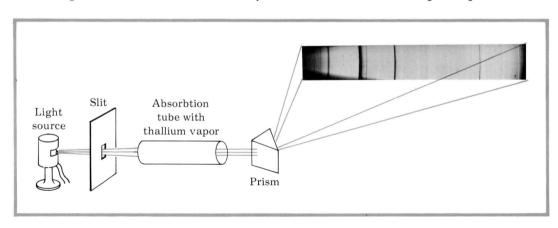

FIG. 19-1

Absorption spectrum. The dark lines of the spectrum are frequencies absorbed by thallium vapor. (Spectrum by J. Gibson Winans)

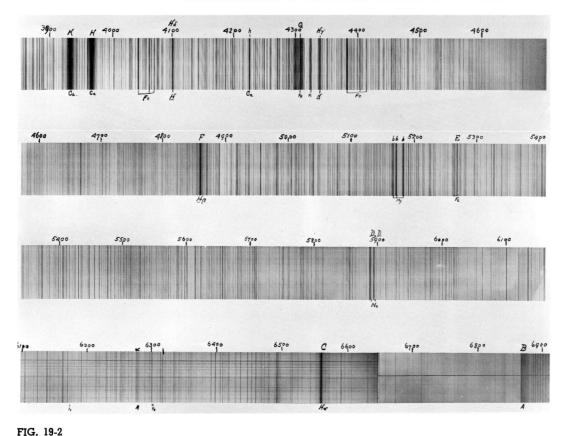

FIG. 19-2

Fraunhofer lines. Many frequencies are missing from the sun's spectrum because of absorption in the sun's chromosphere. Among the lines identified in this spectrum are those of H, Ca, Fe, and Mg. (Photograph from the Mount Wilson and Palomar Observatories)

same frequencies are emitted as absorbed.

Since, through the equation $E = hn$ (Chap. 15), electromagnetic radiation of frequency n_i is associated with photons of a fixed amount of energy E_i, the fact that atomic spectra consist of a few sharp lines only means that something about the structure of atoms causes their electrons to interact with some fixed amounts of energy only and to leave all other amounts of energy alone. This situation has an analogue in tall buildings with elevators (Fig. 19-4). People transported by the elevator can gain or lose potential energy only in amounts that correspond to the heights between the floors. All other amounts of potential energy are forbidden because there are no doors to let the people out and,

of course, no floors to step on if they were let out. The Danish physicist Niels Bohr in 1913 overcame the problems of atomic structure and explained absorption and emission spectra by suggesting similar restrictions to the energies of electrons in atoms.

Suppose that electrons in an atom are like people in a tall building. Suppose they can occupy the "floors" of the atom but not the spaces in between. On any given "floor," they are attracted to the nucleus by a Coulomb's law force that depends upon the charge of the nucleus and of the electron and the distance between them (Chap. 13). The "floors" therefore represent various levels of attractive electrostatic energy around the nucleus and are called *energy*

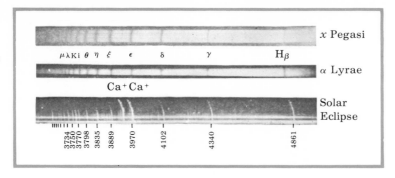

FIG. 19-3

Emission (bottom) and absorption spectrum of hydrogen, with two calcium lines. The emission spectrum was obtained from the solar chromosphere during a total eclipse of the sun. The upper photographs show the same lines absorbed in the gaseous atmospheres of the stars χ Pegasi and α Lyrae. The same lines are emitted by hydrogen when the gas glows in a cathode-ray tube. (After W. Finkelnburg, "Atomic Physics," McGraw-Hill Book Company, New York, 1950, and H. E. White)

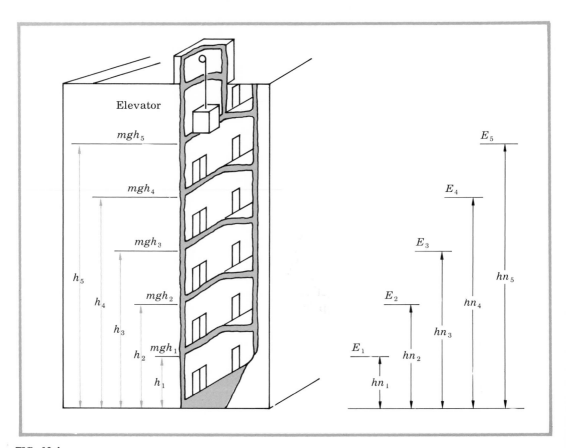

FIG. 19-4

People riding in an elevator can gain potential energy only in amounts that corres-
pond to the heights h_1, h_2, h_3, . . . *of the floors. Similarly, electrons in atoms can*
interact with restricted amounts of electromagnetic energy only, those that cor-
respond to the frequencies, n_1, n_2, n_3, ...

levels. Bohr proposed that electrons can occupy only a restricted number of energy levels, never the spaces between them. In the energy levels the electrons are stable. There they move without emitting energy. Hence stable atoms do not radiate.

Bohr next suggested that interaction with electromagnetic radiation produces jumps between the energy levels. An absorbing electron jumps to a level further removed from the nucleus, and since the allowed energy levels are specified, an electron can absorb only those quantities of energy (frequencies) which propel it exactly to another energy level. Thus only some select frequencies are absorbed and the dark lines of the absorption spectrum result. Conversely, the electrons may be pushed to the more distant energy levels by heating. Then, as they jump back to their original position on energy levels nearer the nucleus, they emit an amount of energy corresponding to the difference between the two levels. The emission spectrum also consists of lines. Since the nuclear charge is a characteristic property of each element and since it determines the attraction for electrons on each energy level, the spectrum is chiefly a function of the nuclear charge and thus is characteristic for each element.

QUANTUM NUMBERS

But on what basis can one restrict the energies permitted the electrons, the "allowed" energy levels? To this question Bohr provided a radical answer. Electrons can occupy only those energy levels in which a component of their energy is equal to whole-number multiples of the quantity $h/2\pi$. In the lowest level, it has the value $h/2\pi$. In the next level, $2h/2\pi$; in the third, $3h/2\pi$; and so forth. The allowed energy levels are consequently characterized by a set of numbers, 1, 2, 3, ... multiplied by $h/2\pi$ (h is Planck's constant). These numbers, the *quantum numbers*, specify both the location and the energy of the permitted energy levels.

The introduction of quantized energy levels in which electrons can move without radiating may seem strange, and it was, indeed, somewhat arbitrary when Bohr first suggested it. But the fact that computations

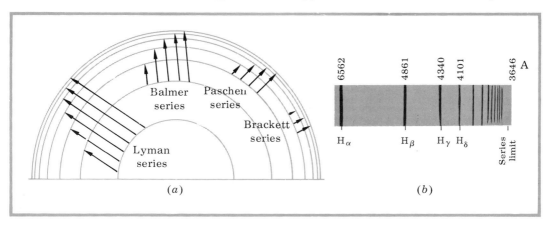

FIG. 19-5

The hydrogen spectrum. (a) According to Bohr's theory, there should be lines corresponding to the differences in energy between each pair of energy levels. (b) The Balmer series, the part of the hydrogen spectrum in the visible region of the spectrum, corresponds to lines starting at energy level 2. The ultraviolet Lyman series and the infrared Paschen and Brackett series are known and also correspond exactly to predicted energy differences. (After G. Herzberg, "Atomic Spectra and Atomic Structure," Dover Publications, Inc., New York, 1944)

based on Bohr's quantum restriction gave energy differences between the allowed energy levels that coincided exactly with the observed spectrum of hydrogen atoms was evidence for its validity (Fig. 19–5). If one calculates the electrostatic energy of an electron in the energy level for which the quantum number is 1 and also for the energy level in which it is 2, the difference between the two energies coincides exactly with the energy of one line of the hydrogen spectrum. The same is true for the first and third levels, the second and third levels, and for all the rest. The evidence was quite overwhelming that for hydrogen, the simplest atom, with only one electron and only one proton in the nucleus, quantization according to Bohr's theory describes the experimental observations. While perhaps strange because it was new and different, the theory met the test of experiment.

The introduction of quantum numbers into electronic structure is no more arbitrary than is the introduction of light quanta or photons into the model of electromagnetic radiation. There is no reason, based on our experience with large objects, to consider light energy as photons, packets of fixed energy, rather than as a continuous flow of any desired magnitude. New conceptions are required to explain the behavior of very small things, and it turns out that the idea of quanta elucidates the puzzles of both electromagnetic radiation and the electronic structure of atoms.

Because of the similarity between quantized photons and quantized electrons, and because photons as electromagnetic radiation are described by the equations of wave motion, an attempt was made to determine whether a wave correlate exists to electrons in atoms as it exists for light photons. In 1924 a Frenchman, Count Louis Victor de Broglie, showed that elementary particles may be described by waves. This was experimentally confirmed by the Americans C. J. Davisson and L. H. Germer in 1927. In the same year the Austrian physicist Erwin Schrödinger succeeded in providing a set of equations based on the mathematics of waves which in more rigorous form produced the quantized energy levels of atoms. In the mathematics of waves, whole numbers (quantum numbers) appear as natural consequences of the equations rather than as arbitrary conditions set on the allowed energy. As discussed in Chap. 12, the number of waves set up in a rope stretched between two points is limited to whole numbers. In such a rope one can have one large wave, or two smaller ones, or three, four, five waves, but since the rope is attached at both ends, the number of waves is always a whole number. Here, even in the world of large, everyday phenomena, a "quantum" restriction appears. And while this analogy is somewhat remote, it helps to indicate how quantum numbers arise directly from the solution of the wave equation Schrödinger developed for atoms. Because of this, the physics of small particles is known as *wave* or *quantum mechanics*. It stems from the initial contribution of Bohr, first refined by Schrödinger and later by many others.

As so frequently happens, an alternate mathematical solution that also led directly to quantized energy levels was developed in the same year by Heisenberg. By 1927 the framework for understanding the electronic structure of atoms had been completed. It is of interest to note the ages of the major contributors to the atomic theory at the time of their contributions: Bohr, 28; de Broglie, 32; Schrödinger, 40; Heisenberg, 26.

ORBITALS

The description of the energy levels of the hydrogen atom is simple because its energy is entirely determined by the attraction of the positive nucleus for one electron. Normally, the electron is in the energy level closest to the nucleus, and it moves to other energy levels when it absorbs energy. The electrons of all other atoms are also in energy levels, but their description is more complex because electron-electron repulsions as well as electron-nucleus attractions exist. This has two effects. Not all electrons can occupy the same energy level. The interactions limit the occupancy of each. Also, not all the electrons in an energy level are alike. Their locations around the nucleus are affected by the repulsive interactions. Consequently, other aspects of the electrons' energies are quantized, and a total of four quantum numbers is required to describe fully each electron in a many-electron atom.

While the uncertainty principle prevents us from specifying precisely the exact location and path of each electron in a many-electron atom, spectra provide a considerable amount of information. The energy of attraction for electrons in energy level 1 is greater than for electrons in energy level 2, in energy level 2 greater than in 3, etc. Consequently, electrons normally occupy low-quantum-number energy levels first, until each level is fully occupied. Also, spectra give the restrictions on the occupancy. There can be no more than two electrons in energy level 1; eight in energy level 2; eighteen in 3; etc.

When the spectra are observed from atoms that are in electric or magnetic fields, the lines split into two or more separate lines of nearly identical frequency. The splitting of the lines, called the *Stark effect* for the electric field and the *Zeeman effect* for the magnetic field in honor of their discoverers, shows that within the energy levels there are slight differences among the electrons. These differences are expressed by a second quantum number and relate to the spatial orientation of the electron around the atom. (Incidentally, Zeeman splitting of the lines emanating from sunspots is the evidence from which their strong magnetic fields are deduced.)

To interpret the second quantum number, we need a pictorial representation of the locations of electrons. These are called *orbitals*, to indicate both the similarity and the difference to the orbits of planets around the sun. Electrons, like planets, move under the influence of a central force. But whereas planets can be precisely located, electrons cannot. An orbital is a region in space where the electron might be found; it is not a path. An orbital is the fuzzy outline (Fig. 19–6) which represents the probability of finding an electron.

The subdivision of energy levels into orbitals is the following. In each energy level there are two electrons which are spatially unrestricted. Their second quantum number is expressed by the letter *s*. Thus the two electrons of the first energy level, 1*s* electrons, are likely to be found anywhere within a spherical shell around the nucleus at a distance appropriate for energy level 1 (Fig. 19–6*a*). In the second energy level, somewhat farther from the nucleus, there are also two electrons which are spatially unrestricted. These are called 2*s* electrons.

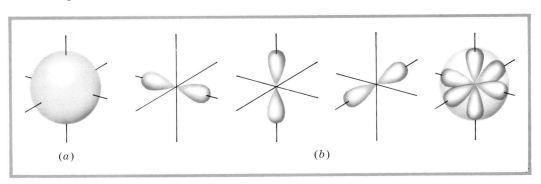

(*a*)   (*b*)

FIG. 19-6

Orbitals. (a) *In* s *orbitals, the electrons occupy a spherical shell around the nucleus.*
(b) p-*type electrons are restricted to the space near one of the coordinate axes.*

There are similar electrons in the third energy level, 3s electrons; etc.

The first energy level can hold only two electrons; hence the 1s electrons completely fill it. In each of the other energy levels, there are electrons which are spatially more restricted. Their second quantum number is expressed by the letter p. p-type electrons are restricted to the region of the energy level near one of the coordinate axes: two of them are found near the x-axis; two near the y axis; two near the z axis (Fig. 19–6b). There is, therefore, room for six p-type electrons within each energy level beyond the first. There are three pairs, each restricted both in distance and angular orientation.

Beginning with the third energy level, there is room for other, still more restricted electrons. There is room for ten d-type electrons, electrons whose second quantum number is expressed by the letter d and which are limited to five spatially equivalent portions of the energy levels. Then there are seven restricted f locations in energy levels above 4; nine restricted g locations in energy levels above 5; etc.

We may now summarize the electronic structure of atoms:

1. Electrons can exist only in a restricted number of energy levels which are designated by a principal quantum number 1, 2, 3, ... Energy levels relate chiefly to the distance between the electron and the nucleus with the lowest-number energy level closest to the nucleus.

2. Electrons within any energy level differ because of restrictions to the parts of the energy level they may occupy. These spatial restrictions are characterized by the letters s, p, d, f, g, h, . . . to denote a second quantum number.

3. One orbital in each energy level, characterized by the letter s, places no angular restriction on the electrons. The 1s, 2s, 3s, . . . orbitals are, therefore, the entire spherical shells at a distance from the nucleus determined by principal quantum numbers 1, 2, 3, ...

4. Each energy level with a principal quantum number of 2 or higher has three p orbitals. These are orbitals which limit the electrons to the regions of space near one of the three principal axes.

5. There are still more complex orbitals. Five d orbitals in energy levels above the third; seven f orbitals in energy levels above the fourth; etc.

6. An orbital is the location of two electrons. There can be, therefore, two electrons in each s orbital; six electrons in each set of p orbitals; ten electrons in each set of d orbitals; etc.

ORBITAL OCCUPANCY AND CHEMICAL BEHAVIOR

Before we describe the relation between electronic structure and chemical behavior, let us review a few of the characteristics of the periodic arrangement of elements. The elements at the end of each row are the noble gases. These are elements which, almost without exception, do not combine at all with other elements. Something about the arrangement of their electrons makes them inert to chemical combination. A second characteristic of the periodic table is that elements listed in the vertical rows are very similar in their chemical properties. Since we might suspect that electrons, the outermost and most accessible parts of atoms, are involved in chemical interactions, we should look for similarities in the electronic structure of the members of each group of elements. With this in mind, let us examine the location of electrons in a number of elements. The rule we shall follow in placing electrons among the allowed energy levels is a simple one: electrons occupy those orbitals first in which the electrostatic attraction to the nucleus is greatest; that is, they fill lower-quantum-number orbitals first. Let us see how this fits the periodic arrangement.

Hydrogen, the first element, has but one electron. Normally it is located in the 1s orbital. (Of course, it is possible to move the electron from that orbital under conditions which produce atomic spectra. The input of some form of energy "excites" the atom and causes transitions of the electron to the other allowed orbitals. But under normal conditions, the stable atom has its electron in the 1s orbital.)

Helium, the next element, has two electrons. Since the 1s orbital can accommodate two electrons, both are found there. But these two electrons completely fill the 1s orbital, and since the first energy level has only that orbital, the two electrons completely fill the first energy level. We refer to this as constituting a *filled shell* or *completed shell*. It is, of course, interesting that helium, an element whose electrons fill the first shell, is inert, a noble gas.

The next element, Li, has three electrons. Two of them are in the 1s orbital; one in the next lowest orbital, the 2s orbital. (For simplicity we shall adopt a shorthand notation which uses a superscript to indicate the number of electrons in each orbital. For lithium the notation gives

$1s^2$, $2s^1$—two electrons in the 1s and one in the 2s orbitals.) Be, with four electrons, has two in the 1s and two in the 2s orbitals. In shorthand, its structure is $1s^2$, $2s^2$. In Be, both the 1s and the 2s orbitals are filled, but Be is not an inert element. The next orbitals available are three 2p orbitals which have room for six electrons. B, the element with five electrons, has the structure $1s^2$, $2s^2$, $2p^1$; C has $1s^2$, $2s^2$, $2p^2$; N has $1s^2$, $2s^2$, $2p^3$; and so on, until in Ne, element 10, with the structure $1s^2$, $2s^2$, $2p^6$, the 2p orbitals are completely occupied and, indeed, the second energy level is completely filled. With Ne we again make the interesting observation that there are two filled electron shells and that the element is inert, a noble gas.

When we turn to the elements of the next period, we find another suggestive coincidence. Element 11, sodium, is chemically very similar to Li. Its electronic structure, according to the rule we follow, is $1s^2$, $2s^2$, $2p^6$, $3s^1$. Na has a single electron in an s orbital beyond two filled shells; Li has a single s electron beyond one filled

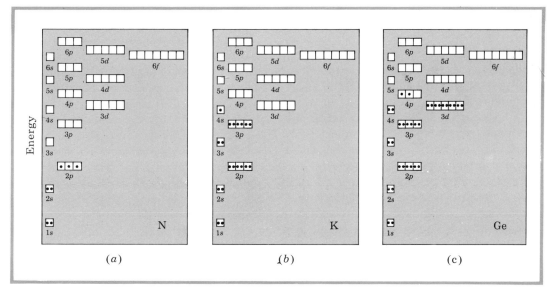

(a)   (b)   (c)

FIG. 19-7

The electronic structure of elements. Electrons occupy lower-quantum-number orbitals before higher-quantum-number orbitals, and s before p. However, 4s orbitals are filled before 3d; 5s before 4d; etc. (a) Electronic structure of N. (b) Electronic structure of K. (c) Electronic structure of Ge.

shell. Mg is similarly related to Be: both have two electrons in s orbitals beyond filled shells. B and Al have two s electrons and one p electron beyond filled shells; C and Si have two s and two p electrons beyond filled shells; and similar relationships hold for N and P, O and S, F and Cl, and Ne and Ar. From these observations, we might formulate two rules:

1. A filled-shell structure signifies chemical inertness.

2. Similarity in electronic arrangement *beyond* inert filled shells signifies similarity in chemical behavior.

Since the electrons beyond the filled shells seem to be the basis for chemical similarities, we shall give them a special name, *valence electrons*. For instance, Na and Li both have one s-type valence electron; C and Si both have four (two s-type and two p-type) valence electrons.

Our thinking about filled shells has to be adjusted when we examine the last element in the third row, Ar. The electronic structure of Ar is $1s^2, 2s^2, 2p^6, 3s^2, 3p^6$. The $3s$ and the $3p$ orbitals are filled, but there is still room in the third energy level for the ten $3d$ electrons. Yet, although the third energy level is not completely filled, argon is inert, a noble gas. Here the chemical evidence indicates inertness for the third energy level with the filling of the s and p orbitals even though d orbitals of that energy level may still be vacant. Comparable electronic structures for the other noble gases, Kr, Xe, and Rn confirm that filled s and p orbitals lead to chemical stability even when d, f, or other orbitals are still entirely vacant. This evidence suggests that rule 1 above be changed to: a filled shell, or one with the s and p orbitals completely filled, signifies chemical inertness.

The altered rule receives further confirmation from the electronic structure of the next element, K, atomic number 19. As an alkali metal like Li and Na, K would be expected to have one s-type valence electron with its other electrons in filled inert shells. Spectroscopic evidence clearly es-

tablishes the electronic structure of K as $1s^2, 2s^2, 2p^6, 3s^2, 3p^6, 4s^1$, another indication of the inertness of the $3s^2, 3p^6$ arrangement in the third energy level even though there still are vacant $3d$ orbitals.

The spectroscopic evidence, moreover, shows that the $3d$ orbitals are bypassed in the electronic structure of the next element, Ca, as well as in K. As an alkaline-earth element, Ca has two s-type valence electrons and the electronic structure $1s^2, 2s^2, 2p^6, 3s^2, 3p^6, 4s^2$.

The question then arises, why are the $3d$ electrons bypassed in the filling of orbitals by K and Ca? As usual, the question "why" has no adequate answer except that the evidence shows that such is the case. The evidence indicates that electrons are more firmly bound in the $4s$ than in the $3d$ orbitals. Electron stability determines the order in which orbitals are filled and, for unknown reasons, the $4s$ orbitals provide greater stability. The same order of stability holds for the $5s$ and $4d$, $6s$ and $5d$, etc., orbitals. In each case, electrons are more firmly held in the s orbitals than in the lower-quantum-number d orbitals and occupy the s orbitals first.

The next element after Ca is Sc. It starts a new set of elements in the periodic table, the ten groups of transition elements, none of which have members of their families in rows 1, 2, or 3. Knowing that the $3d$ orbitals have room for ten electrons and that elements 1 to 20 have no electrons in d orbitals, we can immediately suspect that in the ten groups starting with Sc there are d-type valence electrons. That is the case. Spectroscopic evidence shows that the ten elements between Sc and Zn locate their next electrons in the $3d$ orbitals. The d orbitals are filled in the element Zn.

The thirty electrons of Zn occupy the following orbitals: $1s^2, 2s^2, 2p^6, 3s^2, 3p^6, 3d^{10}, 4s^2$. Filling the $3d$ orbitals has the same effect as filling s and p orbitals; they constitute a filled shell which is inert. The two $4s$ electrons alone determine the chemistry of Zn. Likewise, in element 31, Ga

($1s^2$, $2s^2$, $2p^6$, $3s^2$, $3p^6$, $3d^{10}$, $4s^2$, $4p^1$), the two $4s$ electrons and the one $4p$ electron determine chemical behavior. Zn is quite similar to the alkaline-earth elements in its properties, and Ga belongs to group IIIa, whose elements have three valence electrons.

A correlation between the detailed electronic structure and the chemical characteristics can be given for the remaining elements in the periodic table. We shall limit ourselves, however, to a summary of the characteristics we have already discussed without citing the additional evidence. The summary indicates the basis for dividing the periodic table into four sets of elements (Chap. 17). In columns Ia and IIa, there are elements with one and two valence electrons respectively in s orbitals. Then come ten groups with valence electrons in s and d orbitals, the transition elements. These ten groups resemble each other quite closely besides showing the usual intragroup relationships. Next, in the main portion of the table, are groups IIIa to VIIa and 0. These have their valence electrons in s and p orbitals with the last group, group 0, having filled electron shells. Group 0 is the inert, noble gases. Finally, the lanthanides and actinides are listed separately. These elements have two valence electrons in s orbitals and fill the fourteen vacancies of the $4f$ and $5f$ orbitals respectively. As we indicated before, they are very similar in their chemical properties.

FILLED SHELLS AND BONDING

We can now relate electronic structure to chemical combination of elements. The rule for combination is based on the inertness of filled shells: *elements form compounds by exchanging or sharing valence electrons so that, as a result of the exchange or sharing, each obtains a filled outermost shell.* We shall illustrate this rule by a number of examples.

In chemical combinations the element

fluorine with seven valence electrons ($2s^2$, $2p^5$) adds an electron to the outermost shell, thereby attaining the electronic structure $2s^2$, $2p^6$, a filled shell. In chemical combinations the element sulfur with six valence electrons ($3s^2$, $3p^4$) adds two electrons to the outermost shell, thereby attaining the electronic structure $3s^2$, $3p^6$, a filled shell. Nitrogen with five valence electrons ($2s^2$, $2p^3$) adds three electrons to its outermost shell, thereby attaining the electronic structure $2s^2$, $2p^6$. As these examples illustrate, elements with a few electrons less than eight in their outermost shells add enough electrons to complete the shell.

In chemical combinations the element sodium with one valence electron ($3s^1$) and the element calcium with two valence electrons ($4s^2$) give up electrons to leave only filled electron shells. Other elements with only a few electrons in their outermost shells also attain filled-shell structures by losing the few electrons. One kind of chemical reaction then occurs between this kind of element and the kind discussed in the last paragraph. When they react, electrons are transferred from one element to another:

$$\text{Na} + :\!\overset{\textstyle\cdot}{\underset{\textstyle\cdot\cdot}{\text{F}}}\!: \longrightarrow \text{Na}^+ + :\!\overset{\textstyle\cdot\cdot}{\underset{\textstyle\cdot\cdot}{\text{F}}}\!:^- \qquad (19\text{--}1)$$

An element like sodium transfers its electrons to an element like fluorine and both are left with filled outermost shells. (Equation 19–1 uses *electron-dot* symbols and formulas to represent valence electrons. These help visualize where the electrons are before and after the reaction. The valence electrons are generally indicated in pairs to emphasize the double occupancy of each orbital.)

Another example of this kind of chemical reaction is the reaction between Mg and N:

$$\text{Mg} + \text{Mg} + \text{Mg} + :\!\overset{\textstyle\cdot\cdot}{\text{N}}\!: + :\!\overset{\textstyle\cdot\cdot}{\text{N}}\!: \longrightarrow$$
$$\text{Mg}^{2+} + \text{Mg}^{2+} + \text{Mg}^{2+} + :\!\overset{\textstyle\cdot\cdot}{\underset{\textstyle\cdot\cdot}{\text{N}}}\!:^{3-} + :\!\overset{\textstyle\cdot\cdot}{\underset{\textstyle\cdot\cdot}{\text{N}}}\!:^{3-}$$

$$(19\text{--}2)$$

In this reaction each Mg atom loses two

electrons. Because each N atom must add three electrons to fill its valence shell, the reaction is between at least three Mg atoms and two N atoms. Then, six electrons are lost by three Mg atoms and gained by two N atoms. The formula of the compound is Mg_3N_2.

The reactions illustrated in Eqs. 19–1 and 19–2, in which electrons transfer from one atom to another, lead to the formation of charged particles, ions. Hence the compounds formed are called *ionic* compounds and the forces that hold the ions together are called *ionic* bonds. Ionic bonds are the electrostatic attractions between ions of opposite charge.

There is a second way in which compounds attain the stability of filled outermost electron shells. Instead of the complete transfer of electrons from one atom to another as in ionic compounds, some atoms share electrons in their orbitals and thus attain filled shells. The element chlorine, for instance, occurs in nature as molecules consisting of two atoms (Chap. 16). The reason for the stability of Cl_2 is that the outermost shell of each chlorine atom has seven electrons. By sharing one electron

pair in orbitals from each atom (Fig. 19–8), each atom attains a filled outermost shell—with the shared electron pair. The electron-dot equation for the formation of Cl_2 from atom is:

$$: \overset{..}{\underset{..}{Cl}} \overline{\cdot + \cdot} \overset{..}{\underset{..}{Cl}} : \longrightarrow : \overset{..}{\underset{..}{Cl}} : \overset{..}{\underset{..}{Cl}} : \qquad (19\text{--}3)$$

Compounds formed by this process, the sharing of an electron pair between two atoms, are called *covalent* compounds. The attraction between the joined atoms which results from the nucleus–electron pair–nucleus interactions is called a *covalent bond*. In covalent compounds the individual atoms do not become charged, but the atoms are held together by the shared electron pair bonds. In contrast to ionic compounds, in which single ions are the basic units, the group of atoms linked by shared electron pairs is the basic unit in covalent compounds.

Cl_2O, shown in Eq. 19–4, is another example of a covalent molecule. In its electron-dot formula, for bookkeeping purposes, we show the oxygen electrons as $\times$'s and the chlorine electrons as dots. The result here is the same as in the Cl_2 molecule.

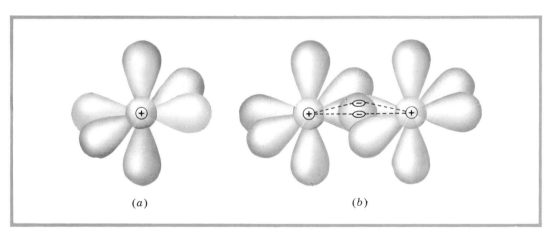

(a)   (b)

FIG. 19-8

Covalent bonding in chlorine. (a) Chlorine has seven valence electrons, $3s^2$, $3p^5$. The spherical s orbital and two p orbitals are fully occupied; the third p orbital has only one electron. (b) When two Cl atoms come together so that the half-filled orbitals overlap in space, each atom provides an electron for the shared orbital and, through the shared electron pair, attains a filled-shell structure. The molecule is held together by the attractions between the nuclei and the shared electron pair.

Sharing gives each of the bonded atoms eight electron outermost shells.

$$: \overset{..}{\underset{..}{Cl}} \boxed{+ \overset{\times}{_\times} \overset{\times\times}{\underset{\times\times}{O}} \times + } \overset{..}{\underset{..}{Cl}} : \longrightarrow : \overset{..}{\underset{..}{Cl}} \overset{\times}{} \overset{\times\times}{\underset{\times\times}{O}} \overset{\times}{} \overset{..}{\underset{..}{Cl}} :$$

$$(19\text{--}4)$$

VALENCE AGAIN

With these rules for combination based on electronic structure, we can now return to the concept of valence or combining power which, in Chap. 17, was an interesting but unexplained corollary of the periodic table. In that chapter we mentioned that elements in groups Ia to IVa have valences of 1 to 4 respectively; elements in groups Va, VIa, and VIIa sometimes show valences of 5, 6, or 7, but more commonly have the valences 3, 2, and 1 respectively. We also mentioned the variable valences of the transition metals and the inertness of group 0. Now, we can relate these to electronic structure.

Valence is related to the number of electrons an element loses, gains, or shares in chemical combination. For instance, group Ia elements have one valence electron to lose and, consequently, have a valence of 1. Group IIa elements have two valence electrons to lose and consequently have a valence of 2. Group IIIa elements have three electrons and a valence of 3. Group IVa elements can gain four, lose four, share four. Whatever they do, their valence is 4. Group Va elements, to show a valence of 5, would have to share their five valence electrons with other atoms or to lose the five. Group Va elements never lose and rarely share all five electrons. They can, however, also gain three or share three electrons with other elements and frequently do so. Hence the most common valence for group Va elements is 3. Similar reasoning then leads to 2 as the most common valence of group VIa elements and to 1 as the common valence for group VIIa elements. These relationships between electronic structure and valence are illustrated in Table 19–1.

The table suggests two additional rules. Elements that have only a few valence electrons, 1, 2, or 3, will lose them in forming compounds. Elements that have more, nearly enough to complete the shell of eight electrons, tend to gain them. Thus we find that the elements on the left side of the periodic table, stretching from groups Ia and IIa through the transition elements to the heavy lines running stepwise and diagonally across the periodic table, are the elements that lose their electrons and form ionic compounds with elements that gain electrons. These elements are also the metallic elements. Indeed, one of their typical properties, metallic conduction of electricity, is related to the ready loss of electrons in chemical combinations. On the other hand, elements which are to the upper right-hand side of the diagonal are nonmetals.

TABLE 19-1

Electronic structure and compound formation

Element	Group	Electrons in outermost shell	Forms compounds by	Valence	Formula of compound
Li	I	$2s^1$	Loss of 1	1 $\big\}$	Li_2S
S	VI	$3s^2, 3p^4$	Gain of 2	2	(ionic)
Ca	II	$4s^2$	Loss of 2	2 $\big\}$	Ca_3N_2
N	V	$2s^2, 2p^3$	Gain of 3	3	(ionic)
P	V	$3s^2, 3p^3$	Sharing 3	3 $\big\}$	PCl_3
Cl	VII	$3s^2, 3p^5$	Sharing 1	1	(covalent)

The second rule concerns the likelihood of forming ionic or covalent compounds. Ionic bonding occurs when one element loses electrons completely and another gains them completely. Consequently ionic compounds are formed between elements that have a strong tendency to lose electrons, metals, and elements that have a strong tendency to gain them, nonmetals. Covalent compounds, on the other hand, share electrons. If both elements in the compound have a tendency to gain electrons, they reach a compromise by sharing, and a covalent compound is formed. Thus covalent compounds are those between two nonmetallic elements. Metallic elements do not form compounds with one another except in a very special sense (Chap. 21).

The stable eight-electron outermost shell determines the valence of elements with two exceptions. One is the hydrogen atom. Since the outermost shell of hydrogen is the first shell, which becomes filled with only two electrons, hydrogen attains closed-shell stability by sharing or gaining only one additional electron. This occurs in co-valent compounds like H:O:H or H:Cl: and ionic compounds such as Li$^+$ + :H$^-$. Another possibility is for hydrogen to lose its one electron to other elements, leaving behind the H$^+$ ion, a proton stripped of all electrons. This is a unique structure among the elements; all other positive ions have inner shells and consequently are not stripped to the bare nucleus when they transfer electrons in ionic compounds. It gives the positive hydrogen ion a peculiar place among the ions.

The second exception to the eight-electron shell is the transition metals, which have some d electrons in the outermost shell. Because of these, the filling of s and p orbitals with eight electrons is not an adequate criterion for stability. The behavior of the transition elements is quite complex. These are elements for which valence cannot be predicted simply from electronic structure alone and which show multiple valences in their compounds. The multiple valence is related to the availability of s and possibly some d electrons for compound formation.

OTHER RELATIONSHIPS IN THE PERIODIC ARRANGEMENT

The location of an element in the periodic table gives its valence, if its outermost shell contains s, or s and p, electrons only. From this, the formulas of compounds between such elements can be predicted. Moreover, the location of the two combining elements in the periodic table suggests the likelihood of covalent or ionic bond formation. Thus a substantial amount of chemistry can be inferred directly from the table. A slight extension of this mode of thinking leads to some rules about the chemical reactivity of the various elements.

A simple model for the reactivity of a metallic element is the following. The atom, for instance sodium, consists of a nucleus of charge +11, surrounded by a shell of charge −2 (the first energy level), another shell of charge −8 (the second energy level), and finally a single electron. Since sodium loses only that one valence electron in forming compounds, its reactivity is governed by the ease with which that electron can be removed from the attraction of the positive nucleus, considering that there are also repulsions due to the other electrons. There is a theorem in electrostatics which states that when looking at a charged sphere from outside the sphere, its charge appears located at the center of the sphere. It allows us to estimate the repulsions. As far as the valence electron is concerned, the completed shells of two and eight electrons respectively repel like charges of −2 and −8 located in the nucleus. The forces that attract the valence electron, then, are simply those between a nucleus with a net charge of +11 −2 −8 = +1 and an electron with charge

−1, at the distance between the nucleus and the valence electron.

The reactivity of potassium is governed by a similar relationship. Its valence electron is attracted by a nucleus of charge +19 surrounded by filled shells of charge −2, −8, and −8. Again because of the theorem stated above, the valence electron notices the effect of a net charge of +1 only from the nucleus (+19 −2 −8 −8 = +1). The valence electrons of both potassium and sodium are held by net attractions of about +1. Their relative reactivities are therefore determined by the relative distances between the nuclei and valence electrons in the two elements. The greater the distance, the less tightly the electrons are bound and the greater the reactivity of the element.

The distance between the valence electron and the nucleus is governed mostly by the number of filled shells that intervene. While the first shell of potassium is somewhat smaller than the first shell of sodium (Fig. 19–9), because of the greater charge of the potassium nucleus, and the same is true of the second shells, the existence of a filled third shell in potassium keeps the 4s valence electron farther from the nucleus than is the case for the 3s valence electron of sodium. Hence, this simplified model for the factors that govern metallic reactivity suggests that the valence electron

in potassium is farther away, predicting less attraction and greater reactivity for the element potassium. This is found experimentally.

This model also suggests that an element with one valence electron should lose that electron more easily, be more reactive, than its neighbor with two valence electrons. Sodium should be more reactive than magnesium; potassium than calcium; rubidium than strontium; etc. The reasoning here is the following. First the charge of +12 on the magnesium nucleus draws the filled shells and valence electrons somewhat closer than does the charge of +11 on the sodium nucleus. Hence the distance between the valence electrons and the nucleus is less in magnesium. In addition, the charge "seen" by each valence electron of magnesium is +12 − 2 − 8 = +2 contrasted with a charge of only +1 "seen" by the valence electron of sodium. Both of these factors tend to hold the valence electrons of magnesium more tightly than that of sodium. This too is found chemically.

An experimental measure of the ease with which electrons are lost by atoms is the *ionization energy*, the energy required to remove an electron from an atom, which can be obtained from the spectrum of its gaseous atoms. Gases are used because in them the atoms are far apart and do not interact with one another. The ionization

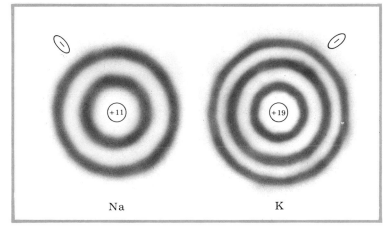

The valence electrons of both Na and K experience a net attraction of about +1 from the nuclei because of the shielding of the filled electron shells. Since the valence in K is farther than that in Na, it is bound less tightly. K is the more reactive metal.

Na   K

FIG. 19-9

TABLE 19-2

Ionization energies of some elements in electron volts

H											
13.5											
Li	Be										
5.4	9.3										
75.3	18.1										
Na	Mg										
5.1	7.6										
47.0	15.0										
K	Ca	Sc	Ti	V	Cr	Mn	Fe	Co	Ni	Cu	Zn
4.3	6.1	6.7	6.8	6.7	6.7	7.4	7.8	7.8	7.6	7.7	9.4
31.7	11.8	12.8	13.6	14.1	16.6	15.7	16.2	17.3	18.2	20.3	17.9

The upper number gives the first ionization energy, for the reaction: $M \rightarrow e- + M+$.
The lower number gives the second ionization energy, for the reaction: $M+ \rightarrow e- + M^2+$.

energy appears in the atomic spectrum as a line that represents the jump of an electron from the valence shell of the atom to an energy level at "an infinite distance from the nucleus," actually so far away that the electron is free and the atom has become ionized. Spectroscopically determined ionization energies, given in Table 19–2, show that the predictions of the simple model of reactivity are confirmed by experiment.

The model predicts, and experiment confirms, that reactivity of metals increases downward in each family and toward the left in each period. Cesium is the most reactive stable metal, the metal with the greatest tendency to lose an electron and become the Cs+ ion. From cesium, the tendency to form positive ions decreases both upward and to the right. The tendency to gain electrons and form negative ions by the nonmetallic elements changes in the opposite directions.

To lose an electron easily during chemical combination, that electron should be as far from the nucleus as possible. To gain an electron and hold it tightly, the con- verse is true; the electron should be as near the nucleus as possible. Fluorine, which gains one electron into its second shell, holds that electron more tightly than chlorine, in which it is in the somewhat more distant third shell. Also, one electron added to a nucleus with charge +9 is held more tightly than two electrons added to a nucleus with charge +8. Hence fluorine gains electrons more readily than oxygen. For the nonmetals reactivity increases toward the upper right of the periodic chart, with fluorine the most reactive nonmetallic element.

A diagonal can be imagined across the entire periodic table from lower left to upper right, along which the tendency to gain electrons decreases gradually—from cesium, least likely to gain and most likely to lose, to fluorine, most likely to gain and least likely to lose. Elements along slanting lines at right angles to the diagonal are approximately equal in their respective reactivities. Near the stepwise heavy lines in the periodic table is the boundary between tendency to gain and tendency to lose. This is the transition between the metallic and

					He
					24.5
					54.1
B	C	N	O	F	Ne
8.3	11.2	14.5	13.6	17.3	21.5
25.0	24.3	29.5	34.9	34.8	40.9
Al	Si	P	S	Cl	Ar
6.0	8.1	10.9	10.3	13.0	15.7
18.7	16.3	19.6	23.3	23.7	27.8
Ga	Ge	As	Se	Br	Kr
6.0	8.1	10.5	9.7	11.8	13.9
20.4	15.9	20.1	21.3	19.1	26.4

The distance of an element along the diagonal from cesium to fluorine is given by the *electronegativity* of the element, a number that represents its tendency to become a negative ion. The smallest electronegativity is that of Cs—0.5; the largest that of F—4.0. For the other elements the electronegativity values are between those two numbers, depending upon their chemical behavior. The formation of ionic or covalent bonds depends upon the difference in the electronegativity of the two elements. Those with nearly equal electronegativity form covalent bonds; those with a considerable difference in electronegativity, ionic bonds. But the formation of ionic or covalent bonds is not an absolute matter. Just like the tendency to gain or lose electrons, it varies gradually from one extreme to the other, but that topic must be reserved for more advanced discussions of bond formation. Hydrogen is unique in this regard, too. In spite of its location far to the left, indicating a lower electronegativity, its electronegativity is 2.1, nearly equal to that of carbon.

nonmetallic elements. Actually, since the transition is gradual, the elements near that boundary line resemble metals in some of their properties and nonmetals in others.

Questions and Problems

1. Give and explain (a) Heisenberg's uncertainty principle (b) the Bohr model of the atom, (c) Zeeman effect.

2. Differentiate between s and p orbitals.

3. Draw electron-dot equations for the reaction of Cl_2 with H_2; Na with S; Ca with Br_2; P with I_2.

4. Write the complete electronic orbital designation for Ar, Sc, P, Al^{3+}, N^{3-}.

5. Write the valence shell orbital occupancy for Ba, Rb, Sb, Pb, Zn.

6. Define and explain (a) absorption spectrum, (b) emission spectrum, (c) quantum number, (d) ionic bond, (e) covalent bond, (f) energy levels, (g) orbitals.

7. Explain the variation in first ionization energy between Li, Be, B; F, Ne, Na.

8. Explain the variation in the second ionization energy between K, Ca, Sc; Na, Mg, Al.

9. Compare first and second ionization energies for Li and Be and explain.

10. Compare the sizes of F^-, Ne, Na^+, Mg^{2+}. Explain.

11. Predict the approximate value of the third ionization energy of Mg.

12. Show that the difference between lines of the hydrogen spectrum corresponds to other lines of the spectrum.

13. Which of the following do you predict to be ionic? covalent?

(a) $AlCl_3$ (d) Ba_3N_2 (g) $SrCl_2$
(b) S_2Cl_2 (e) P_2O_3 (h) IBr
(c) SO_2 (f) CBr_4 (i) Cs_2S

Suggestions for Further Reading

Texts that contain extensive discussions of the contents of this chapter include:

Christiansen, G. S., and Paul H. Garrett: *Structures and Change*, W. H. Freeman and Company, San Francisco, 1960. Chapters 20, 28, and 29.

Holton, Gerald, and Duane H. D. Roller: *Foundations of Modern Physical Science*, Addison-Wesley Publishing Company, Inc., Reading, Mass., 1958. Chapters 33 to 35.

Pauling, Linus: *College Chemistry*, 3d ed., W. H. Freeman and Company, San Francisco, 1964. Chapters 7 to 9.

Quagliano, James V.: *Chemistry*, 2d ed., Prentice-Hall, Inc., Englewood Cliffs, N.J., 1963. Chapters 3, 12 to 14.

Two paperbacks that closely relate to this chapter are:

Ryschkewitsch, George E.: *Chemical Bonding and the Geometry of Molecules*, Reinhold Publishing Corporation, New York, 1963 (paperback).

Sisler, Harry H.: *Electronic Structure, Properties, and the Periodic Law*, Reinhold Publishing Corporation, New York, 1963 (paperback). Chapters 1 and 2.

Chapter 20

Ionic Solutions

As we discussed in Chap. 16, there are two categories of matter—substances and mixtures. Substances are fixed in composition and homogeneous throughout. Pure elements and pure compounds are substances. Mixtures are neither homogeneous nor fixed in their composition. They vary in the relative amounts of their components, and often, as the minerals in granite illustrate (Fig. 5–4), the components are readily distinguishable. But there are some things, like coffee, that are difficult to categorize. Macroscopically, coffee, appears fixed in composition and homogeneous. Every drop in a cup of coffee, or every thousandth of a drop, looks like every other thousandth of a drop and has the same composition. But the composition of coffees can vary greatly—some people drink theirs weak, others strong. Coffee is not fixed

319

in composition. Moreover, if we could examine it submicroscopically, we should find it nonhomogeneous as well. Molecules of water and of the components of coffee alternate in the cup. Coffee is an example of a *solution,* a macroscopically homogeneous mixture.

SOLUTIONS

Solutions contain at least two components, the *solvent,* in which things are dissolved, and one or more *solutes.* The solvent is always in the same state as the solution. If the solution is gaseous, the solvent is a gas; if the solution is liquid, the solvent is a liquid; if the solution is solid, so is the solvent. When solvent and solute are both in the same state, as in a solution of alcohol and water, the substance present in the largest amount is generally considered the solvent. The choice of solvent and solutes is a matter of convenience and rarely presents problems.

Solvents can be solid, liquid, or gaseous, and so can solutes. Alloys, for instance, are solid solutions. Their major component, a metal, is the solid solvent which contains chiefly other metals as solutes; but it may also contain gaseous solutes like H_2 or N_2 or the liquid solute, mercury.

Air is an example of a gaseous solution with the solvent N_2 (79 percent of air), the gaseous solutes O_2, Ar, CO_2, etc.; the liquid solute water vapor; and possibly solid solutes like I_2 or evaporated moth crystals. The most common solutions, however, are liquid solutions, and for ionic compounds the most common solvent is water.

Solution of one substance in another is a very specific property. Only in rare instances can solvent and solutes be mixed in all proportions. Alcohol and water are an example. Solutions of the two exist all the way from a drop of water in a tubful of alcohol to a drop of alcohol in a tubful of water. Much more common are insoluble or hardly soluble solutes. Less than 0.01 gram of $BaSO_4$ and $CaCO_3$, for instance, dissolves in 100 grams of water. The same is true of the gases O_2, N_2, H_2. NaCl is an example of a more soluble compound—up to 30 grams dissolve in 100 grams of water. NH_4NO_3 is unusual—about 300 grams dissolve in 100 grams of water.

The extent to which a substance dissolves in a solvent is its *solubility* in the solvent. For instance, the solubility of NH_4NO_3 is 300 grams/100 grams water. Solutions can be prepared which contain less than that amount but not more than that amount. NH_4NO_3 solutions could con-

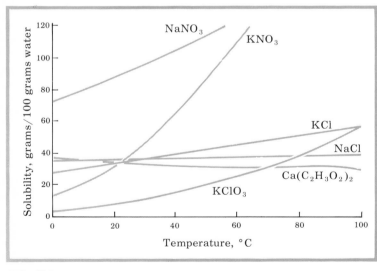

Solubilities of some ionic compounds. Solubility is quite specific for each compound and usually changes greatly with temperature.

FIG. 20-1

tain as little as 1 gram/100 grams water or even 0.001 gram/100 grams water. Solubilities usually change greatly with temperature (Fig. 20–1), either increasing or decreasing. As the examples indicate, the solubility is a specific property of a given solvent and solute.

MOLAR CONCENTRATIONS

The simplest way of characterizing the amount of solute in a solution is grams per grams of solute. This we illustrated above. Another way is by percentage by weight. Thus, a 10 percent by weight aqueous NaCl solution contains 10 parts by weight of NaCl and 90 parts by weight of H_2O. Grams per gram solute and percentage by weight composition are easy to compute, but they have very little chemical meaning. Moles, not grams, are comparable in chemistry. In 100 grams of 10 percent solutions of NaCl, $CuSO_4$, and $C_3H_8O_3$, for instance, there are 0.17 mole of NaCl among 5 moles of water; 0.063 mole of $CuSO_4$ among 5 moles of water; and 0.11 mole of $C_3H_8O_3$ among 5 moles of water. In terms of the number of solute particles dissolved, the three 10 percent solutions are quite different. Because the number of particles of solute in the solution is of much greater chemical significance, chemists express concentrations in terms of moles of solute per liter of solution.

The *molarity* is defined as the number of moles of solute per liter of solution. A 1 *molar* (1M) solution contains 1 mole of solute per liter; a 0.5 molar (0.5M) solution contains 0.5 mole of solute per liter; a 0.0263 molar (0.0263M) solution contains 0.0263 mole of solute per liter. The weights of different solutes which are needed for such solutions then must be computed from their molecular weights. If NaCl (mol. wt. = 58.5) is the solute, the weights needed for the three solutions are 58.5 grams (1M), 29.3 grams (0.5M), and 1.54 gram (0.0263M). If the solute is $CuSO_4$

(mol. wt. = 163), the weights are 163 grams, 81.5 grams, and 4.30 grams, respectively. An analogous computation will give the weights of $C_3H_8O_3$ needed.

One difficulty that many students encounter with the concept of molarity is that it is easy to forget that solutions come in small and large amounts. In some contexts we may deal with as little as a few drops of salt solution. Human tears are a good example. In others, whole oceans are present. Naturally the weight of solute differs greatly in the two. Yet the concentration concept, molarity, applies to both. It is entirely feasible and sensible to compute the molarity of NaCl in seawater—about 0.6M. Each liter of the ocean contains about 35 grams (0.6 mole) of NaCl. The concentration of NaCl in tears is, likewise, about 0.6M. But the total weight of salt in the ocean, is almost infinite because of the fantastically large amounts of ocean water while each tear contains only a grain or two of salt. Molarity expresses amounts of solute in a standard volume—1 liter—of solution. In actual operations, smaller or larger volumes are usually encountered, and for these the weights of solute must be appropriately scaled.

COLLIGATIVE PROPERTIES

With concentration expressed by molarity, we can investigate a set of surprising properties of solutions, the *colligative properties*: vapor-pressure lowering, boiling-point elevation, freezing-point depression, and osmotic pressure. Colligative properties are surprising because they depend only on the concentration of the solute, not on its kind. Despite the general specificity of solvent-solute interactions, as shown by the great variation of solubility among different substances, all solutes affect the solvent vapor pressure, its boiling and freezing points, and its osmotic pressure identically. The magnitude of the changes depends only on the concentration of the solution.

At 25°C the vapor pressure of water in 1M aqueous solutions of nonvolatile solutes like sugar or glycerine is about 23.3 mm Hg, about 0.5 mm Hg less than the vapor pressure of pure water. In 2M solutions the effect doubles. The vapor pressure is reduced about 1 mm Hg. In 0.5M solutions the effect is halved; the vapor pressure drops only about 0.25 mm Hg. This effect occurs for all nonvolatile compounds if they are sufficiently soluble.

It is not too difficult to produce a plausible explanation for this behavior. Vapor pressure is a measure of the equilibrium between molecules escaping from the surface of the liquid and gaseous molecules returning to the liquid (Chap. 11). With nonvolatile solute molecules occupying parts of the surface, the exchange is limited to the remainder of the surface. The rate of exchange drops and the vapor pressure likewise drops. Perhaps the only surprising feature is that the size of the solute molecules is not specifically important and that their number in solution—concentration—alone determines the magnitude of the effect. (While we have specified nonvolatile solutes, the basic effect occurs with volatile solutes, like alcohol, too. The vapor pressure of water is reduced because the exchange of molecules between the liquid water and the water vapor is reduced. But the alcohol molecules themselves set up a liquid-to-vapor exchange. Alcohol also exerts a vapor pressure and the situation thereby becomes more complicated.)

Since the boiling point of a substance is defined as the temperature at which vapor pressure equals atmospheric pressure (Chap. 11), vapor-pressure lowering causes the elevation of the boiling point. The solution must be raised to a higher temperature before its (lower) vapor pressure reaches atmospheric pressure. And since vapor-pressure lowering depends only on concentration and not on kind of solute, boiling-point elevation also depends only on concentration and not on kind of solute (Fig. 20–2). One molar solutions of nonvolatile solutes in water boil at 100.5°C, a change of 0.5°. Solutions of different concentrations change the boiling point proportionately.

At the other end of the liquid range, a solute lowers the freezing point of water about 1.86°C for 1M solutions. This has a practical application in automobile radiators, in which the presence of methyl alcohol or ethylene glycol prevents freezing. Since freezing-point depression also de-

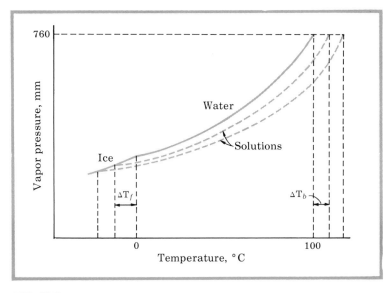

Vapor pressure for water and two aqueous solutions, not to scale. Vapor-pressure lowering due to the solute produces a boiling-point elevation and a freezing-point depression.

FIG. 20-2

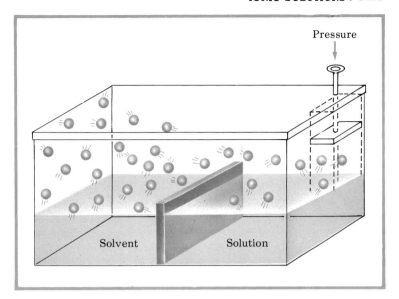

The vapor pressure of pure solvent is greater than its pressure above a solution. If the two are next to each other in an enclosed vessel, there will be transport of solvent to the solution. One way to prevent this would be to increase the pressure of the vapor above the solution—if that could be done.

FIG. 20-3

pends only on the concentration of the solute and not its kind, we can understand why, weight for weight, methyl alcohol, CH_4O (mol. wt = 34), is more effective than permanent antifreeze, ethylene glycol, $C_2H_6O_2$ (mol. wt = 62). A given weight of methyl alcohol contains nearly twice as many moles and consequently reduces the freezing point nearly twice as much as an equal weight of ethylene glycol. However, methyl alcohol has itself a high vapor pressure and thus readily escapes from the radiator, whereas ethylene glycol is non-volatile. This makes permanent antifreeze more desirable in the long run. (While our discussion of colligative properties is in terms of water solutions, all effects occur in other liquid solvents. The numerical values of changes are different for different solvents, however.)

One other property of solutions depends only on the concentration and not on the kind of solute, the osmotic pressure. Like boiling-point elevation and freezing-point depression, osmotic pressure is related to the vapor-pressure decrease. Consider a solution and some pure solvent together in a closed container (Fig. 20–3). Because of its higher vapor pressure, the pure solvent tends to evaporate more extensively than

the solution and there is a net transport of solvent into the solution. One way to stop this transport is to increase the pressure on the solution side so that the solution vapor pressure plus the added pressure equals the solvent vapor pressure. Then the two are in balance. Equilibrium can be attained by somehow adding pressure to the vapor pressure of the solvent.

This experiment can be performed only in the mind. There is no apparatus that allows us to add pressure to the vapor pressure of the solution and still leave some open surface for the vapor to exchange with the pure solvent. However, it is possible to have the exchange of solvent and to apply pressure if the two fluids are separated by a very common biological structure, a *semipermeable* membrane (Fig. 20–4). A semipermeable membrane is a membrane which allows the passage of very small molecules but which has pores too small for bigger molecules. Thus, if it encloses a sugar solution, it allows the passage of water but not of sugar.

Because of the lower vapor pressure of water in the solution, the pressure exerted by water molecules in the pores of the semipermeable membrane on the solution side is less than the pressure exerted on the

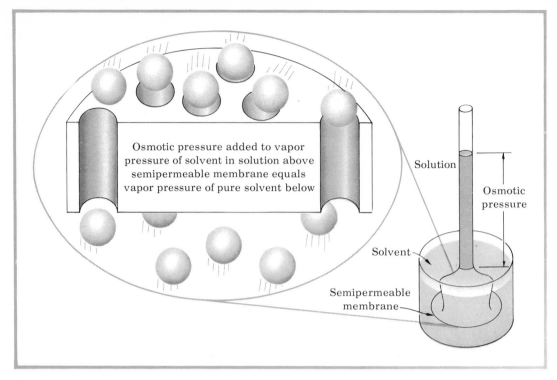

FIG. 20-4

Osmotic pressure. On the solution side of the semipermeable membrane, the solvent is under greater pressure than on the solvent side because of the extra column of liquid. This extra pressure maintains equilibrium of flow through the semipermeable membrane.

pure water side. Water tends to flow into the solution because of this pressure differential. This differential, which depends on concentration, is the *osmotic pressure*.

The actual measurement of osmotic pressure is done somewhat differently. The solution rises in the tube of the osmometer. The column of liquid then exerts a pressure on the solution side of the semipermeable membrane. This pressure, when added to the solution vapor pressure, equals the vapor pressure of the pure solvent. Hence, there is no net flow of water. The extra pressure on the solution side—the osmotic pressure of the solution—is easily computed from the height of solution in the tube.

Semipermeable membranes separate many tissues of plants and animals, and osmotic pressure has an important function in living organisms.

IONIC SOLUTIONS

What we have said about colligative properties is correct only if the solute is a covalent compound. Every example we cited —methyl alcohol, ethylene glycol, glycerine, sugar—is covalent. Solutions of ionic compounds, on the other hand, always produce larger changes. Whereas in $1M$ solutions of covalent compounds the vapor pressure is reduced 0.5 mm Hg at 25°C and the boiling point raised 0.5°C, in $1M$ solutions of NaCl (Na^+ and Cl^-) or $CuSO_4$ (Cu^{2+} and SO_4^{2-}) the vapor pressure is reduced about 1 mm Hg and the boiling point raised 1°C. In $1M$ solutions of $CaCl_2$ (Ca^{2+} and $2Cl^-$) and $(NH_4)_2CO_3$ ($2NH_4^+$ and CO_3^{2-}) the vapor pressure is reduced about 1.5 mm Hg and the boiling point raised about 1.5°C. Other ionic compounds produce comparable changes.

With our background it is not difficult to interpret this evidence though it may be surprising. But when the Swedish chemist Svante Arrhenius (1859–1927) suggested, in his doctoral thesis in 1887, that there are two kinds of chemical compounds, covalent compounds which stay as single units in solution, and ionic compounds which break into separate, independent ions in solution, his professors could not believe it. His doctoral thesis was held up. Later, however, he got the Nobel Prize for his work, the only instance in which doctoral research was so honored.

Arrhenius's reasoning went as follows. Colligative properties measure the number of particles in solution regardless of their kind. If 1 mole of NaCl changes the boiling point as much as 2 moles of sugar, it is because in NaCl solution there are 2 moles of particles—1 mole of Na^+ and 1 mole of Cl^-. Similarly, if 1 mole of $CaCl_2$ changes the vapor pressure as much as 3 moles of sugar, it is because in $CaCl_2$ solution there are 3 moles of particles, 1 mole of Ca^{2+} and 2 moles of Cl^-. Apparently, it does not matter whether the particles are uncharged or charged; their number alone determines the colligative property changes.

IONIC CONDUCTION

Colligative properties provide evidence for the existence of separate ions in water solutions of ionic compounds. This evidence is corroborated by experiments in which solutions are made part of an electric circuit with a device such as that shown in Fig. 20-5. When the electrodes are dipped into a solution of a covalent compound, the bulb does not light. The solution of the covalent compound does not conduct and the circuit is open. When the electrodes are placed in a solution of an ionic compound, on the other hand, the bulb lights. The ionic solution conducts current.

Precisely how an ionic solution conducts

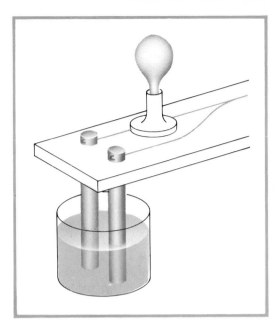

FIG. 20-5

A simple conductance apparatus. The light bulb and the electrodes dipping into the solution are connected in series. The bulb glows only when the solution conducts current.

the current can be deduced from observations of what happens in the solution and at the electrodes that dip into the solution. If the solution happens to be $CuCl_2$, gas bubbles with the strong odor of chlorine appear at the positive electrode (anode). A reddish material looking very much like copper appears at the negative electrode (cathode). Moreover, the blue color of the solution (it is due to aqueous Cu^{2+}) gradually moves toward the cathode, and if the current is left on long enough, the blue color fades entirely and conduction stops. (There is also motion of Cl^-, but it cannot be observed as easily because Cl^- ions are colorless.)

With these observations, we can explain conduction in ionic solutions. The electric current carries electrons toward the cathode. There they attract the positive Cu^{2+} ions, which consequently also move to the cathode. Then electrons join Cu^{2+} ions:

$$Cu^{2+}(aqueous) + 2e^- \longrightarrow Cu(solid)$$

(20–1)

At the same time, electrons are withdrawn by the current from the anode, which then attracts the negative Cl^- ions. They give up their electrons:

$$2Cl^-(\text{aqueous}) \longrightarrow Cl_2(\text{gas}) + 2e^-$$

$$(20\text{-}2)$$

Thus conduction through an ionic solution proceeds in three distinct steps (Fig. 20-6). In the wire there is electron flow. The current carries electrons to one electrode and withdraws them from the other. At the electrodes, electrons are obtained from negative ions and added to positive ions. There are chemical reactions at the electrodes. In the solution, ions move toward the electrodes of opposite polarity. The re-

action at the cathode removes electrons from the wire, and the anode reaction furnishes new electrons to the wire. Moreover, ion flow through the solution brings a new supply of ions to the electrodes to maintain the electrode reactions. Thus ionic conduction, requiring the flow of the separate ions in opposite directions, is additional evidence for the independence of the ions in solution.

THE DISPLACEMENT SERIES

In the conducting solution we have just described, a battery pushes electrons onto Cu^{2+} ions to produce metallic Cu atoms. This effect can be obtained without a bat-

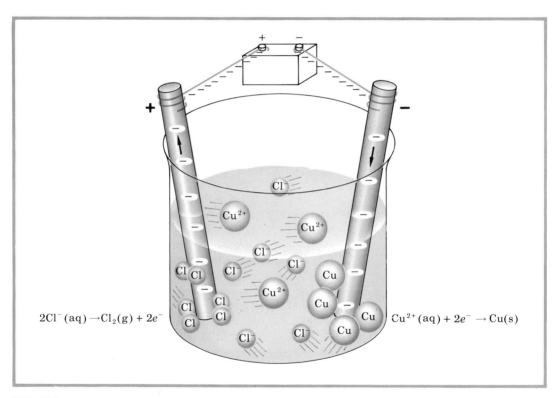

$$2Cl^-(\text{aq}) \rightarrow Cl_2(\text{g}) + 2e^-$$

$$Cu^{2+}(\text{aq}) + 2e^- \rightarrow Cu(\text{s})$$

FIG. 20-6

Ionic conduction in $CuCl_2$. Electrons flow through the wire to the cathode. There they transfer to positive Cu^{2+} ions, which settle on the cathode. To maintain current flow, more Cu^{2+} ions migrate to the cathode, and the blue color of the solution gradually fades in that direction. At the same time, the negative Cl^- ions migrate to the anode, where they transfer their extra electrons to the wire. They change to Cl_2 gas, which bubbles off. Their electrons flow back through the wire to the battery to complete the circuit.

FIG. 20-7

Almost all metals, when dipped into a solution of $CuSO_4$, produce metallic copper. The picture shows the effect of the reaction: $Zn(s) + Cu^{2+}(aq) \rightarrow Cu(s) + Zn^{2+}(aq)$.

tery by an iron nail or a strip of zinc or aluminum (Fig. 20–7). Almost all metals when dipped into a solution containing Cu^{2+} ions will react according to an equation like

$$Cu^{2+}(aq) + Zn(s) \longrightarrow$$
$$Zn^{2+}(aq) + Cu(s) \qquad (20\text{–}3)$$

As this equation shows, solid metallic Zn —the (s) indicates that Zn is a solid— pushes its electrons onto the Cu^{2+} ions— the (aq) indicates that they are in an aqueous solution—to produce Cu metal and dissolved Zn^{2+}. In this reaction the zinc displaces the copper from its combination with Cl^- ions. Consequently, it is called a *displacement* reaction.

If we look separately at what happens to the two metallic species in a displacement reaction, we find that they are involved in exactly opposite processes.

$$Cu^{2+}(aq) + 2e^- \longrightarrow Cu(s) \qquad (20\text{–}4)$$

$$Zn(s) \longrightarrow Zn^{2+}(aq) + 2e^- \qquad (20\text{–}5)$$

Aqueous copper ions add electrons to become metallic copper while metallic zinc atoms lose electrons to become aqueous zinc ions. We find the same to be true if

we study the reactions between Cu^{2+} and Al or between Cu^{2+} and Fe. In both of these cases, too, there is electron loss for one metal:

$$Al(s) \longrightarrow Al^{3+}(aq) + 3e^- \qquad (20\text{–}6)$$

$$Fe(s) \longrightarrow Fe^{2+}(aq) + 2e^- \qquad (20\text{–}7)$$

and its reverse, electron gain (Eq. 20–4), for the other metal, copper. Now suppose we reverse the direction in which we write the copper equation so that it, too, becomes an electron-loss equation:

$$Cu(s) \longrightarrow Cu^{2+}(aq) + 2e^-$$
$$(20\text{–}4 \text{ rev.})$$

Is there some way we can combine the four equations to indicate when displacement occurs and when not? Let us think of every element as an "electron pusher," although not all are equally strong in their tendency to lose electrons. A displacement reaction takes place when a stronger pusher pushes its electrons onto the ions of a weaker pusher. Thus, the fact that Zn displaces Cu^{2+} ions means that Zn is a stronger electron pusher. The fact that both Al and Fe also push their electrons onto Cu means that Cu is the weakest electron pusher of the four.

We can repeat this experiment with other pairs of the four metals. Then the notion of stronger and weaker electron pushers allows us to arrange the four elements in the order in which they displace each other. Al displaces all others. It is the strongest pusher of the four. Zn is next. While Zn^{2+} is displaced by Al, Zn in turn displaces both Fe^{2+} and Cu^{2+}. Fe displaces only Cu^{2+} and Cu displaces none of the other three. This lines up the four elements in the order in which they displace one another. This order of displacement among metals, the *displacement series,* can be extended to include other metals (Table 20–1). In it, the strongest displacers are at the top and the weakest at the bottom. Thus, the fact that Mg is given above Al means that the Mg pushes its electrons onto Al^{3+}. The Mg reaction occurs as

TABLE 20-1

Standard electrode potentials

Reaction		E^0 (volts)
Ca(s)	$= Ca^{2+}(aq) + 2e-$	2.87
Na(s)	$= Na+(aq) + e-$	2.71
Mg(s)	$= Mg^{2+}(aq) + 2e-$	2.37
Al(s)	$= Al^{3+}(aq) + 3e-$	1.66
Zn(s)	$= Zn^{2+}(aq) + 2e-$	0.76
Fe(s)	$= Fe^{2+}(aq) + 2e-$	0.44
Ni(s)	$= Ni^{2+}(aq) + 2e-$	0.25
Pb(s)	$= Pb^{2+}(aq) + 2e-$	0.13
H_2(g)	$= 2H+(aq) + 2e-$	0.00
Cu(s)	$= Cu^{2+}(aq) + 2 e-$	−0.34
$2I-(aq)$	$= I_2(s) + 2e-$	−0.54
Hg(l)	$= Hg^{2+}(aq) + 2e-$	−0.85
$2Br-(aq)$	$= Br_2(l) + 2e-$	−1.07
$2H_2O$	$= O_2(g) + 4H+(aq) + 4e-$	−1.23
$2Cr^{3+}(aq) + 7H_2O$	$= Cr_2O_7{}^{2-}(aq) + 14H+(aq) + 6e-$	−1.33
$2Cl-(aq)$	$= Cl_2(g) + 2e-$	−1.36
$Mn^{2+}(aq) + 4H_2O$	$= MnO_4-(aq) + 8H+(aq) + 5e-$	−1.51
$2F-(aq)$	$= F_2(g) + 2e-$	−2.65

shown in the table, and it is coupled with the reverse of the Al reaction:

$$Al^{3+}(aq) + 3e- \longrightarrow Al(s)$$

(20–6 rev.)

for an overall reaction

$$3Mg(s) + 2Al^{3+}(aq) \longrightarrow 3Mg^{2+}(aq) + 2Al(s)$$

(20–8)

The lower element in the displacement series always accepts electrons from the one listed above and, consequently, its equation is reversed from the way it is shown in the table. In this way the displacement series summarizes a large number of reactions.

ELECTROCHEMICAL CELLS

In displacement reactions, electrons transfer whenever an ion of one element happens to bump into the atoms of another element. At the point of contact there is electron flow, but the electron flow is wasted in a sense. The electrons that jump from the atoms to the ions cannot be used for electrical work. One needs to prevent the direct transfer and to put a wire in between in order to obtain useful energy from the displacement reaction. This can be arranged. The apparatus in Fig. 20–8 produces electric current from displacement reactions. In this apparatus direct contact between ions of one kind and atoms of another is prevented. Two metal electrodes dip into solutions of their own ions, and the solutions are carefully separated. The electrodes are connected by a wire and the solutions by another ionic solution, called a *salt bridge*. The entire setup is called an *electrochemical cell*.

The electrochemical cell shown consists of Cu dipping into $CuSO_4$ solution, Zn dipping into $ZnSO_4$ solution, and a salt bridge connecting the two solutions. While direct contact between Zn atoms and Cu^{2+} ions is not possible, electrons still flow. At the Zn electrode, Zn atoms push off their electrons to the wire and enter the solution as Zn^{2+} ions. The electrons travel to the Cu electrode, where they add to Cu^{2+} ions, which are changed into Cu atoms.

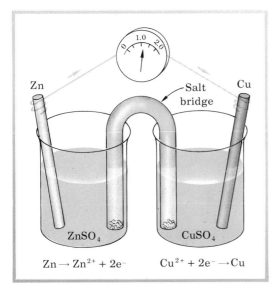

FIG. 20-8

Zn → Zn²⁺ + 2e⁻   Cu²⁺ + 2e⁻ → Cu

Apparatus for producing and measuring the current of electrochemical cells. Zn loses electrons to the wire and Zn^{2+} ions enter the solution. The electrons flow through the wire to the Cu electrode where they add to Cu^{2+} ions, which settle out as Cu atoms. Ion flow through the salt bridge maintains electroneutrality in the two solutions while preventing the mixing of ions.

Thus the cell reaction is the same as that when a Zn strip is in contact with $CuSO_4$. However, the electrode reactions would stop if there were no means to offset the effects of the reaction because Zn^{2+} would pile up near the Zn electrode while SO_4^{2-} would be left in excess near the Cu electrode. To prevent this is the function of the salt bridge. It provides a path for ion flow. Negative ions flow through the salt bridge from the $CuSO_4$ compartment to the $ZnSO_4$ compartment. The ion flow keeps the solutions electrically neutral, and further electron flow occurs through the wire. In electrochemical cells which use the displacement reactions to produce electric current, the reactions take place in two parts at the two electrodes, ions flow through the solutions, and electrons flow through the wire connecting them.

The Zn-Cu electrochemical cell had considerable importance in the days when tele-graph lines strung along railroad tracks were the chief means for communication. A modification of the above apparatus, called the Daniell cell (Fig. 20–9), powered these telegraph lines. Instead of a salt bridge, the Daniell cell had a porous porcelain cup. The cup prevented the mixing of the $ZnSO_4$ with the $CuSO_4$, yet it permitted the passage of SO_4^{2-} ions needed to keep the cell operating. While the Daniell cell has passed into history, other electrochemical cells are in wide use. The common flashlight "batteries" produce current from a complex $Zn—MnO^2—NH_4Cl$ displacement reaction. We shall not discuss it. The lead storage battery commonly used in automobiles and more recently in Ni—Cd storage battery are other electrochemical cells.

In the lead storage battery both electrodes dip into the same ionic solution H_2SO_4. The electrodes are made of metallic Pb and the insoluble lead compound, PbO_2, respectively (Fig. 20–10). When they produce current, both electrode materials change to $PbSO_4$, which is also insoluble and adheres to the electrode surfaces as the reaction proceeds:

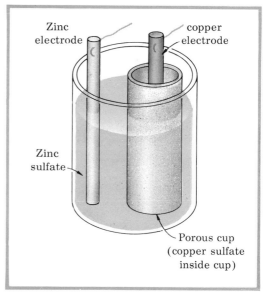

FIG. 20-9

The Daniell cell. Ion transfer between the $ZnSO_4$ and $CuSO_4$ solutions occurs through the pores of a porcelain cup.

$$Pb(s) + SO_4{}^{2-}(aq) \longrightarrow PbSO_4(s) + 2e^-$$

$$(20\text{--}9)$$

$$2e^- + PbO_2(s) + 4H^+(aq) + SO_4{}^{2-}(aq)$$
$$\longrightarrow PbSO_4(s) + 2H_2O$$

$$(20\text{--}10)$$

Equation 20–9 shows the reaction which furnishes electrons to the wires while the reaction given by Eq. 20–10 takes them up.

The most significant aspect of the lead storage battery is that an impressed current, from the automobile generator, can reverse the processes of Eqs. 20–9 and 20–10 many, many times without destroying the battery. The reverse processes, called charging of the battery, form Pb again at one electrode and PbO_2 again at the other. But the real key to charging is the fact that $PbSO_4$ adheres to the electrode surface. Because $PbSO_4$ remains on the electrode, the essential materials for both discharge and charge of the battery are in contact with the electric circuits when they are needed. If the $PbSO_4(s)$ were not there, if it fell off the electrode surfaces, or if Pb^{2+} ions were freely floating around in the solution, the reversal could not take

place and recharging would be impossible. In fact, reversibility is theoretically possible with all electrochemical cells. In practice only a few, like the lead storage battery, can be reversed efficiently. The Daniell cell, for instance, cannot be reversed in practice because the Cu metal produced on discharge fails to adhere to the electrode surface. It falls to the bottom of the $CuSO_4$ compartment, where the impressed current cannot reach it. Hence the cell spends itself on discharge.

STANDARD ELECTRODE POTENTIALS

The displacement reaction can be converted into current-producing electrochemical cells by the appropriate design of the apparatus. Now currents have voltages, and voltages measure potential difference. The potential difference between the reactions at the two electrodes turns out to be the difference in "electron-pushing power," to which we referred before. One only needs to connect a voltmeter to the apparatus shown in Fig. 20–8 to obtain a numerical measure

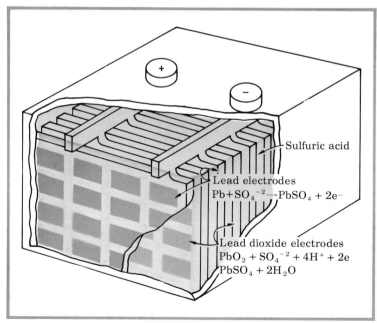

The lead storage battery.

FIG. 20-10

of electron-pushing power, although one must take into account one other factor to make the series completely quantitative. The voltage generated by an electrochemical cell depends on the concentration of ions in solution. Hence one must use the same concentration of ions in all measurements. The common reference concentration is a $1M$ solution of the metallic ion. Each electrode consists of a metal strip dipping into a $1M$ solution. This is called the *standard electrode.*

The potential generated by the standard electrode is related to the ionization energy (Chap. 19) of an atom because both measure a tendency to lose electrons. However, there are three important differences between the measurements: the state of the metal is different; the state of the ions is different; and the process by which electrons are lost is different. The ionization energy refers to the interaction of gaseous atoms with energy to produce gaseous ions and an electron:

$$M(g) \longrightarrow M^+(g) + e^- \qquad (20\text{--}11)$$

In this kind of experiment single gaseous atoms interact with light or cathode rays to produce free, gaseous ions. No other chemical species is involved. The potential of the standard electrode, on the other hand, is for a reaction of the solid atoms to produce aqueous ions and electrons:

$$M(s) \longrightarrow M^+(aq) + e^- \qquad (20\text{--}12)$$

Furthermore, and this is the most important difference, the potential of a standard electrode cannot be obtained except when one electrode is connected to another. The measurement invariably must be done for pairs of electrodes, pairs of chemical species. Nevertheless, the order of reactivities in the two cases is approximately the same. The factors relating to the state of the atoms and the state of the ions are relatively less important than the energy required to lose electrons.

The fact that voltages must be measured for pairs of electrodes means that it is impossible to obtain the standard electrode potential of any single standard electrode. The standard zinc electrode cannot be measured except with some other standard electrode. Thus the 1.10 volts generated by connecting standard Zn and Cu electrodes measure the electron-push potential of Zn less the electron-push potential of Cu against which the electrons are pushed from Zn atoms onto Cu^{2+} ions. Any other measurement of the potentials generated by standard electrodes, likewise, gives the difference between the electron-push potentials of the two electrodes.

When measurements cannot be referred to a natural zero (as in the temperature scale before Kelvin), an arbitrary zero is chosen to which all measurements are referred. An unusual electrode serves as the reference point for *standard electrode potentials.* It consists of $H_2(g)$ flowing past an electrode of the inert metal platinum, which is dipping into a solution containing $1M$ H^+ ions (Fig. 20–11). The platinum is inert and serves merely as the place for electron exchange and as a conductor of

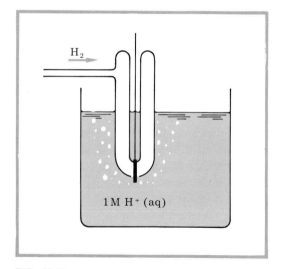

FIG. 20-11

The standard hydrogen electrode. H_2 gas at 1 atm pressure bubbles around an inert electrode of finely divided platinum metal dipping into a solution of $1M$ $H^+(aq)$. The platinum serves merely as a point of contact between electrons, H^+ ions, and H_2 gas.

electrons. It takes no part in the chemical reaction of the *standard hydrogen electrode,* which is

$$H_2(g) \longrightarrow 2H^+(aq) + 2e^- \qquad (20\text{-}13)$$

This is the reference point for which a 0.00-volt electron-push potential—and also a 0.00-electron-pull potential—is assumed. This means that one assumes that the electrons in Eq. 20-13 flow from right to left and from left to right without any resistance so that the voltage measured between this electrode and any other standard electrode is entirely due to the other standard electrode. For instance, the Zn electrode connected to the standard hydrogen electrode generates 0.76 volt. This is treated as if it were entirely due to the electron push of Zn atoms. Hence the standard electrode potential of the Zn standard electrode is 0.76 volt. The Cu electrode connected to the standard hydrogen electrode produces a potential of 0.34 volt. In this case, however, the voltmeter indicates that the electrons flow to the Cu^{2+} ions so that the electron-push potential of Cu is 0.34 volt less than that of the hydrogen electrode. This makes the standard electrode potential of Cu -0.34 volt. Measurements of this sort produced the standard electrode potentials of the reactions of the displacement series given in Table 20-1. From them one can obtain the voltage generated by a given displacement reaction.

To use the standard electrode potentials in Table 20-1, we begin exactly as before. The fact that Mg is listed above H_2 means that Mg transfers electrons onto H^+ ions. But now we look at the right-hand column to find that this reaction produces current flowing with a potential difference of 2.37 volts. Compared to the other numbers listed, 2.37 volts is relatively large. Mg is quite reactive compared to most other materials and vigorously displaces H^+ ions.

For the Al-Zn reaction we proceed similarly. Al being listed above Zn means that Al displaces Zn^{2+} from solution. The reaction proceeds according to:

$$2Al(s) + 3Zn^{2+}(aq) \longrightarrow$$
$$2Al^{3+}(aq) + 3Zn(s)$$
$$(20\text{-}14)$$

The standard electrode potential for Al, 1.66 volts, is for the electron-pushing tendency of Al. The standard electrode potential of Zn, 0.76 volt, is likewise for the electron-pushing tendency of Zn. Hence the standard electrode potential of Al must work against the standard electrode potential of Zn. The cell voltage is the difference between the two, 0.90 volt. This displacement is less vigorous than the one for Mg-H_2.

The Mg-Hg cell is another illustration of the use of the table of standard electrode potentials. Mg is listed above Hg, and so the reaction occurs according to the equation:

$$Mg(s) + Hg^{2+}(aq) \longrightarrow$$
$$Mg^{2+}(aq) + Hg(l)$$
$$(20\text{-}15)$$

The standard electrode potential listed for Mg implies that Mg pushes its electrons with 2.37 volts onto H^+ in the standard hydrogen electrode. The negative voltage, -0.85 for the Hg standard electrode, implies that the standard hydrogen electrode in turn pushes electrons onto Hg^{2+} ions. Consequently, for the Mg-Hg cell, the two voltages add, giving a net voltage of 3.22 volts, another vigorous reaction.

The voltage relationships may be easier to follow with the aid of a diagram. Figure 20-12 contains a few of the standard electrode potentials listed as if they were on a thermometer scale. Then:

1. Electron flow is from the higher listing to the lower listing.

2. The distance between the two listings is the voltage generated by the cell.

3. Electron flow occurs as written for the higher-listed electrode; it occurs in the reverse direction from that written for the lower electrode (which also has the sign of its listed voltage reversed in the computation).

The table of standard electrode potentials allows us to compute the voltage generated

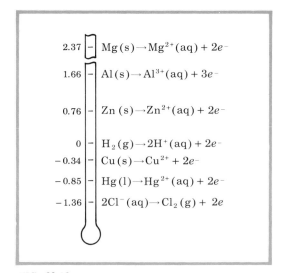

FIG. 20-12

Standard electrode potentials. Electrons are lost by the higher electrode and gained by the lower electrode, with the distance between them proportional to the voltage generated by the cell.

by different combinations of electrodes. It should be noted that not all electrodes are metallic. Reactions not involving metals in which electrons are lost or gained can be included in the table provided inert, conducting electrodes are used for electron transfer. The $H_2(g)$–$2H^+(aq)$ reaction is one example. Another is the reaction

$$2Cl^-(aq) \longrightarrow Cl_2(g) + 2e^- \qquad (20\text{–}16)$$

which occurs at an inert electrode like the hydrogen electrode.

The advantage of including all possible electron-loss reactions in the list of standard electrode potentials is that the table provides information about all kinds of chemical reactions that occur naturally. The $2Cl^-(aq)$–$Cl_2(g)$ reaction is far down the list with a standard electrode potential of −1.36 volts. This implies that, in general, the $2Cl^-(aq)$–$Cl_2(g)$ reaction occurs naturally in the reverse direction. That is, $Cl_2(g)$ readily picks up electrons from some other material to form $Cl^-(aq)$ ions. Moreover, the large positive potential generated when Eq. 20–16 occurs in the reverse direction confirms the ease of the electron-gain for Cl_2 and the relative stability of the Cl^- ion. Analogous reasoning leads us to the relative stability of $Hg(l)$, rather than $Hg^{2+}(aq)$, and $Mn^{2+}(aq)$ rather than $MnO_4^-(aq)$ (another complex electron-exchange reaction). The voltage generated by a cell, in other words, is a measure of the ease with which the reaction proceeds, and easy reactions lead to stable products. Thus we can add a fourth point regarding standard electrode potentials:

4. Large positive voltages imply ready reaction and stable products.

Questions and Problems

1. Compute the weights of $C_3H_8O_3$ required for the solutions on page 321.

2. Compute the weights of the solute required for each of the following solutions:
   (*a*) ½ liter of 0.20M Li_2SO_4
   (*b*) 2.5 liters of 1.2M NaOH
   (*c*) 0.8 liters of 4.5M $Ba(NO_3)_2$
   (*d*) 7.2 liters of 0.75M $C_6H_{12}O_6$

3. Compute the molarity of the solutions prepared in each of the following cases:
   (*a*) 43 grams of $(NH_4)_3PO_4$ to make 0.8 liter
   (*b*) 18 grams of C_2H_6O to make 1.8 liters
   (*c*) 223 grams of $AlCl_3$ to make 2.2 liters
   (*d*) 427 grams of K_2SO_4 to make 0.9 liter

4. Name the colligative properties. In what way are they unusual as solvent-solute interactions?

5. Explain vapor-pressure lowering in terms of kinetic theory. Explain its relation to the boiling point of the solution.

6. 1 gal (about 3,600 grams) of methyl alcohol is used in a 15-liter cooling system. Determine the molarity of the solution. The freezing point is reduced 1.86° × M. At what temperature °C will the radiator freeze? Convert to °F.

7. Repeat the computations of Question 6 for ethylene glycol.

8. Explain why the accumulation of Zn^{2+} ions near the Zn electrode and SO_4^{2-} ions

near the Cu electrode prevents further reaction of the electrochemical cell in Fig. 20–8.

9. Suggest several electrochemical cells which could deliver current at a voltage of at least 3.0 volts; of 4.0 volts; of 5.0 volts.

10. Determine the voltages for the following reactions. Which occur spontaneously?

(a) $2F_2(g) + 2H_2O = 4F^-(aq) + O_2(g) + 4H^+(aq)$

(b) $I_2(s) + 2Cl^-(aq) = 2I^-(aq) + Cl_2(g)$

(c) $3Cu(s) + Cr_2O_7^{2-}(aq) + 14H^+(aq)$
$= 3Cu^{2+}(aq) + 2Cr^{3+}(aq) + 7H_2O$

(d) $Ni(s) + Fe^{2+}(aq) = Fe(s) + Ni^{2+}(aq)$

(e) $Ca(s) + Hg^{2+}(aq) = Hg(l) + Ca^{2+}(aq)$

11. Describe what happens in all parts of the apparatus when one electrode in Fig. 20–8 is Al dipping into $Al(NO_3)_3$ solution and the other is Ni dipping into $Ni(NO_3)_2$ solution, with KNO_3 solution in the salt bridge.

12. Predict the freezing points of $1M$ solutions of:

(a) $Al_2(SO_4)_3$ (d) magnesium chloride
(b) K_2CO_3 (e) iron (III) nitrate
(c) $(NH_4)_3PO_4$ (f) cobalt (II) bromide

(A $1M$ solution of a covalent compound freezes at $-1.86°C$.)

13. Molten NaCl conducts current. Solid NaCl does not. Explain. Suggest how a compound might be tested to determine whether it is ionic. What if it is insoluble in water?

14. List three differences between standard electrode potential and ionization energy. Suggest factors that influence each difference.

15. More current is required to produce 1 mole of Al from its solution than 1 mole of Cu from its solution. Explain.

16. Estimate the solubility in grams/100 ml water for NaCl at 20°C; KCl at 70°C; Na_2SO_4 at 50°C; K_2SO_4 at 80°C. Convert to moles/100 ml.

17. A common test to see whether a compound is an iodide, bromide, or chloride involves the addition of chlorine dissolved in water. If the compound is an iodide, I_2 forms and can be identified by its purple color with a few drops of carbon tetrachloride. If it is a bromide, Br_2 forms and appears pink in carbon tetrachloride. With reference to Table 20–1, explain the chemical basis for this test.

Suggestions for Further Reading

Ionic solutions and electrochemistry are discussed in:

Sienko, Michell J., and Robert A. Plane: *Chemistry*, 2d ed., McGraw-Hill Book Company, Inc., New York, 1961. Chapters 10 and 14.

Christiansen, G. S., and Paul H. Garrett: *Structure and Change*, W. H. Freeman and Company, San Francisco, 1960. Chapters 13, 14, 19, 21, and 22.

Quagliano, James V.: *Chemistry*, 2d ed., Prentice-Hall, Inc., Englewood Cliffs, N. J., 1963. Chapters 15 to 19.

Sisler, Harry H., Calvin A. Vander Werf, and Arthur W. Davidson: *College Chemistry*, 2d ed., The Macmillan Company, New York, 1961. Chapters 13 to 16, 19.

Bonds and Structure

In solutions of ionic compounds the ions are far apart, interactions are negligible, and the ions behave as independent species. In ionic solids, on the other hand, the ions are close together, attractions and repulsions between them are strong. Most of the properties of ionic solids can be related to these interactions.

Solids with covalent bonds reflect the characteristics of their bonds also, and metals, which have a chemically unique bond, have properties that depend on the character of the metallic bond. The structure and properties of all solids can be traced back to the bonds which hold their constituents together.

335

IONIC SOLIDS

The basic structural unit of ionic solids is the ion, and the bonding force is the attraction between ions of opposite charge. Crystals of NaCl or MgO or Li_2SO_4 or NH_4NO_3 result from the electrostatic attraction (and repulsion) between the positive ions, Na^+, Mg^{2+}, Li^+, or NH_4^+, and the negative ions Cl^-, O^{2-}, SO_4^{2-}, or NO_3^-. Now, an important characteristic of electrostatic forces is that they are nondirectional; the force of attraction varies with distance only. Thus any given ion can form as many bonds as there are ions of opposite charge around it, and the strength of the bonds depends only on the interionic distances. For instance, in the NaCl crystal (Fig. 21–1), Na^+ and Cl^- ions do not pair. Every Na^+ ion is surrounded by six Cl^- ions, each at a distance of 2.81 A (angstrom unit = 10^{-8} cm), and similarly, every Cl^- ion is surrounded by six equidistant Na^+ ions. Thus there are six "bonds" per ion. Ionic bonding links each ion to all its neighbors throughout the crystal without breaks. The entire crystal is one giant, chemically bonded unit.

This microscopic situation is reflected in the macroscopic properties of ionic solids.

They are hard and rigid because of the strong bonds throughout. Typically, they melt at fairly high temperatures. This also shows the strength and stability of the bonding. Molten ionic compounds typically remain liquid over fairly large ranges of temperature (NaCl from about 800 to about 1400°C), showing that there remain strong bonding forces—electrostatic attractions— even when the order of the crystal breaks down. Their heats of vaporization, the energy required to tear single units from the molten liquid, are also quite large, again indicating the strength of the interionic attraction.

Another result of the arrangement of ions in the crystal lattice is the appearance of grains of salt (Fig. 10–1a). The right-angle corners and the square or rectangular faces of the crystal reflect the small cubes that are the basic units of the NaCl crystal lattice. When NaCl crystals fracture, as they do with difficulty because of the strong forces of attraction, fracture occurs along a plane of ions in the crystal and the same geometric features are reestablished.

Cubic arrangement of atoms in solids is quite common though it may vary from the NaCl arrangement and is by no means necessary. CsCl is also cubic. Externally,

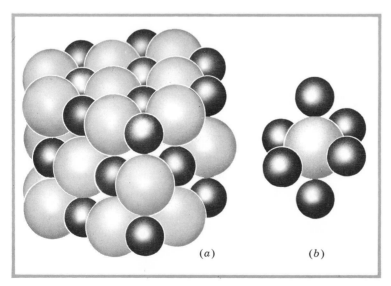

(a)   (b)

Model of the NaCl crystal. Each Na+ ion is surrounded symmetrically by six Cl− ions, and each Cl− ion by six Na+ ions. This arrangement continues in three dimensions throughout the crystal.

FIG. 21-1

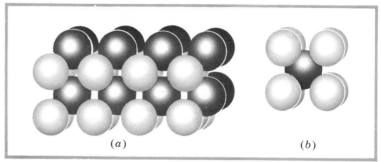

Model of the CsCl crystal. Each Cs+ ion is surrounded by eight Cl− ions, each Cl− ion by eight Cs+ ions, and each set of eight ions forms a small cube.

(a) (b)

FIG. 21-2

CsCl crystals are almost identical to NaCl crystals, but internally they differ markedly. In CsCl each ion is surrounded by eight, not six, neighbors of opposite charge (Fig. 21–2). Calcite crystals reflect a more complex crystal pattern (Fig. 10–1b). Its ions are located to form hexagons, and the crystal faces show the 60° angles typical of that arrangement. Whatever the exact geometry, however, in all ionic crystals, rigidity and firmness are the result of the electrostatic attractions between ions of opposite charge.

COVALENT SOLIDS

Covalent molecules are discrete units. The bonding extends until all atoms within the molecule attain stable filled shells through electron sharing. Then no further bonding occurs. The unit is complete. Crystals of covalent molecules reflect the completeness of bonding *within* molecules. No chemical bonding forces extend beyond the single units because all bonding orbitals are filled. Consequently intermolecular forces in covalent compounds are weak. Covalent crystals are soft, low-melting. The compounds also have low heats of vaporization.

The simple covalent compounds :I:I: illustrates these characteristics of covalent solids. Bonding occurs between pairs of iodine atoms; all other attractions in the crystal are weak and barely hold the molecules together. Solid iodine is soft; it readily sublimes because single molecules easily

leave their neighbors. Iodine crystals melt at a low temperature, 113°C. Forces in the liquid are equally weak, and the liquid boils at 184°C, only 71° higher.

Particularly good evidence for the difference between covalent crystals and ionic crystals comes from X-ray measurements of distances between iodine atoms. In solid iodine there are two I-I distances (Fig. 21–3). Each atom is paired with one other atom at the close distance of 2.70 A. This is the distance between atoms joined by the covalent bond. Then there are other atoms at a distance of 3.54 A. This is the distance to atoms from other molecules which are attracted by very weak forces only. Such weak intermolecular forces, too weak to be considered chemical bonds in

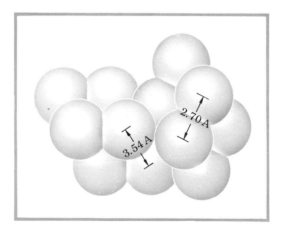

FIG. 21-3

Model of the I₂ crystal. There are two I-I distances, 2.70 A between pairs of covalently bonded atoms and 3.54 A to the nonbonded atoms.

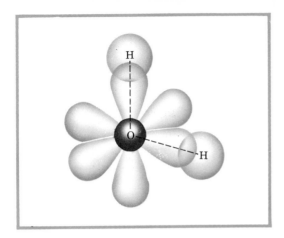

FIG. 21-4

Bond angles in H_2O. Electrons fully occupy the 2s orbitals and one 2p orbital of oxygen. The other 2p orbitals, which are at right angles to each other, can be shared by the hydrogen atoms. Hence the expected H—O—H angle is 90°.

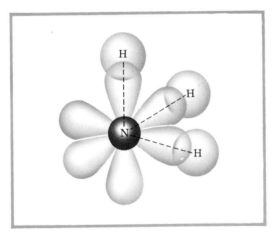

FIG. 21-5

Bond angles in NH_3. Each of the 2p orbitals of N can be shared with a hydrogen atom. The expected H—N—H angles are 90°, and the expected structure for the molecules is pyramidal.

the ordinary sense, are called *van der Waals forces.* The weak van der Waals forces are also responsible for deviations of gases from ideal behavior due to sticking of molecules (Chap. 11).

There is a sharp contrast between ionic solids and covalent solids. In ionic solids

the strong attractions between ions of opposite charge extend throughout the crystal. The crystals are hard and strong. In covalent solids strong bonds terminate within each separate molecule. Intermolecular forces are weak and the compounds are soft.

BOND ANGLES

There is one other important difference between ionic and covalent solids. Since ions are like small charged spheres, the structure of ionic compounds is determined by maximum attractions between ions of opposite charge and minimum repulsion between ions of like charge. The bonds are nondirectional, and there is no specific molecular structure. Covalent bonds are entirely different. The covalent bond results from the sharing of a specific electron pair in specific orbitals of two atoms. These orbitals overlap in space so that the electrons in them can complete the valence shell of both. Hence, the shared electron pair is localized between two atoms and the geometry of the molecule follows the geometry of orbitals.

Let us take H:O:H as an example. The hydrogens use 1s orbitals for sharing electron pairs. These are nondirectional and have no implications for the geometry of H_2O. Oxygen, with an electron configuration of $1s^2$, $2s^2$, $2p^4$, has the 2s orbitals and one 2p orbital of its valence shell fully occupied. Its two other 2p orbitals, which have only one electron in them, are used for bond formation. These are the orbitals which overlap with the H orbitals and which share electrons (Fig. 21–4). p orbitals are perpendicular to one another in space. Consequently H_2O molecules are bent with an angle of 90° between the H—O bonds expected.

Similar considerations suggest the geometry of NH_3. Since N has the electronic configuration $1s^2$, $2s^2$, $2p^3$, the bonding orbitals in N also are $2p$ orbitals. The 90° angles between the p orbitals then indicate a pyramidal structure for NH_3 (Fig. 21–5).

Actually the bond angles in H_2O and NH_3 are not exactly 90° but 105° and 107° respectively. Angles of 90° between the bonds crowd the hydrogen atoms around the small oxygen and nitrogen atoms. Consequently the bonds spread somewhat to relieve the crowding. In H_2S, on the other hand, the crowding is not severe because the S atom is larger. The angle between the two S—H bonds is 92.2°, close to the predicted 90°.

These examples indicate how orbital geometry influences the geometry of molecules as well. Unfortunately, the situation becomes more complex in the compound CH_4 and carbon compounds in general. The electronic configuration of carbon, $1s^2$, $2s^2$, $2p^2$, suggests two bonds at the end of the vacant $2p$ orbital with the other two bonds using the other p orbitals at right angles to the first. Methane, then, would have a pair of bonds 180° apart and the other two at 90° (Fig. 21–6). That is not what experiment shows. There is no distinction among the CH bonds in CH_4. All bonds and bond angles are identical. The structure is that of a regular tetrahedron (Fig. 21–7).

This unexpected bond geometry has been studied in considerable detail and can be explained quite well. (Obviously we have to accept the experimental evidence whether we can explain it or not.) There is a principle which suggests that the strongest covalent bonds form when the overlap between the bonding orbitals is greatest. p orbitals, which are directional, can overlap greatly. However, when an atom forms four covalent bonds, the strongest bonding results from four equivalent orbitals which extend farther into space toward the corners of a regular tetrahedron and thus can overlap still better. These more symmetrical orbitals are called *tetrahedral orbitals*.

One consequence of the specific geo-

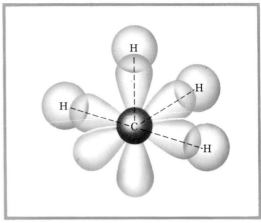

FIG. 21-6

Expected bond angles in CH_4. With one 2p orbital empty and the others half filled, one might expect two H atoms at the ends of the empty orbital and the others at 90° to them. This is not the case.

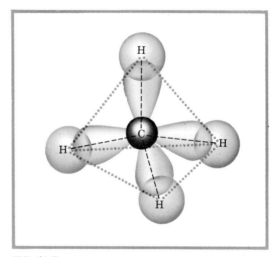

FIG. 21-7

Tetrahedral bond angles. When an atom forms four covalent bonds, the strongest bonds result if the orbitals face the corners of a regular tetrahedron. This is the structure of CH_4 and of most C compounds.

metric structure of molecules is that the crystals must accommodate that structure. This leads to some extremely interesting arrangements. In the structure of solid water (Fig. 21–8), for instance, the hydrogens of one molecule always face toward oxygens from other molecules. This pro-

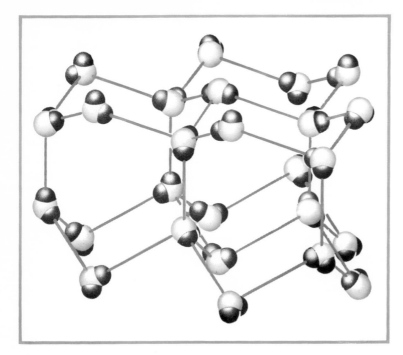

Model of the ice crystal. Hydrogen bonding to other oxygen atoms produces an open structure.

FIG. 21-8

duces an open structure, with much empty space between and is the reason for the expansion of water on freezing. The reason the hydrogens always face toward another oxygen is also interesting. It is another example of the dependence of structure on bonding. But it is bonding of a different kind, which we shall approach through a more detailed study of the interactions in solutions.

SOLUTIONS

Solubility, as we pointed out in the previous chapter, is a specific property of solvent and solute (Fig. 20–1). Each compound seems to interact with the solvent in a quite specific manner. Nevertheless, there are several limited rules governing solubility:

1. In general, ionic compounds dissolve in water but not in covalent liquids like gasoline or kerosene.

2. In general, covalent compounds dissolve in covalent liquids but not in water.

3. However, as pointed out before, there

are many compounds which dissolve in neither and a few compounds that dissolve in both.

This is the extent to which we can generalize solubilities. (Since we feel that we "understand" a topic when we can give precise rules for behavior, this means that solutions and solubility are poorly understood. It is a field that is being actively investigated.)

Now the solubility rules place water in a very peculiar position. It is itself a covalent compound, and yet it dissolves mostly ionic compounds. This seems strange. Even stranger is the fact that ionic compounds dissolve at all. In the first section of this chapter we stressed the strength of the ionic bonds in ionic crystals and the large amounts of energy needed to tear ionic crystals apart.

We can get some insight into the peculiar character of water if we contrast the solubility of the covalent compound I_2 in water and in heptane, a covalent constituent of gasoline. The solubility of I_2 in heptane is about 100 times as great as its solubility in water. This is in accord with the solubility rules. What does it tell us about water?

Four factors govern the solubility of a compound in another compound: (1) a fundamental principle of thermodynamics (the study of energy relationships), which states that all molecules tend to disperse, to take up states of greater randomness; this principle favors any solution over the corresponding separate solvent and solute because the dispersed molecules of solute in the solvent are in a state of greater randomness; (2) the energy required to overcome attractive forces between separate solute molecules; (3) the energy required to separate the solvent molecules in order to admit solute molecules; (4) the energy produced by new attractions between adjacent solute and solvent molecules; if these are strong, they may offset the attractions within the solute or the solvent.

In the I_2-water and I_2-heptane solutions, factors 1 and 2 are identical. The molecules in solution are in the favored state of greater randomness, and I_2 is the solute in both cases. Factors 3 and 4 differ, and the lower solubility of I_2 in water indicates that either water molecules do not separate as easily as heptane molecules to admit the I_2, or the water–I_2 attractions are much less than the heptane–I_2 attractions. Both factors could operate simultaneously.

Since both heptane and I_2 are covalent compounds, their molecules do not attract each other strongly. Strong bonding in covalent compounds is limited to the atoms within single molecules. It does not extend from molecule to molecule. Factor 4 does not provide a likely explanation for the greater solubility of I_2 in heptane. This leaves the other alternative. Despite the fact that water is covalent, its molecules seem to attract each other very strongly.

POLAR COMPOUNDS

As we shall see, the solubility of I_2 is only one bit of evidence which points to strong bonds between water molecules. Furthermore, water is not the only covalent compound which shows this peculiarity. There are many other covalent compounds which show intermolecular attractions much stronger than those due to van der Waals forces. This peculiar bonding arises whenever, for one reason or another, covalent bonds form despite a large electronegativity difference between the bonded atoms that normally leads to ionic bonding. One of the special reasons is the difficulty of removing a large number of electrons from an atom or adding a large number of electrons to an atom. CF_4 is covalent, for instance, despite the large electronegativity difference between C and F because C^{4+} does not form (nor does C^{4-}). Indeed, ions with large charges, like X^{4+}, X^{3+}, X^{3-} and X^{4-}, are rare because of unfavorable energy relationships. Usually covalent bonds form instead.

A second special reason for covalent bonds rather than ionic bonds is the instability of the ion H^+. H^+ is a bare nucleus, a proton without any electrons around it. That ion is not a stable chemical species, and H^+ ions are never found alone. Compounds like H_2O and HF are covalent, not ionic.

But the covalent bonds in these compounds are not quite like ordinary covalent bonds. While the complete transfer of an electron to the more electronegative element does not occur, the shared electron pair is not shared equally between the bonded atoms as in $:\overset{..}{\underset{..}{I}}:\overset{..}{\underset{..}{I}}:$ or $H:H$. Instead, the more electronegative element claims more than an equal share of the bonding electrons, and the other element, correspondingly, has less than an equal share. This makes the covalent bond somewhat like an ionic bond. Through unequal sharing, some part of the charge moves toward the more electronegative element, leaving the bond slightly negative at one end and slightly positive at the other. There is a dipole along the bond. Thus the unequal

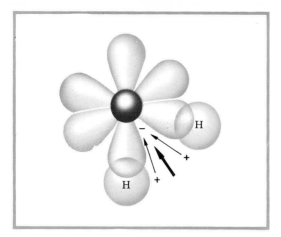

FIG. 21-9

Polar compounds. Because of its greater electronegativity, oxygen tends to draw shared electron pairs closer. This makes the oxygen end of the bonds slightly negative and the hydrogen end slightly positive. The contributions of the two polar bonds add to make the molecule as a whole polar.

electronegativity of the bonded atoms leads to *polar covalent bonds*, with small dipolar electrostatic fields (Fig. 21–9). Since these dipolar fields extend beyond the molecules

according to the laws of electrostatics, they produce intermolecular interactions of some magnitude. Compounds with polar bonds, *polar compounds,* are intermediate between pure covalent compounds, with no purely electrostatic fields outside the molecules, and ionic compounds, in which ions are bonded exclusively by electrostatic attractions.

There is direct evidence for the existence of polar bonds. When polar gases are placed between the plates of a charged condenser, the charge which it can hold without leakage increases. This happens because the field on the charged plates tends to reduce the random thermal motions (Fig. 21–10) and to line up the polar molecules with their positive ends near the negative plate and the negative ends near the positive plate. The fields of the nearby polar bonds oppose the fields of the condenser and permit a measurable increase in the plate charge.

Direct dipole measurements, the characteristics of solids and liquids, and solubility data confirm the existence of polar

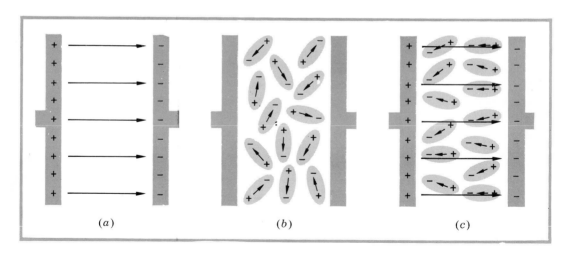

(a)   (b)   (c)

FIG. 21-10

Measurement of molecular dipoles. (a) Without molecules, a certain amount of charge can be built up on the condenser plates. (b) Without a field, the molecules tumble around in all directions. (c) When the molecules are between charged plates, they orient in the electric field and their thermal motions are restricted. Because the small field of the dipoles opposes the field between the plates, more charge can be built up on the plates.

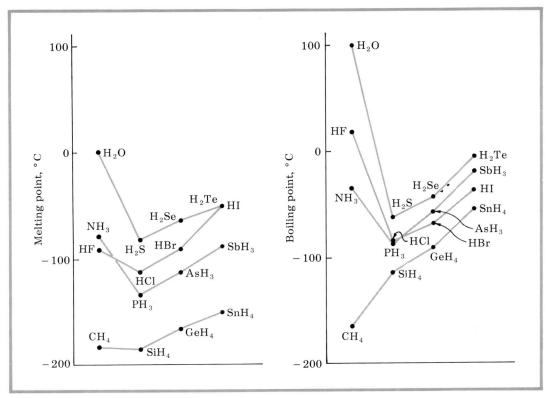

FIG. 21-11

Melting and boiling points of the hydrogen compounds of the elements of groups IVa, Va, VIa, and VIIa. The melting and boiling points of HF, H_2O, and NH_3 are clearly out of sequence because of their strong polar bonds. The effect is not as pronounced for HCl and is nonexistent for the nonpolar CH_4.

bonds in many compounds. However, the polar bonds in HF, H_2O, HCl, and NH_3 are unusually strong and lead to unexpectedly large attractions between molecules (Fig. 21–11). These can be attributed to the peculiar nature of the combined hydrogen atom.

Hydrogen is the only element without a filled electron shell. When it forms a covalent bond, it consists of a nucleus and the shared electron pair. In bonds with strongly electronegative elements, that shared pair is drawn strongly toward the other element, leaving the hydrogen an almost unshielded nucleus, a bare proton (Fig. 21–12). This very small center of positive charge can then strongly attract electron pairs from neighboring atoms to form another strong

electrostatic attraction. This kind of bonding, in which hydrogen from the strongly polar HO or HN or HF or HCl bonds actually bonds with a second strongly electronegative element, is quite common and has been given the name *hydrogen bond*. Although it involves covalent molecules, it is primarily an electrostatic interaction between the small, nearly bare hydrogen nucleus and electrons from two electronegative atoms and does not follow the orbital-filling rules of covalent bonding. Hydrogen bonds are chemically quite strong. They are responsible for the open geometry of the ice crystal which causes water to expand when freezing and for a number of features of molecular biochemistry which we shall mention in the next chapter.

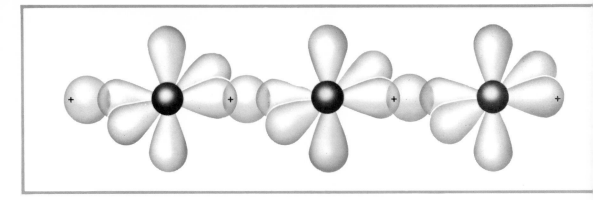

FIG. 21-12

The hydrogen bond. The polar bond between hydrogen and F, O, N, and Cl has the electron pair so far displaced toward the electronegative element that the hydrogen can be considered a bare proton. This proton can attract other electron pairs.

SOLUTIONS OF IONIC COMPOUNDS

Now we can explain the peculiar position of water as a solvent. Strong dipolar interactions between the water molecules prevent covalent compounds from entering solution. Therefore covalent substances tend to be insoluble in water. With ionic substances the situation is entirely differ-

ent. The polar water molecules slip between the ions in the crystal (Fig. 21–13). This weakens the attractions in the ionic solid and helps to break it down. Moreover, in the solution the polar water molecules surround the ions, oxygen toward positive ions and hydrogen toward negative ions. These ion-dipole interactions are strongly attractive, compensating for the disruption of previous ion-ion attractions in the solid and dipole-dipole attractions in the solvent. As

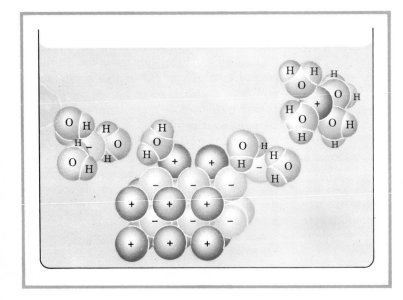

Solution of an ionic solid in water. The polar molecules slip between the ions of the crystal and reduce the interionic attractions. Then, when the ions are in solution, the polar molecules surround them, substituting ion-dipole attractions for the ion-ion attractions of the crystal.

FIG. 21-13

a result, solution of many ionic compounds in water is energetically favored.

Polar bonds thus help explain the solubility rules. Covalent substances dissolve in covalent liquids because molecules held only by weak van der Waals forces are easily dispersed to enter solution and the solvent molecules are easily parted to allow them entry. Little energy is needed, and the randomness principle governs solution. Ionic substances dissolve in polar liquids because ion-dipole interactions provide the energy needed to separate the ions and the dipolar molecules of the liquid. However, many ionic compounds are insoluble because the ion-dipole energy is not enough. Likewise, mixing ionic and covalent substances, or covalent and polar substances, does not form new attractions of sufficient energy to overcome the ion-ion or dipole-dipole bonds which must be disrupted. Hence solubility is low in these mixtures.

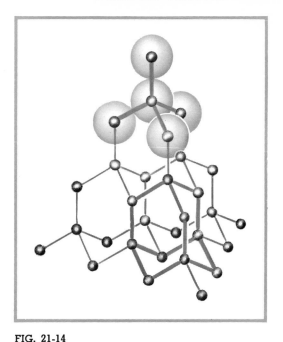

FIG. 21-14

Model of the diamond structure. All bond angles are tetrahedral and a network of six-membered rings gives diamond its hardness and rigidity.

NETWORK SOLIDS

There are two other kinds of solids, different from ionic and covalent solids—network solids and metals. As in ionic solids, their bonds extend throughout the solid structure. They are consequently hard and stable and generally insoluble. They cannot easily be broken into smaller units.

Diamond is an example of a network solid. In diamond (Fig. 21-14) carbon atoms are bonded entirely by covalent bonds. But unlike the covalently bonded crystals we have discussed so far, the covalent bonds in the diamond structure do not define discrete small molecules. In diamond the tetrahedral bonds form a network extending, via interlocking rings of six carbon atoms, throughout the entire solid. Since the covalent bonds of this network are localized in space and cannot be distorted, the entire structure is rigid and hard. Diamond is the hardest and strongest natural material known. It cannot be bent because of the rigidity of its covalently

bonded rings, and it cannot easily be broken because of the strength of the covalent bonds. Diamond is highly resistant to disruption by grinding, by heating, or by chemical means. It sublimes at a very high temperature; its melting point is not known. It is insoluble except perhaps in molten iron.

Other network solids have electron configurations which, likewise, lead to networks of covalent bonds that extend throughout the entire solid. SiC, for instance, a commonly used abrasive like diamond, differs from diamond only in having Si atoms alternate with C atoms throughout the network. Since both have four valence electrons, the basic bond structure is the same. This is also true of BN and AlN, other extremely hard network solids. While these two compounds produce their shared bonds by using five electrons from N and three from the other element, they end up with enough electrons, altogether, for four tetrahedral covalent bonds per atom. Consequently they are hard and rigid like SiC or diamond.

MINERALS

Minerals are also network solids although, except for silica, both ionic and covalent bonds are involved. The basic structural unit of minerals is the SiO_4^{4-} tetrahedron

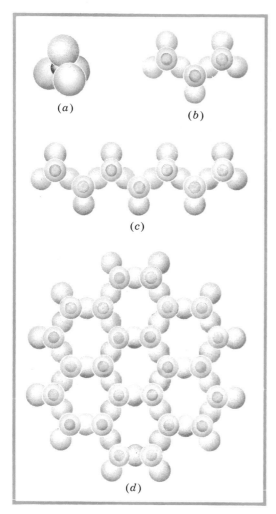

FIG. 21-15

The structure of silicate minerals. (a) The basic unit, SiO_4^{4-}. (b) A three-unit chain, $Si_3O_{10}^{8-}$. (c) An extended chain. (d) A sheet formed through the sharing of three corners of the SiO_4^{4-} tetrahedrons.

(Fig. 21–15a), in which each silicon atom is surrounded tetrahedrally by four oxygen atoms. Single tetrahedrons have a net charge of −4. However, in the minerals the tetrahedrons share one or more oxygen atoms. This reduces the net ionic charge per tetrahedron. For instance, the ion $Si_2O_7^{6-}$, two tetrahedrons sharing one corner, has a net charge of −3 per Si; the ion $Si_2O_6^{4-}$, in which two corners are shared, has a net charge of −2 per Si. These ions, however, are only the precursors of the mineral network structures. Even the simplest minerals have long chains of shared Si tetrahedrons. Thus there is strong covalent bonding in the chain direction, and the mineral has rope-like characteristics. In such minerals, of which asbestos is an example, the strands are held together by positive ions which fit between them.

In a second group of minerals three of the four tetrahedron corners are shared (Fig. 21–15d). These minerals consist of sheets of shared tetrahedrons with positive ions holding the sheets together. They have strong two-dimensional stability but easy cleavage between sheets. Mica and talc are examples of such a two-dimensional network structure.

When all four corners of the silicon tetrahedrons are shared, all electrons are used for covalent bonds. This is the three-dimensional-network mineral, silica, pure SiO_2. However, there are a large number of three-dimensional-network minerals which contain positive ions as well as silicon tetrahedrons. In these, Al and other atoms substitute for the Si at the centers of some of the tetrahedrons. Since Al has one less valence electron than Si, it must gain an electron from some other ion to form four tetrahedral bonds with the surrounding oxygen atoms. Hence, for every Al tetrahedron in the network structure there is a net change of −1. This is balanced by other positive ions, like Na^+ or K^+ or Mg^{2+} or Fe^{2+} in the mineral structure. Such ions are typically very small and fit into the

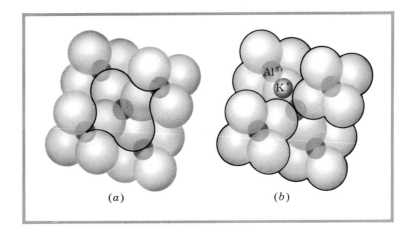

(a) (b)

FIG. 21-16

(a) *In silica all four corners of the SiO₄⁴⁻ tetrahedrons are shared with other tetra-hedrons. A fully covalent network solid results.* (b) *In many minerals some of the Si atoms are replaced by Al atoms. Since Al has only three valence electrons, an additional electron is needed for the covalent bonds. This is supplied by metals like K, Na, and Ca, which are located inside the Al-Si-O networks as the ions K+, Na+ or Ca²⁺.*

spaces between the shared tetrahedrons (Fig. 21–16).

METALLIC SOLIDS

Entirely different kinds of bonds are involved in the formation of metallic solids. Metals have relatively loose electrons in their valence shells. But they do not meet the conditions leading to bond formation as we have discussed them because there is no opportunity for electron exchange. There are electrons to be lost, but there is no place for them to go. From this point of view, the great stability of metals in the solid state is surprising. However, we have at least one additional bit of evidence which suggests that the metallic bond is different. Metallic conduction can be interpreted only through the existence of freely moving electrons, whereas in both ionic and covalent compounds electrons are localized in atomic orbitals. The best model for bonding in a metal regards the metal atoms as positive ions surrounded and held together by their valence electrons. This model, which is based on quantum-me-chanical considerations, then suggests that under the influence of the adjacent atoms, the valence shell orbitals of every atom stretch out, join, and run through the entire metallic solid. Thus the whole metal, instead of selected regions around each atom, becomes accessible to the electrons. This frees the electrons for conduction and also places them between and around the positive metal ions. The structure of metallic solids is sometimes described as positive ions immersed in a "sea of electrons," with metal ion-electron interactions serving as the bonding forces.

The extension of the available orbitals throughout the metallic crystal has a number of corollaries. As in the ionic solid, the bonding forces are nondirectional. Consequently, the atoms tend to crowd as closely as possible, and metallic solids have a structure known as *closest-packed*, one in which each atom is surrounded by twelve others. The arrangement is the same as that obtained when marbles are tossed into a crowded bag. A second corollary is the ease with which metals can be "worked": ductility, malleability. Since there is no favored bond direction in the solid, and since, more-

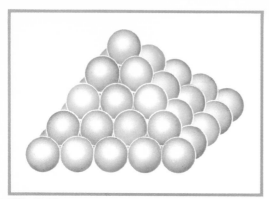

FIG. 21-17

Model of the metallic structure. The atoms are crowded together in the closest-packed arrangement to maximize contacts between them. Since dislocation reestablishes new contacts between atoms, metals can be hammered and drawn and retain their strength.

over, contact between atoms produces only attractions, deformation of the solid does not disrupt the metal structure but leads to new, again strongly attractive contacts between atoms. Thus the model explains these properties. Finally, the "sea of electrons" concept explains the high electrical and heat conductance of metals, both of which are caused by the freely moving electrons.

We have now shown that many of the properties of substances can be traced back to the characteristics of their bonds. For covalent molecules this dependence extends to their chemical behavior. In the next chapter we shall examine some of the relationships between chemical behavior and covalent bond structure.

Questions and Problems

1. Do you expect any influence of orbital geometry on the structure of the Cl_2 molecule? Explain.

2. Predict the geometry of the PH_3 molecule. What orbitals are used? Would you expect the bonds to deviate from the predicted geometry? Explain.

3. Sulfur consists of S_8 molecules which are in the form of a zigzag eight-atom ring. Show that this structure conforms to (a) orbital filling, (b) orbital geometry.

4. Contrast metallic bond, ionic bond, covalent bond, hydrogen bond, and van der Waals forces with respect to bond strength; orientation in space; dependence on orbital geometry. What factors, in each case, determine the geometry of the solids?

5. Predict the character of solid:
   (a) Ar   (c) Ni
   (b) SCl_2 (d) $NiCl_2$

6. GeO_2 is insoluble in water; it melts at 1086°C; $GeCl_4$ melts at −50°C. Explain.

Suggestions for Further Reading

The relationship between bonds and structure is discussed in:

Pauling, Linus: *College Chemistry*, 3d ed., W. H. Freeman and Company, San Francisco, 1964. Chapters 8, 9, 20, and 22.

Pimental, George C. (ed.): *Chemistry: An Experimental Science*, W. H. Freeman and Company, San Francisco, 1963. Chapters 16 and 17.

Sisler, Harry H., Calvin A. Vander Werf, and

Arthur W. Davidson: *College Chemistry*, 2d ed., The Macmillan Company, New York, 1961. Chapter 7.

Ryschkewitsch, George E.: *Chemical Bonding and the Geometry of Molecules*, Reinhold Publishing Corporation, New York, 1963 (paperback).

Sisler, Harry H.: *Electronic Structure, Properties, and the Periodic Law*, Reinhold Publishing Corporation, New York, 1963 (paperback).

Chapter 22

Organic Chemistry

Carbon has a special place among the elements. It forms few ionic compounds because the ions C^{4+} or C^{4-} are energetically unstable. On the other hand, the number and variety of covalent carbon compounds is nearly unlimited because carbon atoms have the unique property of forming stable covalent bonds with other carbon atoms. There are millions of carbon compounds in which two or more—as many as thousands—carbon atoms are linked together. Hundreds of thousands of these have been studied; indeed, the chemistry of carbon and covalent bond chemistry are nearly synonymous. But carbon chemistry is even more interesting for very personal reasons: the chemistry of life is the chemisty of carbon compounds. Whether because carbon compounds show such great variety or just by accident, the molecules of living organisms are molecules of carbon compounds. For this reason, carbon chemistry is called *organic chemistry,* and at one time it was even thought that carbon compounds could be produced only by living organisms. That view, however, was dispelled in 1828, when the German chemist Friedrich Wöhler (1800–1882) heated the ionic compound NH_4NCO and found, much to his surprise, that the organic compound of identical composition, urea, was produced. This accidental result of one of Wöhler's many researches was the precursor of today's chemical industry, which in some processes starts with even simpler materials—coke, air, and water—to produce the organic drugs, plastics, and fibers that seem indispensable to our modern civilization.

HYDROCARBONS

The simplest organic compounds are the *hydrocarbons,* compounds of carbon and hydrogen only. Of this group, the simplest compound is the one-carbon-atom methane, CH_4 (Fig. 22–1a), a tetrahedral molecule. The next member of this series is ethane, C_2H_6 (Fig. 22–1b), which has the structure of two "jacks" joined together. The three-carbon-atom hydrocarbon, propane, C_3H_8, is

next. Because of the tetrahedral geometry of the carbon bonds, the carbon backbone of propane is bent (Fig. 22–1c).

A structural variation occurs in the next hydrocarbon, butane, C_4H_{10}. The fourth carbon atom can add to the end of the propane chain to give a bent four-carbon-atom skeleton, (Fig. 22–2a), or it can bond to the middle atom of the propane chain to produce a *branched* four-carbon-atom molecule (Fig. 22–2b). Both of these have the same chemical composition C_4H_{10}, but they differ somewhat in their properties. A similar situation exists for pentane, C_5H_{12}, which can have three different structures; for hexane, C_6H_{14}, with five different structures; and indeed for all hydrocarbons larger than butane. Such different structures which have the same chemical composition are called *isomers.* Their number increases at a fantastic rate as the molecules get larger. $C_{13}H_{28}$ has 819 isomers; $C_{20}H_{42}$ more than 366,000; $C_{30}H_{62}$ more than 4 billion. Needless to say, not all possible isomers of these compounds have been prepared or isolated.

Table 22–1 summarizes some of the information about hydrocarbons. Except for the first four compounds, which have kept antique and nonsystematic names, the naming convention uses Greek-number prefixes to count the carbon atoms and the suffix *ane* to denote that the compound is a

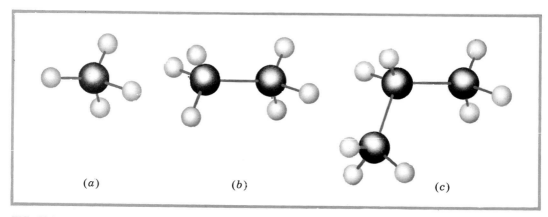

(a)   *(b)*   *(c)*

FIG. 22-1

Models of the structure of (a) *methane,* (b) *ethane, and* (c) *propane.*

hydrocarbon. Additionally, to separate iso- mers, the word *normal,* as in "normal hep- tane," is used for straight-chain isomers and *iso,* as in "isobutane," for branched iso- mers. Obviously, this is an inadequate con- vention for larger hydrocarbons with many branched isomers. A better naming conven- tion has been devised.

Writing adequate chemical formulas for

organic compounds is a difficult problem because of the existence of isomers. C_4H_{10} does not denote a compound unambigu- ously; it refers to both normal butane and isobutane. The problem is worse for larger molecules with more isomers.

The best representation of an organic compound is a model which shows the exact geometry, or a pictorial rendition of

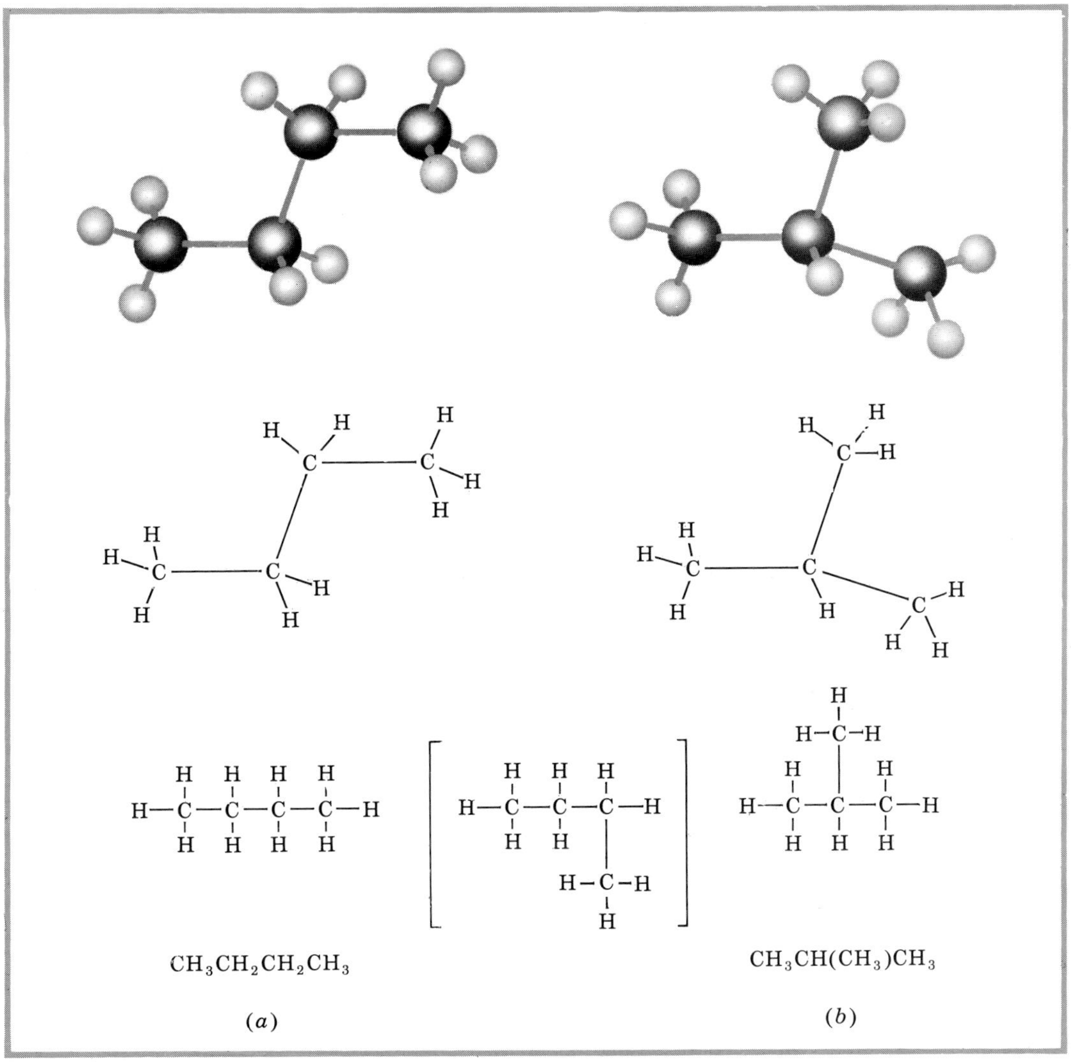

$CH_3CH_2CH_2CH_3$

(*a*)

$CH_3CH(CH_3)CH_3$

(*b*)

FIG. 22-2

Different ways of representing (a) *normal butane and* (b) *isobutane. The upper line is a drawing of a ball-and-stick model. The line below, a letter-and-line drawing in perspective. The third line gives the most common way of representing structural formulas. Perspective is lost and its interpretation requires practice. (The rendition in brackets is not another isomer!) The bottom line shows still another way of show- ing structural arrangements.*

TABLE 22-1

The methane hydrocarbons

Formula	Name	No. of isomers	Freezing* point, °C	Boiling* point, °C	Commercial name
CH_4	Methane	–	−184	−161	Fuel gases
C_2H_6	Ethane	–	−172	−88	
C_3H_8	Propane	–	−190	−45	
C_4H_{10}	Butane	2	−135	1	
C_5H_{12}	Pentane	3	−132	36	Petroleum ether
C_6H_{14}	Hexane	5	−94	69	(naptha)
C_7H_{16}	Heptane	9	−90	98	
C_8H_{18}	Octane	18	−57	125	Gasoline
C_9H_{20}	Nonane	35	−51	154	
$C_{10}H_{22}$	Decane	75	−32	174	
$C_{11}H_{24}$	Undecane	151	−27	197	Kerosene
$C_{16}H_{34}$	Hexadecane	10,359	20	288	

$C_{17}H_{36}$ to $C_{22}H_{46}$: semisolids, constituents of petroleum jelly and lubricating oil
$C_{23}H_{48}$ to $C_{29}H_{60}$: constituents of paraffin

*The data refer to the normal, or straight-chain, compounds. Isomers of these hydrocarbons have somewhat different properties.

such a model as in the top line of Fig. 22–2. This is difficult to do and wasteful of space. The model is often transformed into a line-and-letter diagram, as in the second line of Fig. 22–2. The second line, however, requires that the figures be drawn in perspective, a skill not easily mastered. Often a further simplification is made which changes three-dimensional molecules into two-dimensional structural formulas— line 3 in Fig. 22–2. This further change badly distorts bond angles and produces difficulties with spatial visualization and the transformation of the two-dimensional formulas back into three-dimensional molecules. Considerable practice is usually needed to recognize that the compound in brackets in line 3 of Fig. 22–2 is *not* another isomer but is structurally identical to one of the others when translated back into three dimensions. Nevertheless line 3 is a very common format for *structural formulas* of organic compounds. Another simplification changes the geometric representations into ordinary formulas with parentheses around groups to indicate bonding—line 4. Figure 22–2 shows how

the various ways of writing formulas are related to one another and to the three-dimensional molecules they represent.

Table 22–1 gives the uses of the hydrocarbons and also implies their major chemical characteristics. They are found as natural gas or petroleum, which is refined and used as a fuel.

The separation of petroleum into the different fuels makes use of *distillation,* a process in which the mixture is heated and the components boil off one by one. Because the many petroleum constituents, straight-chain and branched, have high vapor pressures and boiling points near one another, mixtures rather than pure substances are obtained. These are adequate for the use of the petroleum fractions as fuels.

The major product of petroleum is gasoline, which, however, constitutes only a small fraction of the natural crude oil. Hence in petroleum refining some of the larger molecules are broken into fragments of gasoline size—by a process called *cracking*—or combined from smaller molecules. The production of gasoline also involves adding certain compounds to obtain more desirable combustion characteristics. There are additives that assure complete burning to gaseous CO or CO_2 rather than to solid C (soot), additives that reduce corrosion in engines, and additives that reduce engine knock.

Engine knock results from the explosive combustion of the gasoline in the cylinder chamber rather than the gradual burning as the hot gases push the cylinder upward. In knocking engines, the burning is faster than desired. Straight-chain isomers seem to be the chief culprits, whereas branched isomers burn more smoothly.

The basis for the octane rating used to grade gasoline performance is the comparison of the gasoline with mixtures of normal heptane and isooctane,

$$CH_3—C(CH_3)_2—CH_2—CH(CH_3)—CH_3.$$

In early experiments it had been found that, of the known constituents of gasoline, normal heptane knocked most and isooctane knocked least. Hence, pure isooctane —100 octane—was the best fuel while its mixtures with normal heptane were worse, down to the very worst fuel, 0 percent isooctane. In rating a commercial gasoline, its combustion characteristics are compared to mixtures of these two hydrocarbons. The octane rating indicates the percentage of isooctane in the comparison fuel. Since the establishment of the octane scale, improvements in gasoline refining have produced gasolines with octane ratings higher than 100. They burn more smoothly even than 100 percent isooctane.

It is no accident that the petroleum hydrocarbons are used primarily as fuels. Chemically they are rather uninteresting because C—C and C—H bonds are both unreactive. Modification of the molecules for specific purposes, changing only one or two bonds to produce other useful substances, is nearly impossible. On the other hand, the hydrocarbons burn easily and liberate much energy. But combustion with oxygen is a sledgehammer kind of reaction. It disrupts all bonds of the hydrocarbon molecule and leaves only the small fragments H_2O and C, CO, and CO_2.

UNSATURATED HYDROCARBONS

There are other compounds of hydrogen and carbon with structural features that make them more useful for further chemical processes. There is a series of compounds in which two carbon atoms share two pairs of electrons. This type of bond is called a *double bond*. It is represented by two lines in the structural formula, as in $H_2C=CH_2$. Another series contains compounds in which two carbon atoms share three pairs of electrons. This type of bond, called a *triple bond*, is represented in the structural formulas by three lines, as in $HC≡CH$. Double- and triple-bond hydrocarbons are much more reactive than those with single bonds because the second and third pairs of electrons in the multiple bonds can participate in additional chemical combinations. The ease with which these compounds form additional bonds has given them the name *unsaturated* hydrocarbons.

Ethylene, $CH_2=CH_2$, is the simplest double-bond compound. The next member of this series is propylene, $CH_3CH=CH_2$. There are three isomeric butylenes: $CH_3CH=CHCH_3$; $CH_3CH_2CH=CH_2$; and $CH=C(CH_3)_2$; isomeric pentenes; hexenes; etc. The naming of the double-bond hydrocarbons follows the convention for naming single-bond hydrocarbons. The same prefixes are used to count carbon atoms, followed, however, by the suffix *ene* to denote the double bond. (An extra "yl" has remained in the names ethylene, propylene, and butylene from history. They should really be called ethene, propene, and butene.)

The series of triple-bonded compounds begins with acetylene, $H—C≡C—H$, which may also be called ethyne. The next member is propyne, $H—C≡C—CH_3$; then two isomeric butynes, $CH_3—C≡C—CH_3$ and

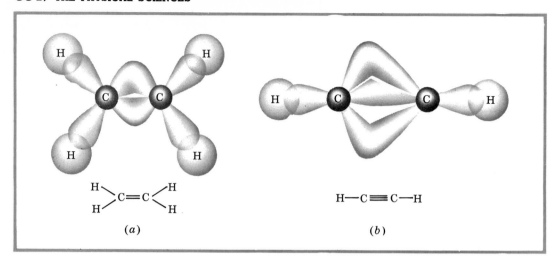

FIG. 22-3

Models for double and triple bonds. (a) The double bond is produced by the sharing of electron pairs in two overlapping tetrahedral orbitals. (b) The triple bond is produced by the sharing of electron pairs in three overlapping tetrahedral orbitals.

$HC\equiv CCH_2CH_3$; etc. The suffix *yne* denotes the presence of a triple bond.

The greater reactivity of the unsaturated hydrocarbons can be interpreted by a simple model in which two of the tetrahedral orbitals of carbon overlap and share electrons in the double-bonded compounds, and three in the triple-bonded compounds (Fig. 22–3). This geometry shows clearly that the electrons of the multiple bonds stick out from the molecules and remain unshielded by the atoms. Hence, these electrons are readily available for new combinations with atoms or molecules that happen to come by and bump into them. (They are completely unlike the electrons of single covalent bonds, which are located exactly between the atoms which they bond and are shielded by the atoms from contacts that might form new bonds.)

The model also suggests another aspect about the geometry of the double and triple bond. The atoms in $H—C\equiv C—H$ are in a straight line in the model, and this is confirmed by crystallographic evidence. Acetylene is a linear molecule. For double-bond compounds, the model suggests that the atoms all lie in one plane and this, too, is confirmed by crystallography. Moreover,

the double bond prevents the rotation of one group around the other and thus suggests the existence of the isomers

because of the impossibility of flipping one =CHCl group about the other. These isomers exist. (Corresponding isomers for the single-bonded compounds, like

do not exist because the $ClH_2C—$ groups can rotate to make the two structures identical.)

ADDITION AND SUBSTITUTION

The differences between single bonds and multiple bonds can be further demonstrated by a detailed examination of the reactions that produce $ClH_2C—CH_2Cl$ from either ethane or ethylene. The process that starts with ethane is difficult to carry out, is slow, and produces other compounds in addition to the desired product. It proceeds according to the equation:

$$CH_3—CH_3 + 2Cl_2 \longrightarrow$$
$$ClH_2C—CH_2Cl + 2HCl \qquad (22–1)$$

Two chlorine atoms *substitute* for two hydrogen atoms; however, HCl is also formed. This means that two additional chlorine atoms are needed to combine with the substituted hydrogen atoms. The reaction proceeds by a scheme like that illustrated in Fig. 22–4. A chlorine molecule somehow finds its way toward a carbon atom. When they collide, the previous bonds are disrupted. One chlorine atom attaches itself to the carbon while the other chlorine atom carries off the hydrogen atom.

There are three barriers to this reaction. The most important barrier is the inaccessibility of the carbon atom. Chlorine molecules reach the carbon only with difficulty because of the other atoms that are crowded around. A second barrier is the Cl—Cl bond which must be disrupted, and the third barrier is the C—H bond which must also be disrupted. All this, however, produces only $CH_3—CH_2Cl$. A second reaction of the same sort must take place at the other carbon atom before $ClH_2C—CH_2Cl$ is formed. It is impossible to control this reaction so that only the desired product

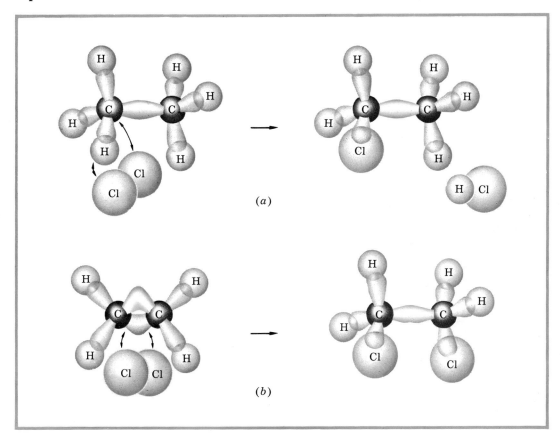

(a)

(b)

FIG. 22-4

Models for the reactions between (a) $CH_3—CH_3$ and Cl_2 and (b) CH_2=CH_2 and Cl_2. (Molecules are not as open as the ball-and-stick representation suggests.) In (a) Cl_2 must find its way to a C atom, disrupt two bonds, and rearrange to form CH_3CH_2Cl. Then another Cl_2 molecule must repeat the process to form CH_2ClCH_2Cl. In (b) Cl_2 reacts with a relatively accessible electron pair to form CH_2ClCH_2Cl directly.

TABLE 22-2

Commercially important addition products of ethylene and their derivatives

Addend, % of use	Product	Further reactions
HCl 10%	CH_3CH_2Cl ethyl chloride	
H_2O 30%	CH_3CH_2OH ethyl alcohol	$\xrightarrow{-H_2}$ $CH_3CH{=}O$ acetaldehyde $\xrightarrow{-H_2O}$ $CH_3CH_2{-}O{-}CH_2CH_3$ diethyl ether
HOCl 25%	CH_2ClCH_2OH ethylene chlorohydrin	$\xrightarrow{-HCl}$ CH_2CH_2 ethylene oxide $\xrightarrow{+H_2O}$ $CH_2(OH)CH_2OH$ ethylene glycol $\xrightarrow[-HCl]{+NH_3}$ $CH_2(NH_2)CH_2NH_2$ ethylene diamine $\xrightarrow{-H_2O}$ $ClH_2CCH_2OCH_2CH_2Cl$ dichloroethyl ether $\xrightarrow[-HCl]{+CH_3OH}$ $CH_2{=}CHCOCH_3$ methyl acrylate

(benzene structure) 10% → (ethylbenzene structure) $\xrightarrow{-H_2}$ (styrene structure) styrene

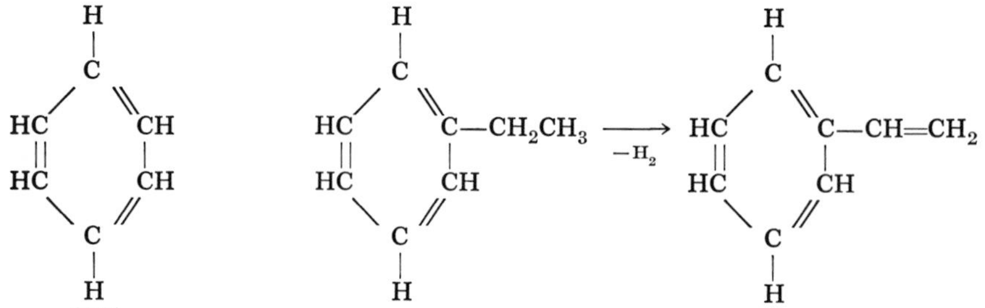

$CH_2{=}CH_2$ 15%   polyethylene

Other uses 10%

---

forms. All possible substitutions of Cl for H take place and the result is a mixture of compounds with one to six chlorine atoms.

The reaction that begins with $CH_2{=}CH_2$ follows an entirely different scheme:

$$CH_2{=}CH_2 + Cl_2 \longrightarrow ClH_2C{-}CH_2Cl \quad (22{-}2)$$

Only one chlorine molecule is needed because the chlorine atoms *add* to the ethyl-

Uses of products

Solvent, refrigerant, used in manufacture of tetraethyl lead for gasoline

Solvent, antifreeze, used in further manufacture

Used in further manufacture

Solvent, anesthetic

Antifreeze and many other products

Textile finishes

Solvent

Acrylic plastics (plexiglas, lucite, etc.)

Polystyrene plastics

Plastic films

present. But since the double-bond electrons are readily accessible to the reacting Cl_2 molecules, there is little difficulty in getting the two together (Fig. 22–4b). The reaction proceeds rapidly, and it produces only the desired compound because the addition removes the double bond and thereby stops further rapid reactions.

Reactions which add groups to a double or triple bond are called *addition* reactions. They are the typical reactions of unsaturated compounds. Because they are rapid and easily controlled, they are extremely important in chemical processes. The kind of reaction illustrated by ethane (Eq. 22–1), on the other hand, is slow and cannot be precisely controlled. It is much less important. Because it involves the substitution of one atom for another, it is called a *substitution reaction*.

Table 22–2 lists a number of compounds produced commercially from ethylene by addition to show the prevalence of addition reactions and the importance of ethylene as an industrial chemical. Over 3 billion lb is used annually. The products include a consumer product like ethylene glycol, the antifreeze, and a large number of chemicals which are used as solvents or for further manufacture. Each is produced after the initial addition of one simple molecule to the ethylene double bond.

Another exceedingly important addition reaction of ethylene differs slightly from the simple scheme discussed above. This kind of reaction is illustrated by the last entry in the table, the production of polyethylene, a widely used packaging material. In it, many ethylene molecules are added together in a process called *polymerization*. The product of the polymerization reaction, which may consist of thousands of identical small units, is a *polymer*.

The polymerization of ethylene begins with a "starter," a substance which has one unbonded electron. This electron forms a bond with an electron from one pair of the double bond to form a starter-ethylene unit (Fig. 22–5). Because of the second electron

ene molecule instead of substituting for one of its atoms. In this reaction Cl_2 molecules also must collide with the $CH_2=CH_2$ molecules and bonds in both must be disrupted. These barriers to reaction are still

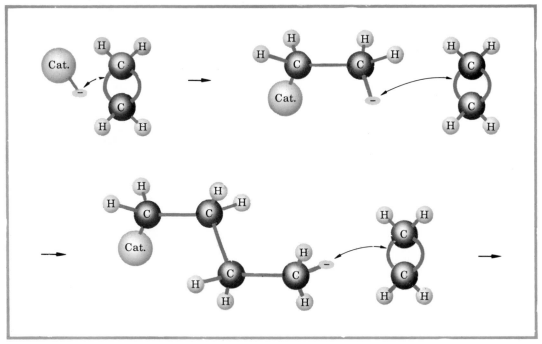

FIG. 22-5

Representation of an addition polymerization reaction. A starting material with a single electron disrupts the double bond and adds to the ethylene. The product also has a single electron which can disrupt another double bond and add to a second molecule of ethylene. The product again has a single electron which can continue the addition reactions.

from the disrupted double bond, the starter-ethylene unit then also has an extra electron. Hence, it can attack another ethylene molecule, disrupting its double bond and forming a starter-two-ethylene unit, also with one extra electron. This new unit attacks a third ethylene in an analogous reaction; the product attacks a fourth ethylene; and thus the reaction proceeds until a polymer of thousands of ethylene units is formed. The addition of ethylene to the growing molecule stops only when two growing ends of molecules happen to meet and join their lone electrons into a bond or when the ethylene has completely reacted. How quickly growing ends meet—the size of the molecules which are produced—can be controlled by the relative amounts of starter and ethylene.

Polymerization reactions are extremely common in industrial processes. Most plas-

tics are produced in this way; however, not all polymerizations are of the kind illustrated here, *addition polymerization,* in which the simple molecules add together. In other polymerization reactions (see below, Eqs. 22–3 and 22–4) hydrogen and oxygen atoms are split from the reagents, and water as well as the polymer is produced.

BENZENES

There is one kind of double-bond hydrocarbon which is surprising in its properties. Benzene, C_6H_6, and compounds like it have the double bonds alternating with single bonds around a six-carbon-atom ring (Fig. 22–6). Yet, despite the presence of three double bonds in the molecule, benzene reacts chiefly by substitution. Moreover, substitution on the benzene ring is much more rapid than with single-bond hydrocarbons. The electrons of the alternating single and double bonds behave unlike those of either the saturated or the unsaturated compounds; they appear spread out evenly over the entire ring with something like 1½ bonds between all carbon atoms.

The unique character of alternating single and double bonds is confirmed by another kind of evidence: colored compounds typically contain benzene rings, or chains with alternating bonds, or both. Since color in a molecule results from the absorption of light by electrons just as it does in atomic spectra, this evidence also indicates a different kind of electron arrangement. We shall encounter benzene rings in a number of molecules later on.

HALOGEN DERIVATIVES

Equations 22–1 and 22–2 illustrate two methods for producing hydrocarbon *derivatives*, compounds which are derived from a CH compound by reaction (though they might be found in nature). In theory, most other elements can form derivatives; in practice, only six elements are at all common. Most organic compounds found in nature contain oxygen, many also contain nitrogen, and halogen derivatives are of considerable commercial importance though they are not typically found in nature.

The basic chemistry of the halogen derivatives is fairly simple. Like hydrogen, the halogens form single covalent bonds. Consequently, they substitute for hydrogen on a one-to-one basis. The derivatives CH_3F, CH_2F_2, CHF_3, and CF_4, and comparable compounds with Cl, Br, and I are all known. Nine different derivatives of C_2H_6 with one to six halogen atoms exist, of which some are isomers. Nearly any hydrocarbon derivative which can be imagined and which replaces one or more hydrogen atoms has been or can be produced in the laboratory, and many have found commercial application. For instance, two of the chlorinated methanes are used widely: $CHCl_3$, chloroform, as an anesthetic and CCl_4, carbon tetrachloride, as a solvent and as a nonflammable dry-cleaning fluid.

The chlorinated methanes demonstrate the influence of polar bonds on the properties of molecules. CH_4 is nonpolar because its bonds are nonpolar; CCl_4 is nonpolar because the dipoles of the four C—Cl bonds

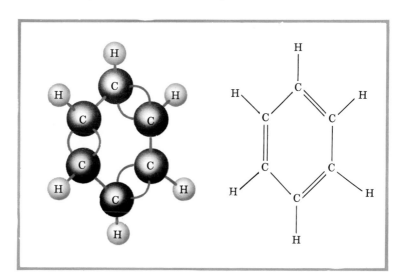

Models of benzene, C_6H_6.

FIG. 22-6

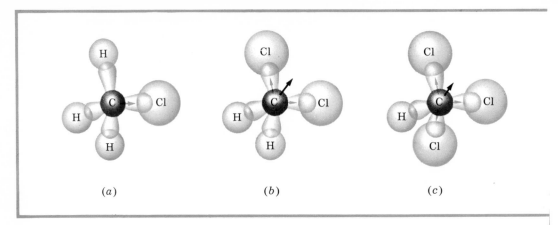

(a)   (b)   (c)

FIG. 22-7

add vectorially in the molecule to give a resultant of zero. In the other three derivatives the polar bonds add to make the molecules polar (Fig. 22–7). Table 22–3 shows the effect. The solubility in water, particularly, separates the polar from the the nonpolar chlorinated methanes with CH_3Cl, CH_2Cl_2, and $CHCl_3$ more than 10 times as soluble in water as the other compounds. The melting- and boiling-point changes are more difficult to interpret because in addition to the differences in polarity of the molecules, the added chlorine atoms greatly change the molecular weight of the compounds.

Substitution need not be restricted to single halogens. The freons, a group of compounds used as refrigeration fluids, include $C_2H_2Cl_2F_2$ and $C_2Cl_2F_4$.

TABLE 22-3

Physical properties of chlorinated methanes

Compound	Melting point, °C	Boiling point, °C	Solubility, grams/ 100 ml water
CH_4	−184	−161.5	0.006
CH_3Cl	− 97.7	− 24.2	0.9
CH_2Cl_2	− 96.7	40.1	2.0
$CHCl_3$	− 63.5	61.3	1.0
CCl_4	− 22.8	76.8	0.08

OXYGEN DERIVATIVES

A number of different oxygen derivatives exist because oxygen forms two covalent bonds (Table 22–4). For instance, both of the bonds may be to hydrocarbon groups, giving a compound of the type R—O—R'. (R represents a hydrocarbon group.) This type of compound is an ether. Alternatively, one of the bonds may be to a hydrogen atom, giving a compound of type R—OH, an alcohol. The chemical properties of the oxygen derivatives depend primarily on the nature of their oxygen groups, called *functional groups,* because the hydrocarbon portions of the molecules are generally unreactive.

Alcohols, type formula R—OH, contain the —OH or *hydroxyl* functional group. The simplest alcohol is CH_3OH, methyl or wood alcohol, a very poisonous liquid. The next member of the series is ethyl or grain alcohol, CH_3CH_2OH. Two isomers of propyl alcohol exist, normal propyl alcohol, $CH_3CH_2CH_2OH$, and isopropyl alcohol, $CH_3CH(OH)CH_3$. There are several isomeric butyl alcohols, etc. The small alcohols are chiefly used as solvents and as intermediates in the production of larger, more complex chemicals; larger and more complex alcohols are biochemically important.

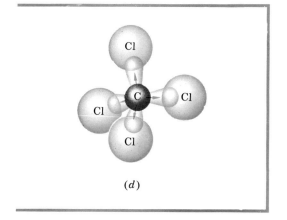

(d)

Dipoles of chlorinated methanes. In CH_2Cl_2 and $CHCl_3$ the dipoles of the C—Cl bonds add to produce strongly polar molecules. In CCl_4 they add to produce a zero resultant for the molecule. CCl_4 is nonpolar.

The alcohols show the importance of polar bonds in a compound. The hydroxyl group is strongly polar. Moreover the hydrogen can form hydrogen bonds. The C—O bond is slightly polar, while the remaining bonds in the molecule are nonpolar. In the small alcohols the polar group determines most of the behavior. Methyl, ethyl, and both propyl alcohols are soluble in water in all proportions. The butyl alcohols are much less soluble, and the solubility of the higher alcohols in water drops very rapidly. On the other hand, sugars, which have five OH groups on a six-carbon-atom chain, are quite soluble because polar groups again predominate.

As the sugars indicate, substitution of OH is not restricted to one per molecule. Other common polyhydroxy compounds are ethylene glycol, $CH_2(OH)CH_2OH$, the common antifreeze, and glycerine, $(HO)H_2CCH(OH)CH_2OH$.

TABLE 22-4

Common derivatives of the hydrocarbons

Name of derivative	Functional group	Name of function group	Type formula
Alcohol	—OH	Hydroxyl	R—OH
Ether	—O—	...	R—O—R'
Aldehyde	$-\overset{\displaystyle O}{\overset{\displaystyle \|}{C}}-H$	...	$R-\overset{\displaystyle O}{\overset{\displaystyle \|}{C}}-H$
Ketone	$-\overset{\displaystyle O}{\overset{\displaystyle \|}{C}}-$	Carbonyl	$R-\overset{\displaystyle O}{\overset{\displaystyle \|}{C}}-R'$
Acid	$-\overset{\displaystyle O}{\overset{\displaystyle \|}{C}}-OH$	Carboxyl	$R-\overset{\displaystyle O}{\overset{\displaystyle \|}{C}}-OH$
Ester	$-\overset{\displaystyle O}{\overset{\displaystyle \|}{C}}-O-$	...	$R-\overset{\displaystyle O}{\overset{\displaystyle \|}{C}}-O-R'$
Amine	$-NH_2$	Amino	$R-NH_2$

The functional group of *ethers* is the —O— group, type formula R—O—R'. CH_3—O—CH_3 is dimethyl ether. The common anesthetic ether is diethyl ether, CH_3CH_2—O—CH_2CH_3. Ethers demonstrate the smaller polarity of the C—O bond and its lesser contribution to the whole molecule. They have rather low boiling points, low solubility in water, etc. Some ethers are used as solvents, but members of this group are not very common in nature.

All other oxygen derivatives contain the oxygen double-bonded to carbon in the

$$-\overset{\overset{\textstyle O}{\|}}{C}-$$

or carbonyl group. Aldehydes, general formula

$$R-\overset{\overset{\textstyle O}{\|}}{C}-H,$$

have an R group and an H attached to the carbonyl carbon.

The simplest, formaldehyde,

$$H-\overset{\overset{\textstyle O}{\|}}{C}-H,$$

is used as a disinfectant and preservative and is well known to students of biology. Some of the larger liquid aldehydes have pleasant odors and are found in flower extracts. Bakelite, a common plastic, is a polymer of formaldehyde with the benzene derivative phenol.

(22–3)

While the polymerization reaction involves

the double-bonded oxygen, the reaction produces water from hydrogen atoms of two phenol molecules and the formaldehyde oxygen. It is not an addition polymerization.

Compounds in which the carbonyl group

$$\text{is attached to two R groups, } R-\overset{\overset{\textstyle O}{\|}}{C}-R',$$

are called *ketones*. The reactivity of the ketone carbonyl group is like that of the aldehydes. Some ketones are solvents, and many important natural products contain the ketone carbonyl group.

Another group of derivatives contains both the carbonyl and the hydroxyl groups,

$$R-\overset{\overset{\textstyle O}{\|}}{C}-OH,$$

often abbreviated R—COOH. These are *organic acids*. Organic acids are quite common: acetic acid in vinegar; citric acid in citrus fruit; lactic acid in sour milk; oxalic acid in rhubarb, for example. However, one group of organic acids, the amino acids, is important beyond all others. Amino acids are the simple compounds of which proteins are built. They have the amine-functional group, —NH_2, as well as the acid-functional group, both attached to the same carbon atom. Their type formula is

$$H_2N-\overset{\overset{\textstyle H}{|}}{\underset{\underset{\textstyle R}{|}}{C}}-COOH$$

There are about 20 amino acids in proteins which differ in their R groups. Their number and arrangements vary in different proteins and in different organisms. Glycine has only another H atom for its R,

$$H_2N-\overset{\overset{\textstyle H}{|}}{\underset{\underset{\textstyle H}{|}}{C}}-COOH$$

alanine has a methyl group,

$$H_2N-\overset{\overset{\textstyle H}{|}}{\underset{\underset{\textstyle CH_3}{|}}{C}}-COOH$$

phenyl alanine, a benzene ring attached to the methyl of alanine (see below); threonine, a hydroxyl attached to the alanine,

$$\begin{array}{c} H \\ | \\ H_2N-C-COOH \\ | \\ CH_2OH \end{array}$$

Other amino acids differ in comparable ways.

The amino acids polymerize into proteins by splitting water between the —COOH and —NH₂ groups of adjacent molecules:

$$\begin{array}{cc} \begin{array}{c} H \quad H \\ | \quad | \\ H-N-C-COOH \\ | \\ CH_2 \\ | \\ C \\ HC \diagup \diagdown CH \\ HC \diagdown \diagup CH \\ C \\ | \\ H \end{array} & \begin{array}{c} H \quad H \\ | \quad | \\ H-N-C-COOH \\ | \\ CH_2 \\ | \\ OH \\ \text{Threonine} \\ \\ H \quad H \\ | \quad | \\ H-N-C-COOH \\ | \\ CH_3 \end{array} \end{array}$$

Phenyl alanine   Alanine

$$\begin{array}{c} H \quad H \quad O \quad H \quad H \quad O \quad H \quad H \quad O \\ | \quad | \quad || \quad | \quad | \quad || \quad | \quad | \quad || \\ \rightarrow -N-C-C-N-C-C-N-C-C- \; + \; H_2O \\ \quad | \qquad | \qquad | \\ \quad CH_2 \quad CH_2 \quad CH_3 \\ \quad | \qquad | \\ \quad C \qquad OH \\ HC \diagup \diagdown CH \quad \text{Threo-} \quad \text{Alanine} \\ HC \diagdown \diagup CH \quad \text{nine} \\ C \\ | \\ H \\ \text{Phenyl} \\ \text{alanine} \end{array}$$

(22–4)

Formally, this is a straightforward reaction which can be carried out in the laboratory although it is impossible to control the order and sequence. The mystery is how organisms have found it possible to regulate the reaction so that proteins maintain their specific structures and sequence. We shall return to that topic later.

Acids also combine with alcohols in a water-splitting reaction:

$$\begin{array}{c} O \\ || \\ CH_3-C-OH \; + \; H-O-CH_2CH_3 \longrightarrow \\ \text{Acetic acid} \qquad \text{Ethyl alcohol} \\ O \\ || \\ CH_3-C-O-CH_2CH_3 \; + \; H_2O \\ \text{Ethyl acetate} \end{array}$$

(22–5)

The product of this reaction is called an *ester*, formula $R-\overset{\overset{\textstyle O}{||}}{C}-O-R'$. Most esters are pleasant-smelling substances. They are found in perfumes and flavors.

It should be obvious that we could go on and on with organic chemistry to study the reactions that produce different derivatives; to study some of the complex organic molecules and their isomers; to study their physical properties and their biological activity. That kind of study is going on in many industrial research centers, where new paints and plastics, fibers and drugs are sought. It goes on in chemical, biochemical, medical, and pharmaceutical research laboratories, where an understanding of the functioning of healthy and sick organisms is sought. It is a growing field and many undergraduate and graduate courses in organic chemistry are taught to describe its findings. We shall stop here.

The remaining sections speculate on two kinds of biological processes—the action of specific molecules in normal body functions and the production of proteins—both of which illustrate the great structural specificity of biological processes. Indeed, structural details which we have met so far in tetrahedral carbon-atom bonds, isomerism, multiple bonds, and the benzene hydrocarbons seem to be vital in the chemical processes that sustain life.

VITAMINS AND HORMONES

Many vitamins and hormones have been identified and completely analyzed. They are combinations of hydrocarbon structures and functional groups. For instance, niacinamide, one of the B vitamins, has the structure shown below. It contains a benzenelike ring with a nitrogen atom in place of one CH, to which a carbonyl and NH_2 group are attached. Also shown are two poisons which are chemically quite similar. Their similarity is so great that the vitamin has been produced by easy chemical reactions from the poisons.

Niacinamide   Coniine

Nicotine

It is interesting to speculate how these poisons function. Some evidence comes from an experiment with certain bacteria which require *para*-aminobenzoic acid (PABA) to produce the vitamin folic acid. PABA is structurally very similar to the sulfa drugs.

PABA   Sulfa drug (different
                drugs have different R's)

In the experiment the bacteria were grown in a medium containing some PABA. Growth occurred. This growth was stopped when some sulfa drug was added. When more PABA was added, however, growth

of the bacteria started again. The addition of further sulfa drug stopped this growth, and then further PABA started it again. In this manner the bacteria were taken through several cycles of growth and stoppage by the alternate additions of PABA and the sulfa drug.

The evidence suggests strongly that there are two parts to the metabolic processes involving PABA. Something in the bacteria combines with the NH_2—C_6H_5— structure of either PABA or the sulfa drug. Then, if the —COOH is at the other end, further metabolic activity takes place; if the sulfa-drug groups are there, no further reaction can take place. Hence, when a bacterium attaches to the PABA NH_2—C_6H_5—, bacterial growth occurs, and when it mistakes the sulfa drug NH_2—C_6H_5— for the needed structure, growth stops. Apparently there is a specific interaction with the NH_2—C_6H_5— structure first, and then a reaction involving the —COOH group.

In the experiment growth was supported and then stopped in cycles because the bacterium-$NH_2C_6H_5$— combinations are not permanent but form and then separate. When PABA was present in excess, the combinations that formed were chiefly bacterium-PABA combinations and further growth occurred. When the drug was present in excess, the combinations that formed were chiefly bacterium-drug combinations and no further growth took place. These reactions suggest an explanation for the operation of poisons that are structurally very similar to substances needed for metabolic processes. Their structure may be so similar that the body mistakes them for the necessary material, yet sufficiently different to prevent subsequent vital reactions.

The medical use of sulfa drugs is through their growth-stopping function. PABA is needed by bacteria, including those which cause the infection, whereas body cells do not need PABA because they cannot manufacture the vitamin folic acid. Folic acid must be obtained from foods. Hence, stopping the PABA metabolic process damages

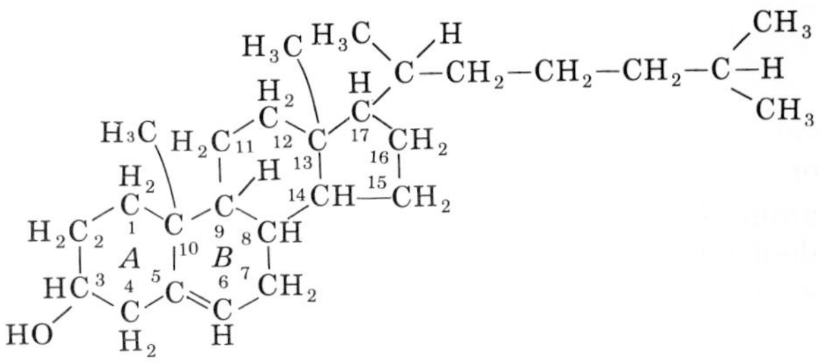

The structure of cholesterol, one of many steroid hormones.

FIG. 22-8

the growth of the bacteria only, without affecting the functions of the body cells. With the reduction in the growth rate of the bacteria, other body defense mechanisms have a chance to attack them and to destroy them.

Another illustration of the great structural specificity of the molecules involved in biological processes is found in the steroid hormones. This group of hormones and vitamins of related structure regulate many body processes, from the antiarthritic functions of cortisone to the participation in sexual development of estradiol and testosterone to some unknown involvement of progesterone in the normal growth of the human embryo. Cholesterol (Fig. 22–8) apparently has many regulatory functions, for it is present in very large amounts; a 160-lb man has nearly ½ lb of cholesterol. Yet its specific biological activity is almost completely unknown.

TABLE 22-5

Structure of some steroids

Name	Double bonds between C Nos.	Substituent groups and position	Function
Cholesterol	6, 7	—OH at C_3; CH_3 at C_{10}; —$CH(CH_3)CH_2CH_2CH_2CH(CH_3)_2$ at C_{17}	Unknown
Cortisone	4, 5	=O at C_3 and C_{11}; CH_3 at C_{10}; —OH and $\overset{\text{O}}{\overset{\|}{-\text{C}}}$—$CH_2OH$ at C_{17}	Treatment of rheumatoid arthritis
Progesterone	4, 5	=O at C_3; —CH_3 at C_{10}; $\overset{\text{O}}{\overset{\|}{-\text{C}}}$—$CH_3$ at C_{17}	Related to pregnancy
Testosterone	4, 5	=O at C_3; —CH_3 at C_{10}; —OH at C_{17}	Male reproduction
Estradiol	6, 10	—OH at C_3; —OH at C_{17}	Growth and function of female reproductive organs
Ergosterol	6, 7 8, 9	—OH at C_3; —CH_3 at C_{10}; —$C(CH_2)$—CH=CH—$CH(CH_3)CH(CH_3)_2$ at C_{17}	Found in yeast Vitamin D_2

It is again remarkable how closely related the structures of different steroids are
since their functions are so specific. All
have four connected rings of carbon atoms
with most carbons also bonded to two hydrogens, and a CH_3 group at C_{13}. The chief
differences occur in the groups attached to
carbon atoms 3, 11, and 17; in the presence
or absence of a —CH_3 group on carbon
atom 10; and in the presence or absence of
double bonds in rings A and B. Yet, as small
a change as the shift of one double bond
in ring A, the addition of a methyl group
at C_{10}, and the substitution of the carbonyl
for the hydroxyl on carbon 3 changes the

female hormone estradiol into the male hormone testosterone (Table 22–5).

DNA, RNA, AND PROTEINS

We have already referred to another puzzle
of structural specificity: how the body adds
20 amino acids in a specific order to fashion
the proteins which make up our arms or
legs, our kidneys or lungs, or the many
smaller proteins which act as hormones and
regulate body processes. The larger proteins
are still pretty well unknown though the
presumption is strong that they are also
structurally specific. For the smaller pro-

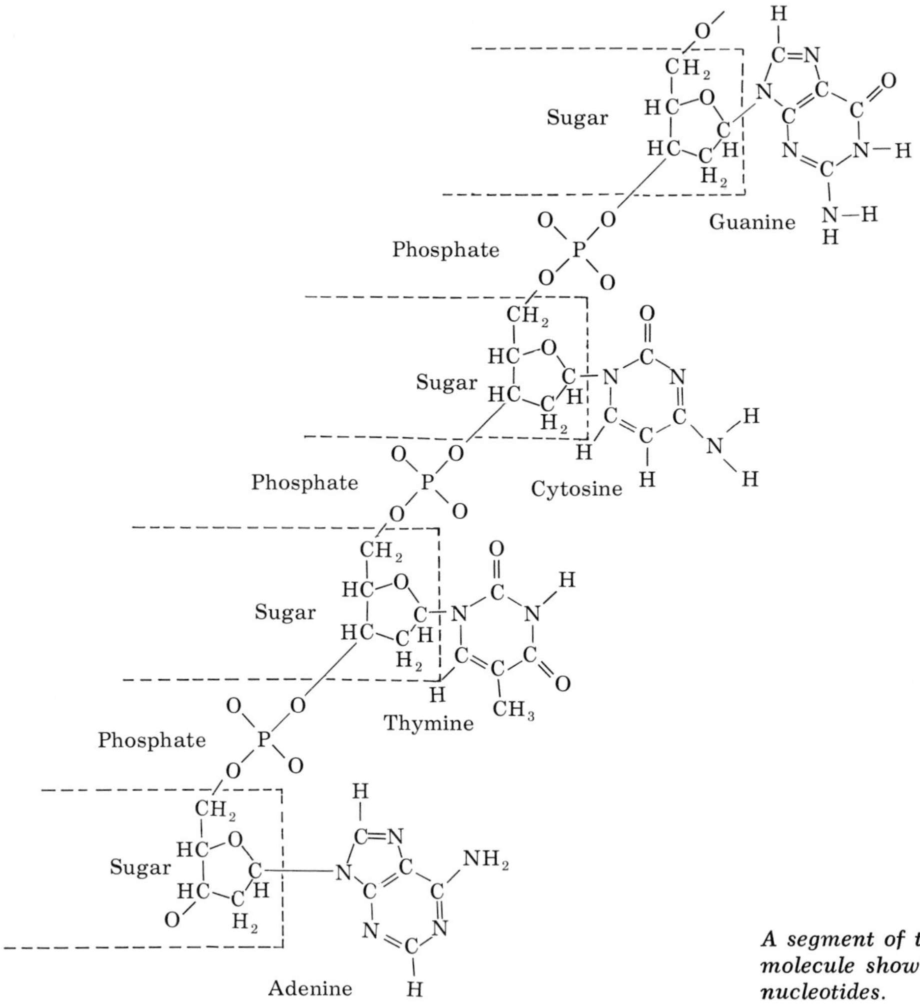

*A segment of the DNA
molecule showing four
nucleotides.*

FIG. 22-9

teins this presumption has been demonstrated. Many smaller proteins have been isolated, purified, and crystallized. This is possible only if the material is a compound of fixed structure and composition. Indeed, several smaller proteins have been taken apart, amino acid by amino acid, and their specific composition has been established.

The British biochemist Frederick Sanger received the Nobel Prize for the first complete identification of a protein. In a series of researches lasting from 1945 to 1953, he and his coworkers established the order of the 51 amino acids in insulin. At about the same time, the American Vincent du Vigneaud completed the synthesis of a small protein, the 8-amino-acid oxytocin. He too was awarded the Nobel Prize for his research. But while this work was tremendously important in clarifying the structure and regularity of proteins, it did not clear up the puzzle of how the body puts together amino acids in this orderly fashion.

The investigation of protein synthesis in the body followed a different line. Biologists had identified stringlike bodies in the nucleus of cells, called *chromosomes,* as the transmitters of heredity. Early in this century the chromosomes had been analyzed. Their major constituent is the polymeric substance DNA, *deoxyribonucleic acid.* DNA, when analyzed further, contains only four basic units, called *nucleotides* (Fig. 22–9). Each of the four nucleotides has a phosphate group attached to a deoxyribose group and these two alternate in the polymeric chain of DNA. The nucleotides differ in their third constituents, nitrogen-containing ring structures. Each nucleotide has a different nitrogen ring, and these rings are attached apparently at random along the deoxyribose-phosphate chain.

Confirmation that the DNA in the chromosomes is the transmitter of heredity came in 1944 from an experiment in which DNA from dead smooth-coated pneumococcus cells was added to live rough-coated pneumococcus cells. The DNA from dead cells added the coat-smoothing character-

Adenine   Thymine

Guamine   Cytosine

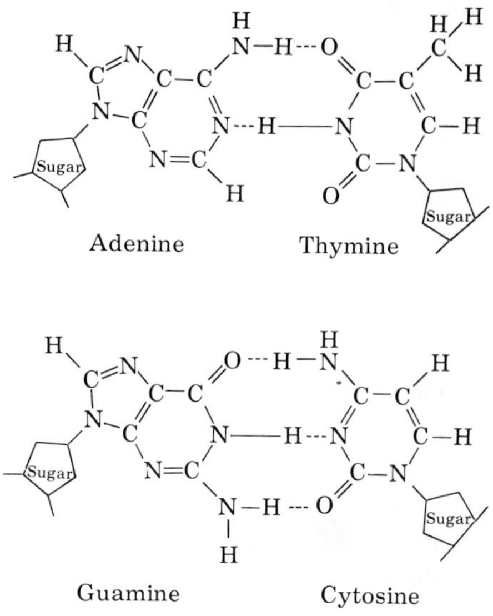

FIG. 22-10

Hydrogen bonding in DNA. Oxygen and nitrogen atoms in the pairs adenine-thymine and guanine-cytosine are so arranged that hydrogen bonds can easily form.

istic and the cells grew with smooth coats. This pinpointed DNA as the carrier of inheritance.

Suggestions for the manner in which hereditary information is transmitted by DNA first came from the finding that the amount of the nucleotides in DNA is not completely independent. There is as much adenine as thymine and as much cytosine as guanine. A model of these pairs of nucleotides shows that strong hydrogen bonds can easily form between them (Fig. 22–10). Moreover, structural studies indicate that the DNA molecules coil into a helix and come in pairs. All this evidence, which had accumulated by the early 1950s, suggested to the British biologists J. D. Watson and F. H. C. Crick that two DNA molecules take on a twisted-rope-ladder structure (Fig. 22–11), which is maintained by hydrogen bonds between the nitrogen rings of the two DNA molecules.

The Watson-Crick structure suggests a mechanism for producing new DNA of identical chemical composition. If the two strands of the molecule unwind, new nu-

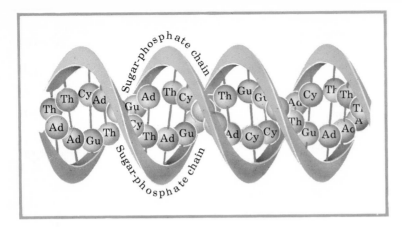

The Watson-Crick model of DNA. Hydrogen bonding between two DNA molecules keeps them together in a helical structure.

FIG. 22-11

cleotide units can be brought to them by some process to fit exactly into the hydrogen-bonded templates: adenines opposite thymines and cytosines opposite guanines. Hence the new DNA must fit the order of the existing nucleotides. This notion about DNA reproduction has been confirmed by adding nucleotides with radioactive N atoms to DNA. New DNA molecules are formed which are radioactive but are otherwise identical to the old DNA. Thus, heredity seems to be transmitted via new DNA molecules that match the nucleotides on the old DNA molecules by means of hydrogen bonds.

This leaves a final puzzle because the four nucleotides not only must duplicate themselves to transmit hereditary information, but must also somehow act as templates for the 20 amino acids to put together proteins with their constituents in the right order. This is a still unsolved puzzle although some further clues are available. It is being researched very actively and might be solved by the time this book appears in print.

The American astronomer George Gamow and F. H. C. Crick both showed that four nucleotides taken three at a time produce twenty different arrangements. There are four arrangements consisting of a sequence of the same nucleotide—three guanines or three thymines or three cytosines or three

adenines; twelve arrangements of two identical nucleotides with one other; and four arrangements of three different nucleotides. Thus successive triads of nucleotides along the DNA chain might determine the order of amino acid placement in the building of a protein. There is some confirmatory evidence for this. However, the theory does not explain how the amino acids get to the DNA in the first place, nor how they know at which point on the DNA molecule to start counting nucleotides, because different starting points change the order of the nucleotides in the triads.

Protein synthesis does not occur in the chromosomes which contain the DNA. Instead, there is a substance closely related to DNA, called RNA, *ribonucleic acid,* which acts as an intermediary. There are several RNAs which differ from DNA only in the presence of an OH on the deoxyribose group and the absence of a CH_3 on the nitrogen ring of thymine. One kind of RNA, messenger RNA, takes the information from the DNA to the site of protein synthesis. The other RNAs, called transfer RNAs, attach themselves to amino acid molecules and carry them to the messenger RNA. There they fit the template and leave their amino acids in the correct sequence. These processes are sketched in Fig. 22–12. While the details of hereditary transmission and protein synthesis are far from known, it

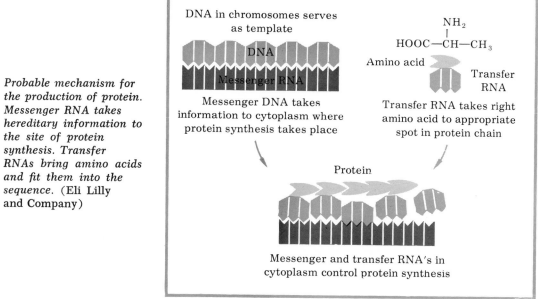

DNA in chromosomes serves as template

DNA

Messenger RNA

Messenger DNA takes information to cytoplasm where protein synthesis takes place

$$HOOC—\overset{\overset{\displaystyle NH_2}{|}}{CH}—CH_3$$

Amino acid

Transfer RNA

Transfer RNA takes right amino acid to appropriate spot in protein chain

Protein

Messenger and transfer RNA's in cytoplasm control protein synthesis

Probable mechanism for the production of protein. Messenger RNA takes hereditary information to the site of protein synthesis. Transfer RNAs bring amino acids and fit them into the sequence. (Eli Lilly and Company)

FIG. 22-12

appears that DNA is the stable substance that transmits the genetic information from mother cell to daughter cell and that it serves as the template for the production of RNAs which, in a series of probably complex steps, arrange amino acids into proteins following the nucleotide sequence in the original DNA.

LEFT-HANDED PROTEINS

After the description of so many structurally specific chemical processes among the vital reactions of the body, it is perhaps not surprising that protein synthesis can use only left-handed amino acids as starting materials, not right-handed ones. These terms arise from the fact that all amino acids except glycine interact with polarized light (Chap. 15) and rotate the plane of polarization either to the right or to the left. (This adds another kind of isomerism, *optical isomerism.*)

Rotation of polarized light occurs in carbon compounds whenever four entirely different groups are attached to a single tet-

rahedral carbon atom. These four groups can attach themselves in two distinct ways which are mirror images of one another but which, like the fingers of our two hands, cannot in any way be rotated into one another. Figure 22–13 shows an example of a simple *optically active* molecule. Chemically and structurally, optical isomers are identical; all bond angles and bond lengths are the same. Yet they interact differently with polarized light and with other optically active compounds.

In amino acids the carboxyl group, the amine group, a hydrogen atom, and the R group that identifies the specific amino acid are all attached to one carbon atom. This makes that carbon atom optically active because the four groups can arrange themselves in two ways which are mirror images of one another. Hence the optical isomerism of the amino acids. In ordinary chemical production of amino acids, the four groups are added to a carbon atom one at a time and the optically active carbon atom is formed stepwise. Equal amounts of the two isomers are formed because the reaction is not optically directive. But if this mixture of the two optical isomers is fed

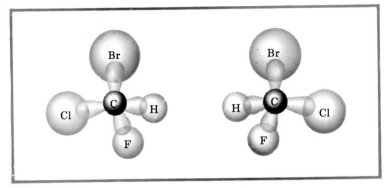

Optical isomers. When four different groups are attached to a tetrahedral carbon atom, they can do so in two distinct ways. No amount of rotation can make the two structures identical.

FIG. 22-13

to organisms as a raw material for protein production, the amino acid which rotates polarized light to the right is rejected and only the amino acid which rotates to the left can be utilized. A man would literally starve if he were fed a diet of only right-handed proteins.

Fortunately, all organisms we eat, indeed all organisms that have been studied, have proteins formed from left-handed amino acids. (There may be some primitive organisms which are exceptions.) The fact that in nonliving processes the two optical isomers of amino acids form in equal amounts, whereas living organisms all have only the left-handed form, suggests strongly that there is a connection between them. It is an additional justification for the theory of evolution of life from simple forms.

Questions and Problems

1. The chemical industry in some processes starts with coke, air, and water. What needed elements are obtained from each?

2. Draw structural formulas for normal heptane and isooctane.

3. Write balanced equations for the combustion of isooctane. A gallon of isooctane weighs about 2,500 grams. Compute the weight of oxygen required for complete combustion. What volume of air is needed to burn 1 gal of isooctane? (Air is 20 percent O_2.)

4. Write structural formulas for:
   (a) $CH_3CH=C(CH_3)CH_3$ (c) a pentyne
   (b) $HC\equiv CC(CH_3)_3$ (d) a hexene

5. Draw structural formulas for all Cl-substituted ethanes. Show that their number is 9, as cited in the text.

6. Suggest reasons for the high boiling point of ethylene glycol contrasted to the lower boiling point of methyl alcohol.

7. Explain why glycine $H_2N-\overset{\overset{\displaystyle H}{|}}{\underset{\underset{\displaystyle H}{|}}{C}}-COOH$ is not optically active.

8. Explain why ethylene and acetylene hydrocarbons are considered unsaturated.

9. Why must the methane-series hydrocarbons react by substitution?

10. Make a table listing two properties of the methane, ethylene, acetylene, and benzene hydrocarbons.

11. Write the formulas of oxygen derivatives if R is CH_3CH_2- and R' is CH_3-. Name as many as you can.

12. Distinguish between an optical isomer, a double-bond isomer, and another kind of isomer.

13. Ethyl alcohol and dimethyl ether are isomers. Explain. What acid is an isomer of

$$CH_3-\overset{\overset{\displaystyle O}{||}}{C}-OC_2H_5?$$

14. Vinyl chloride $CH_2=CHCl$, forms a polymer by addition polymerization. Suggest how the reaction might proceed.

15. Is glycerine optically active? Explain. Is the sugar glucose, $CH_2OHCH(OH)CH(OH)CH(OH)CH(OH)\overset{\overset{\displaystyle O}{||}}{C}-H$, optically active? (It has

also been called dextrose. Look up the meaning of the prefix *dextro* and suggest a reason for its name. Another sugar is called levulose. Suggest a reason for its name.)

16. When benzene was discovered more than 100 years ago, it was suggested that the carbon atoms might be arranged in the form of a triangular prism rather than a ring. The structure was decided on the basis of the number of isomers of dichlorobenzene (two hydrogens replaced by chlorine). How many isomers are possible for the ring structure? the prism? How many exist?

Suggestions for Further Reading

Among the many textbooks in organic chemistry are the following, which are listed in order of increasing complexity:

Leffler, John E.: *A Short Course of Organic Chemistry*, The Macmillan Company, New York, 1959.

Morrison, Robert T., and Robert N. Boyd: *Organic Chemistry*, Allyn and Bacon, Boston, 1959.

Cram, Donald J., and George S. Hammond: *Organic Chemistry*, McGraw-Hill Book Company, Inc., New York, 1959.

Roberts, John D., and Marjorie C. Caserio: *Basic Principles of Organic Chemistry*, W. A. Benjamin, New York, 1964.

Chapter 23

Equilibrium and Kinetics

Chemical systems are dynamic systems; the molecules are moving, bumping into each other, perhaps reacting. In the vessels holding the reactants and products of a chemical reaction all sorts of reactions occur, and the ultimate result of these reactions is an equilibrium among the species. Since acid-base reactions illustrate the fundamental principles of chemical equilibrium, our discussion will begin with this important group of chemical reactions.

ACIDS AND BASES

Acids and bases are relatively well-known compounds. Acids are sour to the taste. They corrode most metals. Bases taste bitter and feel slippery. They are also corrosive.

A simple distinction between acids and bases is by means of *indicators*, dyes which change to a different color when acids are added and back again when bases are added. Indicators are quite common. Tea, for instance, contains an indicator which changes to a lighter shade of tan when lemon juice—citric acid—is added. Red cabbage contains an indicator which changes from bluish to red when vinegar —acetic acid—is added. Both of these color changes can be reversed by the addition of excess base, although lye or ammonia are rarely found in recipes.

The chemistry of acids and bases depends on the peculiar nature of the element hydrogen. In acids, hydrogen is bonded to a highly electronegative element. It forms a strongly polar bond with the shared electron pair displaced away from hydrogen. The displacement occurs to such an extent that the acid hydrogen is essentially a proton attached to the electron pair. This proton is rather mobile. It can easily attach itself to an available electron pair of some other group. Acid-base reactions are the proton-transfer reactions. *Acids are proton donors* and *bases are proton acceptors.*

We can illustrate this by the action of acids and bases with the indicator methyl orange (*MO*), which in its yellow, basic form has the structure shown in Fig. 23-1. *MO* has many alternating single and double bonds in the two rings and the —N=N— bridge between them. This is the kind of electron arrangement which interacts with

light and produces color in a compound. Also, *MO* has several nitrogen atoms with available, unshared electron pairs. These can accept protons when acids are added. The addition of the proton then produces a rearrangement of the electrons throughout the *MO* molecule, which also changes the color to pink.

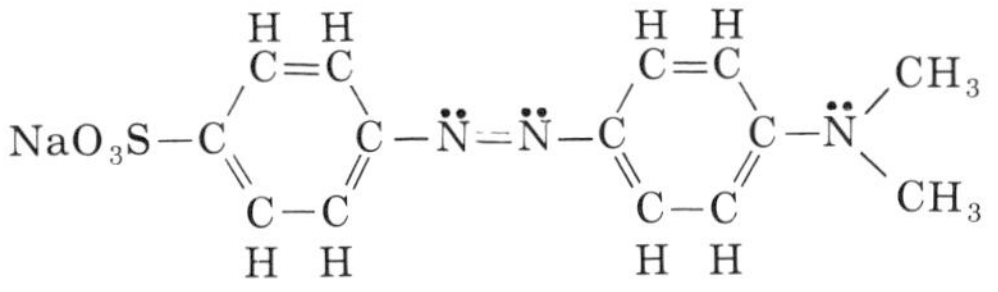

The reaction of an acid—we shall use HCl for illustration—with the indicator *MO* is given schematically in Eq. 23–1:

$$H:\overset{..}{\underset{..}{Cl}}: + \quad MO \quad \rightarrow HMO^+ + :\overset{..}{\underset{..}{Cl}}:^-$$
$$\text{(yellow)} \quad \text{(pink)}$$
$$(23\text{–}1)$$

The proton donor HCl transfers its proton to the proton acceptor *MO*. The reaction is an acid-base reaction. To reverse the color change by the addition of a base requires that the proton be removed from HMO^+. This is illustrated by the reaction of the base NH_3:

$$\overset{\textstyle H}{\underset{}{H:\overset{..}{N}:H}} + HMO^+ \rightarrow \overset{\textstyle H}{\underset{\textstyle H}{H:\overset{..}{N}:H^+}} + \quad MO$$
$$\text{(pink)} \qquad\qquad \text{(yellow)}$$
$$(23\text{–}2)$$

The proton acceptor NH_3 accepts a proton from the proton donor HMO^+. Equation 23–2 also shows an acid-base reaction.

The two equations illustrate a number of important aspects of acid-base reactions. Each equation shows two pairs of related species which differ only by a proton. In Eq. 23–1 the pairs are HCl–Cl⁻ and HMO^+–*MO*; in Eq. 23–2, HMO^+–*MO* and NH_4^+–NH_3. The first member of each of the pairs has a proton which it can donate; it is an acid. The second member has an available electron pair to accept a proton; it is a base. These pairs are acid-base pairs. Second, in acid-base reactions the acid from one pair donates its proton to the base of the other. In Eq. 23–1 the acid HCl donates a proton to the base *MO*; in Eq. 23–2 the acid HMO^+ donates a proton to the base NH_3. Finally either the acid or the base of an acid-base pair can participate in an acid-

FIG. 23-1

The structure of the indicator methyl orange. The many alternating double bonds are typical of the electron arrangement in colored compounds. In addition, there are three nitrogen atoms with available electron pairs to which H+ ions can attach.

base reaction. For instance, in 23–1 the base *MO* of the pair *HMO*+–*MO* reacts. In 23–2 the acid *HMO*+ reacts.

The characteristics of acid-base reactions are very similar to the characteristics of displacement reactions. In displacement reactions a metal loses electrons or its ion gains them. The electron-loss tendency orders displacement reactions. In acid-base reactions the acid of an acid-base pair donates protons or the base accepts them. Acid-base reactions, too, can be ordered by means of their proton-loss tendency. Strong acids readily donate protons; weak acids tend to hold on to them.

We can set up a partial list of acid-base pairs with the information from Eqs. 23–1 and 23–2. Equation 23–1 shows that the acid HCl donates its protons to the base *MO*. It implies that the acid *HMO*+ does not donate protons to the base Cl⁻, or the arrow in the equation would point the other way. The pair HCl–Cl⁻ has a stronger acid than the pair *HMO*+–*MO*. Equation 23–2, by analogous reasoning, shows that the pair *HMO*+–*MO* has a stronger acid than the pair NH_4+–NH_3. Hence the order of the three pairs, in the direction of decreasing acid strength, is HCl–Cl⁻, *HMO*+–*MO*, NH_4+–NH_3.

ACID-BASE SERIES

While the indicator *MO* was convenient to illustrate how an acid-base series can be set up, water is a much more useful reference for ordering acid-base pairs; slightly different techniques are used to produce the list. Water is unusually well suited for this task even aside from its ready availability. It has two strongly polar O—H bonds which can serve as the source of protons; it also has two available unshared electron pairs to which protons can attach. H_2O can be either an acid or a base and, indeed, in pure water there is a small amount of acid-base behavior. About two water molecules in a billion donate their

protons to the electron pairs of other water molecules:

$$H : \overset{..}{\underset{..}{O}} : H + H : \overset{..}{\underset{..}{O}} : H \longrightarrow$$
$$H$$
$$H : \overset{..}{\underset{..}{O}} : H^+(aq) + : \overset{..}{\underset{..}{O}} : H^-(aq)$$
$$(23\text{--}3)$$

Evidence for this reaction comes from the slight conductance of electric current due to the presence of H_3O+ and OH⁻ ions. While these ions are present in all water solutions, their number is so small that it can usually be ignored when other reactions are discussed.

The reactions which occur when acids are added to water are all similar to

$$HCl(g) + H_2O \rightarrow$$
$$H_3O^+(aq) + Cl^-(aq)$$
$$(23\text{--}4)$$

Since the reaction produces ions, acid strength in the solution is measured by electric conductance and by changes in the colligative properties. With respect to these properties, HCl solutions behave exactly like NaCl solutions. This is good evidence that HCl in water exists as the ions H_3O+ and Cl⁻ only. HCl is a very strong acid.

Acetic acid, CH_3COOH, contrasts sharply with HCl. Its solutions conduct poorly. It changes colligative properties only slightly more than the nonacid covalent compound ethyl alcohol. There are few ions in CH_3COOH solutions; most of the molecules retain their protons. We indicate this by the short arrow in Eq. 23–5 with an arrow of comparable length in the opposite direction.

$$CH_3COOH(aq) + H_2O \rightleftharpoons$$
$$CH_3COO^-(aq) + H_3O^+(aq)$$
$$(23\text{--}5)$$

The short double arrow means that reaction to the right occurs to a slight extent. Acetic acid is a weak acid.

Table 23–1 lists other acids, from the very strong acids HCl and H_2SO_4 at the top to the very weak acids NH_4+ and H_2O

at the bottom. We use Table 23–1 exactly as we used the displacement series. Each listing is of an acid-base pair reacting with the H_3O^+–H_2O pair. Then, the acid from the acid-base pair listed higher in the table donates its proton to the base of the acid-base pair listed lower. This means that in writing the equation for the actual reaction, the direction of the lower equation is reversed. For instance, the table tells us that the acid HF, listed higher, donates its protons to the base paired with the acid H_2S. A chemical reaction occurs between HF and HS^-. To write the equation, we combine the equation for HF as listed with the equation for H_2S reversed.

$$HF(aq) + H_2O \longrightarrow$$
$$H_3O^+(aq) + F^-(aq)$$
$$(23\text{–}6)$$

$$HS^-(aq) + H_3O^+(aq) \longrightarrow$$
$$H_2O + H_2S(aq)$$
$$(23\text{–}7)$$

Then we add these two but omit H_2O and H_3O^+ from the final equation since they occur both on the product and the reactant side.

$$HF(aq) + HS^-(aq) \longrightarrow$$
$$H_2S(aq) + F^-(aq)$$
$$(23\text{–}8)$$

The equation and the table show that the stronger acid, HF, pushes its protons onto the base paired with the weaker acid, H_2S. It means that if we should add HF, the highly corrosive glass-dissolving acid, to a solution of NaHS, an ionic compound, they would react to produce H_2S, highly poisonous and obnoxious because of its rotten-egg odor, and leave noncorrosive NaF in the solution. The $Na^+(aq)$, however, does not appear in Eq. 23–8 because ions in water solution are independent species. $Na^+(aq)$ has no vital part in the reaction.

It is important to note that at the bottom right of Table 23–1 there are some substances typically considered as bases. They are paired with very weak acids. This is as expected from the definitions of acid-base pairs. The acid-base pair of a strongly proton-donating acid like HCl contains a weakly proton-accepting base like Cl^-, whereas the pair of a strongly proton-accepting base like OH^- contains a weakly donating acid like H_2O. The table can therefore be used for all kinds of substances, whether they are commonly considered acids or bases. For instance, the reaction between the strong acid HNO_3 and the strong base KOH uses the second and the last equations on Table 23–1:

$$HNO_3(g) + H_2O \longrightarrow$$
$$H_3O^+(aq) + NO_3^-(aq)$$
$$(23\text{–}9)$$

TABLE 23-1

Relative strengths of acid-base pairs

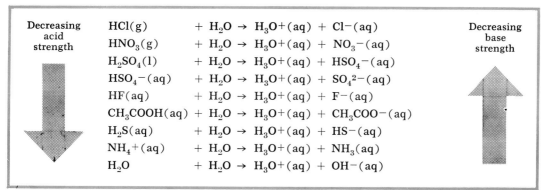

Decreasing acid strength			Decreasing base strength
	$HCl(g)$	$+ H_2O \rightarrow H_3O^+(aq) + Cl^-(aq)$	
	$HNO_3(g)$	$+ H_2O \rightarrow H_3O^+(aq) + NO_3^-(aq)$	
	$H_2SO_4(l)$	$+ H_2O \rightarrow H_3O^+(aq) + HSO_4^-(aq)$	
	$HSO_4^-(aq)$	$+ H_2O \rightarrow H_3O^+(aq) + SO_4^{2-}(aq)$	
	$HF(aq)$	$+ H_2O \rightarrow H_3O^+(aq) + F^-(aq)$	
	$CH_3COOH(aq)$	$+ H_2O \rightarrow H_3O^+(aq) + CH_3COO^-(aq)$	
	$H_2S(aq)$	$+ H_2O \rightarrow H_3O^+(aq) + HS^-(aq)$	
	$NH_4^+(aq)$	$+ H_2O \rightarrow H_3O^+(aq) + NH_3(aq)$	
	H_2O	$+ H_2O \rightarrow H_3O^+(aq) + OH^-(aq)$	

$$OH^-(aq) + H_3O^+(aq) \longrightarrow$$
$$H_2O + H_2O$$
$$(23\text{-}10)$$

Addition leaves:

$$HNO_3(g) + OH^-(aq) \longrightarrow$$
$$H_2O + NO_3^-(aq)$$
$$(23\text{-}11)$$

The ion $K^+(aq)$ with which the OH^- in Eq. 23–10 was associated is an independent species which has no important part in the reaction.

None of the products of Eq. 23–11 is strongly acid. Hence the reaction between the strong acid HNO_3 and the strong base OH^- produces water and the nonacid, nonbasic ionic species NO_3^- which is associated with the K^+ ion. The products are no longer corrosive; they do not affect indicators either as acids or as bases. Strong acids and strong bases neutralize each other, usually producing water and ionic compounds called *salts*.

Two final points are of interest. In acids like H_2SO_4 there are two potentially available protons, and both can be lost to bases. However, the acid strength of the two pro-

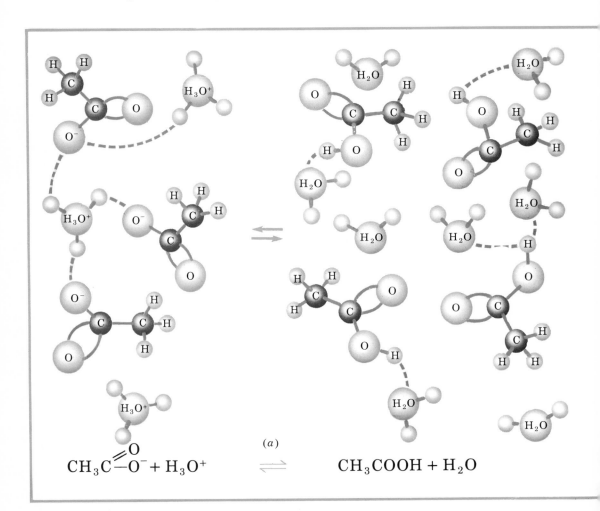

(a)

$$CH_3C{\overset{\displaystyle O}{\Vert}}O^- + H_3O^+ \rightleftharpoons CH_3COOH + H_2O$$

FIG. 23-2

Changing the CH_3COOH equilibrium. (a) The equilibrium reflects the probability that CH_3COO^- and H_3O^+ ions combine compared to the probability that CH_3COOH

tons is not the same. The first acid reaction of H_2SO_4 occurs completely:

$$H_2SO_4(l) + H_2O \longrightarrow$$
$$H_3O^+(aq) + HSO_4^-(aq)$$
$$(23\text{–}12)$$

No H_2SO_4 is left. But the second acid reaction, the loss of the proton from HSO_4^-, leaves some HSO_4^- ions.

$$HSO_4^-(aq) + H_2O \longrightarrow$$
$$H_3O^+(aq) + SO_4^{2-}(aq)$$
$$(23\text{–}13)$$

HSO_4^- is not as strong an acid as H_2SO_4.

There are many other acids with more than one proton, like H_2S and H_2CO_3 in the table.

Finally, the reaction between acids and metals is not an acid reaction—proton transfer—at all. Instead, it is an electron-transfer reaction. $H^+(aq)$, which is listed in the table of standard electrode potentials, is the same species as $H_3O^+(aq)$ in acid solutions; both are H^+ attached to the electrons of H_2O molecules. But the reaction of $H^+(aq)$ with an active metal is a reaction in which the metal pushes its electrons onto the acid proton and forms H_2 gas; it is not proton transfer.

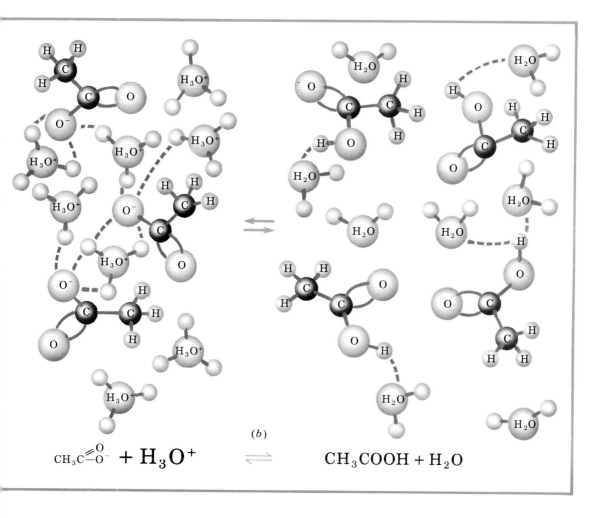

(b)

$$CH_3C{\overset{O}{\underset{O^-}{\diagup}}} + H_3O^+ \rightleftharpoons CH_3COOH + H_2O$$

and H_2O molecules combine. (b) The addition of H_3O^+ ions from some other acid increases the probability that they combine with CH_3COO^-.

EQUILIBRIUM

In our discussion so far, we have ignored the dynamic character of acid-base reactions and, indeed, of all chemical reactions. We implied that in weak acid solutions a small fraction of the acid molecules donate their protons to water and that the reaction then stops. This is not so. All systems of molecules react continually. Some of the acid molecules, at any instant, donate protons to water molecules while some of their paired bases, at the same instant, accept protons from water. A more accurate representation of the reactions that occur is by an equation that includes a double arrow to indicate that reactants and product are continuously being formed and unformed. This was one purpose of the double arrow in Eq. 23–5. In this dynamic interchange a state is reached in which the net concentrations no longer change because the rates of formation and reversal are equal. This is a state of equilibrium. While individual molecules and ions continue to accept or donate protons, their total concentrations do not change.

A dynamic situation of this sort is governed by probability considerations. If a $0.01M$ solution of CH_3COOH in water forms about 5 percent CH_3COO^- and H_3O^+ ions, this implies that the probability of CH_3COOH donating its protons to water is relatively slight compared to the probability of H_3O^+ donating its protons back to the CH_3COO^-. If a $0.01M$ solution of HF forms about 25 percent F^- and H_3O^+ ions, this implies that the probability of HF donating its proton is relatively greater than the probability for CH_3COOH. The dynamic equilibrium implies that acid strength is related to the probability that H_3O^+ and X^- form from the acid HX without recombining as the species move through the solution and are jostled about by their neighbors. Conversely, base strengths relate to the probability that the species X^- will hold the proton as HX rather than donating it again to another base.

Because of the dynamic nature of the reactions, changes can be made in the solutions in unusual ways. For instance, one can diminish the amount of CH_3COO^- in a solution of acetic acid (Eq. 23–5) simply by adding a strong acid like HCl. HCl furnishes H_3O^+ ions. These combine in the dynamic-equilibrium-reaction processes with CH_3COO^- to form CH_3COOH while the latter at the same time forms the ions. But if there are more H_3O^+ ions present than before (from HCl) the probability of their combination with CH_3COO^- increases. The reaction that removes CH_3COO^- from the equilibrium system is favored. Less CH_3COO^- remains.

In a similar manner one can increase the concentration of CH_3COO^- ions by diminishing the concentration of H_3O^+—for instance, by the addition of OH^-, which is a stronger base than CH_3COO^- and removes H_3O^+ preferentially. With fewer H_3O^+ present, the reaction that removes CH_3COO^- proceeds more slowly than before, and the amount of those ions present increases.

LE CHÂTELIER'S PRINCIPLE

A statement credited to the French physicist H. L. Le Châtelier (1850–1936) describes how changes affect all systems at equilibrium. *Le Châtelier's principle* states that *if a stress is applied to a system in equilibrium, the equilibrium system will adjust to relieve that stress.* The previous section provided one illustration of Le Châtelier's principle. In a solution of CH_3COOH, protons jump from CH_3COOH to H_2O with a certain probability and from H_3O^+ to CH_3COO^- with another probability. At equilibrium the two processes occur at the same rate; no net change in the species occurs. Then H_3O^+ is removed by the addition of OH^-. The equilibrium is disturbed—a stress is applied—and proton jumps from H_3O^+ to CH_3COO^- cannot occur as frequently. The system adjusts to relieve the stress be-

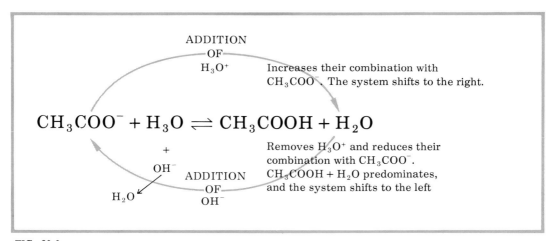

FIG. 23-3

Le Châtelier's principle and the CH₃COOH equilibrium.

cause the proton jumps from CH_3COOH to H_2O, which have not been affected, now predominate and produce additional H_3O^+. Thus the system tends to replenish the species H_3O^+ which was disturbed in the first place. (Of course, the formation of more CH_3COO^- ions accompanies the production of more H_3O^+.)

When excess H_3O^+ is added to the system, as in the other example above, the stress is relieved by adjustment in the other direction. The added H_3O^+ from HCl increase the rate of H_3O^+ combining with CH_3COO^-. This now-favored reaction removes the excess H_3O^+ which were the stress on the equilibrium system. In both

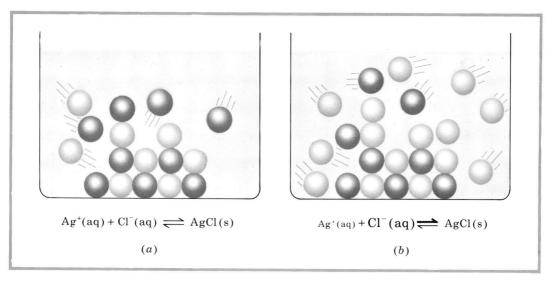

$$Ag^+(aq) + Cl^-(aq) \rightleftharpoons AgCl(s)$$
(a)

$$Ag^+(aq) + Cl^-(aq) \rightleftharpoons AgCl(s)$$
(b)

FIG. 23-4

Le Chatelier's principle and the AgCl solubility equilibrium. (a) In AgCl solution, Ag+ and Cl− ions settle on a crystal of AgCl as rapidly as the ions break away and enter solution. (b) Addition of Cl− (perhaps from NaCl) increases the rate at which Cl− ions settle. They take with them additional Ag+ ions, and the equilibrium is reestablished with a smaller number of Ag+ ions left in solution.

cases the stress-reducing reaction predominates over its reverse until new concentrations of all species reestablish equilibrium, in a new situation in which the rates of formation and reversal are again equal.

Le Châtelier's principle can be applied to other equilibrium systems as well. Solubility of a substance implies that a point is reached in which its particles deposit from solution as quickly as they enter solution from the solid residue. A dynamic equilibrium exists. For instance, in $10^{-5}M$ AgCl solution, Ag^+ and Cl^- ions settle as quickly as others leave the crystal (Fig. 23–4). If additional Cl^- is added from HCl or NaCl, settling of Ag^+ and Cl^- occurs more rapidly than before the equilibrium was disturbed because there are more Cl^- ions to settle and they take with them additional Ag^+ ions to keep the crystal electrically neutral. Deposition of ions on the solid occurs until a new equilibrium is set up in which the settling rate of the new amounts of Ag^+ and Cl^- again equals their rate of solution from the solid. That new rate, however, is established with some of the added Cl^- — the stress—no longer in solution. The adjustment has been in the direction of relieving the stress.

Another example of Le Châtelier's prin-ciple is the vapor-pressure equilibrium above liquids. Compressing the molecules in equilibrium with a liquid increases their concentration and their rate of striking the liquid surface (Fig. 23–5). Hence more molecules return to the liquid than leave it. The amount of vapor above the liquid is reduced until only enough molecules are left in the now smaller vapor space to maintain the vapor-pressure equilibrium. The effect has been to relieve the stress of compression by reducing the number of molecules in the vapor. Adding heat to the vapor-liquid system also produces an effect that offsets the stress. The added heat increases the energy of the molecules so that a larger fraction can overcome the potential energy that binds them to their neighbors in the liquid. More leave and the vapor pressure increases. Hence the result of the addition of heat is to increase the heat-absorbing evaporation processes that relieve the stress of the added heat.

COMPLETION OF REACTIONS

The previous section suggests that all chemical systems are dynamic, with reactants colliding to produce products and

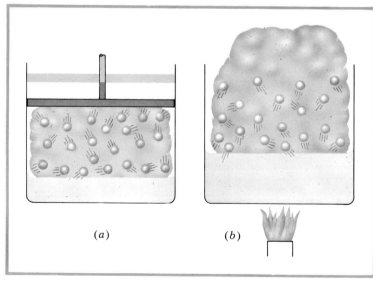

(a)   (b)

Le Chatelier's principle and the vapor-pressure equilibrium. (a) Compressing the vapor produces condensation of the molecules, which reduces the pressure. (b) Heating increases the rate of evaporation, a process which absorbs the heat of vaporization.

FIG. 23-5

products colliding to re-form the reactants. This raises the very real question of how chemical reactions occur at all. How are things like H_2SO_4 or NH_3 manufactured if the reactants and products constantly form and reverse? The answer is given by Le Châtelier's principle. Stresses are applied to the equilibrium system so that it continuously adjusts to relieve the stress.

One stress on an equilibrium system is to produce a gaseous product which escapes. Since the gaseous product is no longer present in the reaction system, recombination cannot occur. In each of the following equations, gas formation produces adjustments in the equilibrium that make the reaction go to completion:

$$H_2SO_4(aq) + Cl^-(aq) \xrightarrow[\text{heat}]{} HSO_4^-(aq) + HCl(g)$$

$$(23\text{--}14)$$

$$CH_3COOH(aq) + HCO_3^-(aq) \longrightarrow CH_3COO^-(aq) + H_2O(l) + CO_2(g)$$

$$(23\text{--}15)$$

$$OH^-(aq) + NH_4^+(aq) \longrightarrow H_2O + NH_3(g)$$

$$(23\text{--}16)$$

A second stress, more common among ionic solutions, is to produce an insoluble solid product which is removed from the solution equilibrium by settling to the bottom:

$$Ag^+(aq) + Cl^-(aq) \longrightarrow AgCl(s)$$

$$(23\text{--}17)$$

$$Ba^{2+}(aq) + SO_4^{2-}(aq) \longrightarrow BaSO_4(s)$$

$$(23\text{--}18)$$

In both of these reactions, only the ions which combine to form the insoluble compound are written. They come, of course, with another ion of opposite charge which, however, is independent in the solution and takes no part in the reaction. It is an onlooker, a *spectator* ion. Thus, Eq. 23–17

represents all the following possible reactions, and more:

$$AgNO_3(aq) + NaCl(aq) \longrightarrow NaNO_3(aq) + AgCl(s)$$

$$(23\text{--}19)$$

$$AgNO_3(aq) + HCl(aq) \longrightarrow HNO_3(aq) + AgCl(s)$$

$$(23\text{--}20)$$

$$AgCH_3COO(aq) + NaCl(aq) \longrightarrow NaCH_3COO(aq) + AgCl(s)$$

$$(23\text{--}21)$$

$$2AgNO_3(aq) + CuCl_2(aq) \longrightarrow Cu(NO_3)_2(aq) + 2AgCl(s)$$

$$(23\text{--}22)$$

In all of them the reverse reaction, recombination of product ions to produce the reactant ions, is impossible because AgCl is removed from contact with the product ions by the formation of the insoluble solid, a process called *precipitation.*

A third factor which leads to the completion of chemical reactions is electron transfer. The attraction of ions for electrons differs so greatly, as we saw in Chap. 20, that reversal of an electron-transfer reaction in the equilibrium sense is always possible in principle but rarely occurs in fact. Thus $Cu(s)$ holds its electrons so much more strongly than $Zn(s)$ that the displacement reaction goes to completion. And the same is true of nearly every other displacement reaction. Only those with very small standard electrode potential differences—say about 0.10 volt or less—are in fact equilibrium systems in which substantial forward and reverse reactions take place. Very few of the common displacement reactions produce such small potentials.

The fourth factor is the formation of a strong covalent bond which is difficult to break. The reverse reaction, which requires the breaking of that bond, has a small probability and the reaction goes to completion.

For instance, the H—O bond in H_3O^+ is relatively strong compared to the H—Cl bond (Eq. 23–4). Consequently HCl(g) reacting with water forms H_3O^+ and Cl^- exclusively because the chance of the breaking up of H_3O^+ is relatively very small.

The breaking of covalent bonds as a factor governing the completion of chemical reactions, like electron transfer, is a relative matter. The HCl + H_2O reaction goes to completion because the bonds in H_3O^+ are much stronger than the H—Cl bond. Likewise, the HNO_3 + H_2O reaction (Table 23–1) goes to completion because of the great difference in bond strength between H—NO_3 and H_3O^+. But in CH_3COOH the O—H bond is nearly as strong as in H_3O^+. Consequently the breaking of bonds in the forward and reverse reactions occurs with nearly equal probabilities. The reaction does not go to completion but remains a dynamic equilibrium system.

Covalent bonds of similar strengths are quite common in organic reactions. Equilibrium systems, implying small yields, are the rule, and the task of the chemical engineer and chemist is to apply stresses to equilibrium systems in such a manner that the desired reactions go more nearly to completion. This requires making use of one or several of the factors we have just discussed. It also means keeping undesirable side reactions to a minimum since the processes that take place in chemical-reaction vessels are rarely as neat and simple as those we write on paper in a text. To explore the complexities of such situations in detail, however, takes us far beyond the purpose of this book, which is to stress the simple understandings that have been developed to analyze complex situations found in nature.

KINETICS

Equilibrium focuses on the reactions that go on in a chemical system, the collisions between reactant molecules that lead to the formation of products and the collision of product molecules that re-form the reactants. Not all collisions actually produce a reaction. H_2 and O_2 molecules can be mixed and will not react although the molecules collide incessantly. They merely bump and separate again. The mixture is potentially explosive but actually unreactive. We saw the reasons for this in the previous chapter when we discussed the reactions that produce ClH_2CCH_2Cl, Eqs. 22–1 and 22–2. New bonds do not simply form, even if they are stronger, unless old bonds are first broken. And a number of factors hinder the breaking of old bonds. The study of the actual progress of chemical reactions, from collision to breaking of bonds to rearrangement and the formation of new bonds is the subject of *chemical kinetics*. What happens to the bonds is inferred from measurements of the rates with which the molecules combine.

In the theoretical analysis of chemical reactions we focus on five distinct parts of the process which leads from reactants to products (Fig. 23–6). The part of the figure between A and B describes the approaching molecules. Their energy is the energy of their bonds. Since they are not yet in contact, there is no interaction between them. At point B the molecules collide. From there onward to C they disrupt each other, distorting bonds and dislocating electrons as suggested by the colliding molecules in the figure. These disruptive processes require energy, and the curve rises along the energy axis. At C the molecules have reached an intermediate structure. Here the old bonds are almost completely disrupted and the new bonds are just beginning to form. Neither reactants nor products are distinctly recognizable, and the bonds of both are partly formed. From C to D the structure becomes distinctly that of the products and the new bonds stabilize. As they form more firmly, the system becomes more stable and its energy decreases. Finally, from D to E the product molecules separate and the energy of the system is that of the bonds of the products.

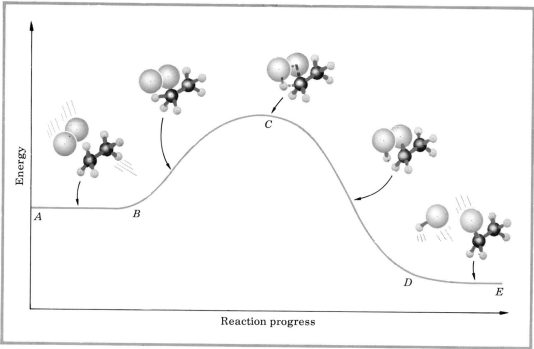

FIG. 23-6

The reaction coordinate. At A two separate molecules approach, but they are too far apart to interact. At B they just begin to touch. As they bump and dislocate bonds and electrons, from B to C, their energy goes up. If the collision geometry is favorable and the collision sufficiently energetic, old bonds begin to break and new ones form in an intermediate structure, at C. The partial bonds of the intermediate structure may stabilize as the bonds of the product molecules, from C to D, with a drop in the energy of the system. The product molecules then separate from D to E.

In any chemical reaction, the molecules must pass through these steps, and the rate of the chemical reaction is governed by the ease with which they can pass through the steps. The first step, from *A* to *B*, is the collision of the molecules. Few collisions mean a slow reaction. In the next step, from *B* to *C*, two factors operate. Molecules must collide vigorously enough to produce the disruptions needed to reach the intermediate structure. This normally happens in only a small fraction of the collisions, those between the most rapidly moving molecules of the speed distribution. Slower molecules bump, begin to disrupt, and move partway up the slope from *B* to *C*. But then their energy is insufficient to lead to rearrangement of the bonds, and they separate again as they had existed before collision,

moving downward and to the left on the reaction coordinate. Second, the vigorous collisions must be so oriented that the initial disruptions easily lead to the formation of new bonds. The collision geometry must be right. If it is not, the colliding molecules will be thoroughly shaken up, but since new bonds cannot form, they will separate again toward the left on the reaction coordinate without forming the intermediate structure.

The final factor which may preclude the formation of products is the behavior of the intermediate structure itself. This structure is halfway between reactants and products. Its bonds are partially those of the reactants and partially those of the products. After it forms as the result of a high-energy collision with favorable geometry, it may separate again in the same manner as it was formed. It can separate into reactants as well as into products. Hence only about half the collisions which lead to the formation of the intermediate structure actually lead on to the formation of product molecules.

This analysis indicates the manner in which a chemical reaction can be manipulated to increase the speed with which product is produced. Since we cannot affect individual molecules, there is no way of influencing collision geometry or the manner in which the intermediate structure separates. But it is possible to influence the number of collisions per second and also the vigor of the collisions.

One can increase the number of collisions per second by increasing the concentration of a reactant in solution or increasing the pressure of the gases in a gas-phase reaction. In both cases the number of molecules per unit volume increases and their frequency of collision likewise increases. The relationship is quite direct. Doubling the concentration of a reactant doubles its rate of collision and also the rate of chemical reaction. The rate of chemical reaction is directly proportional to the concentration of the reacting species.

For solids it is not possible to increase the concentration. Reaction occurs only at the surface. But increasing the available surface increases the rate. Finely powdered solids react much more rapidly than big particles, so much so that fine steel wool burns in a bunsen burner, powdered aluminum explodes in oxygen, and powdered dust may explode in air. Many silos have been lost because the dust of the grain stored in them exploded.

But collision is not enough to produce a reaction. The molecules must collide with enough vigor to break old bonds before new ones can be formed. Since the faster the molecules move, the more vigorous their collisions, temperature has an important effect on the rate of reaction. Temperature effects are not alike for all reactions be-

cause the strengths of the bonds to be broken differ and the molecular geometries involved in collision also differ. Typically, chemical reactions double to quadruple their rates for each 10°C rise in temperature. Concentration and temperatures are the direct ways for changing the speed of chemical reactions.

CATALYSTS

There is one other means for increasing the rate of chemical reactions, the addition of a catalyst. *Catalysts* are substances which are added to a chemical reaction to influence its rate and which appear unchanged after the reaction is complete. Figure 23–7 helps to explain how they function.

The line from A to B indicates the average energy of separated reactant molecules; the line from D to E, the average energy of separated product molecules. As the diagram is drawn, the reactant molecules contain more energy than the product molecules. During reaction this amount of energy is produced as the *heat of reaction*. As the reaction proceeds, heat is given off to the surroundings.

But there is another energy of interest to the chemist. Molecules that reach point C have the minimum energy required for the bond rearrangement that produces the intermediate structure at C. The difference between their energy at C and the average is called the *activation energy*. Activation energy is the energy that must be supplied to average molecules in order to produce the rearranged intermediate structure in the reaction. The larger the activation energy, the smaller the fraction of the molecules that possess enough energy to rearrange. Hence a large activation energy means a slow reaction. Conversely, a small activation energy means a fast reaction.

Both temperature and catalysts affect the reaction rate through the activation energy. Heating a reaction mixture increases the fraction of energetic molecules in the dis-

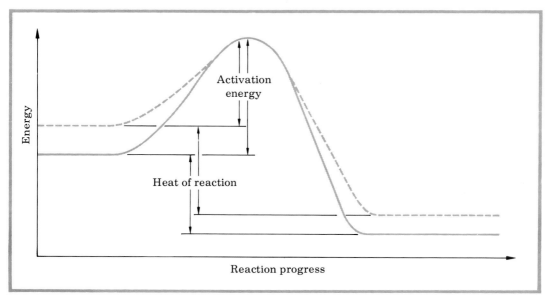

FIG. 23-7

Energy relations in a chemical reaction. The difference between reactant energies and product energies is the heat of reaction. The difference between reactant energy and the energy required to produce the intermediate structure is the activation energy. At higher temperatures (dashed lines), both reactants and products have higher energies. The activation energy is smaller, implying a faster reaction.

tribution. Hence a larger fraction of the collisions occurs between molecules that possess the activation energy or more. More product-producing collisions occur. Heating raises the total energy of the colliding molecules, the level between *A* and *B*. Catalysts affect the level at *C*.

Activation energy implies a particular intermediate arrangement with certain bonds broken and a particular intermediate electron distribution among the intermediate species. Catalysts change the rate by providing alternative routes to product formation which require less disruption and, therefore, require less energy to reach the intermediate point *C*. We can illustrate this with the ethylene polymerization, Fig. 22-5. Ethylene is a quite stable substance. Spontaneous polymerization due to rearrangement of the double-bond electrons on collisions is practically nonexistent. The activation energy for this simple collision process, in which two ethylenes open their double bonds simultaneously, is extremely

high (Fig. 23-8). But when the starter is added, a new reaction route becomes available. The intermediate structure now has the ethylene double bond partially open and the single electron of the starter nearby, ready to form the products. This rearrangement requires much less energy, its activation energy is low, and this polymerization proceeds rapidly at quite low temperature. The reactants and the products in both reactions, direct collision of ethylene molecules or catalyzed addition, are the same. The energy levels at *A* and *E* are unchanged, but the "mountain" in between, the activation energy, is greatly reduced.

Because they increase the rates of chemical reactions, catalysts are extremely helpful in industrial processes. In the body, too, most chemical reactions are catalyzed by the organic catalysts called *enzymes*. But while a starter, like the one used in ethylene polymerization, reacts with nearly any double-bond compound and other common industrial catalysts like finely divided plati-

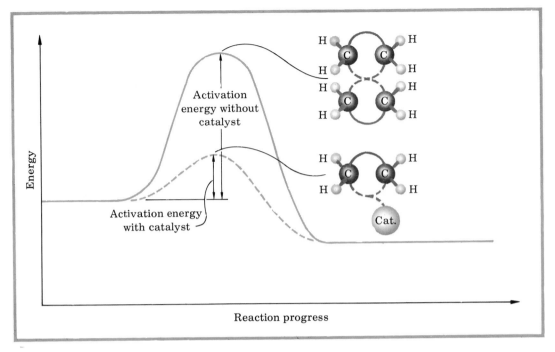

FIG. 23-8

Catalyst influence on reaction rate. In a catalyzed reaction the reaction path goes through an intermediate structure which forms much more easily—has a lower activation energy.

num or nickel catalyze a variety of reactions, enzymes are quite specific. Structural fit and structural specificity mark most processes of living organisms. There seem to be specific enzymes for nearly every body process. Amylases for splitting sugars, lipases for splitting fats, pepsin for splitting proteins are a few examples. Indeed, the transfer RNAs, which apparently are specific for one amino acid and probably for one kind of protein, are simply catalysts in the building of proteins.

KINETICS, CATALYSTS, AND EQUILIBRIUM

The reaction path from A to E in Fig. 23–6 describes the intermediate steps for reactants colliding, rearranging, and forming products. The reverse reaction in an equilibrium system, the reaction that re-forms the reactants from products, follows the

path in reverse. The products begin at E, some collide with sufficient energy to form the intermediate structure at C, and some of these proceed on to re-form the reactants at A. For this reverse process, the activation energy is the difference between the average energy of products, the level at E, and the energy of the intermediate structure at C. If the reaction from A to E produces energy, the reverse reaction has a higher activation energy and proceeds more slowly.

At equilibrium in this case there are more of the products present than of reactants because there a greater number of collisions between product molecules offsets the lesser probability that any collision re-forms reactants. Thus by balancing numbers with the probability that reaction proceeds, the rate of the reverse reaction is kept equal to the rate of the formation of products. At equilibrium, therefore, the amounts of reactants and the amounts of products are related to the relative heights of the two activation energies, which in turn depend on the heat of reaction. The relative composition of the equilibrium mixture is related to the heat of reaction. But the speed with which the reactions proceed at equilibrium, how fast they approach the equilibrium when mixed, and then how fast the interchange between reactants and products, backward and forward, takes place, depends on the absolute height of the activation energy. Reactions with large activation energy approach equilibrium slowly.

This point is particularly well illustrated by the schematic representation of the reaction between H_2 and O_2 to form water. The heat of reaction is quite high; much heat is liberated when two moles of H_2 burn in O_2. The equilibrium mixture of these two gases has nearly all of the system in the form of water. But the rate of approach is very slow. A mixture of H_2 and O_2 is

quite stable because the activation energy for the process is very high. Hardly any H_2 and O_2 molecules collide with enough energy to rearrange. A catalyst changes all this. A bit of powdered platinum will explode the mixture. Then, because of a path with a smaller activation energy for the forward reaction, equilibrium is reached very quickly—explosively—and forward and backward reactions both take place rapidly. Still, the equilibrium system remains mostly water because nearly all forward collisions lead to water production while few water collisions re-form H_2 and O_2. When these two rates occur equally rapidly, there must be many more collisions between water molecules; most of the system must be H_2O.

We have studied the concept of a dynamic equilibrium in the context of chemical reactions where it has the most direct and immediate practical application. The notion

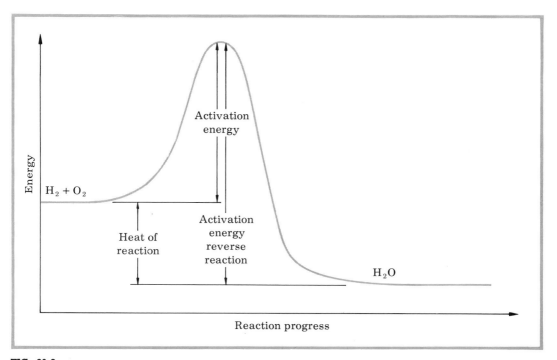

FIG. 23-9

Schematic representation of the $2H_2 + O_2 \rightarrow 2H_2O$ reaction. The heat of reaction is large, implying great stability of H_2O, but the activation energy of the uncatalyzed reaction is also very large, implying a very small rate of combination of H_2 and O_2.

of dynamic equilibrium transcends chemistry, however. Our estimates of the processes that go on within stars, in Chap. 3, were based on the supposition of a dynamic balance between them. The concept of uniformitarianism is a concept of dynamic balance and so is the principle of isostasy. Since we postulate the birth of a star and the origin of the earth, the balance has persisted for a limited time only. Four or more billion years ago our earth congealed presumably from hot gases, and around 5 to 10 billion years ago, probably, the sun was formed. Whether these processes of creation were part of a dynamic balance between creation and decay that extends throughout the universe in time and space, or whether they were part of a catastrophic beginning of planets, stars, and even galaxies is an open question. Cosmology, the study of the nature of the universe, is the last chapter of this book.

Questions and Problems

1. Each of the following are acids. What species are the base members of their acid-base pairs? H_3O^+, H_3PO_4, HSO_3^-, NH_4^+, H_2O.

2. Each of the following are bases. What species are the acid members of their acid-base pairs? CH_3COOH, HPO_4^{2-}, H_2O.

3. Determine from Table 23–1 which of the following reactions take place:

   (a) $HS^-(aq) + H_2O \rightarrow$
       $H_3O^+(aq) + S^{2-}(aq)$

   (b) $H_2SO_4 + NaF \rightarrow HF + NaHSO_4$

   (c) $NH_4^+(aq) + HSO_4^-(aq) \rightarrow$
       $NH_3(aq) + H_2SO_4(l)$

   (d) $HNO_3(g) + NH_3(aq) \rightarrow$
       $NH_4^+(aq) + NO_3^-(aq)$

4. $Ag(NH_3)_2^+(aq) + Cl^-(aq) \rightleftharpoons AgCl(s) + 2NH_3(aq)$. This equation describes a complex equilibrium system. Suggest at least two ways in which the relative amounts of $Ag(NH_3)_2^+$ and $AgCl(s)$ can be changed without adding or removing either. (Think of ways you can affect the other species.)

5. List the factors that promote completion of reaction. Illustrate each with two equations.

6. Each of the following reactions goes to completion. State all factors that promote completion of reaction:

   $Ba^{2+}(aq) + SO_4^{2-}(aq) \rightarrow BaSO_4(s)$

   $Ba(OH)_2(aq) + H_2SO_4(aq) \rightarrow$
     $BaSO_4(s) + 2H_2O$

   $NH_4^+(aq) + OH^-(aq) \rightarrow H_2O + NH_3(g)$

   $Mg(s) + 2HCl(aq) \rightarrow H_2(g) + MgCl_2(aq)$

7. Describe Le Châtelier's principle and illustrate it.

8. In a certain reaction two gases A and B combine. Discuss what happens to the rate of the chemical reaction if (a) the temperature is lowered, (b) the pressure is doubled.

9. Distinguish between heat of reaction and activation energy. How does each influence the rate of a chemical reaction? the equilibrium between reactants and products?

10. Most salts absorb heat on dissolving. According to Le Châtelier's principle, how should their solubility change with temperature?

11. In terms of a reaction-path diagram, explain why reactions of ions in solution are almost instantaneous.

12. Write all chemical equations described in the first paragraph of the section on Le Châtelier's principle.

Suggestions for Further Reading

Further treatment of the contents of this chapter may be found in:

Christiansen, G. S., and Paul H. Garrett: *Structure and Change*, W. H. Freeman and Company, San Francisco, 1960. Equilibrium and kinetics (chap. 12).

Pauling, Linus: *College Chemistry*, 3d ed., W. H. Freeman and Company, San Francisco, 1964. Equilibrium and kinetics (chap. 18); acids and bases (chap. 19).

Pimentel, George C. (ed.): *Chemistry: An Experimental Science*, W. H. Freeman and Company, San Francisco, 1963. Kinetics (chap. 8); equilibrium (chap. 9, 10); acids and bases (chap. 11).

Quagliano, James V.: *Chemistry,* 2d ed., Prentice-Hall, Inc., Englewood Cliffs, N.J., 1963. Acids and bases (chap. 20); equilibrium (chap. 21, 22); kinetics (chap. 23).

Sienko, Michell J., and Robert A. Plane: *Chemistry,* 2d ed., McGraw-Hill Book Company, Inc., New York, 1961. Kinetics (chapter. 12); equilibrium (chap. 13).

Further discussions of chemical equilibrium are found in:

Vander Werf, Calvin A.: *Acids, Bases and the Chemistry of the Covalent Bond,* Reinhold Publishing Corporation, New York, 1961 (paperback).

Strong, Laurence E., and Wilmer J. Stratton: *Chemical Energy,* Reinhold Publishing Corporation, New York, 1965 (paperback).

Chapter 24

Special Problems

We have reached the end of this brief study of the physical universe. In 23 chapters we have described selected aspects of the sky, of the earth, and of the things on it. We have discussed the basic laws that connect diverse phenomena—the laws of motion; of electricity, magnetism, and electromagnetism; of light and radiation; of nuclear particles and nuclear processes; of atomic structure and chemical combination—and the theories that explain them. The applications of this knowledge are everywhere around us. Scientific theory is the foundation upon which are built the hundreds of technological devices that make our lives easier and more comfortable. The advances in medicine that make our lives longer and healthier are also based on scientific theory. These practical results are an important reason for the emphasis on science in modern civilization.

But scientists are dreamers as well as tinkerers. Understanding and doing go hand in hand in the progress of science. Alongside the military results of space research is research into the origins of the universe. Alongside the practical medical results of health research is research into the origin of life. These two lines of research are among the most active and speculative investigations of today. Their aim is the understanding of how we and our universe came to be.

EARLY SCIENTIFIC COSMOLOGY

The earliest theories of the creation of the universe concerned only the solar system. The Copernican theory put the sun at the center with all planets revolving about from west to east and rotating also in the same direction. Newton's theory of gravitation described the planetary orbits and showed how the solar system hung together. But there was no scientific theory to suggest how it had got there. Newton at one time speculated that the sun and planets might have condensed from a diffuse gas that filled all space evenly. He concluded, however, that only the Creator could have formed a hot sun and six cold planets from this gas and then set them into motion in their peculiar ways. At the end of the seventeenth century a divine act of creation dominated cosmology. No one had seen a way to explain the formation of the universe by means of mechanical laws.

This was changed, within 50 years when two different ideas, both dependent in some way upon gravity, were suggested. One hypothesis first proposed by a Frenchman, Georges Buffon (1707–1788), assumed that a star had passed so close to the sun that gravity had pulled the planets from it (Fig. 24–1). Buffon's idea did not receive much attention until early in this century, when Sir James Jeans (1877–1946) in England and the Americans F. R. Moulton (1872–1952) and T. C. Chamberlin (1843–1928)

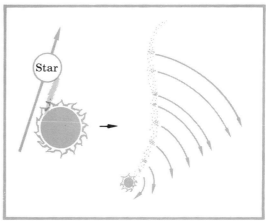

FIG. 24-1

Buffon's hypothesis. A passing star pulled gases from the sun which condensed into the planets. (Redrawn from Yerkes Observatory Photograph, University of Chicago, Williams Bay, Wis.)

independently developed it in some mathematical detail. They ran into serious trouble, and since about 1940 the passing-star hypothesis has not been considered likely by most astrophysicists. Its serious consideration by these outstanding scientists early this century is interesting because it is related to the history of the other hypothesis.

The second hypothesis was first proposed by Immanuel Kant (1724–1804), better known for his metaphysics. Kant, like Newton, proposed that the universe began as a diffuse cloud of material particles. The particles were in continuous chaotic motion under the influence of forces of attraction and repulsion. Because of attraction they eventually gathered into heavenly objects; because of repulsion they began to rotate and revolve. This method of creation accounted for the formation of the solar system, of rotating galaxies, and even of rotating supergalaxies.

There is one important difference between Buffon's and Kant's hypotheses. Buffon's was limited to the solar system; Kant's encompassed the universe. Kant used information, which had been amassed during the eighteenth century, that there were many rotating systems in the universe. This idea had originated with Thomas Wright (1711–1786), who in 1750 first suggested that the Milky Way is a wheel of stars as the solar system is a wheel of planets. Five years later Kant pointed to the then recently discovered elliptical light sources in the sky as other wheels of stars. Soon thereafter Sir William Herschel, discoverer of Uranus, made several careful surveys of the sky and found some 2,000 of the elliptical light sources now known as galaxies. He agreed with Kant and Wright and even went one step further. He divided the galaxies into four groups which to him suggested stages of development. Thus an origin and successive development are inherent in his groups. Moreover, Herschel discovered 269 pairs of revolving binary stars. These findings brought to light other revolving and rotating systems in the heavens, all of which Kant used in his theory.

But Kant's and Buffon's theories were also alike in one respect. Both were speculative and descriptive, not mathematical. This was changed early in this century for Buffon's theory. For Kant's theory it happened much earlier.

Soon after its publication, the French mathematician Pierre S. de Laplace (1749–1827) worked out the mathematics of Kant's theory for the solar system. An initially hot, rotating mass of diffuse matter cooled and condensed (Fig. 24–2). As it condensed, it had to rotate more rapidly in order to conserve angular momentum. As a result of the rapid rotation, the whirling mass lost rings of matter from time to time. These rings then broke up and some matter gathered into the precursors of planets, called *protoplanets*. Through their greater mass and gravitational attraction, the protoplanets gathered more of the primordial matter into themselves and eventually swept the rings clean. But the protoplanets were also spinning and condensing, and they too lost rings of matter. These rings of matter also broke up into what became the satellites, except for the rings of Saturn which have not yet condensed.

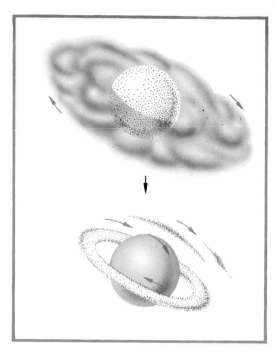

FIG. 24-2

The Kant-Laplace hypothesis. A cloud of gas began to rotate and to condense into the sun and the planets. (Redrawn from Yerkes Observatory Photograph, University of Chicago, Williams Bay, Wis.)

And while protoplanets grew into planets and protosatellites into satellites, the central mass of matter contracted to form the sun.

The Kant-Laplace hypothesis of rotating and condensing gas governed cosmological thought until late in the nineteenth century, when James Clerk Maxwell made a detailed calculation of the possibility of a ring of matter breaking up into Laplace's protoplanets. Assuming the initial ring particles to be similar in density to terrestrial matter, his conclusion was unambiguous. Rings like those surrounding Saturn are stable structures. They will not break up and condense into larger aggregates. The gravitational forces between the particles is insufficient to produce protoplanets. Thus Maxwell's calculations demolished the Kant-Laplace hypothesis, and serious work returned to the Buffon hypothesis. But as we mentioned above, the revival of the collision or near-miss hypothesis was short-lived because it, too, ran into mathematical trouble. Then, in 1944, Maxwell's calculation was reexamined in the light of new data. The German astrophysicist Karl von Weizsäcker recalculated the probability of ring condensation, using for the composition of the rings a mixture of about three-fourths hydrogen and one-fourth helium slightly contaminated by about 1 percent of all the other elements. This distribution of the elements in the universe as a whole had been established in the meantime by spectrographic studies of the absorption of light by stellar atmospheres and interstellar gases. It seemed more reasonable to assume that the protoplanets had formed from such a medium rather than from earthlike matter. Weizsäcker concluded that condensation of protoplanets could take place in such a low-density medium quite naturally by gravitational effects (although not in the denser rings of Saturn, as Maxwell had correctly shown). The crucial flaw of the condensation theory had been removed. The Dutch-American G. P. Kuiper then extended the work, and there is now a fairly detailed and coherent theory for the formation of the sun and planets along the lines initially suggested by Kant and Laplace. Not every aspect of the solar system has been completely explained, however. The high inclinations of the orbits of Pluto and Mercury, for instance, are troublesome, as is the origin of comets. Many of these unusual orbits are now thought to have resulted from interactions with planets in which initial orbits were changed. For instance, it seems quite probable that the extremely massive planet Jupiter had something to do with the formation of the asteroids, presumably through the disruption of an earlier planet, and its influence on other solar-system bodies seems equally likely. However, the exact solution of the problem requires an analysis of the mutual interactions of the three bodies—Jupiter, sun, and the other body—and completely adequate mathematical solutions of this prob-

lem, the so-called three-center problem, have not yet been found.

There is one interesting corollary to the question of the collision hypothesis versus the Kant-Laplace hypothesis. If collision was the method of forming the solar system, then it is extremely unlikely that there are many other planetary systems in the entire universe because encounters between stars are extremely rare. The distances between them are simply too large. On the other hand, the Kant-Laplace hypothesis suggests that planetary systems should form nearly every time a star condenses from rotating gas so that planets should be about as plentiful in the universe as stars. As we shall discuss at the end of this chapter, this has important implications for the likelihood that other life exists in the universe.

(While many astronomers still believe that there may be life on other planets, the existence of life on Mars was put considerably in doubt by photographs returned to earth from the Mariner IV spacecraft, which passed within 5,500 miles of Mars on July 14, 1965. Despite the seasonal variation in

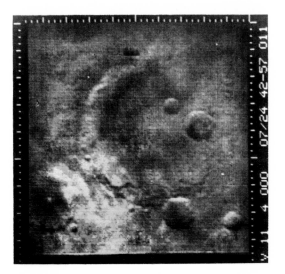

FIG. 24-3

A picture relayed to earth by Mariner IV, the space probe which passed within 5,500 miles of Mars on July 14, 1965. Mars's surface is very similar to the moon's (Fig. 2–11). (NASA/ Jet Propulsion Laboratory Photo)

the telescopic appearance of Mars, its surface was found to be as barren and pockmarked as the moon's [Fig. 24–3]. This casts serious doubt on the possibility that there is enough atmosphere on Mars to sustain any life processes.)

THE EXPANDING UNIVERSE

The suggestion that the elliptical objects in the sky might be aggregations of stars like those in the Milky Way was, as we saw, due to Kant. Sir William Herschel and his son, Sir John (1792–1871), catalogued a large number of galaxies and discovered that while they seemed to aggregate into clusters, they were more or less uniformly scattered throughout the celestial sphere. The universe is populated by galaxies in all directions and as far as the telescope can see (Fig. 3–17). More powerful telescopes later isolated individual stars in the galaxies, and spectral analysis showed that they were identical in color and distribution to those of the Milky Way. This, of course, was definite proof that galaxies are "island universes" of stars. Rotation of galaxies around their centers and motion of the galaxies through space were confirmed by means of the Doppler effect.

We have mentioned spectrographic findings in astronomy several times. Let us briefly review their character. Light produced within the photosphere of stars is absorbed in part by the elements of their coronas and also by interstellar and intergalactic matter. Absorption occurs by means of electron transitions between energy levels. Hence the absorbed lines are of discrete frequencies and are specific for different elements. The absorption lines thus give clues about stellar compositions. But the Doppler effect shifts the frequencies of absorbed lines toward the red end of the spectrum for receding sources and toward the blue for approaching sources. Hence relative velocities can also be determined from spectrographic analyses.

To determine galactic rotation, for instance, the telescope is focused on one edge of the galactic disk and then on the other. If one edge shows an approaching source while the other shows a receding source— as is actually found—rotation of the disk is indicated. If the absorption lines from the center of the disk, where the stars revolve neither toward nor away from us but at right angles to the line of sight, are also shifted, then the whole galaxy is moving relative to us. The Great Galaxy in Andromeda, for instance, shows a blue shift and is approaching us with a velocity of about 75 miles/sec. Most galaxies, however, show red shifts and are receding from us.

In the 1920s Edwin P. Hubble (1889–1956) used the then new 100-in. telescope on Mount Wilson in California for another exhaustive study of galaxies. Among his discoveries were Cepheid variables in the distant galaxies, which permitted a distance estimation (Chap. 3); some regularity in the way galaxies vary, which suggested a development sequence for them (Figs. 3–14 to 3–17); and finally limits to their range of brightness. Galaxies varied in total brightness from about one-half of the average observed value of the brightness to about twice the average. This last finding was of great importance because with the known loss of brightness with distance, a statistical study of the distribution of brightness among clusters of very distant galaxies gave a clue to their distance. By means of this technique, Hubble extended the range of vision to about 500 million light-years. (This has been extended by the 200-in. Mount Palomar telescope to about 2 billion light-years.)

Hubble and his colleague Milton L. Humason also measured red shifts in the light of the galaxies with the conclusion that all except nearby galaxies are receding from ours with a velocity that increases in proportion to their distance from us. The entire universe is expanding with each cluster of galaxies moving away from all others (Fig. 24–4).

From the recessional velocities Hubble

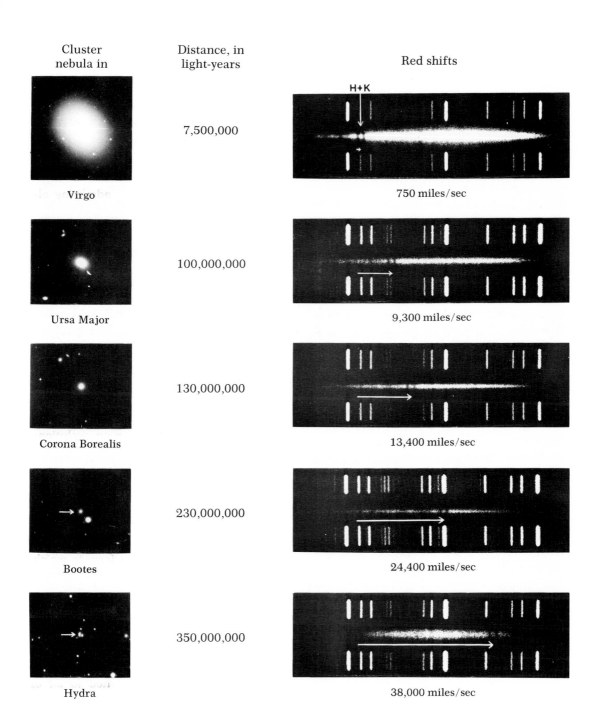

Cluster nebula in	Distance, in light-years	Red shifts

H+K

Virgo — 7,500,000 — 750 miles/sec

Ursa Major — 100,000,000 — 9,300 miles/sec

Corona Borealis — 130,000,000 — 13,400 miles/sec

Bootes — 230,000,000 — 24,400 miles/sec

Hydra — 350,000,000 — 38,000 miles/sec

FIG. 24-4

The increase in red shift with distance. The farther the galaxy, the greater its velocity of recession. Red shifts are expressed as velocities. Arrows indicate shift for calcium lines H and K. One light-year equals about 6 trillion miles, or 6×10^{12} miles. (Photograph from the Mount Wilson and Palomar Observatories)

computed the time when all were clustered together and found it to be an embarrassingly short 1.8 billion years ago. Since geologic dating of rocks had given a rather firm age of around 4.5 billion years for the earth, and since theories of stellar evolution likewise suggest an age of around 5 billion years, Hubble's calculation implied that the universe was substantially younger than the earth or the stars. Fortunately this paradox has been resolved. Recalibration of the distance data by Walter Baade in 1952 showed that Hubble's astronomical distances were too short by a factor of 2.8. Multiplying the previous distances (and ages) by 2.8 gives about 5 billion years for the time when the galaxies were all together, in excellent agreement with other age estimates.

Just as the structure of the solar system was the basic datum to be explained by the early cosmologies, the expansion of the disklike galaxies is the basic datum of the current studies. There are two major candidates: a "big bang" theory of an exploding universe and a theory of continuous creation. Both have among their proponents scientists of impeccable competence and reputation. Here is an excellent illustration of the fact that scientific theories are creations of the mind to be checked against the universe and that, when the universe fails to give unambiguous answers that conform to one and not the other of the alternatives, both are pursued until contradictions occur.

Actually the two theories of the origin of the universe are being reevaluated at this time. Extremely intense radio sources at great distances in the universe have recently been discovered. They may be the evidence which will decide the issue in favor of some form of explosion theory. In 1965 the British astrophysicist Fred Hoyle, one of the inventors of the continuous creation theory, abandoned it because he became convinced that these radio sources demonstrate that the universe has a time scale. It does not reach continuously into the infinite past and the infinite future as continuous creation implies.

Because explosion implies a beginning and a time scale for the universe while continuous creation implies unchanging continuity, a resolution between the two theories must eventually come. This is unlike the wave-particle and mass-energy problems which have faced physics before and which have been resolved by admitting alternative forms of the same entity. The alternative cosmologies demand a beginning to the universe or none; these can hardly be reconciled as alternative forms.

THE EXPLOSION THEORY

Let us review the basic data that must be explained by a theory for the formation of the universe:

1. Rotating galaxies must be formed with stars of various ages.

2. The galaxies must show an evolutionary sequence.

3. The galaxies must recede from each other.

4. The composition of the universe must be mostly hydrogen and helium with only minor amounts of the heavier elements.

5. Planetary systems must form in which the planets have compositions like those of the solar planets.

Modern explosion theory derives chiefly from the initial work of the Belgian Georges Lemaître, extended primarily by the Russian-born American George Gamow, although many others contributed to all or part of it.

According to this theory, initially a portion of the universe was populated exclusively by a dense mass of protons, electrons, and neutrons, the *ylem*, at fantastically high temperatures. The temperatures were so high that the mass associated with the radiation in the ylem ($E = hn = mc^2$) was greater than the gravitational mass of the particles. The radiation exerted pressure which caused expansion of the ylem from time zero onward with the following results. (In answer to the question what existed before time zero, Gamow has written, "One might give a metaphysical answer in the words of St. Augustine of Hippo, who wrote in his *Confessions:* 'Some people say that before He made Heaven and Earth, God prepared Gehenna for those who have the hardihood to inquire into such high matters.' ")

During the first 5 minutes the ylem was so hot and dense with radiation that protons, neutrons, and electrons coexisted in equilibrium with one another. But during this time, the initial expansion of the ylem cooled it to around 1 billion degrees. At this point conditions for the equilibrium between the three particles no longer existed, but conditions were now appropriate for nuclear reactions which first fused neutrons and protons into helium nuclei and then fused additional neutrons and protons to them to form the heavier elements. Theoretical studies by R. Alpher, H. Bethe, and Gamow (the α, β, γ paper) and also by R. C. Hermann, J. S. Smart, and Enrico Fermi and A. Turkevich show that the nuclear reactions that could have occurred at the temperatures of the ylem would lead to the production of amounts of the elements that conform rather closely to their distribution in the universe as given by spectral studies. Thus, during the next 25 minutes, as the ylem expanded further and its temperature dropped further also, the elements were formed in the proportions in which they are found. At this point, about half an hour after time zero, no further element production occurred because the ylem temperature had dropped so low that the particles no longer had sufficient energies to fuse. (It should be pointed out that the theory runs into one snag. Addition of protons and neutrons to form isotopes of masses 2, 3, 4, and 6 up to 238 and higher is without problems. Known nuclear reactions provide the proper sequence and the proper abundances. But there is no known isotope of mass 5. How the addition of particles in the ylem jumped

the gap from 4 to 6 is unknown. At this point the explosion and the continuous creation theories meet head on, apparently in favor of the continuous creation theory. But as we shall see, that also is not entirely satisfactory.)

During the next 250 million years or so, the gas of elements expanded further and also cooled further. Now a few of the atoms in the gas condensed into submicroscopic dust particles. At the end of this period, a much larger portion of the universe was filled by a mixture of gas with a little dust. But by this time, the radiation density which had provided the repulsive force had dropped to below the value of the mass density, and now gravitational effects could set in.

Sir James Jeans has calculated that a huge gas mass is not stable but will break up into smaller gas clouds. This results from the existence of random fluctuations in the density which bring a few particles closer together than average in a perfectly random manner. These slight random condensations then remain stable because greater than average gravitational attractions exist between their particles which are less than average distances apart. The local condensations, in turn, affect the entire gas mass and lead to its rupture into smaller parts (Fig. 24–5). Jeans's calculations permit an estimate of the minimum dimensions and masses of the smaller gas clouds. They must be at least 40,000 light-years in diameter and have 200 million times the mass of our sun. These numbers fit in well with the dimensions and masses observed for galaxies.

The separation of the initial mass into smaller gas masses produced turbulence in them, enough to account for their rotation as a whole and also enough to form local eddies of gas. Hence after separation, each smaller gas mass began to rotate as a whole, as observed in galaxies. In addition, within it there were millions of eddies like the eddies of water flowing over rapids. Gravity then maintained the eddies and trans-

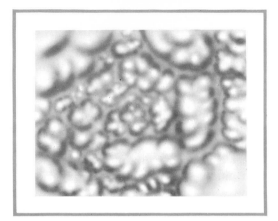

FIG. 24-5

The breakup of the huge gas cloud into smaller clouds and the formation of eddies. Calculations indicate that this can easily occur in a randomly moving large gas cloud.

formed them into smoothly rotating masses that condensed into stars. Thus the sequence of galaxy and star formation occurred. While it took place, the whole universe still expanded and the protogalaxies and later the galaxies receded from each other as we still observe.

According to the theory, the eddies in the gas clouds were of different masses and different degrees of turbulence. They formed stars of different sizes and they formed them at different rates. Consequently we see galaxies that appear to be at different stages of their evolution and also stars which seem to be of different ages and at different points in their evolution (Chap. 3). This picture is particularly difficult to interpret in detail because as we look at a galaxy in the distance, we see it in the past. Light reaching us from a galaxy 500 million light-years away shows us that galaxy when it was 500 million years younger than the Milky Way or that galaxy are right now (whatever "right now" means with respect to that galaxy). The age of galaxies is a second point of confrontation between the explosion and continuous creation theories. All galaxies began at the same time in the explosion theory; since we look at younger and younger galaxies as we look

farther into space, the appearance of galaxies should change in a systematic manner that corresponds to the developmental sequence of the galaxies. Continuous creation predicts no such difference with distance. Unfortunately, with current instruments, the evidence is not at all clear. Galaxies far enough away to represent substantial time differences simply cannot be studied in sufficient detail to show firm differences or the absence of differences. (Recently discovered quasars—quasi-stellar radio sources—which are of stellar size and yet emit radio signals of such intensity that they seem to be of galactic dimensions, may be young galaxies at extremely large distances which show the necessary age difference with distance and time.)

The last stage in the successive condensations of the initial gas mass is from the eddies. Several things can happen here. The gas within an eddy might split into two or more major portions to form a binary or a multiple star system. It might condense into a single star and shed rings of its gases in the manner first postulated by Kant and Laplace to form a planetary system similar to our own.

The events we have described adhere rather closely to current theories of the dynamics of gas masses. Hence the picture is coherent and continuous with what has been learned in laboratories on the earth itself. The same is true if the calculations are extended to the solar system. A detailed treatment of the mechanics of a mass of gas of the size that ultimately formed the solar system provides rather good estimates of the planetary sizes as they are found. The difference in the abundance of the elements among the planets and in the universe can easily be traced back to the expulsion of hydrogen, helium, and other light elements by the radiation pressure of the solar energy, and by the differential rate of escape of the light elements from the planets of smaller mass. This left the inner planets with very little hydrogen and helium.

(An interesting additional aspect of solar-system cosmology is the case of our moon. The moon is unique among the satellites because its mass is relatively large compared to that of the planet. Observations show that the moon is gradually slowing down on its revolution about the earth, about 4.3 seconds of arc each century, which means that it is also receding 5 in. per year. Calculating these values backward, we find that the moon touched the earth about 4 billion years ago and that, at the time, it revolved with the earth's rotation. Hence earth-moon may at one time have been a binary planet system or an unstable protoplanet which broke in two.)

CONTINUOUS CREATION

The theory of an expanding universe suffers from two problems and one arbitrary assumption. The arbitrary assumption is the ylem and the relation of temperature and radiation pressure during the first half hour which permitted the formation of the elements and caused the expansion of the mass of gas. The problems relate to the isotope of mass 5 and the question whether gas breakup would occur in such a manner that galaxies and stars form later. The theory is not conclusive on these two points. Also, the expansion of the universe implies that time had a zero point and that, on a cosmic scale, it will have an end. Eventually the galaxies will have receded from one another and each will die. (There is a possibility in relativistic cosmology that the universe is pulsating and that after some time of expansion the universe will eventually contract again.)

To remedy the problems above, H. Bondi, and T. Gold, D. W. Sciama, and F. Hoyle have proposed the alternative theory of the continuous creation of the universe, although Hoyle abandoned it in 1965. This theory has only one arbitrary assumption; namely, that hydrogen is continuously created in the universe. The problem of

mass 5 and the question of gas breakup do not arise in this theory.

While the creation of matter is entirely contrary to our known laws of nature and thus seems at first glance to be totally unacceptable, the requirement is really quite small. One hydrogen atom created each year in the space of a small skyscraper produces enough hydrogen. Clearly this small amount could not be detected by measurement. In the weighings which produced the law of conservation of matter, single hydrogen atoms—even billions of them—could be lost without any notice whatsoever.

Except for the different means for creating matter initially, the continuous creation theory is quite similar to the explosion theory. Under the influence of existing galaxies, which expand because of the pressure of the newly created hydrogen atoms, the new atoms condense into protogalaxies. Then protogalaxies break up into stars, and protostars shed gas to form planets. The only other major distinction between the two theories is in the formation of the heavy elements.

In the explosion theory the ylem was at a sufficient temperature during the first half hour to produce the heavy elements by the accretion of protons and neutrons, although there is a gap at mass 5 which has not yet been bridged. The continuous creation theory also needs a very hot place for the production of the heavy elements. It finds it in the interiors of supernovae. Supernovae are stars which suddenly change their brightness by factors of millions, and shed substantial amounts of gases at the same time. The Crab Nebula (Fig. 3–11) is direct evidence for this. Such an explosion, it has been calculated, requires an interior temperature in the supernova of at least 100 million degrees. That is hot enough to form the heavy elements which are then expelled by the explosion and join the newly created hydrogen. The helium of the universe is produced by the energy-producing reactions in stars.

Thus the continuous creation takes only observed events—in contrast to the assumed ylem and the assumed initial temperatures. However, there is a dispute whether the number of supernovae explosions—about one per galaxy per 400 years—is large enough to produce the required amount of the heavy elements. Continuous creation theorists say yes; explosion theorists say no. They agree that the mass 5 gap is not a problem in the supernova production of the heavy elements.

The production of protogalaxies is also in dispute between the two theories. In the continuous creation theory, the gravitational fields from older surrounding galaxies naturally condense the newly formed hydrogen gas into protogalaxies and give them the properties needed for star formation. In the explosion theory, protogalaxy formation is possible but not necessary. If it happened, it was a lucky accident. Hence continuous creation theorists suggest continuous creation conforms more fully to established theory and is less dependent on fortuitous circumstances.

The implications of the two theories for the ages of the galaxies have already been mentioned. In the explosion theory the universe is like a single person. He has a youth and prime and an old age. Then he dies and his existence as an individual ceases. So does the explosion theory universe. And just as all parts of the human body age at the same rate— more or less—so all parts of the universe age at the same rate. All galaxies compared for the same age should be alike, and with increasing time they should show increasing development. In the continuous creation theory, on the other hand, the universe is like the population of a city. Some people grow old and die, some are born, and the rest are of all intermediate ages. Hence everywhere galaxies should show all stages of galactic development and no differences should be found dependent on time. It is in this connection that quasars are so important. If further study corroborates what has already been accepted tentatively by many astronomers, namely, that they are young galaxies at great distance from us and therefore sending us energy that originated in the youth of the universe, they may be the evidence which will weigh the scale in favor of the acceptance of the explosion theory despite its theoretical problems.

THE ORIGIN OF LIFE

Speculations concerning the origin of life are much more recent than speculations concerning the origin of the universe. Indeed, the problem has been studied experimentally for only about 20 years and has been treated as a scientific problem for only about 50 years. Consequently it is today in about the same position as scientific cosmology was in Newton's time. Much of the needed theoretical understanding is still missing; many of the needed observations have not yet been made; and most of the conclusions point strongly in the direction of a special act of creation. However, the problem may evolve like the cosmological problem. Three hundred years from now the unsettled question may be which of two possible paths was taken by spontaneous creation of life, not whether life could have arisen spontaneously.

Until about 100 years ago the question of whether life could arise spontaneously occurred to very few individuals. The appearance and growth of bacteria everywhere, apparently without sources, was considered to prove spontaneous generation. It took the genius of Louis Pasteur (1822–1895) to devise a series of experiments that demonstrated conclusively that life came only from other life. Only then did the problem of the origin of the first life arise as a scientific problem. But it took until 1924 to treat it in detail. Then the Russian A. I. Oparin developed a theory which spurred further research. That research went on slowly until World War II, and rapidly since.

The spontaneous creation of life has three

requirements: there must have been the raw materials for the first organisms; the raw materials must have come together into the first primitive living structure; and this first living structure had to find a way to keep itself alive and to reproduce. We must not equate living structure with the simple one-cell organisms we know today. These are much more complex than the possible minimum "living structure." Indeed, one of our problems is that we cannot specify what the precise requirements of this primitive living structure are. We know that it must have lived in a much simpler environment than the one-cell organisms we know, and it could not use the same metabolic processes as they. The substances that they require were not available because most are the products of other living things.

The early earth in which life arose was a barren thing like the moon's surface today. Its atmosphere differed drastically from our present atmosphere. Oxygen was certainly absent, for oxygen is a very reactive substance. In the aeons between the formation of the earth and the genesis of life, any oxygen present when the earth congealed certainly had reacted to form CO_2, H_2O, and the many silicate and aluminate minerals which form the crust of the earth. (The oxygen present in our atmosphere is the result of the metabolic processes of plants which produce oxygen, and these plants were certainly absent at the time life originated.) Hence the first living structures operated in a very different environment and probably had to react quite differently to obtain their energy.

OPARIN'S HYPOTHESIS

Oparin wrote at a time when Moulton and Chamberlin's and Jeans's theories about the origin of the earth were dominant. His starting point is the time when a passing star tore hot gases from the sun and they cooled and congealed into the earth.

The first reactions which Oparin dis-

cusses are those likely to have taken place in the hot earth atmosphere. Molten metals, carbon, and the gases oxygen, nitrogen, and hydrogen must have reacted with one another to produce a number of small, highly reactive carbon compounds, like acetylene, and other common small molecules, like ammonia, which easily fit into a scheme for producing the organic compounds of life. These earliest small molecules reacted with water to form amino acids and sugars, and alcohols, aldehydes, and ketones of the kind known to be part of the processes in living beings. They dissolved in the ocean, which thus became a reservoir of organic molecules. Since the ocean was not shielded from the sun by carbon dioxide and oxygen in the atmosphere, it was much warmer than today. It has been called a hot, dilute soup of chemicals from which life arose.

The simple molecules of the hot dilute soup did not remain static. They reacted with one another. Amino acids grew into proteinlike chains. As the chains increased in size, they began to curl up and to separate as droplets in the soup. But they did not separate alone. A type of hydrogen bonding (hydrogen bonding was discovered after Oparin's book) kept water associated with the proteinlike materials in the droplets so that they resembled living cells (Fig. 24–6). Moreover, similar weak bonds brought other organic molecules into the droplets. Thus Oparin proposed the formation of the simplest living structure. It was a droplet of proteinlike material containing other organic compounds and water, which separated from the hot dilute soup.

Life—energy production and replication —arose because of the difference between the droplet and the soup. The higher concentration of organic substances within the droplet developed osmotic pressure. Hence additional exchange occurred between the droplet and the soup. This brought new organic compounds and led to further chemical reactions. Some of the compounds served as catalysts, thus facilitating a few favored reactions. For many of the drop-

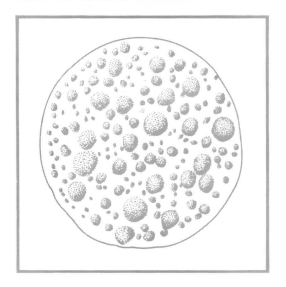

FIG. 24-6

A droplet of proteinlike material with its bound water and smaller molecules.

lets, these reactions meant disintegration. They were broken into small fragments and dissolved again. But for a few, purely by chance, these reactions led to greater differentiation and stability. These few were the true precursors of life. They gathered onto themselves a few stable enzymes and the means for replication.

Oparin's theory was largely speculative. The formation of the basic compounds among the hot gases torn from the sun was speculative although their change into organic chemicals was based on known reactions. But the combination of the organic compounds into proteinlike polymers, the droplet formation, and all further reactions of the droplets were speculative. Hence his theory was important for its basic idea—the possibility of spontaneous generation of life —rather than for its details. Indeed, his first assumption, that the earth was formed by the encounter of a star with the sun, is no longer considered probable.

LATER EXPERIMENTS

The firm transition of the generation of life from a speculative to an experimental prob-

lem came in 1953, when S. L. Miller reported the result of exposing a mixture of CH_4, NH_3, and H_2O to an electric discharge. These gases were chosen because H. C. Urey had shown that they were likely components of the original, oxygen-free earth atmosphere. The electric discharge was chosen because its energy is similar to energy available from the sun. The yield of Miller's experiment was a number of amino acids as well as other organic compounds associated with metabolic processes. Here was direct evidence for something Oparin had only speculated about. The organic compounds needed for our forms of life were produced in a simulated early-earth atmosphere by a completely natural process.

Miller's experiments have been repeated and extended by many others. Ultraviolet light, high-frequency vibrations, radioactive rays, X rays, and light have been used as sources of energy, and variations in the kinds of gases to duplicate a range of possible initial-earth atmospheres have been used. The harvest in all cases has been rich. Most of the simple organic compounds known in the reactions of living things are produced, and a number of the more complex molecules of life have also been identified—among them, nucleotides and precursors of nucleic acids, small proteins, enzymes, and sugars and polysaccharides. There is very little question that the raw materials for producing a living structure and for feeding and replicating it were present at some time early in the earth's history.

Concerning the second requirement, assembling the materials into the living structure, there is also some experimental evidence. S. W. Fox has found it possible to separate microscopic spheres of proteinlike materials from soups like the one presumably in existence on the early earth. Hence the concept proposed by Oparin has found some experimental verification. But the third requirement, the special energy-producing and replicating reactions, has not been found. The microscopic spheres seem to react actively in some lifelike processes. But unlike cells, they react only when the environment is brought to them; they do not seek their food or respond to stimuli that indicate its presence. Nor do they show any indication of replicatory reactions. They are complex proteinlike molecules gathered into a cell-like structure, but they are nothing more than molecules.

This leaves us with the basic question still unanswered. We know quite definitely that the early-earth environment had the raw materials for spontaneous generation of living things. We know that these can be gathered into more complex molecules that begin to resemble the simple basic components of living structures, and we know enough already to be able to predict that some experiments now going on will produce even more complex basic components of living structures. But does that mean that life originated spontaneously?

Both speculative and realistic points of view are possible. The realistic point of view suggests that the spontaneous formation of complex, lifelike molecules means nothing more than the formation of complex, lifelike molecules. It does not mean life or even the likelihood of spontaneous generation of life. The experiments we have described in this chapter are interesting, but they are proof only of the ingenuity of scientists with their test-tubes. Life, on the other hand, would require a special act of creation.

The speculative point of view stresses that in only about 20 years of work, experiments have produced something very similar to life. Let us extend this to the several billion years during which reactions occurred constantly in the hot dilute soup. Surely in that long a time among the billions of lifelike molecules produced there was one (or maybe several) that was not only lifelike but living. This point of view extends what is known and suggests that it is enough to assume the creation of life by a chance and spontaneous reaction.

Unless life is actually created in a test-

FIG. 24-7

Apparatus used to produce organic compounds by the irradiation of simulated early-earth atmospheres. (NASA-Ames Research Center)

tube, there is no way to test either conclusion except in a very special sense. We mentioned early in this chapter that the formation of the solar system from the sun by a passing star makes the earth a very special planet in the universe; the formation of the earth from a cloud of congealing gas, on the other hand, makes it only one of hundreds of millions or billions of similar planets. Each of these similar planets is at about the same distance from its star—which produces about as much energy as the sun—and has about the same mass.

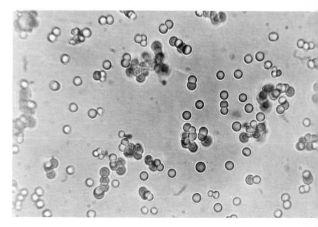

FIG. 24-8

Microscope photograph of proteinlike spheres which separate from soups of compounds similar to those which probably existed in early times. (Photo by Sidney W. Fox)

403

This means that it too at one time had, or still has, a hot dilute soup filled with organic compounds.

If that is the case, then in the other planets, too, billions of reactions have occurred which produced lifelike molecules, and in the billions of reactions, a primitive living structure should have appeared purely by a chance combination. Thus, if we can identify anything as living on another planet, we can feel reasonably assured of the spontaneous origin of life here on earth.

Clearly this point of view is highly speculative. It brings science very close to what is generally considered metaphysics. But then, until quite recently, science was called natural philosophy and the name was not accidental.

Suggestions for Further Reading

Some short popular books on cosmology by astrophysicists who have contributed to modern theory are:

Bondi, Herman: *The Universe at Large*, Anchor Books, Doubleday & Company, Garden City, N.Y., 1960 (paperback). Considers the alternative theories regarding the origin of the universe and other problems in cosmology.

Gamow, George: *The Creation of the Universe*, Mentor Books, New York, 1952 (paperback). An exposition of the explosion theory of the origin of the universe.

Hoyle, Fred: *The Nature of the Universe*, Harper & Row, Publishers, New York, 1960. Lectures on the problems of modern cosmology.

Hoyle, Fred: *Galaxies, Nuclei, and Quasars*, Harper & Row, Publishers, New York, 1965. Reexamines cosmological problems in the light of the newly discovered quasars.

A book which contains excerpts from the original contributions is:

Munitz, Milton K.: *Theories of the Universe*, The Free Press, Glencoe, Ill., 1957. The latter half deals with modern theories.

On the origin of life are:

Keosian, John: *The Origin of Life*, Reinhold Publishing Corporation, New York, 1964 (paperback). A survey of the work regarding the origin of life from the early Greek to the most recent times, including a chapter on Oparin's important contribution.

Oparin, A. T.: *The Origin of Life*, Dover Publications, Inc., New York, 1953 (paperback). A reprint of a translation of Oparin's original thesis; not highly technical.

A book which combines speculation regarding the origin of the universe with speculation regarding life is:

Shapley, Harlow: *Of Stars and Men*, Beacon Press, Boston, 1958.

Index

Format by Susan Bishop
Set in Linotype Primer
Composed by V & M Typographical, Inc.
Printed and bound by The Haddon Craftsmen, Inc.
HARPER & ROW, PUBLISHERS, INCORPORATED

70 71 72 9 8 7 6 5 4 3

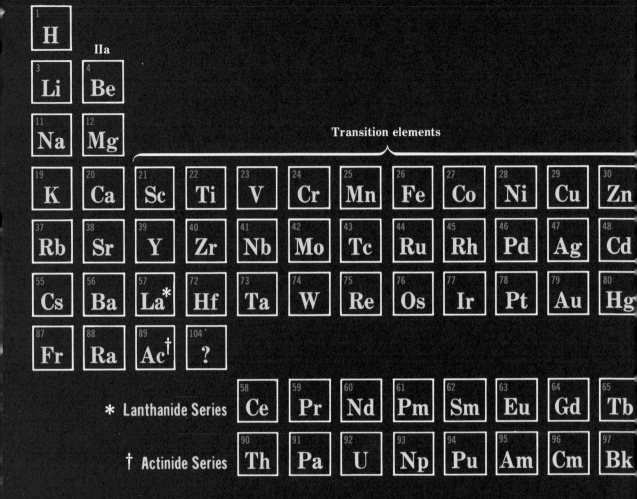

Periodic table of the elements